Genetic Mechanisms In Human Disease

CHROMOSOMAL ABERRATIONS

Edited by

M. F. ASHLEY MONTAGU

CHARLES C THOMAS · PUBLISHER

Springfield · Illinois · U.S.A.

CHARLES C THOMAS · PUBLISHER

BANNERSTONE HOUSE

301-327 East Lawrence Avenue, Springfield, Illinois, U.S.A.

© 1961, *by* CHARLES C THOMAS · PUBLISHER

Library of Congress Catalog Card Number: 61-15377

With THOMAS BOOKS careful attention is given to all details of manufacturing and design. It is the Publisher's desire to present books that are satisfactory as to their physical qualities and artistic possibilities and appropriate for their particular use. THOMAS BOOKS will be true to those laws of quality that assure a good name and good will.

Printed in the United States of America

CONTRIBUTORS

A. G. BAIKIE, M.B. Glasg., M.R.C.P.E., The M.R.C. Group for Research into the General Effects of Radiation, Western General Hospital, Edinburgh, Scotland

MURRAY L. BARR, M.Sc., M.D., Department of Microscopic Anatomy, University of Western Ontario, London, Canada

SIDNEY BECK, The Institute for Cancer Research, The American Oncologic Hospital; Department of Pathology, School of Medicine, University of Pennsylvania, Philadelphia, Pennsylvania

J. M. BERG, M. B. W'SRAND, M.Sc. Cape Town, The Fountain Hospital, London, England

S. BERGMAN, M.D. Lund, The Bacteriological Institute, University of Lund, and Allmänna, Sjukhuset, Malmö, Sweden

P. M. F. BISHOP, Guy's Hospital, London, England

C. E. BLANK, M.B. Wales, Ph.D. Lond., University of Sheffield, Sheffield, England

ADRIEN BLEYER, M.D., St. Louis, Missouri

J. A. BÖÖK, M.D., Institute for Medical Genetics, University of Uppsala, Uppsala, Sweden

CASSIO BOTTURA, M.D., Department of Endocrinology and Metabolic Disorders, Hospital das Clinicas, São Paulo; Department of Clinical Medicine, Faculty of Medicine, Ribeirão Preto, Brazil

B. D. BOWER, M.D. Birm., M.R.C.P., D.C.H., Department of Genetics and Paediatrics, University of Birmingham, The Children's Hospital, Birmingham, England

ELIZABETH BOYD, B.Sc. Glasg., Department of Pathology, Western Infirmary and University, Glasgow, Scotland

J. H. BRIGGS, M.B. Lond., M.R.C.P., Guy's Hospital Medical School, London, England

W. M. COURT BROWN, M.B., B.Sc. St. And., F.F.R., The M.R.C. Group for Research into the General Effects of Radiation, Western General Hospital, Edinburgh, Scotland

KARIN E. BUCKTON, Medical Research Council, Clinical Effects of Radiation Research Unit, Western General Hospital, Edinburgh, Scotland

v

A. H. CAMERON, M.D. Durh., Children's Hospital, Birmingham, England

J. CAMPBELL, M.B. Glasg., Deputy Physician-Superintendent

PETER J. CARPENTIER, M.D., Department of Obstetrics and Gynecology, University of Chicago, Chicago Lying-in Hospital, Chicago, Illinois

C. O. CARTER, B.M. Oxon., M.R.C.P., Medical Research Council's Clinical Genetics, Research Unit, Institute of Child Health, London, England

B. CHIARELLI, D.Sc. Florence, Institute of Genetics, University of Pavia, Pavia, Italy

E. H. Y. CHU, Biology Division, Oak Ridge National Laboratory, Oak Ridge, Tennessee

C. M. CLARKE, Ph.D. Durh., Medical Research Council Radiobiological Research Unit, Harwell, Berks, England

H. G. CLOSE, M.D. Lond., Joyce Green Hospital, Dartford, Kent, England

HERBERT L. COOPER, M.D., New York University, Research Associate in Medicine, U.S.P.H.S. Trainee in Human Genetics, New York, New York

LLOYD H. COTTER, M.D., Department of Pediatrics, University of California School of Medicine, Pacific State Hospital, Pomona, California

V. MARY CROSSE, O.B.E., M.D. Lond., D.P.H., Birmingham Regional Hospital Board, Birmingham, England

LOIS H. CROSSWHITE, B.A., Roswell Park Memorial Institute, The Medical Foundation of Buffalo, Buffalo, New York

J. C. DE ALMEIDA, M.D. Brazil, Guy's Hospital, London, England

LICIO MARQUES DE ASSIS, M.D., Department of Endocrinology and Metabolic Disorders, Hospital das Clinicas, São Paulo; Department of Clinical Medicine, Faculty of Medicine, Ribeirão Preto, Brazil

L. DE CARLI, D.Sc. Pavia, Institute of Genetics, University of Pavia, Pavia, Italy

WAYNE H. DECKER, M.D., New York Medical College, New York, New York

JOY D. A. DELHANTY, B.Sc. Lond., The Galton Laboratory, University College, London, England

C. J. DEWHURST, M.B. Manc., F.R.C.S.E., M.R.C.O.G., Department of Obstetrics and Gynaecology, University of Sheffield; Honorary Consultant, Obstetrician and Gynaecologist, City General Hospital, Sheffield, England

WAYNE H. DICKER, M.D., Department of New York Medical College, Obstetrics and Gynecology, New York, New York

A. J. DONNELLY, The Institute for Cancer Research, The American Oncologic Hospital, Department of Pathology, School of Medicine, University of Pennsylvania, Philadelphia, Pennsylvania

J. H. EDWARDS, M.R.C.P., The Population Genetics Research Unit, Medical Research Council, Headington, Oxford, England

J. R. ELLIS, Ph.D. Manc., The Galton Laboratory, University College, London, England

DORINA REICHHARDT EPPS, M.D., Department of Endocrinology and Metabolic Disorder, Hospital das Clinicas, São Paulo; Department of Clinical Medicine, Faculty of Medicine, Ribeirão Preto, Brazil

M. A. FERGUSON-SMITH, M.B. Glasg., Department of Medicine, The Johns Hopkins University, Baltimore, Maryland

IRIS FERRARI, M.D., Department of Endocrinology and Metabolic Disorders, Hospital das Clinicas, São Paulo; Department of Clinical Medicine, Faculty of Medicine, Ribeirão Preto, Brazil

C. E. FORD, Ph.D. Lond., Medical Research Council, Radiobiological Research Unit, Harwell, Didcot, Berks, England

HUGH FORREST, M.B. Glasg., Surgical Registrar, Royal Hospital for Sick Children, Western Infirmary, Glasgow, Scotland

M. FRACCARO, M.D. Pavia, Institute of Medical Genetics, University of Uppsala, Uppsala, Sweden

JEAN H. FRASER, M.B. Glasg., Senior House-Officer, Department of Pathology, Western Infirmary, Glasgow, Scotland

MARTHE GAUTIER, Chaire d'Hygiene et Clinique de la Ire Enfance, Institut de Progénèse, Faculté de Médecine, Paris, France

J. GOLDSTEIN, M.D. Vienna, Joyce Green Hospital, Dartford, Kent, England

R. R. GORDON, M.C., M.D. Glasg., M.R.C.P., City General Hospital, Sheffield, England

EDWIN GORDY, M.D., Roswell Park Memorial Institute, The Medical Foundation of Buffalo, Buffalo, New York

A. GUNLAP, M.D. Ankara, Medical Research Unit, National Spastic Society, Department of Child Health, Guy's Hospital, London, England

H. HABICH, M.D., Department of Paediatrics, University of Zurich, Zurich, Switzerland

J. L. HAMERTON, B.Sc. Lond., Medical Research Unit, National Spastic

Society, Department of Child Health, Guy's Hospital, London, England

S. D. HANDMAKER, A.B. Johns Hopkins, Research Student, Division of Medical Genetics, Department of Medicine, Johns Hopkins University School of Medicine, Baltimore, Maryland

D. G. HARNDEN, Ph.D. Edin., Medical Research Council, Group for Research on the General Effects of Radiation, Department of Radiotherapy, Western General Hospital, Edinburgh, Scotland

C. W. H. HAVARD, M.A., D.M., M.R.C.P., St. Bartholomew's Hospital, London, England

M. D. HAYWARD, B.Sc. Wales, Department of Genetics and Paediatrics, University of Birmingham, The Children's Hospital, Birmingham, England

KURT HIRSCHHORN, M.D., New York University, Department of Medicine, New York, New York

T. C. HSU, Section of Cytology, The University of Texas, M. D. Anderson Hospital and Tumor Institute, Houston, Texas

DAVID A. HUNGERFORD, The Institute for Cancer Research, The American Oncologic Hospital, Department of Pathology, School of Medicine, University of Pennsylvania, Philadelphia, Pennsylvania

D. IKKOS, Department of Endocrinology, Karolinska Hospital, Stockholm, Sweden

STANLEY L. INHORM, M.D. New York, Department of Pathology and Pediatrics, University of Wisconsin Medical School, Madison, Wisconsin

PATRICIA A. JACOBS, B.Sc. St. And., The M.R.C. Group for Research into the General Effects of Radiation, Western General Hospital, Edinburgh, Scotland

A. W. JOHNSTON, M.B. Cantab., M.R.C.P., Division of Medical Genetics, Department of Medicine, Johns Hopkins University School of Medicine, Baltimore, Maryland

K. W. JONES, Ph.D. Wales, The Medical Research Council Radiobiological Research Unit, Harwell, England

K. KAIJSER, M.D. Stockholm, The Paediatric Department, Central Hospital of Eskilstuna, Eskilstuna, Sweden

JACQUES LAFOURCADE, Chaire d'Hygiene et Clinique de la Ire Enfance, Institut de Progénèse, Faculté de Médecine, Paris, France

JÉROME LEJEUNE, Chaire d'Hygiene et Clinique de la Ire Enfance, Institut de Progénèse, Faculté de Médecine, Paris, France

BERNARD LENNOX, M.D. Durh., Ph.D. Lond., F.R.F.P.S., M.R.C.P.,

Department of Pathology, University and Western Infirmary, Glasgow, Scotland

J. Lindsten, Med. kand., fil. kand., Institute of Medical Genetics, University of Uppsala, Uppsala, Sweden

R. Luft, Department of Endocrinology, Karolinska Hospital, Stockholm, Sweden

R. C. MacGillivray, M.B. Edin., F.R.F.P.S., D.P.M., Lennon Castle Hospital, Stirlingshire, England

T. N. MacGregor, M.D. Edin., F.R.C.O.G., F.R.C.S.E., Department of Obstetrics and Gynaecology and Pathology, Western General Hospital, Edinburgh, Scotland

N. Maclean, M.B. Edin., M.R.C.P.E., Department of Obstetrics and Paediatrics and Pathology, Western General Hospital, Edinburgh, Scotland

J. S. Mile, M.B., B.Sc. Edin., East Lothian

Ursula Mittwoch, Ph.D. Lond., Galton Laboratory, University College, London, England

Keith L. Moore, B.A., M.Sc., Ph.D. Western Ontario, Department of Anatomy, Faculty of Medicine, University of Manitoba

H. David Mosier, M.D., Department of Pediatrics, University of California School of Medicine, Los Angeles, California, Pacific State Hospital, Pomona, California

Inga Marie Nilsson, M.D. Lund, Department of Medicine, University of Lund and Allmänna, Sjukhuset, Malmö, Sweden

Peter C. Noel, The Institute for Cancer Research, The American Oncologic Hospital, Department of Pathology, School of Medicine, University of Pennsylvania, Philadelphia, Pennsylvania

F. Nuzzo, D.Sc. Rome, Institute of Genetics, University of Pavia, Pavia, Italy

F. J. P. O'Gorman, M.B. Glasg., F.R.C.S.E., M.R.C.O.G., City General Hospital, Sheffield, England

Klaus Patau, Ph.D. Berlin, Department of Pathology and Pediatrics, University of Wisconsin Medical School, Madison, Wisconsin

L. S. Penrose, M.D. Cantab., F.R.S., Galton Laboratory, University College, London, England

P. E. Polani, M.D. Pisa, M.R.C.P., Guy's Hospital Medical School, London, England

E. Poli, M.D., Fatebenefratelli Hospital, Milan, Italy

Edith L. Potter, M.D., Department of Obstetrics and Gynecology, University of Chicago, Chicago Lying-in Hospital, Chicago, Illinois

A. Prader, M.D., Department of Paediatrics, University of Zurich, Zurich, Switzerland

T. T. Puck, Department of Biophysics, Florence R. Sabin Laboratories, Department of Pediatrics, University of Colorado Medical Center, Denver, Colorado

J. Reitalu, Ph. cand. Lund, The Cancer Chromosome Laboratory, Institute of Genetics, University of Lund and Allmänna Sjukhuset, Malmö, Sweden

M. Ridler, F.I.M.L.T., Harperbury Hospital, Shenley, Herts, England

A. Robinson, Department of Biophysics, Florence R. Sabin Laboratories, Department of Pediatrics, University of Colorado Medical Center, Denver, Colorado

J. R. Roy, M.B. Glasg., F.R.F.P.S., M.R.C.P.E., D.P.M., Southern General Hospital, Glasgow, Scotland

Avery A. Sandberg, M.D., Roswell Park Memorial Institute, The Medical Foundation of Buffalo, Buffalo, New York

Ann R. Sanderson, B.Sc., Ph.D. St. And., Zoology, Queen's College, University of St. Andrews, Dundee, England

Berta Santesson, Fil. Lic., Institute for Medical Genetics, University of Uppsala, Uppsala, Sweden

Lawrence W. Scott, Department of Pediatrics, University of California School of Medicine, Los Angeles, California; Pacific State Hospital, Pomona, California

A. Shapiro, M.D. Lond., D.P.M., Harperbury Hospital, Shenley, Herts, England

David W. Smith, M.D. Baltimore, Department of Pathology and Pediatrics, University of Wisconsin Medical School, Madison, Wisconsin

A. W. Spence, M.A., M.D., F.R.C.P., St. Bartholomew's Hospital, London, England

Curt Stern, Department of Zoology, University of California, Berkeley, California

John S. S. Steward, M.D. Glasg., Department of Surgery, Royal Infirmary, Glasgow, Scotland

J. A. Strong, B.A., M.B. Dubl., F.R.C.P.E., M.R.C.P., Department for Endocrine and Metabolic Diseases, Western General Hospital, University of Edinburgh, Edinburgh, Scotland

J. M. Tanner, M.D., D.Sc. Lond., Institute of Child Health, University of London, London, England

Eeva Therman, Ph.D. Helsinki, Department of Pathology and Pediatrics, University of Wisconsin Medical School, Madison, Wisconsin

J. H. TJIO, NIAMD Building, National Institutes of Health, Bethesda, Maryland

ISHBEL M. TOUGH, Medical Research Council, Clinical Effects of Radiation Research Unit, Western General Hospital, Edinburgh, Scotland

RAYMOND TURPIN, Chaire d'Hygiene et Clinique de la Ire Enfance, Institut de Progénèse, Faculté de Médecine, Paris, France

HANS P. WAGNER, M.D. Berne, Department of Pathology and Pediatrics, University of Wisconsin Medical School, Madison, Wisconsin

J. WALDENSTRÖM, M.D. Lund, Department of Medicine, University of Lund, Physician to Allmänna, Sjukhuset, Malmö, Sweden

ARNOLD N. WEINBERG, M.D., Senior Assistant Surgeon, Clinical Endocrinology Branch, National Institute of Arthritis and Metabolic Diseases, Bethesda, Maryland

S. D. V. WELLER, M.D. Lond., M.R.C.P., Bromley and Dartford Hospital Groups, Bromley, England

E. WITSCHI, Department of Embryology and Endocrinology, State University of Iowa, Iowa City, Iowa

O. H. WOLFF, M.D. Cantab., M.R.C.P., D.C.H., Department of Paediatrics, University of Birmingham, Birmingham, England

PREFACE

THE present work makes available in a single volume most of the basic contributions which have appeared in recent years which throw light on the chromosomal origins of a variety of disorders or diseases in man.

The main purpose of the book is to introduce the interested reader to the discoveries thus far made concerning the relation of chromosomal anomalies or aberrations to development, mental as well as physical. These discoveries are fundamental, opening up a completely new approach to the diagnosis and investigation of many disorders and diseases, as well as to the determination of sex.

It is the editor's hope that this book will be found useful by all who are interested in human development, whether they be physicians, geneticists, or behavioral scientists, and that it will supply the knowledge and encourage the inquiries which will lead to further discovery.

It is clear that we are at the frontier of a new era in medicine in which the advances yet to be made will be of far-reaching importance in the prevention, diagnosis, and treatment of disease. The contributions contained in this volume make it evident what direction those advances will take. No field of science is developing more rapidly than this. New and important observations are published virtually every week, indeed, at such a rate that it is hard to keep up with the literature. It is a most gratifying development, even though the speed of discovery allows only those to read who can run. The contributions are reprinted in fairly chronological order, although I have also endeavored to place related ones together and at the same time to approximate a systematic development of the role played by chromosomal aberrations in human disease.

As a final contribution I have reprinted Dr. Adrien Bleyer's remarkable paper of 1934 in which he accurately suggested the chromosomal mechanism operative in producing mongolism. This brilliant speculation had to wait a quarter of a century before it was confirmed by Lejeune and his co-workers.

My colleagues at the University Seminar on Genetics and the Evolution of Man at Columbia University, Drs. Kurt Hirschhorn and Herbert L. Cooper, have prepared the introductory chapter to this volume, a task which they generously undertook in the midst of an unusually busy academic year. I am extremely grateful to them for this service, as the reader will be who desires to follow the development of the subject and acquire a knowledge of the methods which will enable him to pursue investigations into the chromosomal bases of disease.

Finally, I am greatly indebted to the authors of the contributions reprinted in this volume, and to the editors of the journals in which they originally appeared, for permission to reprint. I am especially grateful to the editors and proprietors of *The Lancet* (London) who generously allowed me to reprint so many articles from the pages of that esteemed journal.

M. F. Ashley Montagu

Princeton, New Jersey

CONTENTS

Genetic Mechanisms
In Human Disease

1

CHROMOSOMAL ABERRATIONS
IN HUMAN DISEASE

A Review of the Status of Cytogenetics in Medicine

Kurt Hirschhorn, M.D., and Herbert L. Cooper, M.D.

INTRODUCTION

SINCE the beginning of 1959 a number of discoveries have led to an appreciation of a formerly unknown mechanism in the causation of human disease. These discoveries have demonstrated that some types of human pathology may have as their basic defect an abnormality of the number or morphology of the chromosomes. The sudden rapid progress that has been made in this direction is due to the application to human material of new techniques that have recently become available in the field of cytogenetics.

Cytogenetics may be defined as the direct study of the chromosomes, the bearers of the genetic material, by means of cytological techniques. It differs in its approach from that of transmission genetics where information is obtained by statistical analysis of characteristics transmitted from one generation to the next. In cytogenetics information is obtained by direct observation of the chromosomes and other cellular elements in terms of their behavior and appearance in cytological preparations. Correlations may then be made with the phenotypic characteristics of the organism and genetic information thereby obtained.

The methods of cytogenetics applied to lower organisms such

Reprinted from *The American Journal of Medicine, XXXI,* 1961.

From the Department of Medicine, New York University Medical Center.

The authors would like to express their appreciation to Dr. Marco Fraccaro of the Medical Research Council Unit for Population Genetics, Oxford, England, for his critical reading of the manuscript and valuable suggestions. We would also like to thank Dr. Herbert S. Kupperman for referring several of the patients used in this study, and Mr. Orlando Rendon for his technical assistance.

3

as the fruit fly (Drosophilia species) and corn (*Zea mais*) have provided much important information and corroboration in conjunction with transmission genetics.[1, 2] In contrast, human cytogenetics until recently has been a relatively unexplored field, contributing little information relating specifically to human problems. It is the purpose of this paper to review some of the recent developments in this field which bear directly on an understanding of certain specific human disorders and which may present us with a means of increasing our knowledge of the basic pathology of others.

EARLY DEVELOPMENTS

Prior to 1952, the scope of human cytogenetics was limited to attempts to count accurately the number of human chromosomes, and to verify that in the human species, as in other mammalian species, there was a sexual dichotomy in the chromosomes. The male was found to have an X and a Y chromosome while the female had two X chromosomes. This dichotomy was believed to be basic in sex differentiation.[1, 2]

Hansemann[3] in 1891 first succeeded in counting the chromosomes in human testicular tissue, and in three cells arrived at numbers of 18, 24, and 40. This work was done before the realization by Sutton[4] and Boveri[5] in 1903 that the chromosomes actually contained the hypothesized hereditary units, the genes. In 1912, DeWiniwarter,[6] also working with histological sections of testicular tissue, arrived at a human diploid number of 47, claiming that the human male had 23 autosomal paired chromosomes and an X chromosome, but no Y chromosome, while the female had 24 pairs. In 1921, Painter[7] in his preparations of fresh testicular tissue noted chromosome numbers ranging from 45 to 48. He also noted the existence of the Y chromosome, a small unpaired chromosome visible during meiosis. It is interesting, in the light of recent work, to quote Painter's actual words at that time:

In my own material the counts range from 45 to 48 apparent chromosomes although in the clearest equatorial plates so far studied only 46 chromosomes have been found.

Two years later, in 1923, Painter[8] unhesitatingly reported a diploid number of 48 chromosomes—23 autosomal pairs and two unmatched chromosomes—in normal testicular tissue. This seemed to clear away all doubt as to the human chromosome number, and the count of 48 was apparently verified by several other investigators.[9, 10] As will be pointed out later, the techniques employed at that time were inadequate for much further progress along the lines of the direct study of human chromosomes, and the situation remained essentially unchanged in that sphere until 1952.

THE SEX CHROMATIN

While progress in the direct examination of human chromosomes was slow, a significant development occurred in another direction which had important effects on the study of the heredity of sex. In 1950, Barr et al.[11] observed a difference in the morphology of cell nuclei depending on the sex of the individual providing the tissue. This consisted of a small darkly staining body located at varying positions within the nucleus, depending on the type of tissue examined. In human skin and buccal mucosa it is recognizable as a distinct chromatin body, usually closely adherent to the inside of the nuclear membrane (Fig. 1). It is found almost exclusively in the normal female ("chromatin positive") in up to 80% of cells of a section of skin 5 micra in thickness, and rarely if ever in the normal male ("chromatin negative").[12]

This sexual dimorphism is apparently present in many human tissues, including blood. Close study of well prepared peripheral blood films reveals the presence of accessory nuclear lobules or "drumsticks" in normal female polymorphonuclear leukocytes[13] (Fig. 2). They are observable in low frequencies (average: 3%) and some skill is required to differentiate them from other nuclear irregularities.

The exact nature of the sex chromatin body is still under investigation, and a full discussion is beyond the scope of this paper. The reader is referred to several excellent discussions of the subject.[12, 14–16] Most recent work suggests that the sex chromatin body represents the heterochromatic portion of one or both X chromosomes. It had been widely felt that the presence of two X chromosomes was necessary for and always associated with the presence of the sex chromatin body. Recent work has generally

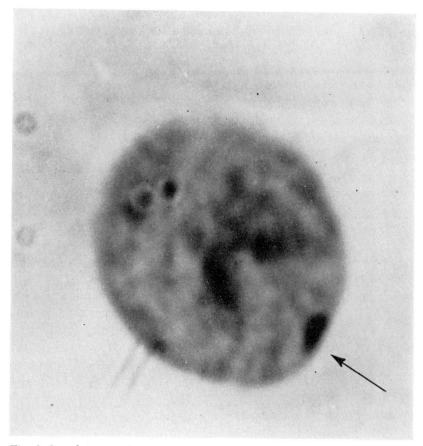

Fig. 1. Sex chromatin body (arrow) in nucleus of buccal mucosal cell from normal female.

confirmed this idea, but the finding by Grumbach *et al.*[17] of two cases of chromatin positive Turner's syndrome, each with only one X chromosome, has cast doubt upon the necessity of two X chromosomes for the presence of the sex chromatin body.*

Application of the technique of "nuclear sexing," as it was called, yielded some interesting results when applied to certain cases of human infertility and abnormal sexual development.[18] In the condition known as Klinefelter's syndrome,[19] usually char-

---

* At least one of these cases is a mosaic (see below), with some cells having two X chromosomes (Grumbach, M., personal communication).

acterized by male appearance associated with sterility, testicular atrophy, hyalinization of the seminiferous tubules and gynecomastia, a chromatin positive pattern is found in approximately 80% of cases.[12] These individuals may appear to be perfectly normal males or may have some degree of gynecomastia,

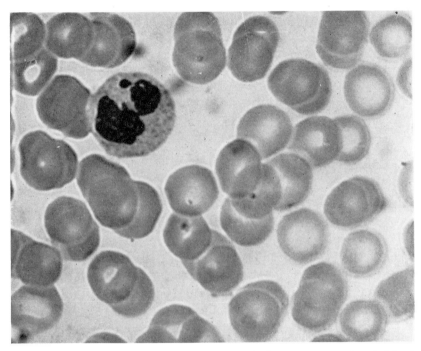

Fig. 2. "Drumstick" in polymorphonuclear leukocyte in peripheral blood smear from normal female.

but are certainly male in appearance. Conversely, in the condition known as Turner's syndrome (or gonadal dysgenesis) the patient appears as a sexually infantile female whose ovaries are represented only by some streaks of connective tissue attached to the broad ligaments. However, the patient is unmistakably female. In these cases, some 80% will have a chromatin negative pattern despite female appearance.[12] While these syndromes are interesting from the endocrinological viewpoint, they are even more fascinating from the genetic one and will be dealt with in detail below.

TECHNICAL DEVELOPMENT

Before discussing the recent rapid strides in human cytogenetics, some explanation of the technical progress in this field is necessary. Before the work of DeWiniwarter, most studies of human chromosome morphology were carried out on bits of testicular tissue obtained some time after the death of executed criminals. Invariably, some time elapsed before the tissue was secured and fixed. This undoubtedly resulted in undesirable tissue changes and in large part explains the conflicting results obtained by Hansemann, Bardeleben, Flemming, Duesberg and others.[8] De-Winiwarter[6] realized the importance of careful handling of the tissue, and obtained fresh surgical specimens. Using meticulous care, he prepared the tissue and sectioned it in 5 to 7.5 micron thicknesses. His drawings indicate a high degree of clarity, but nevertheless crowding and overlapping, together with the possibility of sectioning through a chromosome bent upon itself, make a definite determination of chromosome number uncertain. Painter used essentially similar technique, employing surgically obtained testicular tissue, fixed, imbedded in paraffin, stained and sectioned. It is subject to the same errors.

The use of testicular tissue seemed logical to these workers because it was the site of frequent meiotic divisions, and it might be expected to provide large numbers of cells for study. However, as indicated earlier, the rapid degenerative changes that take place in excised testicular material and the necessity for histological preparation requiring fixation, dehydration, clearing, imbedding in paraffin, sectioning and staining all provide ample opportunity for alterations in the specimen that would lead to faulty interpretation. In addition to these difficulties, the human meiotic chromosomes seen in such preparations present themselves as poorly outlined, closely clumped and overlapping bodies, and are extremely difficult to count accurately.

The recent improvements in technique are due mainly to the introduction of the methods of tissue culture into this field. Kemp[20] in 1929 was probably the first to apply tissue culture methods to the examination of human chromosomes. However, his methods did not permit very clear visualization of the chromosomes. In 1952, Hsu[21] found that the addition of colchicine to cultures of human cells grown in vitro provided large numbers of cells in the metaphase of mitosis due to the unique action of colchicine in arresting dividing cells at the metaphase. This was coupled with the use of a hypotonic salt solution during the prep-

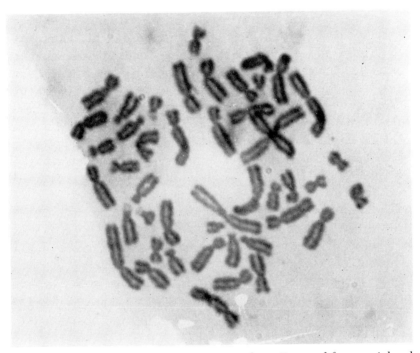

Fig. 3. Human mitotic chromosomes at metaphase. Prepared from peripheral blood grown in tissue culture (see appendix for method). Forty-six chromosomes.

aration of the cells. The hypotonic solution had the effect of swelling the cells and apparently disrupting the mitotic spindles, thereby greatly spreading the chromosomes and making them amenable to study. The chromosomes examined by this method present themselves as sharply outlined X-shaped bodies, each representing a single chromosome in the process of dividing (i.e., a pair of chromatids) (Fig. 3). There is a minimum of overlapping in good preparations and the chromosomes can be counted fairly easily, especially by means of photomicrography.

With the use of this technique Hsu again confirmed Painter's finding of 48 chromosomes as the normal diploid number in man. However, examination of the published photographs of Hsu's preparations might lead one to a different result, and in later work Hsu reports 46 chromosomes, as do most other workers at present.[21] Nevertheless, the figure of 48 remained unquestioned until 1956, when Tjio and Levan[23] working with cultures of fetal lung tissue reported only 46 chromosomes at mitosis. This finding was soon confirmed by Ford and Hamerton[24] and by other workers, including Chu and Giles[25] and Tjio and Puck.[26] At the present time, the normal human diploid chromosome number seems unmistakably established as 46. The possibility of the existence of supernumerary chromosomes, a phenomenon known in lower organisms, has been raised by Kodani[27] who describes the presence of small unmatched chromosomes in several of his preparations of testicular tissue. However, his findings have not been confirmed by others.

The use of the methods of tissue culture introduces new difficulties, but these are gradually being overcome. One important problem is the fact that cells in long-term tissue culture tend to change their chromosome number after many serial passages. The cells may become polyploid (contain more than twice the haploid number), translocations may occur, or the chromosomes may fragment, increasing the number of apparent chromosomes. In one line of originally normal human synovial tissue in our laboratory, after more than one year of repeated serial passages, using techniques in use prior to those of the past two years, the chromosome number had become exceedingly variable, ranging from 52 to over 60. The alteration may be a result of fragmentation of the chromosomes at the centromere (Fig. 4).

In practice, two methods are now available to circumvent such alterations of chromosome number. First, very short term tissue cultures are used, thus preventing the cumulative effect of long-term cultures with serial passages. Freshly drawn bone marrow is incubated for several hours, followed by another period of incubation in the presence of colchicine. The cells are exposed to hypotonic saline, centrifuged, stained, and spread on slides for direct

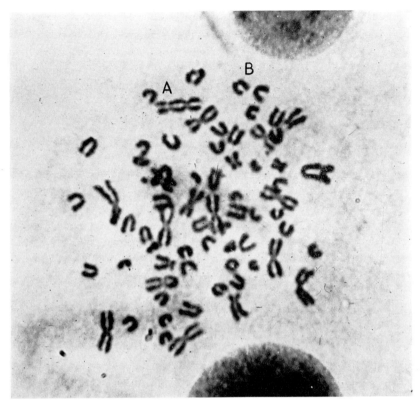

Fig. 4. Chromosomes at metaphase in originally normal human synovial tissue. Sixty-nine chromosomes. Cells grown in culture with multiple passages over a period of two years. Note abnormal chromosome number and morphology. One large chromosome with secondary constriction is seen at (A). Several chromosomes appear to have terminal centromeres (B).

examination. This is essentially the method of Ford and Jacobs[28] and with modifications is used by many workers.

Other innovations which appear to inhibit alteration of chromosome numbers as demonstrated by Puck et al.,[29] are the use of a growth medium which is optimal for the cells, rigid control of temperature and pH of the medium with an atmosphere of 5% CO_2 in which to grow the tissue, and periodic regrowth of the entire culture from single isolated cells. These modifications seem to allow long term growth of human tissues without significant chromosomal alterations. At any time after the establishment of the cells in tissue culture, they may be grown directly on cover slips, incubated in the presence of colchicine, swelled with hypotonic solution, stained and examined. For more exact details as to procedure, the reader is referred to the papers cited.

The use of colchicine has been avoided by several workers, including Lejeune,[30] Fraccaro,[31] and ourselves. It is their feeling that to study the morphology of the chromosomes accurately, it is necessary to introduce the least possible amount of distortion into the preparations. It is known that, in addition to halting the process of mitosis at metaphase, colchicine has the effect of contracting and widening the chromosomes, making their finer morphology difficult to observe. To obviate the necessity of using colchicine, these workers use a technique involving growth of the tissues for an intermediate length of time, long enough to permit growth of a single cell layer on a glass cover slip. The tissue culture medium is refreshed 12 to 16 hours prior to examining the cells, which has the effect of producing a growth spurt, providing many mitotic figures suitable for examination.

The advantages of using colchicine lie primarily in the larger number of mitoses available for examination and in the greater uniformity of the chromosomes in different cells and different preparations. This uniformity is of importance when the careful measurement of the characteristics of the individual chromosomes is undertaken.

In the appendix are presented the methods currently in use in our laboratory for the examination of chromosomes in cells cultured from bone marrow, skin, and peripheral blood.

NORMAL CHROMOSOMES—THE HUMAN KARYOTYPE

The use of the techniques just described has enabled us to prepare clear, easily examined preparations of human chromosomes (Fig. 3), and has allowed us to characterize the normal human chromosome complement in some detail. As in any new, rapidly advancing field, differences of terminology among the different workers have occurred, but they do not cause any undue confusion. The main source of difficulty has been the use of different systems to number the chromosomes. At a conference held in

Denver, Colorado in April 1960[32] it was generally agreed to use a numbering system similar to that first proposed by Chu and Giles,[25] with some modifications. In this paper that numbering system will be followed.

In good preparations the photographs of the chromosomes may be enlarged, the individual chromosomes cut out and paired to provide us with a matched set arranged and numbered in order of

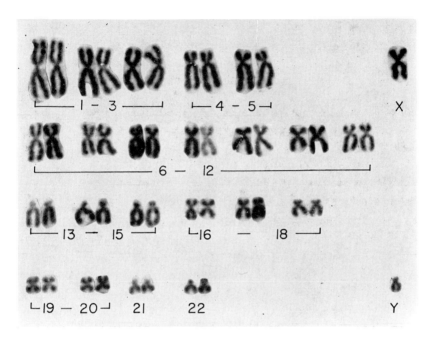

Fig. 5. Karyotype of normal male mitotic chromosomes. Numbered according to the Denver system. Note unmatched X and Y chromosomes.

decreasing size (Figs. 5, 6). Such an arrangement is called an idiogram or karyotype.

Each chromosome is characterized by the presence of a centromere, a constriction located somewhere along the chromosome at which the two chromatids that constitute the chromosome in the process of division are closely joined. The location of the centromere, the overall length of the chromosome, and the length of the "arms" on either side of the centromere are the basic distinguishing features of each chromosome, and permit identification and matching (Fig. 7). Three types of placement of the centromere are recognized: (1) Median or submedian, where the centromere is at, or fairly close to the midpoint of the chromosome, (2) subterminal or acrocentric, where the centromere is near, but not at, the tip of the chromosome, (3) terminal or telocentric, where the

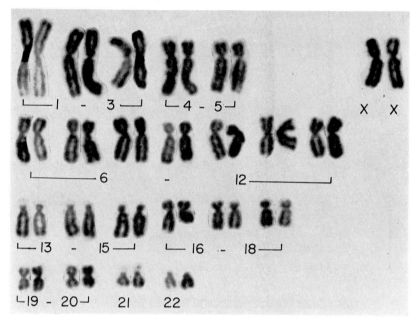

Fig. 6. Karyotype of normal female mitotic chromosomes. Numbered according to the Denver system. Note matching pair of X chromosomes.

centromere is at the tip of the chromosome and no short arm projects beyond it. In the normal human chromosome set there are no truly telocentric chromosomes, although some of the acrocentrics have extremely small "short arms."

In the normal human male (Fig. 5) five pairs of the longest chromosomes can be distinguished in gradually decreasing size. They all have median or submedian centromeres and can usually be further subdivided into two groups, the first with three pairs, and the second with two pairs. These are followed by another seven pairs of submedians, smaller and very similar to each other. Together with these twelve pairs a single unmatched median chromosome is found which falls midway between the two groups in size, and actually cannot always be distinguished from the members of the sixth or seventh pairs. In the female, however, there is no unmatched chromosome, but instead another matched pair making thirteen matched pairs of median or submedian chromosomes of large to moderate size (Fig. 6). By inference, the un-

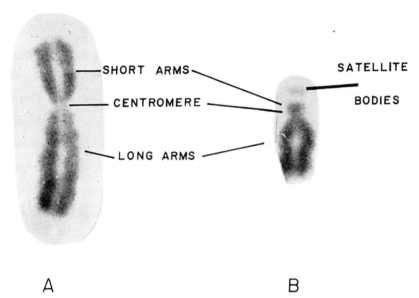

A   B

Fig. 7. Identifying features of human mitotic chromosomes. (A) Submedian or metacentric. Note location of centromere, long and short arms, overall length. (B) Subterminal or acrocentric. Note location of centromere, extremely small short arms, overall length. Also note presence of satellite bodies.

matched chromosome in the male has been labelled the X chromosome and the corresponding sized pair in the female is felt to be the pair of X chromosomes distinguishing the female sex.

Following these twenty-five or twenty-six chromosomes, we can identify three pairs of smaller acrocentric chromosomes, quite similar in appearance. Two of these pairs can sometimes be distinguished from the other one by the presence (in the best preparations) of two small "satellite bodies" extending from their short arms (Fig. 7). These three pairs are followed by five pairs of small submedian chromosomes in decreasing size, the last two being much smaller than the first three. Following these, we find two pairs of tiny acrocentrics. The larger of these pairs is distinguished by satellite bodies similar to those mentioned above. Finally, in the male, a single small acrocentric chromosome, without satellite bodies, remains unmatched.* Together with the previously described unmatched submedian, it completes the male's twenty-third "pair," making 46 chromosomes in all. The normal female never possesses this extra small chromosome, and it is presumed to be the Y chromosome of the XY male sex-determining pair.

In addition to the features just described, there appears to be considerable variation in the length of the chromosomes observed, depending on whether the cell is found in early or late metaphase. In early metaphase, the chromosomes are long and filamentous, with a knobby appearance. The two chromatids of each chromosome are not widely separated, and often one cannot discern the division between them at all. As metaphase progresses, the chromosomes appear to contract and become broader, while the chromatids spread more widely apart, their only point of conjunction being the centromere. Finally, they may rarely be seen to have severed their connection even at the centromere, just preparatory to entering anaphase. These differences are not always observed in colchicine preparations because of its effect of stopping mitosis at more-or-less the same point in all cells.

HUMAN CHROMOSOMAL ABNORMALITIES

Possessed of a technique for adequately examining human chromosomes, workers in this field turned their attention quite naturally toward applications of their methods in human pathology. In 1959, Lejeune *et al.*[33] and Jacobs *et al.*[34] described a consistently abnormal chromosome number in the somatic cells of "mongoloid" idiots. These patients were discovered to have 47 rather than 46 chromosomes at mitosis. By forming a karotype it is seen that these individuals have three rather than two of the small acro-

---

* Recent work has shown that all the acrocentric chromosomes except the Y carry satellites, although they are not always visible.

centric chromosomes with satellite bodies (Fig. 8). This is thought by most to be an extra 21st chromosome, although in some numbering systems it has been considered the 22nd. Nevertheless, the presence of a whole extra chromosome can be demonstrated consistently, and it is felt that this is the basic defect in the disease.

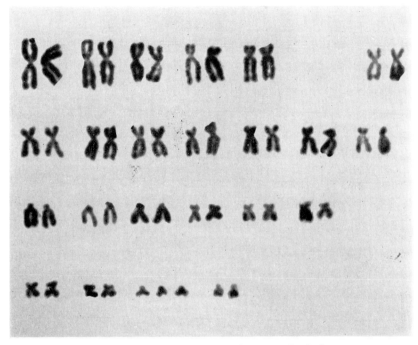

Fig. 8. Karyotype of mitotic chromosomes of a mongoloid idiot. Note trisomy of chromosome 21. Forty-seven chromosomes. Arranged according to the Denver sytem.

The possibility that mongolism was due to a chromosomal abnormality had long been suspected. In the 1930's, Waardenburg,[35] Bleyer,[36] and Penrose[37] each independently suggested that an abnormal chromosome number might explain the facts then known about mongolism.

The reasons for postulating a chromosomal abnormality are basically:

(1) There is 100% concordance between monozygous (identi-

cal) twins, both of the pair always being affected, never one
without the other. In dizygous (fraternal) twins the reverse
is usually the case, only one twin being affected.[38] This information essentially rules out the possibility of an intrauterine cause or
of any other environmental agent affecting the developing embryo, and suggests a genetic defect.

(2) In any family it is very unusual for more than one child to
be affected, and the parents are always normal. Exceptional cases
of two or more mongoloid children in one family have been reported, but these are exceedingly rare.[39] This mode of occurrence would suggest that the genetic factor for mongolism is inherited as a rare recessive trait, or that it is a fresh mutation in
each case. The possibility of fresh mutation is rendered unlikely
by the frequency of occurrence of the condition, which is about
one per 700 live births.[40] No gene is known in man that has such
a high mutation rate. The possibility that the condition is due to
a dominant gene with much reduced penetrance is also small,
since the occurrence of mongolism is almost always a single event
in any given family tree.[39]

(3) On rare occasions mongol females have borne children. To
our knowledge, seven such cases have been reported to date.[41-46]
These mothers have produced mongoloid children more frequently than could be expected on the basis of a simple recessive type
of inheritance. Two of the seven offspring of mongol mothers were
also mongols, and another had some other type of mental retardation, probably of another origin. This strongly suggests a dominant type of inheritance. The explanation of these contradictory
facts must be that some alteration must be present in the genetic
material of mongols which is expressed and transmitted as a dominant factor. This alteration must occur much more often than any
single gene mutation is ever known to occur in man. Finally, the
widespread abnormalities found in these individuals also suggest
more than one gene effect, although this is not definite.

There are two types of alterations in genetic material that can
produce changes in an organism and which can be transmitted to
future progeny. One of these is mutation of single genes. The foregoing discussion indicates that the situation in mongolism is not
explainable by the assumption of single gene mutations. The

other type of genetic alteration is chromosomal aberration. In this case genetic material is altered by deficiency or excess of all or part of a chromosome, or by a positional effect due to rearrangement of its parts. In the case of mongolism, all the preceding facts are consistent with chromosomal aberration as the cause of the abnormality.

The particular chromosomal aberration in mongolism is now seen to be the presence of an extra chromosome. The result of this excess is to produce changes in almost every tissue and physical characteristic of the affected individual. Even the basic biochemistry of the mongol seems to be distorted, as evidenced by the abnormal glucose tolerance and basal metabolic rate these individuals exhibit.[47]

The problem of how this extra chromosome arises is a key one, and may be elucidated by examining some basic facts well known to genetics in the study of lower organisms. Since we are dealing with an abnormality of chromosome number, it is necessary to understand the process by which the human chromosome number is kept constant from individual to individual and from cell to cell.

At fertilization, the zygote is formed by the union of two cells, the ovum and the sperm, each of which contains, normally, one chromosome of each of the 23 pairs of chromosomes—the haploid number. These haploid cells arise from originally diploid (46 chromosome) cells by the process of meiosis. The basic features of this process are (Fig. 9):

(1) Each chromosome in the nucleus comes to lie next to its homologue (other member of the pair). This is called synapsis, and is essential for normal meiosis. The X and Y in the male are partly homologous and therefore lie adjacent to one another, but are not completely synapsed as are the other chromosomes.

(2) Each chromosome is seen to be split longitudinally in two, forming two chromatids. The synapsis of such a pair of doubled chromosomes results in a four-stranded condition, a tetrad. It is at this stage, seemingly that crossing-over occurs between the chromatids of the homologous chromosomes, resulting in new arrangements of genetic material and preserving genetic variability in the species.

(3) The first meiotic division occurs, in which the two doubled

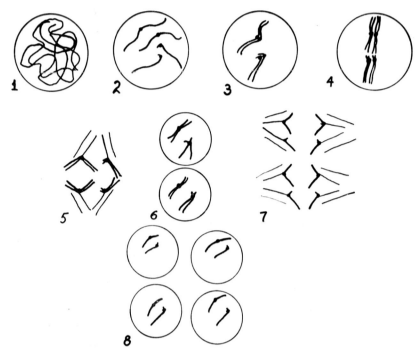

Fig. 9. Meiosis. (1) Nucleus of 1° gametocyte in prophase, leptotene stage. (2) Pachytene stage. Individual chromosomes discernible. (3) Synapsis. Members of each chromosome pair are associated. (4) Diplotene stage. Members of chromosome pairs are seen to be reduplicated. Tetravalents arranged around equator of cell, nuclear membrane disappears, meiotic spindle appears. (5) Diakinesis. Members of chromosome pairs are separated toward opposite poles (disjunction). (6) Completion of first meiotic division. Two cells now present, each with half the diploid number of chromosomes present as divalents. (7) Second meiotic division. Pairs of chromatids comprising each chromosome are separated (disjunction). (8) Completion of second meiotic division. Four cells, each carrying the haploid number of chromosomes.

chromosomes in each tetrad are separated into different cells. This is the process of disjunction and is of vital importance to the preservation of chromosome number. The result of disjunction at the first meiotic division is to produce two cells, each containing one member of each of the 23 pairs of chromosomes in the form of a pair of chromatids.

(4) The second meiotic division then occurs, in which the two

chromatids comprising each chromosome are separated and drawn into separate cells. This is disjunction at the second meiotic division and is also essential for proper maintenance of the chromosome number. The result is the formation from each primary germ cell of four cells, each containing the haploid number of chromosomes. These are the gametes that will take part in fertilization. In the male, all four persist as spermatozoa; in the female three of the products of meiosis degenerate into "polar bodies" while the fourth becomes a fertilizable ovum.

The new individual begins, then, as a diploid cell formed from two haploid cells, and possesses thereby the normal diploid number of chromosomes, 46, in the form of 23 matched pairs (or 22 pairs plus the X and Y in the male). From this one cell, the new individual develops by repeated multiplications. The chromosome complement of each cell remains constant during this series of multiplications by means of the process of mitosis. In this process the chromosomes come to lie more or less centrally in the nucleus, but no synapsis occurs. Instead, the two chromatids of each chromosome are directly separated into different cells, thus producing two cells with the normal diploid number (Fig. 10). From the mechanical point of view, the basic difference between meiosis and mitosis is that in meiosis two cell divisions occur with only one chromosome replication, while in mitosis each cell division is accompanied by chromosomal replication.

With these facts in mind, one may explain the occurrence of an extra chromosome, i.e., a triad instead of a pair. It should be noted that it is fairly certain that every cell in the mongoloid's body contains this defect.* It appears that the original zygote from which the mongol developed had the defect, and it was dutifully preserved by the process of mitosis. For the original zygote to have been defective, it must either have become defective after fertilization, or have received a defective gamete from one of its parents. While there is no definite evidence from mongoloid

---

* The process of cell division ceases in many tissues, such as skin, when the cells reach their mature state. Many cytologists believe that at the final mitosis before ceasing to divide, the cells may acquire abnormal chromosome numbers. This qualification to the preceding statement does not affect its general application.[48]

material to support either of these hypotheses, facts known from
the genetics of lower organisms support the theory that a defect
in one of the parental gametes is responsible. This defective
gamete apparently possessed an extra 21st chromosome (i.e., two
rather than one) and on union with a normal gamete from the
other parent resulted in a zygote with three rather than two of

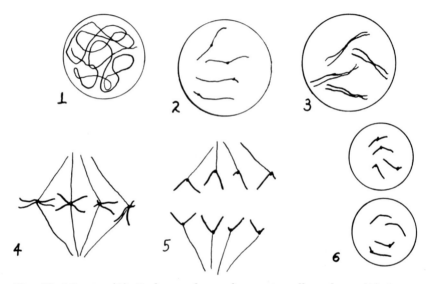

Fig. 10. Mitosis. (1) Early prophase of somatic cell nucleus. (2) Later
prophase. Individual chromosomes apparent. (3) Late prophase—early
metaphase. Each chromosome is seen to be reduplicated. (4) Metaphase.
Nuclear membrane disappears. Chromosomes arranged on mitotic spindle.
No association of homologous chromosomes. (5) Anaphase. Two chromatids comprising each chromosome are drawn to opposite poles. (6) Completion of mitosis. Two cells each containing the diploid number of
chromosomes.

the 21st chromosome. A probable explanation for the cause of
such defective gametes comes from the work of Bridges[49] with
Drosophila. He was observing the inheritance of sex-linked characters in fruit flies. It will be recalled that the theory of sex-linked
inheritance, as proposed by Morgan,[50] concerns characters that
follow a peculiar pattern of inheritance. A father who shows the
character will produce all normal-appearing progeny. His sons
produce only normal offspring. His daughters, although they

themselves appear normal, will transmit the character to half their sons. Females rarely, if ever, show the character in question. Morgan postulated that the gene for a character showing this sort of inheritance pattern was located on the X chromosome and was a recessive (Fig. 11).

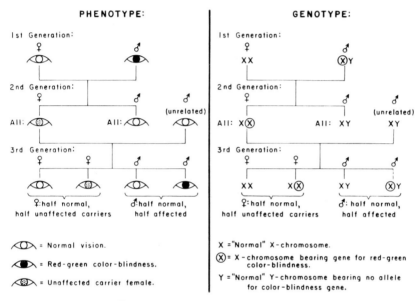

Fig. 11. Diagram illustrating recessive sex-linked inheritance. Red-green color-blindness is taken as an example. Note that affected individuals are all males, sons of unaffected carrier females. These females generally are daughters of affected males, but may be the daughters of unaffected carriers. For a female to be affected, her father would have to be affected and her mother a carrier. Note that the trait follows the transmission of the X chromosome from the affected male.

The following facts about sex-determination should be understood. All normal ova produced by the mother contain an X chromosome. Two types of sperm are produced by the father: half carry an X chromosome and half carry a Y. If an ovum is fertilized by an X-bearing sperm, the zygote formed will be XX and will become a female. If fertilization is accomplished by a Y-bearing sperm, the zygote will be XY and will become a male.

It will be observed that a father transmits his Y chromosome to his sons and his X chromosome to his daughters, never the reverse. Males always receive their X chromosomes from their mothers. Thus, by Morgan's theory, the sex-linked (or rather X-linked) gene will go from an affected father to all his daughters, who will carry the gene as a recessive, having a normal gene at the same location on the other X chromosome to offset its effect. His sons, receiving only the innocent Y from the affected father, will be perfectly normal, having received their X from their normal mother. When the carrier daughters produce ova, half of them will carry an X-chromosome bearing the normal gene, while half will carry an X-chromosome bearing the abnormal gene. Thus, these daughters will transmit an affected X to half their sons, who will show the recessive trait because their Y will not offset it. Similarly, half their daughters will again be carriers.

In order for a female to show a recessive sex linked trait, she must carry two genes for the trait, one on each of her X chromosomes. This is easily arranged with *Drosophila* in the laboratory. Bridges was working with female *Drosophila* of this type. They carried two X-linked genes for the recessive trait "white eye" and therefore showed the condition. When he crossed these white-eyed females to normal (red-eyed) males the vast majority of offspring were as predicted by Morgan's theory. The males, all receiving an abnormal X from their mother and a Y from their father, were white-eyed. The female offspring, all receiving an abnormal X from their mother and a normal one from their father, were red-eyed but could be shown by further breeding to be carrying the recessive trait.

Among many crosses of this type, however, on rare occasions white-eyed *females* and red-eyed *males* were produced instead of the reverse. These occurred in about one out of every 2,000 to 3,000 offspring of such a cross. Such an occurrence did not seem explainable by Morgan's theory. It meant, if Morgan were correct, that the white-eyed daughters did not receive a normal X from their father, but must have received two abnormal X's which could only have come from their mother. Likewise, the red-eyed sons must have received their father's normal X and not their mother's abnormal one. Such a series of events was unprecedented. Bridges suggested a means whereby these irregularities

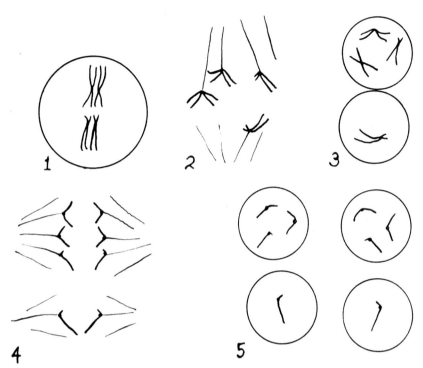

Fig. 12. Meiotic nondisjunction. (1) Diplotene stage, meiotic metaphase. Synapsed pairs of homologous chromosomes. (2) Nondisjunction at first meiotic division. Both members of one synapsed pair of chromosomes are drawn to the same pole instead of being separated. (3) Completion of first meiotic division. One cell contains both members of one chromosome pair, the other lacks any member of that pair. (4) Second meiotic division. (5) Completion of second meiotic division. Half of the gametes contain one more than the haploid number of chromosomes while half contain one less.

could have occurred. He postulated that, in the formation of the ovum during meiosis, an accident had occurred. At the time of disjunction in the first meiotic division, the two synapsed X chromosomes had not been drawn into separate cells. Instead, *nondisjunction* had occurred and both X chromosomes migrated to the same pole. This resulted in an ovum with either two X chromosomes, or none at all, instead of the usual single X (Fig. 12). If the ovum contains two X chromosomes and mates with a normal Y-bearing sperm, it should produce an offspring with the unusual sex-chromosome constitution of XXY. If mated with an X-bearing sperm, an XXX offspring was expected. Now the XXY offspring in the above example carried two abnormal genes for white eye, both obtained from the mother. Bridges predicted that the abnormal white-eyed females would have such an XXY constitution. When such females were subjected to cytological examination it was indeed found to be the case that they carried an extra chromosome and that they did have an XXY constitution, thus confirming Bridges' brilliant series of predictions. Similarly, if the ovum that had received no X chromosome at all were fertilized with an X-bearing sperm the resultant offspring would be X-O in its sex determining chromosomal make-up (i.e., it would have only one sex chromosome instead of two). Fertilization with a Y-bearing sperm would produce a Y-O individual. Bridges predicted that the unexpected red-eyed male flies he had found were these postulated X-O individuals. Again cytological examination proved him correct. As for the XXX and YO individuals also predicted, some XXX's were found, but they were underdeveloped females and usually did not survive. Because of their three X chromosomes, Bridges dubbed them "superfemales" although there was nothing "super" about them in any way. As for YO individuals, none were found, and it is presumed that such zygotes were totally nonviable. This might be expected, considering the complete absence of any of the genetic material normally carried by the relatively large X chromosome.

The occurrence of non-disjunction in meiosis is thus seen to account for abnormal chromosome numbers, both above and below the normal number. In particular, here is a process that might produce three instead of two chromosomes of one type. That the process is not restricted to the sex-chromosomes is shown by its widespread occurrence among plants. In general, being trisomic (having three rather than two of a given chromosome) results in decreased viability, as does being monosomic (only one chromosome instead of two). However, in the Jimson Weed, which has twelve pairs of chromosomes, twelve variants have been found, each of which is trisomic for a different chromosome.[1]

The process of non-disjunction, then, supplies us with a mechanism by which the individual with mongolism may have come to possess an extra chromosome in every cell of his body. While it does not tell us anything about the exact pathogenesis of the symtom-complex, an understanding of this process at least provides us with insight into the basic defect in the condition. At present, it can be postulated that mongolism is the end result of a non-disjunction in the formation of one of the parental gametes. A gamete is produced that contains the normal haploid set of chromosomes plus an extra 21st chromosome. When this gamete mates with a normal one from the other parent, the resulting zygote is trisomic for the 21st chromosome, and the effect of this trisomy is to distort the development of the embryo and produce the condition of mongolism.

It is generally felt that in the case of mongolism the defective gamete is most often the maternal ovum. This is suggested by the correlation between the incidence of mongolism and advancing maternal age, while there is no such correlation with paternal age.[62]

This effect of increasing age of the mother, but not of the father previously led to the leading hypothesis of the etiology of mongolism—that of poor intrauterine environment in an older woman. Now that the primary defect in mongolism has been placed much earlier in time, during the formation of the ovum, a different hypothesis is suggested to explain the fact that increased maternal age is correlated with the occurrence of mongolism, while paternal age seems unrelated. Although there is some difference of opinion, it is believed that all of a woman's germ cells are already present in the oocyte state while the ovary is still in its fetal state. These oocytes then remain dormant until adult life, when they divide to form the ova. Mintz[51] has recently suggested that at the time of birth, the oocytes may even have begun the process of first meiotic division, and may finish dividing only shortly before ovulation. This is quite different from the situation in the male, in whom new spermatocytes are constantly formed from puberty on. If aging of a cell is capable of causing damage to the normal spindle mechanism, thereby predisposing to the occurrence of non-disjunction, then the constantly aging maternal germ cells have a far greater chance of becoming abnormal than have the paternal germ cells, which are constantly being newly produced.

CHROMOSOME STUDIES IN INTERSEXES

As mentioned earlier, application of the technique of sex-chromatin examination produced unusual results in the majority of patients with Klinefelter's syndrome. These individuals, while

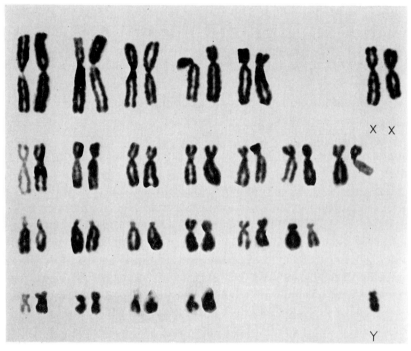

Fig. 13. Karyotype of mitotic chromosomes from an individual with Klinefelter's syndrome. Note the presence of two X-chromosomes together with a Y-chromosome. Forty-seven chromosomes. Arranged according to Denver system.

apparently male, were found to have nuclear chromatin bodies characteristic of female tissue. The incidence of Klinefelter's syndrome has been estimated as being as high as one in 1,000-3,000 live male births in the general population.[52-54] Among mental defectives, however, the incidence may be as high as 1-3%.[52, 54, 56]

Speculation as to the cause of Klinefelter's syndrome led to an analysis of the incidence of the X-linked condition of red-green color blindness in patients with this condition. Polani *et al.*[57]

found an incidence of color blindness among such individuals that suggested the presence of two X chromosomes. The following year Jacobs and Strong[58] reported such a case in which they counted the chromosomes in bone marrow cells. They found a

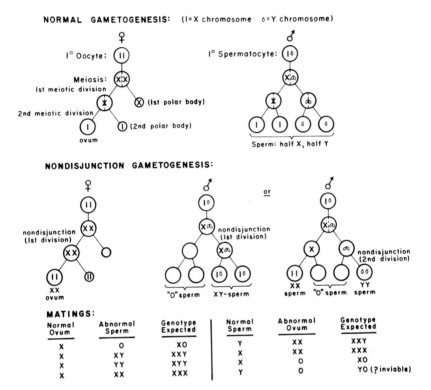

Fig. 14. Diagram illustrating the formation of normal gametes and the types of gametes resulting from nondisjunction involving the sex chromosomes. Predicted results from matings involving such abnormal gametes and normal gametes from the opposite sex are shown.

chromosome number of 47. There were 8 pairs of submedian chromosomes in the medium size range, indicating the presence of two X chromosomes. However, there were also five small acrocentrics, indicating the presence of a Y chromosome (Fig. 13). The patient had, apparently, a sex chromosomal constitution of the XXY type, and was phenotypically a male. Subsequent workers have confirmed this finding[59, 60] and it is now accepted that the majority, if not all, individuals showing the Klinefelter syndrome have this chromosomal aberration.

It is of interest to observe that the XXY individual found among *Drosophila* by Bridges was a fully viable, fertile female, while in the human an XXY individual is a sterile male. This fact was important implications in the general genetic theory of sex-determination, and will be discussed later.

In the Klinefelter syndrome, we have another situation where an extra chromosome occurs in every cell examined allowing for occasional different counts due to technical errors. In mongolism there was also an extra chromosome, one of the small acrocentric autosomes. (An autosome is any chromosome other than the X or Y.) The patient with Klinefelter's syndrome, however, has an extra chromosome of the sex-determining pair. The origin of the extra chromosome here, as in mongolism, is thought to be non-disjunction. Thus, at meiosis, abnormal gametes are produced as a result of non-disjunction of the sex chromosomes. In the female, this would produce either an XX ovum or an "O" ovum devoid of sex chromosomes. In the male, either an XY sperm or an "O" sperm would be produced. There are two ways in which an XXY constitution might arise, depending on which parent produced the abnormal gamete (Fig. 14). These are either fertilization of an XX ovum by a normal Y sperm, or of a normal X ovum by an XY sperm.

In mongolism, there is good evidence to support the idea that most cases arise through maternal rather than paternal non-disjunction. However, in Klinefelter's syndrome the evidence pointing toward one or the other parent as the more frequent cause is less definite. Stern[61] has analyzed data on the incidence of red-green color blindness in these patients and on statistical grounds feels that the most common causative event is maternal non-disjunction. As yet no correlation with maternal age has been reported.

TURNER'S SYNDROME

From the foregoing discussion it seems probable that XO individuals as well as XXY ones will be produced as a result of non-disjunction of the sex chromosomes. The possibility of an XO constitution in human subjects had been postulated in 1956 by Polani[63] after an analysis of the incidence of color blindness in females with the Turner syndrome. These individuals were usually found to have negative sex chromatin patterns and a male incidence of red-green color blindness. On the basis of these findings Polani postulated the presence of only one X chromosome in

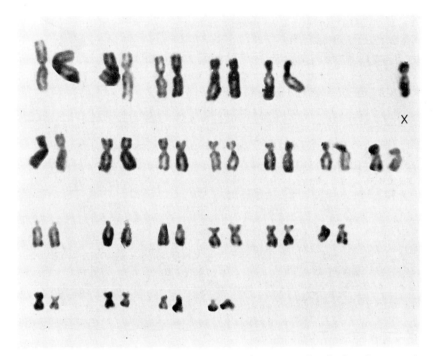

Fig. 15. Karyotype of mitotic chromosomes from an individual with Turner's syndrome. Note the presence of only one X-chromosome. No other sex chromosome is present. Forty-five chromosomes. Denver system.

these patients and possibly an XY or XO constitution. In 1959 Ford, *et al.*[64] reported the first chromosome analysis of a case of Turner's Syndrome and verified Polani's suggestion that these patients have only one X chromosome. The chromosome number in their patient was 45 and the sex chromosome constitution was XO (Fig. 15). The patient's karyotype revealed an unmatched medium sized submedian chromosome which was interpreted as a single X chromosome. There was no corresponding small acrocentric or Y chromosome. There was, therefore, only one member of the sex determining pair, a single X. This finding was confirmed by other investigators[65, 66] shortly thereafter, and it is now considered established that Turner's syndrome is the result of a sex chromosome constitution of the XO type.

The Turner syndrome, then, may be classed with mongolism and the Klinefelter syndrome as a disease due to abnormality of the chromosome number. The cause of these abnormal chromosome numbers is most probably non-disjunction during the production of parental gametes. Again, as in Klinefelter's syndrome, there is no definite evidence as to whether maternal or paternal non-disjunction is the more frequent cause.

It should be observed that among *Drosophila* XO individuals are sterile males, while among humans they are sterile females. In addition, the human XO condition is associated with a variety of other congenital malformations, while the *Drosophila* XO suffers only from sterility.

THE SUPERFEMALE

It will be recalled that as a result of the fertilization of a non-disjoined XX ovum by an X sperm, Bridges found a class of female flies that had poor viability and were physically below normal. Because of the XXX constitution he called them *superfemale*. If the occurrence of Klinefelter's and Turner's syndromes is actually due to the effect of parental non-disjunction and the resultant abnormal chromosome number, extension of the theory suggests that XXX humans should also exist.

It was only a question of time before such an individual was discovered. In 1959 Jacobs *et al.*[67] reported a sexually infantile female who had scanty menses which eventually ceased altogether. This patient had a positive sex chromatin pattern and even showed two nuclear chromatin bodies in most of the cells of a buccal mucosa scraping. Examination of her chromosomes revealed that she had a chromosome number of 47 with a karyotype indicating three X chromosomes. Jacob *et al.* have recently discovered another case of the same type.[68] The discovery of these cases, whose existence was predicted by theory, is the strongest confirmation of the correctness of the theory. It may be stated with practically complete assurance that the Klinefelter syndrome, the Turner syndrome and the superfemale represent the human counterparts of the XXY, XO and XXX in *Drosophila,* and that the etiology of the chromosomal abnormality is the same in both cases.

In a recent survey conducted among institutionalized mental defectives, Ferguson-Smith studied two individuals whose buccal smears showed two sex chromatin bodies in each nucleus.[69] These individuals were phenotypically males, but had 48 chromosomes, with 44 autosomes (normal) and a sex chromosome constitution of XXXY type. The mode of origin of such a condition is uncertain. Non-disjunction may have occurred by chance in both parents, or an XXX ovum may have been produced by the mother because of non-disjunction at both first and second meiotic divisions.

CHROMOSOMAL ABERRATIONS IN OTHER CONDITIONS

Just as the identification of an XXX condition in a human was an important theoretical confirmation, the discovery of another type of chromosomal aberration has given further evidence of the specificity of the defects produced by such aberrations.

In 1959, Ford *et al.*[70] reported a patient who exhibited clinically the features of both mongolism and the Klinefelter syndrome. As might be expected this patient's karyotype showed trisomy for the 21st chromosome and an XXY sex chromosome pattern. The chromosome number was 48. In our laboratory we have examined the chromosomes of a similar case[71] with the same results (Fig. 16). It would seem that trisomy for the 21st chromosome produces mongolism regardless of the condition of the other chromosomes; the same may be said for specificity of the XXY condition. However, the complete specificity of such abnormalities of chromosome number is doubtful, in view of a recent report by Fraccaro *et al.*[72] These workers report a case of mongolism with 46 rather than 47 chromosomes, but only one 21st chromosome. One of the 46 chromosomes was an unmatched small submedian, resembling the normal chromosome 19. At first it was postulated that the patient did have trisomy for the 21st chromosome, but that two of the three chromosomes had become translocated (see below) and fused into one to form the extra submedian that was found. However, examination of the chromosomes of the normal father of the patient revealed that this man was trisomic for the 19th chromosome. At present it cannot be decided whether the original explanation is the true one, or whether the mongol child

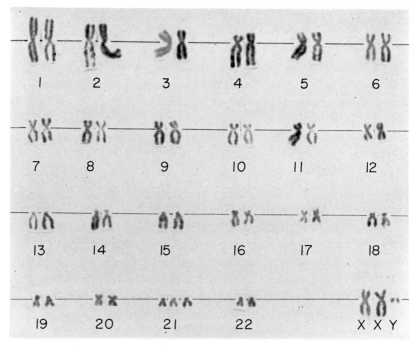

Fig. 16. Karyotype of mitotic chromosomes from an individual with both mongolism and Klinefelter's syndrome. Forty-seven chromosomes. Note trisomy for chromosome 21 and XXY sex chromosome constitution. Numbering system used is one applied prior to the Denver meeting.

is in fact trisomic for the 19th chromosome like his father and is actually *monosomic* for the 21st chromosome. If this is the case, it would seem that the imbalance caused by absence of a 21st chromosome is phenotypically indistinguishable from that caused by the presence of an extra one. It is also evident that trisomy for the 19th chromosome is a benign condition producing no easily demonstrable abnormalities. A preliminary report by Böök describes a triple 19.[73] This patient's only apparent abnormality was an interatrial septal defect. The patient's son was also examined, and was found to have the same abnormalities as his mother—trisomy for the 19th chromosome and interatrial septal defect.

Several other trisomic states have also been reported. Edwards *et al.*[74] report a case having multiple congenital anomalies with trisomy of the 17th chromosome. Patau *et al.*[75] have described two cases with congenital abnormalities where there was trisomy for one of the medium sized acrocentrics (i.e., number 13, 14, or 15). They do not believe they can determine which of these three very similar chromosomes is actually trisomic. Patau *et al.*[76] have also found six cases with another group of congenital anomalies where trisomy for the 18th chromosome has occurred. The triple 17 of Edwards and the triple 18 of Paton are probably the same entity. It is difficult to differentiate 17 and 18 with certainty. Fraccaro *et al.*[77] have reported a patient who had 49 chromosomes and exhibited facial and cephalic peculiarities and an intersexual state. This individual was thought to be trisomic for the 8th and 11th chromosomes with either XXY sex chromosome constitution, or triple 22 with XX constitution. It is now thought to be a case of XXXXY with normal autosomes.[102] Finally, Böök and Santesson[78] have reported an individual with mental retardation and central nervous system pathology who has 69 chromosomes. This patient is a complete *triploid, i.e.,* he has three of each chromosome instead of the expected pair. Further work has shown this subject to be a mosaic (see below) with both normal and triploid cells present.[103]

Undoubtedly other trisomic syndromes will be described in the near future. It is probable that trisomy for any of the 23 chromosome pairs, and combined states with any two or more chromosomes present in triplicate will also be found. Some of these situations will be lethal and therefore will be discovered in aborted fetuses, but it is apparent from the preceding group of cases that it is impossible to predict the extent of the pathology that any given trisomic state will produce.

The fact that trisomy for the 19th chromosome is compatible with normal development is especially important. It suggests that the abnormalities found in mongolism are not the result of the imbalance produced by an excess of a whole chromosome's content of genetic material, but only of such imbalance at one or a few key gene loci. Such a possibility brings mongolism closer to the class of diseases caused by single gene mutations which produce specific biochemical abnormalities. Examples of such conditions are phenylketonuria and galactosemia, both of which produce severe mental deficiency. In both of these conditions the basic biochemical defect is fairly well understood and attempts at treatment are being met with some success.[79] The importance of these speculations lies in the possibility that an underlying biochemical defect in mongolism, due to the action of one or a few genes on the 21st chromosome, may yet be uncovered, with the end result that mongolism too may eventually become a treatable disease. Recent work by Jérôme *et al.*[104] suggests an accelerated pathway in tryptophane metabolism in mongols.

TRANSLOCATION

All of the conditions thus far discussed involve an excess or deficiency of at least one entire chromosome. Another type of chromosomal aberration may occur and may be associated with disease. In this case, the aberration involves parts of chromosomes rather than whole chromosomes. During the course of mitosis (or meiosis) chromosomes may become fragmented. Such chromosome fragments frequently become joined to other fragmented chromosomes, producing a "new" chromosome. Such alterations are called *translocations*. Turpin *et al.*[80] were the first to report such an occurrence in a human. His case presented as a child with multiple abnormalities of the spine, and chromosome analysis revealed the apparent absence of one of the small acrocentrics. The chromosome number was 45. Careful study suggested that the missing chromosome had been translocated and was attached to the short arm of one of the longer acrocentrics. It is probable that some chromosomal material was lost, since translocations usually take place between the broken ends of two chromosome fragments. Also, it is questionable whether any disease would have been produced if the only abnormality were the attachment of two intact chromosomes.

Polani *et al.*[81] have found a case of mongolism where the extra chromosome characteristic of that disease was translocated and attached to one of the longer acrocentrics. The chromosome number was apparently normal, *i.e.,* 46. However, the discovery of the translocated extra chromosome indicates again that mongolism occurs when the genetic material of the 21st chromosome is present in "triple dose."

Another case found by Lejeune *et al.*[82] was a patient with Klinefelter's syndrome, but with only 46 chromosomes instead of the usual 47. On careful analysis two of the six medium sized acrocentrics (probably one number 13 and one number 15) were found to be missing. Their place had apparently been taken by a single long median chromosome. It is believed that this long chromosome is actually made up of both of the missing acrocentrics, translocated end to end.

MOSAICISM

During the development of a new individual from a zygote, a series of mitotic divisions, each involving replication of the whole chromosome set, occurs. It occasionally happens that a chromosome becomes translocated or lost altogether during mitosis in the early stages of growth. This might result in a portion of the body containing normal cells and another portion containing replications of the abnormal cell. Such a condition is referred to as *mosaicism.*

The occurrence of mosaicism due to a chromosomal aberration in humans was suggested by Ford *et al.*[83] when they reported the findings of a chromosomal analysis of a case of Klinefelter's syndrome. The majority of bone marrow cells examined showed 47 chromosomes with XXY sex chromosome constitution. However, a significant number of cells, more than could be attributed to technical error, were of XX constitution. It was felt that this individual was a mosaic, where the Y chromosome had been lost from one of the earliest cells of the embryo, resulting in a significant proportion of XX cells. Such loss of a sex chromosome has been known among *Drosophila* and is one cause of so-called gynandromorphs, where part of the body is female (XX) and part "male" (XO).[1] A similar case has been reported by Crooke and Hayward.[84]

Studies of a patient at our laboratory have been done on another case of a related type.[85] In this case, an infant was born with female genitalia and a much enlarged clitoris, or small phallus. Sex chromatin studies revealed consistently negative (male) patterns. Laparotomy revealed the presence of a uterus and fallopian tubes with two gonads. Histological sections of these gonads revealed grossly disordered structure, but most pathologists agree that both ovarian and testicular elements are present. It is probable that this patient is a true hermaphrodite.

Analysis of the chromosomes showed two types of cells in the bone marrow. About 40% had an XY constitution with a Y chromosome that seemed somewhat larger than usually found. (In our experience, as well as in the experience of other workers[86] the Y chromosome is more variable in length than the other chromosomes.) The remaining cells showed an XO constitution. It is probable that in this case the Y chromosome was lost in one of the early cells of the embryo, producing the picture seen. The extent and distribution of the mosaicism is not yet known, since the proportion of atypical cells in the bone marrow may not reflect the distribution throughout the body.

To date, chromosomal analysis of two other cases of true hermaphroditism have appeared in the literature.[87, 88] One of these was phenotypically female, while the other was an apparent male. Both showed the presence of an ovo-testis, confirming the diagnosis of true hermaphroditism. On chromosome analysis, both showed the XX sex chromosome constitution. The origin of partly functional testicular tissue in these individuals is problematical, and it has been suggested that such patients are actually mosaics. The finding of only one cell type in the bone marrow, skin and peripheral blood in these cases does not rule out the presence of a mosaic in the gonadal tissue. The case of XY/XO mosaicism described above supports the idea that true hermaphrodites may be mosaics. In the cases where only XX cells were found it is possible that a mosaicism of the XX/XXY or XX/XO type actually exists but has not been detected.

As implied above, other types of sex chromosome mosaics may occur, and some have been found. Ford[59] and Fraccaro et al.[89] have found cases of mosaicism of the XX/XO type where some of the cells are normal (XX) and some have only a single sex chromosome (XO). These cases all presented clinically with Turner's syndrome, but were sex chromatin positive. Such mosaicism may account for some of the chromatin positive Turner's syndromes that have been reported.

Jacobs *et al.*[68] have studied another interesting type of mosaic. This patient had primarily XXX sex chromosome constitution in cells cultured from skin, while the peripheral blood and bone marrow were largely of XO constitution. The case came to their attention because of the presence of double sex chromatin bodies in buccal mucosa scrapings (related to the XXX constitution). The peripheral blood, however, showed no "drumsticks" (related to the XO constitution).

In the cases of mosaicism just described, the individual's body was found to be composed of two types of cells. At least one of these cell types possessed an abnormal sex chromosome constitution (XXY, XO or XXX). It is apparent that these atypical cells can be responsible for abnormal sexual development despite the presence of a large number of normal cells in the body. The exact location of the abnormal cells is probably critical. If they comprise a large proportion of the gonadal tissue, abnormalities of sexual development may be expected.

Court Brown *et al.*[90] have discussed the subject of mosaicism and suggest certain criteria which should be met in order to diagnose mosaicism by chromosome counts:

(1) The frequency of the cells with non-modal chromosome number should be greater than that expected by chance alone.

(2) The determination should be made on repeated specimens from different tissues, if possible.

(3) All the non-modal cells should have the same karyotype.

It is to be expected that mosaicism for the autosomes will also be discovered, but to date none have been reported.

ISOCHROMOSOMES

Another chromosomal anomaly has been mentioned by Fraccaro.[91] He has found three cases that present some of the features of Turner's syndrome (primary amenorrhea, short stature, elevated urinary gonadotrophins) but lack others (no webbed neck, sex chromatin positive). These cases all had 46 chromosomes, but the chromosomes thought to be the XX pair did not match one another. One was considerably longer than the other and, unlike the usual X chromosome, had a perfectly median centromere. Fraccaro postulates that this chromosome arose by the splitting of the centromere the wrong way at the second meiotic division. Instead of splitting vertically down the middle, thereby separating the two chromatids, the centromere split horizontally. The long arms of both chromatids remain joined and went to the same daughter cell, while the short arms went to the other. The long arms then behaved as a new chromosome and were replicated as such at each cell division thereafter. This new "isochromosome" carries none of the genetic material of the short arm of the X chromosome and a double dose of the material of the long arm. It is possible that the genetic material in the short arm of the X chromosome is required in double dose for normal female development. Its absence, either in the XO individual or because of a long arm isochromosome, results in primary amenorrhea, with or without the complete Turner's syndrome.

DISCUSSION

It is apparent that significant contributions to medical knowledge have been made by the application of the techniques of cytogenetics to human disorders. The basic defect and its probable mode of origin have been discovered for three well known diseases: mongolism, Klinefelter's syndrome, and Turner's syndrome. In addition, one possible etiology for multiple congenital anomalies and intersexes is now recognized, and merits investigation in appropriate cases. While the frequency of chromosomal aberration as a cause for these conditions is not known, further investigation will undoubtedly produce many such cases. In particular, chromosomal analysis may clarify the pathology in individual cases. Thus, Harnden and Stewart[92] have reported a case of "pure gonadal dysgenesis" in an apparent female. This patient was tall, thin and sexually undeveloped, but otherwise had none of the stigmata of Turner's syndrome. The patient had a vagina, uterus and fallopian tubes, and artificial menses occurred following estrogen treatment. Cases of this sort have been generally considered to be variants of Turner's syndrome, lacking the short stature, webbed neck and other recognized characteristics of the disease, but having the major defect of secondary sexual and gonadal underdevelopment. Harnden and Stewart's case, however, on chromosome analysis was shown to be of XY constitution, i.e., a male karyotype, unlike the XO usually found in Turner's syndrome. This case emphasizes the importance of considering more than the chromosomes themselves in trying to understand the development of the human phenotype. The patient in question, while chromosomally a male developed as a female either because of intra-uterine hormonal influences, or perhaps as a result of some rare dominant single gene mutation. A possible explanation of this case is suggested by some of the work of Jost.[93, 94] He has shown in rabbits that males castrated in utero developed the female phenotype, presumably because of maternal hormonal feminizing effects. In the case under discussion, as a result of some genetic factor or of some intrauterine accident, it is possible that the fetus did not develop any functioning testicular tissue. It was effectively castrated, and the result was the same as in Jost's rabbits.

This case should not be confused with the syndrome of testicular feminization, where XY sex chromosome constitutions have also been found in apparently female individuals.[95] These cases, unlike Harnden and Stewart's case, have definite undescended testes and no uterus or tubes. The vagina ends as a blind pouch of varying length and the clitoris is of normal size. This condition is inherited as a single gene defect.[95]

The foregoing speculations bring up the knotty problem of sex determination, which until recently was felt to be fairly well settled by the work of Bridges.[96] It will be recalled that among Drosophilae, flies of XXY constitution are normal females, while flies of XO constitution are healthy but sterile males. Thus, the XXY and XX conditions are indistinguishable, and the XY and XO conditions differ only by the factor of sterility. The presence of two X chromosomes makes the fly a female, and an added Y has no effect. If one of the two X's is "subtracted" the result is a male. Apparently the presence of two X chromosomes provides enough female determining genetic material to produce a female fly, while one X chromosome does not, its effect being overcome by male determining genes which have been shown to be carried on the autosomes.[96] The "female" genes on the X chromosome are sufficiently potent in double dose to overcome the effect of a diploid set of male determining autosomes and produce a female. A single X, however, does not provide sufficient feminizing influence to overcome a diploid set of male determining autosomes, so that the XY or XO drosophila is a male.

Thus, the Y chromosome appears to have little or nothing to do with the production of male characteristics in the *Drosophila*. However, in the human, this is obviously not the case, since the XO individual is a female and the XXY a male. Seemingly the addition of a Y chromosome to a female (XX) constitution converts it to a male phenotype. Similarly, the lack of a Y chromosome (XO) is not insignificant and any autosomal male sex-determiners are apparently unable to overcome the effect of a single X chromosome. These facts suggest that in man potent male determiners are linked with the Y chromosome, since maleness apparently cannot occur in its absence, and its presence produces maleness even when two X chromosomes are also present.

Similarly, Welshons *et al.*[97] have shown in mice that the XO condition produces a female which, unlike the human XO, is usually fertile. It is of interest that Bahner *et al.*[98] have reported a case of a woman with XO sex chromosome constitution who bore a child, showing that the XO human may also be fertile in rare cases. Thus, it seems that among the mammals that have been studied the Y chromosome is a bearer of male sex determiners.

It would appear then, at first glance, that the balance theory of sex determination has been shown to be non-applicable for mammals, but that the X and Y chromosomes are themselves the bearers of the necessary sex determinants. However, it is important to bear in mind the fact that placental mammals do not develop independently of maternal sexual effects as Drosophilae do. A well known example of the effect of the intrauterine hormonal environment is the masculinization of female fetuses by administration of progesterone to the mother during pregnancy.[99] As shown by Jost, a castrated mammalian embryo develops the female phenotype, possibly as a result of endogenous maternal feminizing secretions.[94] In order to combat this feminizing effect, functioning embryo testicular tissue seems necessary. The presence of a Y chromosome is apparently required for the development of such testicular tissue, since the human XO individual usually has no gonads to speak of. It would seem that such an individual, without functioning testicular tissue, develops as a female because of the combined effects of the single X chromosomes and the maternal hormonal milieu. Any autosomal male determiners are apparently overwhelmed. In the same way, in the XXY human the addition of the Y chromosome results in the production of apparently functional testicular tissue, and masculinization occurs, in spite of a double dose of X chromosome female determiners and the maternal hormonal milieu. It cannot be confidently stated that this is because the Y chromosome is the sole factor involved in male determination. It may be that the addition of the Y chromosome to the autosomal male determiners already present is sufficient to tip the balance in favor of maleness.

It is of interest in this connection that the previously mentioned case of Böök's with complete triploidy (69 chromosomes)[78] seemed to have normal sexual differentiation. His sex chromosome constitution was of the XXY type, but he differed from a case of Klinefelter's syndrome by having an extra set of autosomes. The presence of this extra set of autosomes may have increased the "maleness" of the patient. It can be tentatively postulated, on the basis of this information, that the autosomes do contain masculinizing factors.

Thus, with present evidence, the balance theory of sex determination cannot be considered to be inapplicable to mammalian sex determination. With the modifications indicated above it may still be valid.

SUMMARY

(1) A brief history of the development of techniques in human cytogenetics is presented. Early and recent information obtained by these techniques is reviewed.

(2) Application of these techniques to the study of human disease is illustrated. The basic chromosomal defects in several disease states are presented. The best studied conditions to date

are mongolism, Klinefelter's syndrome, and Turner's syndrome. In mongolism there is trisomy for the 21st autosome. In Klinefelter's syndrome there is an XXY sex chromosome constitution. In Turner's syndrome there is an XO sex chromosome constitution. The chromosome numbers in these conditions are, respectively, 47, 47, and 45, while the normal human chromosome number is 46.

(3) Non-disjunction of chromosomes at meiosis in the production of parental gametes is postulated as the mechanism for the production of these chromosomal aberrations in the above-mentioned conditions. The process of non-disjunction is discussed in detail. It results in the production of parental gametes with either more or less than the normal haploid number of chromosomes. Fertilization involving such a gamete and another normal one may result in a zygote that is either trisomic for the chromosome involved, or is deficient in one chromosome.

(4) Other types of chromosomal aberrations are discussed. Some of these are translocation, mosaicism, and isochromosome formation.

(5) The importance of the techniques and new information described is discussed. The bearing of recent information on the theory of sex determination is also discussed.

Appendix

The methods and materials used by the authors for chromosome preparations vary with the tissue to be examined. We shall describe those used for bone marrow, skin, and peripheral blood.

BONE MARROW

Approximately 1 cc of bone marrow is aspirated under sterile conditions from the sternum or iliac crest and suspended in 3 cc of nutrient medium, consisting of 60% medium 199 (Difco), 35% single donor AB serum and 5% freshly prepared chicken embryo extract. The medium also contains 200 u/cc penicillin, 100 μg/cc streptomycin and 20 u/cc mycostatin (Squibb, suspension). This is then distributed into sterile 60 mm Petri dishes containing a cover slip, with 1 cc in each Petri dish. Two to 3 cc of the nutrient medium is added to each dish, and the covered dishes are placed into a 37°C incubator in a 5% CO_2 atmosphere. Depending on the cellularity of the original inoculum, the dishes are removed from 24 to 72 hours later, the higher cell concentrations requiring less time. No colchicine is used in this method. The cover slips are removed with sterile forceps, and the dishes returned to the incubator for eventual passage of the cells. The cover slips are placed into 0.7% sodium citrate for 10 minutes, and then into 2% acetic orcein (2 grams natural orcein (Matheson, Coleman and Bell), dissolved in 45 cc glacial acetic by heating with a reflux condenser, then add 55 cc distilled water while still warm; filter before use) for 5 minutes. The cover slip is inverted on a clean slide, squashed gently and examined. If spreading is insufficient, one may squash more strongly. Seal with Kronig's cement. This method is a modification of that described by Fraccaro, Kaijser and Lindsten.[31]

SKIN

After injection of 1% procaine deep to the area to be biopsied (usually the posterolateral aspect of upper thigh or buttock), not intradermally, a superficial fold of skin is grasped with pointed tissue forceps and is cut with a sharp scalpel blade, under sterile conditions. The resulting fragment is usually approximately 5 x 4 mm and is 2 mm thick. This procedure leaves no scar. The skin is kept in sterile saline until preparation. The fragment is cut into small explants (app. 1 x 1 mm), which are distributed into 2 or 3 60 mm Petri dishes with cover slips, some pieces lying on and some off the cover slip. No plasma clot is required. Nutrient medium, consisting of 70% medium 199, 20% single donor AB serum and 10% chicken embryo extract, with the same antibiotics as in the bone marrow medium, is added to not quite cover the explants (usually 1.5 cc). The covered dishes are incubated at 37°C in a 5% CO_2 atmosphere. The medium is changed three times a week without disturbing the explants. After one to three weeks, a monolayer of cells has grown from the explants onto the glass, and a deeper layer of medium (3 cc) may be used. When growth appears to be active, the cover slips are treated as in the bone marrow technique. Since these preparations will usually not give many mitoses for study, the remaining cells are removed from the Petri dishes by incubating for 20 minutes with 2 cc of a 50/50 mixture of trypsin and Versene, made up in calcium and magnesium free Hanks' solution. The resulting cell suspension is centrifuged gently for 5 minutes (4 - 500 RPM), resuspended in 2 to 10 cc of the nutrient medium, the amount depending on the cell dentisty. 2 cc aliquots of the suspension are placed in 60 mm Petri dishes with cover slips and replaced into the CO_2 incubator. After 3 to 4 days a heavy growth of cells covers the bottom of the dish. The cover slips are removed with sterile forceps and treated as in the bone marrow method. Again no colchicine is necessary. The cells remaining in the dishes may be subcultured for future examinations. This method is a modification of that described by Harnden.[100]

PERIPHERAL BLOOD

Ten to 20 cc of venous blood is obtained in sterile vacuum tubes, which have previously been prepared with 0.1 cc of a 5,000 μ/cc solution of heparin (Liquaemin). Within 2 hours, 0.25 cc Phytohemagglutinin (Bacto) is added to each 10 cc of blood. After standing for 2 minutes, the blood is centrifuged at 200 RPM for 5 minutes. The serum, containing the white blood cells, is pipetted off, and 2 cc aliquots are placed in wide 35 cc centrifuge tubes. Medium 199 is added so as to make the final cell concentration 1 to 3 million/cc (usually 8 cc of 199 to 2 cc of cell suspension). The tubes are closed and placed in a 37°C water bath for 72 hours. At this time, colchicine (final concentration 3 gamma/cc) is added without removing the tubes from the bath. All steps until this point are done with sterile technique. Colchicine is not necessary, but helps to obtain greater numbers of countable mitoses. After 2 hours, the tubes are emptied into conical 15 cc centrifuge tubes, which are centrifuged at 400 RPM for 5 minutes. The supernatant is pipetted off, 2 cc of 1% sodium citrate is added to each tube and the cells suspended. After 3 minutes, the tubes are centrifuged at 200 RPM for 4 minutes, and the supernatant is pipetted off. A 3:1 mixture of absolute ethyl alcohol and glacial acetic acid is added slowly, drop by drop, resuspending after each drop, until 2 cc have been added. After 10 minutes, the suspension is centrifuged at 200 RPM for 4 minutes, and the supernatant is pipetted off. The cells are now suspended in 2 cc of 45% acetic acid, where they are permitted to settle for 12 hours or more in the refrigerator. The supernatant is pipetted off, and the cells are resuspended in 1-2 cc of the alcohol-acetic acid mixture. Several small drops are distributed on a clean cover slip and permitted to dry. Temporary preparations may be made by placing a drop of acetic orcein (as above) on a slide, inverting the cover slip on the drop, and removing the excess stain by placing filter paper along the edges of the cover slip. This preparation is sealed with Kronig's cement. Permanent preparations are made by placing the unstained cover slip in a staining rack, which is taken through the following solutions: acetic orcein, 25 minutes; tertiary butyl alcohol, 1 minute; tertiary butyl alcohol, 1 minute; tertiary butyl alcohol, 2 minutes; 1:1 tertiary butyl alcohol/xylene, 2 minutes; xylene, 6 minutes; xylene, 2 minutes. While still wet with xylene, the cover slip is inverted on a slide into a drop of Diaphane, Euparol or Permount. This method is a modification of those described by Miller,[101] and Hungerford *et al.*[87]

All types of preparations are then studied by microscopic examination under oil immersion, microphotography, and cutting out individual chromosomes from enlargements for final matching.*

ADDENDUM

Since this paper was submitted for publication, many articles have appeared in the literature which describe material of importance to human cytogenetics. We have selected a group of these references and listed them below, together with our comments. No attempt has been made to be comprehensive. The works cited are ones which seem to have general importance.

(1) DeGrouchy, J., Cottin, S., Lamy, M., Netter, A., Netter-Lambert, A., Trevoux, R., and Delzant G. Un cas de dysgenesie gonadique a formule chromosomique male (XY) normal. *Rev.*

---

* This work was done during the tenure of an Established Investigatorship of the American Heart Association of one of the authors (K. H.), and was aided by grants from the American Heart Association, the U.S. Public Health Service (H-2202) and the New York City Health Research Council (U-1030).

Franc. Etudes Clin. et Biol. 5:377, 1960. Similar to Harnden's case of XY constitution in a phenotypic female, but has laparotomy findings of one small primitive gonad.

(2) Stewart, J. S. S. and Sanderson, A. R. Fertility and Oligophrenia in an apparent triplo-X female. *Lancet ii*:21, 1960.

(3) Fraser, J. H., Campbell, J., MacGillivray, R. C., Boyd, E., and Lennox, B. The XXX syndrome: frequency among mental defectives and fertility. *Lancet ii*:626, 1960. Indicates relatively unimpaired fertility in XXX humans generally. High correlation with mental deficiency is suggested, but incidence in the general population is unknown.

(4) Carr, D. H., Barr, M. L., and Plunkett, E. R. An XXXX sex chromosome constitution in two mentally defective patients. *Canad. Med. Ass'n. J.* 84:131, 1961. Association between multiple numbers of X chromosomes and mental retardation. Demonstrates relationship of "Sex chromatin" to X chromosomes: 3 chromatin masses found in many buccal mucosal cells presumably carrying 4 X chromosomes, i.e.—one less chromatin mass than number of X chromosomes,

(5) Barr, M. L. and Carr, D. H. Sex chromatin, sex chromosomes and sex anomalies. *Can. Med. Ass'n. J.* 83:979, 1960.

(6) Miller, O. J. and Breg, R. XXXXY sex chromosome constitution. Personal communication. (5) and (6) demonstrate masculinizing effect of Y chromosome in the presence of multiple X chromosomes (XXXY in (5)). These patients had Klinefelter's syndrome and mental deficiency.

(7) Muldal, S. and Ockey, C. H. The "double male": a new chromosome constitution in Klinefelter's syndrome. *Lancet ii*:492, 1960. An XXYY individual with Klinefelter's syndrome.

(8) Cooper, H. L., Kupperman, H. S., Rendon, O. R., and Hirschhorn, K. Sex chromosome mosaicism of type XYY/XO. In press, 1961. Another type of mosaicism in a phenotypic female with gonadal dysgenesis.

(9) Carter, C. O., Hamerton, J. L., Polani, P. E., Gunalp, A., and Weller, S. D. V. Chromosome translocation as a cause of familial mongolism. *Lancet ii*:678, 1960.

(10) Penrose, L. S., Ellis, J. R., and Delhanty, J. D. A. Chromosomal translocation in mongolism and normal relatives. *Lancet*

ii:46, 1960. Together with reference 81, these papers demonstrate the existence of a class of mongols who have triple dose of chromosome 21, but only 46 chromosomes. This is due to a translocation and fusion of two chromosomes into one. Also shows that normal parents and relatives of these mongols frequently have only 45 chromosomes including the translocation. These parents have a high expectancy of producing mongoloid children because of the abnormal translocation chromosome they carry.

(11) Moorhead, P. S., Mellman, W. J., and Wenar, C. A familial chromosome translocation associated with speech and mental retardation. *Am. J. Hum. Genet.* 13:32, 1961. Reports familial transmission of translocation chromosomes. Also suggests an increased risk of meiotic nondisjunction in subjects carrying such translocations. Indicates the importance of studying normal relatives of patients with chromosomal anomalies.

(12) Tough, I. M., Buckton, K. E., Baikie, A. G., and Court Brown, W. M. X-ray induced chromosome damage in man. *Lancet ii*:849, 1960. Demonstrates chromosome abnormalities in circulating leukocytes after therapeutic radiation.

(13) Nowell, P. C. and Hungerford, D. A. Chromosomal studies on normal and leukemic human leukocytes. *J. Nat. Canc. Inst.* 25:85, 1960.

(14) Nowell, P. C. and Hungerford, D. A. A minute chromosome in human chronic granulocytic leukemia. *Science* 132:1497, 1960.

(15) Baikie, A. G., Court Brown, W. M., Buckton, K. E., Harnden, D. G., Jacobs, P. A., and Tough, I. M. A possible specific chromosome abnormality in human chronic myeloid leukemia. *Nature* 188:1165, 1960.

(16) Tough, I. M., Court Brown, W. M., Baikie, A. G., Buckton, K. E., Harnden, D. G., Jacobs, P. A., King, M. J., and McBride, J. A. Cytogenetic studies in chronic myeloid leukemia and acute leukemia associated with mongolism. *Lancet ii*:411, 1961. A series of important papers demonstrating a specific chromosomal abnormality related to chronic myelocytic leukemia. A minute chromosome is found in place of either a number 21 or 22 in the leukemic cells.

(17) Hayward, M. D. and Bower, B. D. Chromosomal trisomy

associated with the Sturge-Weber syndrome. *Lancet ii*:844, 1960. Suggests trisomy of number 22 in Sturge-Weber syndrome, but not supported by further work of the same and other authors.

(18) Tjio, J. H., Puck, T. T., and Robinson, A. The human chromosomal satellites in normal persons and in two patients with Marfan's syndrome. *Proc. Nat. Acad. Sci. 46*:532, 1960.

(19) Cooper, H. L. and Hirschhorn, K. Enlargement of chromosomal satellites: an asymptomatic familial condition. In preparation, 1961. These papers demonstrate that chromosomal satellites may be markedly enlarged. Most such cases have been found in subjects with some congenital or genetic disease, but they have also been found in completely normal individuals. The chromosome bearing the enlarged satellite may be followed through several generations and used as a chromosomal marker for genetic studies.

(20) Hirschhorn, K., Cooper, H. L., Rendon, O. R., and Meyer, L. M. A case of mongolism with chromosomal translocation, familial giant satellites and leukemia. In preparation, 1961.

(21) German, J. L., III, DeMayo, A. P., and Bearn, A. G. Chromosomal translocation in a mongol with leukemia. Personal communication. Mongolism and monocytic leukemia in translocation-type mongols.

(22) Harnden, D. G. The Chromosomes. In: *Recent Advances in Human Genetics* (ed. L. S. Penrose), Churchill, London, 1960. Review of chromosome techniques; describes phenomenon of association between satellited chromosomes.

(23) Hastings, J. E., Freedman, S. D., Rendon, O. R., Cooper, H. L., and Hirschhorn, K. An improved method for human white cell culture using differential leukocyte separation. In preparation, 1961. Describes method of mononuclear cell culture after separation of polymorphonuclear leukocytes by phagocytosis of iron and magnetization, giving more reproducible results.

BIBLIOGRAPHY

1. Sinnott, E. W., Dunn, L. C. and Dobzhansky, T., *Principles of Genetics*, McGraw-Hill, 1958, 5th Ed.
2. Swanson, C. P., *Cytology and Cytogenetics*, Prentice-Hall, 1957.
3. Hansemann, D. v., Ueber pathologische Mitosen, *Virch. Arch. 123*:356, 1891.

4. Sutton, W. S., The Chromosomes in Heredity, *Biological Bulletin* 4:231-251, 1903.
5. Boveri, T., Ueber den Einfluss der Samenzelle auf die Larvencharaktere der Echiniden, *Arch. Ent. der Organismen*, 1903, XVI.
6. DeWiniwarter, H., Études sur la spermatogenese humaine, *Arch. Biol.* 27:91, 1912.
7. Painter, T. S., The Y Chromosome in Mammals, *Science*, 53:503, 1921.
8. Painter, T. S., Studies in Mammalian Spermatogenesis, *J. Exp. Zoöl.* 37:291, 1923.
9. Evans, H. M. and Sweezy, O., The Chromosomes in Man, Sex and Somatic, *Mem. U. of Calif.* 9:1, 1929.
10. King, R. L. and Beams, H. W., The sex chromosomes in man with special reference to the first spermatocyte. *Anat. Rec.* 65:165, 1936.
11. Barr, M. L., Bertram, L. F. and Ludwig, H. A., The Morphology of the Nerve Cell Nucleus According to Sex, *Anat. Rec.* 107:283, 1950.
12. Barr, M. L., Sex Chromatin and Phenotype in Man, *Science*, 130:679, 1959.
13. Davidson, W. M. and Smith, D. R., A Morphological Sex Difference in the Polymorphonuclear Neutrophil Leukocytes, *Brit. Med. J.* 2:6, 1954.
14. Graham, M. A. and Barr, M. L., A Sex Difference in the Morphology of Metabolic Nuclei in Somatic Cells of the Cat, *Anat. Rec.* 112:709, 1952.
15. Serr, D. M., Ferguson-Smith, M. A., Lennox, B., Paul, J., Representation of the X Chromosome in Intermitotic Nuclei in Man, *Nature*, 182:124, 1958.
16. Klinger, H. P., Fine Structure of the Sex Chromatin Body, *Exptl. Cell Res.* 14:207, 1958.
17. Grumbach, M. and Morishima, A., Two cases of chromatin positive Turner's syndrome with XO chromosomal constitution; presented at meeting of *Soc. for Ped. Research*, May, 1960.
18. Briggs, D. K. and Kupperman, H. S., Sex Differentiation by Leukocyte Morphology, *J. Cl. End. and Metab.* XVI:1163, 1956.
19. Klinefelter, H. F. Jr., Reifenstein, F. C. Jr. and Albright, F., Syndrome characterized by gynecomastia, aspermatogenesis without a-lydigism and increased excretion of FSH, *J. Cl. End.* 2:615, 1942.
20. Kemp, T., Über das Verhalten der Chromosomen in den somatischen Zellen des Menschen, *Zeits. f. mikr.-anat. Forsch.* 16:1, 1929.
21. Hsu, T. C., Mammalian Chromosomes *in vitro:* The Karyotype of Man, *J. of Heredity*, 43:167, 1952.
22. Hsu, T. C., Pomerat, C. M. and Moorhead, P. S., Mammalian Chromosomes *in vitro:* VIII Heteroploid Transformation in the Human Cell Strain Mays, *J. Nat. Can. Inst.* 19:867, 1957.
23. Tjio, J. H. and Levan, A., The Chromosome Number of Man, *Hereditas*, 42:1, 1956.

24. Ford, C. E. and Hamerton, J. L., The Chromosomes of Man, *Nature,* 178:1020, 1956.

25. Chu, E. H. Y. and Giles, N. H., Human Chromosome Complements in Normal Somatic Cells in Culture, *Am. J. Hum. Gen.* 11:63, 1959.

26. Tjio, J. H. and Puck, T. T., Somatic Chromosomes of Man, *Proc. Nat. Acad. Sci.* 44:1229, 1958.

27. Kodani, M., Three Diploid Chromosomes of Man, *Proc. Nat. Acad. Sci.* 43:285, 1957.

28. Ford, C. E., Jacobs, P. A. and Lajtha, L. G., Human Somatic Chromosomes, *Nature, 181:*1565, 1958.

29. Puck, T. T., Cieciura, S. J., Robinson, A., Genetics of Somatic Mammalian Cells: III Long-term Cultivation of Euploid Cells from Human and Animal Subjects, *J. Exp. Med.* 108:945, 1958.

30. Lejeune, J., Turpin, R. and Gautier, M., Le Mongolisme: premier exemple d'aberration autosomique humaine, *Ann. de Gen.* 1:41, 1959.

31. Fraccaro, M., Kaijser, K. and Lindsten, J., Somatic Chromosome Complement in Continuously Cultured Cells of Two Individuals with Gonadal Dysgenesis, *Ann. Hum. Gen.* 24:45, 1960.

32. A Proposed Standard System of Nomenclature of Human Mitotic Chromosomes, *Lancet* 1:1063, 1960.

33. Lejeune, J., Gautier, M. and Turpin, R., Les Chromosomes Humains en Culture de Tissus, *Comptes Rendus Acad. Sci.* (Paris) 248:602, 1959.

34. Jacobs, P. A., Baikie, A. G., Court Brown, W. M. and Strong, J. A., The Somatic Chromosomes in Mongolism, *Lancet,* 1:710, 1959.

35. Waardenburg, P. J., Das Menschliche Auge und seine Erbanlagen *Bibliographica Genetica (VII),* M. Nijhoff, The Hague, 1932.

36. Bleyer, A., Indications that mongoloid imbecility is a gametic mutation of a degressive type. *Am. J. Dis. of Children,* 47:342, 1934.

37. Penrose, L. S., Maternal Age, Order of Birth and Developmental Abnormalities, *Proc. Edinb. Congr. Genet.* 1941, p. 235.

38. Verschuer, O. V., Menschliche Erblehre hinsichtlich ihrer Bedeutung für den Kinderarzt, *Jahrbücher der Gesellschaft für Kinderheilkunde* v. 1, 1926.

39. Brousseau, K., *Mongolism,* Williams and Wilkins, 1928.

40. Penrose, L. S., *The Biology of Mental Defect,* Grune and Stratton, N. Y., 1949.

41. Lelong, M., Mongolien issu de Mere Mongolienne, *Arch. Franc. Pediat.* 6:231, 1949.

42. Sawyer, G. M., Reproduction in a Mongoloid, *Am. J. Ment. Def.* 54:204, 1949.

43. Forsmann, H. and Thysell, T., A Woman with Mongolism and Her Child, *Am. J. Ment. Def.* 62:500, 1957.

44. Rehu, A. T., Family history of a mongoloid girl who bore a mongoloid child, *Am. J. Ment. Def.* 62:496, 1957.

45. Schlang, R., A Mongolian Mother and Her Child. A Case Report, *Acta Genet.* 7:533, 1957.

46. Stiles, K. A., Reproduction in a Mongoloid Imbecile, *Proc. X Int. Cong. Gen.*, Montreal 2:276, 1958.

47. Benda, C. E., *Mongolism and Cretinism*, Grune and Stratton, 1946.

48. *Symposium on Mitogenesis*, Ed.: H. S. Ducoff and Ehret, C. F., U. Chic. Press, 1959.

49. Bridges, C. B., Non-disjunction as Proof of the Chromosome Theory of Heredity, *Genetics* 1:1-52, 107-163, 1916.

50. Morgan, T. H., Sex Limited Inheritance in *Drosophila*, *Science*, 32:120, 1910.

51. Mintz, B., Continuity of the Female Germ Cell Line from Embryo to Adult, *Arch. Anat. Micr. et Morph. Exper.* 48 (Suppl.):155, 1959.

52. Prader, A., Schneider, J., Zublin, W., Frances, J. M. and Rüedi, K., Die Häufigkeit des echten, chromatin-positiven Klinefelter Syndromes und seine Beziehungen zum Schwachsinn. *Schweiz. med. Wchnschr.* 88:917, 1958.

53. Moore, K. L., Sex Reversal in Newborn Babies, *Lancet* 1:217, 1959.

54. Ferguson-Smith, M. A., The Prepubertal Lesion in Chromatin-positive Klinefelter's Syndrome (primary microrchidism) as Seen in Mentally Handicapped Children, *Lancet* 1:219, 1959.

55. Ferguson-Smith, M. A., Chromatin-positive Klinefelter's Syndrome (primary microrchidism) in a Mental Deficiency Hospital, *Lancet* 1:928, 1958.

56. Mosier, D. H., Scott, L. W. and Cotter, L. H., The Frequency of the Positive Sex-chromatin Pattern in Males with Mental Deficiency, *Pediatrics*, 25/2:291, 1960.

57. Polani, P. E., Bishop, P. M. F., Lennox, B., Ferguson-Smith, M. A., Stewart, J. S. S., and Prader, A., Color Vision Studies and the X Chromosome Constitution of Patients with Klinefelter's Syndrome, *Nature*, 182:1092, 1958.

58. Jacobs, P. A. and Strong, J. A., A Case of Human Intersexuality Having a Possible XXY Sex-determining Mechanism, *Nature*, 183:302, 1959.

59. Ford, C. E., Human Cytogenetics: Its Present Place and Future Possibilities, *Am. J. Hum. Gen.* 12:104, 1960.

60. Bergman, S., Reitalu, J., Nowakowski, H. and Lenz, W., The Chromosomes in Two Patients with Klinefelter's Syndrome, *Ann. Hum. Gen.* 24:81, 1960.

61. Stern, C., Colour Blindness in Klinefelter's Syndrome, *Nature*, 183:1452, 1959.

62. Penrose, L. S., Parental Age in Achondroplasia and Mongolism, *Am J. Hum. Gen.* 9:167, 1957.

63. Polani, P. E., Lessof, M. N., Bishop, P. M. F., Color Blindness in Ovarian Agenesis, *Lancet*, 2:118, 1956.

64. Ford, C. E., Jones, K. W., Polani, P. E., Almeida, J. C. de, Briggs,

J. H., A Sex-chromosome Anomaly in a Case of Gonadal Dysgenesis (Turner's Syndrome), *Lancet*, 1:711, 1959.

65. Fraccaro, M., Kaijser, K. and Lindsten, J., Chromosome Complement in Gonadal Dysgenesis (Turner's Syndrome), *Lancet*, 1:886, 1959 (Letter to the Editor).

66. Tjio, J. H., Puck, T. T., Robinson, A., The Somatic Chromosomal Constitution of Some Human Subjects with Genetic Defects, *Proc. Nat. Acad. Sci.* 45:1008, 1959.

67. Jacobs, P. A., Baikie, A. G., Court-Brown, W. M., MacGregor, T. N., Maclean, N. and Harnden, D. G., Evidence for the Existence of the Human "Super-Female," *Lancet*, 2:423, 1959.

68. Jacobs, P., Harnden, D. G., Court-Brown, W. M., Goldstein, J., Close, H. G., MacGregor, T. N., Maclean, N. and Strong, J. A., Abnormalities Involving the X Chromosome in Women, *Lancet*, 1:1213, 1960.

69. Ferguson-Smith, M. A., Chromosomal Abnormalities in Man: Recent Developments, Symposium on Medical Genetics, *Am. Soc. Hum. Gen. Meeting*, Memphis, Tenn. April 29, 1960.

70. Ford, C. E., Jones, K. W., Miller, O. J., Mittwoch, U., Penrose, L. S., Rider, M. and Shapiro, A., Chromosomes in a Patient Showing Both Mongolism and the Klinefelter Syndrome, *Lancet*, 1:709, 1959.

71. Lanman, J. T., Sklarin, B. S., Cooper, H. L. and Hirschhorn, K., Klinefelter's Syndrome in a Ten Month Old Mongolian Idiot, *New Eng. J. Med.* 263:887, 1960.

72. Fraccaro, M., Kaijser, K., Lindsten, J., Chromosomal Abnormalities in Father and Mongol Child, *Lancet*, 1:724, 1960.

73. Böök, J. A., Personal communication.

74. Edwards, J. H., Harnden, D. G., Cameron, A. H., Mary Crosse, V. and Wolff, O. H., A New Trisomic Syndrome, *Lancet*, 1:787, 1960.

75. Patau, K., Smith, D. W., Therman, E., Inhorn, S. L., Wagner, H. P., Multiple Congenital Anomalies Caused by an Extra Autosome, *Lancet*, 1:790, 1960.

76. Patau, K., Therman, E. and Smith, D. W., Abnormal Chromosome Constitutions in Man as Cause of Multiple Congenital Anomalies, *Am. Soc. Hum. Gen. Meeting*, Memphis, Tenn. April 29, 1960.

77. Fraccaro, M., Personal communication.

78. Böök, J. A. and Santesson, B., Malformation Syndrome in Man Associated with Triploidy (69 chromosomes), *Lancet*, 1:858, 1960.

79. Knox, W. E., An Evaluation of the Treatment of Phenylketonuria with Diets Low in Phenylalanine, *Pediatrics*, 26:1, 1960.

80. Turpin, R., Lejeune, J., Lafourcade, J. and Gautier, M., Aberrations Chromosomiques et Maladies Humaines. La Polydysspondylie a 45 Chromosomes, *Comptes Rend. Acad. Sci. (Paris)*, 248:3636, 1959.

81. Polani, P. E., Briggs, J. H., Ford, C. E., Clarke, C. M. and Berg, J. M., A Mongol Girl with 46 Chromosomes, *Lancet* 1:721, 1960.

82. Lejeune, J., Turpin, R., Decourt, J., Aberrations Chromosomiques et Maladies Humanies. Syndrome de Klinefelter XXY a 46 Chromosomes par Fusion Centromerique T-T, *Comptes Rend. Acad. Sci. (Paris), 250:*2468, 1960.
83. Ford, C. E., Polani, P. E., Briggs, J. H., and Bishop, P. M. F., A Presumptive Human XXY/XX Mosaic, *Nature, 183:*1030, 1959.
84. Crooke, A. C. and Hayward, M. D., Mosaicism in Klinefelter's Syndrome, *Lancet, 1:*1198, 1960 (letter to the Editor).
85. Hirschhorn, K., Decker, W. H., Cooper, H. L., A Case of True Hermaphroditism with Mosaicism of Type XY/XO, *New Engl. J. Med. 263:*1044, 1960.
86. Fraccaro, M., Personal communication.
87. Hungerford, D. A., Donnelly, A. J., Nowell, P. C. and Beck, S., The Chromosome Constitution of a Human Phenotypic Intersex, *Am. J. Hum. Gen. 11:*215, 1959.
88. Harnden, D. G. and Armstrong, C. M., The Chromosomes of a True Hermaphrodite, *Br. Med. J. 2:*1287, 1959.
89. Fraccaro, M., Gemzell, C. A. and Lindsten, J., Plasma Level of Growth Hormone in Four Patients with Gonadal Dysgenesis (Turner's syndrome), *Acta Endocr. 34:*496, 1960.
90. Court-Brown, W. M., Jacobs, P. A. and Doll, R., Interpretation of Chromosome Counts Made on Bone Marrow Cells, *Lancet, 1:*160, 1960.
91. Fraccaro, M., Ikkos, D., Lindsten, J., Luft, R., and Kaijser, K., A New Type of Chromosomal Abnormality in Gonadal Dysgenesis. *Lancet 2:*1144, 1960.
92. Harnden, D. G. and Stewart, J. S. S., The Chromosomes in a Case of Pure Gonadal Dysgenesis, *Br. Med. J. 2:*1285, 1959.
93. Jost, A., Recherches sur la Differentiation Sexuelle de L'embryos de Lapin. III. Role des Gonades Foetales dans la Differentiation Sexuelle Somatique, *Arch. d'anat. Micr, et de Morph. Exper. 36:*271, 1947.
94. Jost, A., Problems of Fetal Endocrinology: The Gonodal and Hypophyseal Hormones, *Recent Progress in Hormone Research* 8:379, 1953.
95. Puck, T. T., Robinson, A. and Tjio, J. H., Familial Primary Amenorrhea Due to Testicular Feminization: A Human Gene Affecting Sex Differentiation, *Proc. Exp. Biol. 103:*192, 1960.
96. Bridges, C. B., Sex in Relation to Chromosomes and Genes, *Amer. Nat.* 59:127, 1925.
97. Welshons, W. J. and Russell, L. B., The Y Chromosome as the Bearer of Male Determining Factors in the Mouse, *Proc. Nat. Acad. Sci.* 45:560, 1959.
98. Bahner, F., Schwartz, G., Harnden, D. G., Jacobs, P. A., Hienz, H. A. and Walter, K., A Fertile Woman with XO Sex Chromosome Constitution, *Lancet, 2:*100, 1960 (letter to the Editor).

99. Wilkins, L., Masculinization of Female Fetus Due to Use of Orally Given Progestins, *J. Am. Med. Assn. 172*:1028, 1960.
100. Harnden, D. G., A Human Skin Culture Technique Used for Cytological Examinations, *Br. J. Exp. Path. 41*:31, 1960.
101. Miller, O. J., Personal communication.
102. Fraccaro, M. and Lindsten, J. A Child with 49 Chromosomes. *Lancet ii*:1303, 1960. (Letter to the editor.)
103. Böök, J. A. and Santesson, B. Further Studies in Clinical Cytogenetics. *Lunds univ. Arsskrift N. F. Avd. 2, 56*:19, 1960.
104. Jérôme, H., Lejeune, J., and Turpin, R. Étude de l'Excrétion Urinaire de Certains Metábolites du Tryptophane chez les Enfants Mongoliens. *C. R. Acad. Sci. Paris 251*:474, 1960.

2

A PROPOSED STANDARD SYSTEM OF NOMENCLATURE OF HUMAN MITOTIC CHROMOSOMES

Arthur Robinson, M.D.

THE rapid growth of knowledge of human chromosomes in several laboratories, following advances in technical methods, has given rise to several systems by which the chromosomes are named. This has led to confusion in the literature and so to the need for resolving the differences. Consequently, at the suggestion of Dr. C. E. Ford, a small study group was convened to attempt the formulation of a common system of nomenclature. The meeting was arranged, through the good offices of Dr. T. T. Puck, to be held at Denver, in the University of Colorado, under the auspices of the Medical School. The meeting of this study group was made possible by the support of the American Cancer Society, to whom grateful thanks are due. For practical reasons, it was decided to keep the group as small as possible and to limit it to those human cytologists who had already published karyotypes. (In contemporary publications the terms, karyotype and idiogram, have often been used indiscriminately. We would recommend that the term, karyotype, should be applied to a systematized array of the chromosomes of a single cell prepared either by drawing or by photography, with the extension in meaning that the chromosomes of a single cell can typify the chromosomes of an individual or even a species. The term, idiogram, would then be reserved for the diagrammatic representation of a karyotype, which may be based on measurements of the chromosomes in several or many cells.) In addition, three counselors were invited to join the group to guide and aid the discussions and, if necessary, to arbitrate. Fortunately, the last office did not prove necessary,

Reprinted from *J.A.M.A.*, *174*, Sept. 10, 1960.

and it was possible by mutual agreement to arrive at a common system which has flexibility.

It was agreed that the principles to be observed by the system should be simplicity and freedom, as far as possible, from ambiguity and risks of confusion, especially with other systems of nomenclature in human genetics. It should also be capable of adjustment and expansion to meet the needs of new knowledge of

TABLE 1

CONSPECTUS OF HUMAN MITOTIC CHROMOSOMES

Group 1-3	Large chromosomes with approximately median centromeres. The three chromosomes are readily distinguished from each other by size and centromere position.
Group 4-5	Large chromosomes with submedian centromeres. The two chromosomes are difficult to distinguish, but chromosome 4 is slightly longer.
Group 6-12	Median-sized chromosomes with submedian centromeres. The X chromosome resembles the longer chromosomes in this group, especially chromosome 6, from which it is difficult to distinguish. This large group is the one which presents major difficulty in identification of individual chromosomes.
Group 13-15	Medium sized chromosomes with nearly terminal centromeres ("acrocentric" chromosomes). Chromosome 13 has a prominent satellite on the short arm. Chromosome 14 has a small satellite on the short arm. No satellite has been detected on chromosome 15.
Group 16-18	Rather short chromosomes with approximately median (in chromosome 16) or submedian centromeres.
Group 19-20	Short chromosomes with approximately median centromeres.
Group 21-22	Very short, acrocentric chromosomes. Chromosome 21 has a satellite on its short arm. The Y chromosome is similar to these chromosomes.

human chromosomes. The system should be agreed to by the greatest possible proportion of cytologists working in the field, but the risk that a minority may be unable to accept the system as a whole should not be allowed to delay adoption by a majority.

It was agreed that the autosomes should be serially numbered, 1 to 22, as nearly as possible in descending order of length, consistent with operational conveniences of identification by other criteria. The sex chromosomes should continue to be referred to as X and Y, rather than by a number which would be an additional and, ultimately, a superfluous appellation.

It was generally agreed that the 22 autosomes can be classified into seven groups, distinction between which can readily be made. Within these groups, further identification of individual chromosomes can in many cases be made relatively easily. Within some groups, especially the group of chromosomes numbered 6-12, including also the X chromosome, the distinctions between the chromosomes are very difficult to make by presently available criteria. However, lesser difficulties are encountered in separating chromosomes 6 and the X from the remainder of this group. It is believed that, with very favorable preparations, distinction can be made between most, if not all, chromosomes.

It is proposed that the autosomes first be ordered by placing the seven groups as nearly as possible in descending order of size. Within each group the chromosomes are arranged, for the most part, by size. It was desired specifically to avoid the implication that size relationships have been permanently decided in every instance, but it is hoped that the assignment of numbers will be permanently fixed. In those cases where distinction is at present doubtful, final definition of each chromosome can be left until further knowledge has accrued, though an attempt is made to provide a characterization of each. These principles make it possible to draw up a conspectus of the chromosomes, a table of their quantitative characteristics and a table of the synonyms which authors have already published. These are appended (tables 1, 2, and 3).

In table 2, showing the diagnostic characters of the chromosomes, three parameters are relied upon. These are (1) the length of each chromosome relative to the total length of a normal, X-containing, haploid set, i.e., the sum of the lengths of the 22 autosomes and the X chromosome, expressed per thousand; (2) the arm ratio of the chromosomes expressed as the length of the longer arm relative to the shorter one; and (3) the centromeric index expressed as the ratio of the length of the shorter arm to the whole length of the chromosome. The two latter indices are, of course, related algebraically quite simply, but it is thought useful to present both here. In some chromosomes, the additional criterion of the presence of a satellite is available (table 1), but, in view of the apparent morphological variation of satellites, they and their connecting strands are excluded in computing the indices.

TABLE 2
QUANTITATIVE CHARACTERISTICS OF THE HUMAN MITOTIC CHROMOSOMES*

	Tjio and Puck[1]			Chu and Giles[2]			Levan and Hsu[3]			Fraccaro and Lindsten[†]			Lejeune and Turpin[†‡]			Buckton, Jacobs, and Harnden[†]			Range		
	A	B	C	A	B	C	A	B	C	A	B	C	A	B	C	A	B	C	A	B	C
1	90	1.1	48	90	1.1	48	85	1.1	49	82	1.1	48	87	1.1	48	83	1.1	48	82-90	1.1	48-49
2	82	1.6	39	83	1.5	40	79	1.6	38	77	1.5	40	84	1.5	40	79	1.6	38	77-84	1.5-1.6	38-40
3	70	1.2	45	72	1.2	46	69	1.2	45	65	1.2	45	67	1.2	46	63	1.2	46	63-72	1.2	45-46
4	64	2.9	26	63	2.9	26	63	2.7	27	62	2.6	28	62	2.6	25	60	2.6	28	60-64	2.6-2.9	25-28
5	58	3.2	24	58	3.2	24	59	2.6	28	60	2.4	29	57	2.4	30	57	2.4	30	57-60	2.4-3.2	24-30
X	59	1.9	34	57	2.8	38	52	1.6	38	54	1.6	38	58	2.2	32	51	1.7	37	51-59	.6-2.8	32-38
6	55	1.7	37	56	1.8	36	56	1.7	37	54	1.6	38	56	1.7	37	56	1.6	38	54-56	1.6-1.8	36-38
7	47	1.3	43	52	1.9	35	51	1.9	35	50	1.7	37	51	1.8	36	50	1.7	37	47-52	1.3-1.9	35-43
8	44	1.5	29	46	1.7	29	48	1.6	33	47	1.7	37	48	2.4	29	46	1.5	40	44-48	1.5-2.4	29-40
9	44	1.9	40	46	2.4	38	47	1.8	36	45	2.0	33	47	1.9	35	44	2.1	32	44-47	1.8-2.4	32-40
10	43	2.4	27	45	2.3	30	45	2.0	33	45	2.6	34	45	2.6	27	44	1.9	35	43-45	1.9-2.6	27-35
11	43	2.8	34	44	2.1	32	44	2.2	31	43	2.2	31	44	1.6	39	43	1.5	40	43-44	1.5-2.8	31-40
12	42	3.1	24	43	3.1	24	42	1.7	32	43	1.7	37	42	2.8	27	42	2.1	32	42-43	1.7-3.1	24-37
13	35	8.0	11	32	9.7	10	32	5.0	16	34	4.8	17	33	6.8	14	36	4.9	17	32-36	4.8-9.7	10-17
14	32	7.3	12	34	9.5	9	37	4.0	18	35	4.4	19	32	7.0	13	34	4.3	19	32-37	4.3-9.5	9-19
15	29	10.5	9	31	11.9	8	35	4.7	17	33	4.6	22	31	10.0	9	34	3.8	22	29-35	3.8-11.9	8-22
16	32	1.8	36	27	1.6	38	30	1.4	42	31	1.4	42	29	1.4	41	33	1.4	31	27-33	1.4-1.8	31-42
17	29	2.8	26	30	2.1	33	29	2.4	30	30	1.9	35	29	3.1	23	30	1.8	36	29-30	1.8-3.1	23-36
18	24	3.8	21	25	3.8	22	25	2.6	28	27	2.5	29	26	4.2	21	27	2.4	29	24-27	2.4-4.2	21-29
19	22	1.4	41	22	1.9	34	24	1.2	40	25	1.3	43	22	1.4	42	26	1.2	45	22-26	1.2-1.9	21-29
20	21	1.3	44	19	1.3	44	21	1.2	40	23	1.3	43	20	1.2	43	25	1.2	46	19-25	1.2-1.3	34-45
21	18	3.7	21	15	6.8	13	13	2.5	28	19	2.5	29	15	2.3	31	20	2.5	29	13-20	2.3-6.8	13-31
22	17	3.3	23	12	6.0	14	16	2.0	33	17	2.3	30	13	4.0	20	18	2.7	27	12-18	2.0-6.0	14-33
Y	19	..	0	11	..	0	18	4.9	17	22	2.9	26	18	..	0	18	4.9	17	11-22	2.9-..	0-26

* All measurements were made from cells of normal individuals, except those made by Fraccaro and Lindsten, which included cases of Turner's syndrome. The column A is the relative length of each chromosome, B is the arm ratio and C the centromere index, as defined in the text.

† Unpublished data.

Table 2 shows the range of measurements determined by various workers. Some of the variation expresses the uncertainty due to measurement of relatively small objects; but many of the discrepancies between different workers' observations are due to the

TABLE 3

SYNONYMY OF CHROMOSOMES AS PUBLISHED BY VARIOUS WORKERS

New Chromosome Number	Tjio and Puck[1]	Chu and Giles[2]	Levan and Hsu[3]	Ford, Jacobs, and Lajtha[5]	Böök Fraccaro, and Lindsten[6]	Lejeune, Turpin, and Gautier[4]
1	1	1	1	1	1	G1
2	2	2	2	2	2	G2
3	3	3	3	3	3	G3
4	4	4	4	4	4	G4
4	5	5	5	5	5	G5
6	6	6	6	6*	6	M1
7	7	7	7	(8)	7	M2
8	8	8	8	(9)	8	Md1
9	9	9	9	(11)	9	M3
10	10	10	10	10	10	Md2
11	11	11	11	(12)	11	M4
12	12	12	12	(13)	12	Md3
13	18	14	20	14	14	T1
14	19	15	18	15	15	T2
15	20	13	19	16	13	T3
16	13	17	15	19	16	C1
17	14	16	13	17	17	P1
18	15	18	14	18	18	P2
19	16	19	16	20	19	C2
20	17	20	17	21	20	C3
21	21	21	22	22	21	Vh
22	22	22	21	23	22	Vs
X	X	X	X	?(7)	X	X
Y	Y	Y	Y	Y	Y	Y

* In the published idiogram the chromosomes of group 6-12 (including X) were indicated by discontinuous lines and left unnumbered owing to the uncertainty of discrimination at that time. For the purpose of this table, these chromosomes have been assigned the numbers shown in brackets, in serial order of length.

measurement of chromosomes at different stages of mitosis and to maxima and minima of the means found by different workers us-for microscopic study. The ranges shown, therefore, represent the maxima and minima of the means found by different workers using different techniques. However, within any one worker's observations, the variations are not so broad.

Reference should be made to two other matters of nomenclature. In the first place, it is considered that no separate nomenclature for the groups is needed. It is considered that any group to which it may be necessary to refer will be a sequence of those designated by Arabic numerals. Hence, any chromosome group may be referred to by the Arabic numerals of the extreme chromosomes of the group, joined together by a hyphen, e.g., the group of the three longest chromosomes would be Group 1-3. This scheme has the merit of great flexibility. For instance, chromosomes X and 6 may be separated from the Group 6-12 whenever they can be distinguished.

Secondly, there is the problem raised by the abnormal chromosomes which are being encountered in the more recent studies. Their nomenclature was discussed without a definite conclusion being reached. Broadly, it was agreed, however, that any symbol used should avoid incorporating a specific interpretation which was not reasonably established. It was suggested that arbitrary symbols, prefixed by a designation of the laboratory of origin, should usually be assigned to the abnormal chromosome.

In this connection, two further requisites for co-ordination of research were discussed. One is the storage of documentation for reference, perhaps in a central depository, additional to what it may be possible to publish. The other is the desirability that cultures be preserved, by the satisfactory methods now used, so that they are available for reference, comparison, and exchange.

Some consideration was also given to the desirability of using a uniform system for presenting karyotypes and idiograms, but recognizing that individual variation in taste is involved, rigidity of design was thought undesirable. However, it was recommended that the chromosomes should be arranged in numerical order, with the sex chromosomes near to but separated from the autosomes they resemble. It is desirable that similar ones be grouped together with their centromeres aligned.

It is recognized that choice between the different possible schemes of nomenclature is arbitrary, but that uniformity for ease of reference is essential. Hence, individual preferences have been subordinated to the common good in reaching this agreement. This human chromosomes study group therefore agrees to use this notation and recommends that any who prefer to use any other scheme should, at the same time, also refer to the standard system proposed here.

We are well aware of the wide interest in the work of this study group and realize that this meeting is merely a preliminary to a larger meeting. It is believed that two needs have to be met in this respect. One is for seminars and workshops at which workers in the field may exchange information; such seminars are best arranged regionally. The second need, which may come later, is for international conferences; and we believe that Congresses and other organizations whose interests include human genetics, should promote such meetings.

LIST OF SIGNATORIES
INCLUDING ADDRESSES

Participants

J. A. Böök
University of Uppsala
The Inst. for Medical Genetics
V. Agatan 24
Uppsala, Sweden

E. H. Y. Chu
Biology Division
Oak Ridge National Laboratory
P. O. Box Y
Oak Ridge, Tennessee, U. S. A.

C. E. Ford
Medical Research Council
Radiobiological Research Unit
Harwell, Didcot, Berks, England

M. Fraccaro
The Inst. for Medical Genetics
V. Agatan 24
Uppsala, Sweden

D. G. Harnden
Medical Research Council
Group for Research on the General
   Effects of Radiation
Dept. of Radiotherapy

Western General Hospital
Crewe Road
Edinburgh 4, Scotland

T. C. Hsu
Section of Cytology
The University of Texas
M. D. Anderson Hospital
   and Tumor Inst.
Texas Medical Center
Houston 25, Texas, U. S. A.

D. A. Hungerford
The Inst. for Cancer Research
7701 Burholme Avenue
Fox Chase
Philadelphia 11, Pa., U. S. A.

P. A. Jacobs
Medical Research Council
Group for Research on the
   General Effects
   of Radiation
Dept. of Radiotherapy
Western General Hospital
Crewe Road
Edinburgh 4, Scotland

J. Lejeune
University de Paris
Chaire d'Hygiene et de
    Clinique de la Premiere Enfance
Hospital Trousseau
158, Av. du General Michel-Bizot
Paris (12), France

A. Levan
Institute of Genetics
University of Lund
Lund, Sweden

S. Makino
Zoological Institute
Faculty of Science
Hokkaido University
Sapporo, Japan

Theodore T. Puck
Department of Biophysics
University of Colorado
    Medical Center
4200 East Ninth Avenue
Denver 20, Colorado, U. S. A.

A. Robinson
Department of Biophysics
University of Colorado
    Medical Center
4200 East Ninth Avenue
Denver 20, Colorado, U. S. A.

J. H. Tjio
NIAMD-Bldg. 10-3N-116
National Institutes of Health
Bethesda 14, Maryland, U. S. A.

Counselors

D. G. Catcheside, Chairman
Department of Microbiology
The University
Edgbaston
Birmingham 15, England

Curt Stern
Department of Zoology
University of California
Berkeley 4, California,
    U. S. A.

H. J. Muller
Department of Zoology
Indiana University
Bloomington, Indiana,
    U. S. A.

REFERENCES

1. Tjio, J. H., and Puck, T. T., Somatic Chromosomes of Man, *Proc. Nat. Acad. Sc. 44*:1229-1237 (Dec.) 1958.
2. Chu, E. H. Y., and Giles, N. H., Human Chromosome Complements in Normal Somatic Cells in Culture, *Am. J. Human Genetics 11*:63-79 (March) 1959.
3. Levan, A., and Hsu, T. C., Human Idiogram, *Hereditas 45*:665-672 (Nov.) 1959.
4. Lejeune, J., Turpin, R., and Gautier, M., Le Mongolisme, Premier exemple d'aberration Autosomique Humaine, *Ann. Genet. 1*:41-49 (July) 1959.
5. Ford, C. E.; Jacobs, P. A., and Lajtha, L. G., Human Somatic Chromosomes, *Nature 181*:1565-1568 (June 7) 1958.
6. Böök, J. A., Fraccaro, M., and Lindsten, J., Cytogenetical Observations in Mongolism, *Acta Paediatrica 48*:453-468 (Sept.) 1959.

3

GÉNÉTIQUE

Etudes des Chromosomes Somatiques de Neuf Enfants Mongoliens

Note de M. Jérôme Lejeune, Mlle Marthe Gautier, et
M. Raymond Turpin

CHEZ neuf enfants mongoliens l'étude des mitoses de fibroblastes en culture récente[1] nous a permis de constater régulièrement la présence de 47 chromosomes. Les observations faites dans ces neuf cas (cinq garçons et quatre filles) sont consignées dans le tableau ci-aprés.

Le nombre decellules comptées dans chaque cas peut sembler relativement faible. Ceci tient au fait que seules ont été retenues

NOMBRE DE CELLULES EXAMINÉES DANS CHAQUE CAS

	Cellules diploïdes						Cellules tétraploïdes			
	CELLULES « DOUTEUSES »			CELLULES « PARFAITES »			CELLULES « PARFAITES »			
Nombre de chromosomes	46	47	48	46	47	48	—	94	—	—
Filles. ⎧ Mg 1 ...	6	10	2	—	11	—	—	1	—	30
⎪ Mg 2 ...	—	2	1	—	9	—	—	—	—	12
⎨ Mg 3 ...	—	1	1	—	7	—	—	2	—	11
⎩ Mg 4 ...	—	3	—	—	1	—	—	—	—	4
Garçons. ⎧ Mg 5* ..	—	—	—	—	8	—	—	—	—	8
⎪ Mg A ...	1	6	1	—	5	—	—	—	—	13
⎨ Mg B ...	1	2	—	—	8	—	—	—	—	11
⎪ Mg C ...	1	2	1	—	4	—	—	—	—	8
⎩ Mg D ...	1	1	2	—	4	—	—	—	—	8
	10	27	8		57			3		105

* Cet enfant est issu d'une grossesse gémellaire. Son cojumau normal, examiné parallèlement possède 46 chromosomes dont 5 petits télocentriques.

La culture de fibroblastes de neuf enfants mongoliens révèle la présence de 47 chromosomes, le chromosome surnuméraire étant un petit télocentrique. L'hypothèse du déterminisme chromosomique du mongolisme est envisagée.

Extrait des *Comptes rendus des séances de l'Académie des Sciences*, t. 248, p. 1721-1722 séance du 16 mars 1959.

dans ce tableau les images ne prêtant qu'à un minimum d'inter-
prétation.

L'apparente variation du nombre chromosomique dans les
cellules « douteuses », c'est-à-dire celles dont chaque chromosome
ne peut être individualisé avec une absolue certitude est signalée
par de nombreux auteurs.[2] Ce phénomène ne nous semble pas cor-
respondre à une réalité cytologique, mais reflète simplement les
difficultés d'une technique délicate.

Il nous semble donc logique de préférer un petit nombre de
dénombrements absolument certains (cellules « parfaites » du
tableau) à une accumulation d'observations douteuses dont la
variance statistique ne dépend que de l'imprécision des observations.

L'analyse de la garniture chromosomique des cellules « parfaites » révèle chez les garçons mongoliens la présence de 6 petits
télocentriques (au lieu de 5 chez l'Homme normal) et chez les
filles mongoliennes de 5 petits télocentriques (au lieu de 4 chez la
Femme normale).

Les cellules « parfaites » d'individus non-mongoliens, ne
présentant jamais ces caractéristiques,[1] il nous semble légitime
de conclure qu'il existe chez les mongoliens un petit chromosome
télocentrique surnuméraire, rendant compte du chiffre anormal
de 47.

Discussion.—Pour expliquer l'ensemble de ces observations,
l'hypothèse de la non-disjonction lors de la méiose, d'une paire de
petits télocentriques pourrait être envisagée. Comme on sait que
chez la Drosophile la non-disjonction est fortement influencée
par le vieillissement maternel, un tel méchanisme rendrait compte
de l'accroissement de fréquence du mongolisme en fonction de
l'âge avancé de la mère.

Il n'est cependant pas possible d'affirmer que le petit télocentrique surnuméraire soit certainement un chromosome normal
et l'on ne peut écarter à l'heure actuelle la possibilité qu'il s'agisse
d'un fragment résultant d'un autre type d'aberration.

REFERENCES

1. J. Lejeune, M. Gautier et R. Turpin, *Comptes rendus*, 248, 1959, p. 602.
2. P. A. Jacobs et J. A. Strong, *Nature*, 183, 1959, p. 302-303.

4

THE CHROMOSOMES IN A PATIENT SHOWING BOTH MONGOLISM AND THE KLINEFELTER SYNDROME

C. E. Ford, Ph.D. Lond., K. W. Jones, Ph.D. Wales, O. J. Miller, M.D. Yale, Ursula Mittwoch, Ph.D. Lond., L. S. Penrose, M.D. Cantab., F.R.S., M. Ridler, F.I.M.L.T., and A. Shapiro, M.D. Lond., D.P.M.

FOR many years the diploid number of chromosomes in normal men and women was believed to be forty-eight. Since the observations of Tjio and Levan (1956)and of Ford and Hamerton (1956), using improved methods, forty-six has been generally accepted as the correct number, twenty-two pairs of autosomes and one sex chromosome pair. The chromosomes of a case of Klinefelter's syndrome, with skin cells exhibiting the Barr chromatin body as in the female, have been studied by Jacobs and Strong (1959) and found to number forty-seven. This was interpreted as the result of the presence of two X chromosomes as well as one Y. The chromosome complement in mongolism was first investigated by Mittwoch (1952) who reported an approximate diploid number of forty-eight chromosomes in spermatocytes. Techniques at that time were not adequate to give exact results. However, Lejeune, Gautier, and Turpin (1959) reported the finding of a small extra chromosome in tissue cultures from the connective tissue of three cases of mongolism, making a total count of forty-seven.

The patient described here is an imbecile, aged 45, who shows signs typical both of Klinefelter's syndrome and of mongolism. He is fourth in a sibship with three normal sisters. The father was 40 years old and the mother 42 at his birth and they are not consanguineous. The Barr chromatin body is present in cells of the

Reprinted from *The Lancet*, April 4, 1959, pp. 709-710.

The writers wish to thank Mr. B. D. Stutter, Dr. R. F. Welch, and Dr. T. H. Howells for conducting the biopsies at Barnet General Hospital.

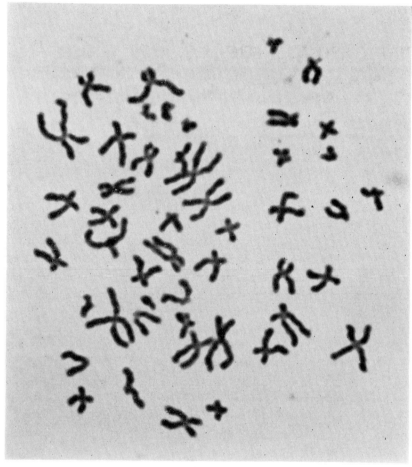

Fig. 1. Mitotic metaphase in a bone-marrow cell.

skin and buccal mucosa; leucocytes with drumstick appendages have been identified, as in a normal female. He has small testes, scanty facial, axillary and pubic hair, slight gynæcomastia and feminine distribution of fat. Testicular biopsy revealed advanced atrophy with no spermatogenesis, only ghost tubules and rare interstitial cells. The mongoloid traits are very well marked, including typical palmar patterns, single creases on the minimal digits, fissured tongue, cataract, and slight cyanosis.

Bone-marrow specimens, obtained by sternal puncture, were

treated by a modification of the method described by Ford, Jacobs and Lajtha (1958). Squash preparations were made from the final, Feulgen-stained, cell suspension. These were searched systematically for cells in metaphase of mitosis. More than fifty cells, in which the chromosomes could be counted accurately, were recorded. Each of them contained forty-eight chromosomes. The de-

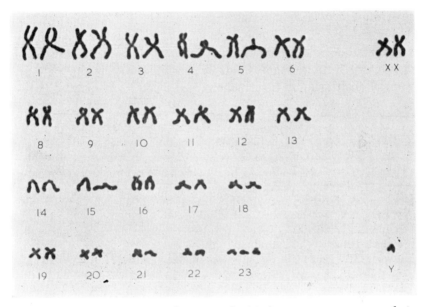

Fig. 2. Chromosomes arranged to size; the X chromosomes are seventh in this order.

tailed chromosome morphology was examined carefully in ten cells. Each appeared to contain a normal set of twenty-three pairs, as in a female, with, in addition, a Y chromosome and an extra acrocentric chromosome. There are two very similar pairs of acrocentric chromosomes in the normal complement, one pair probably slightly larger than the other, pairs 22 and 23 of Ford et al. (1958)—alternatively, nos. 21 and 22 of Tjio and Puck (1958). In the present case, these four chromosomes and the additional acrocentric chromosome are almost indistinguishable from one another: it is possible that two are a little longer than the other three. A representative cell is shown in fig. 1. In fig. 2 the chromosomes from this cell are arranged as far as possible in pairs. The five short acrocentric chromosomes are arranged as a pair and a group of three, and the Y chromosome, which, though very similar, is usually distinguishable from them, is shown by itself. Identification of the X chromosome pair is still uncertain: it is believed to be the seventh in order of length and is shown as such in fig. 2.

This appears to be the first time that a human being with two supernumerary chromosomes has been described. He possesses an additional sex chromosome, as found in Klinefelter's syndrome, and an additional small chromosome which seems likely to be characteristic of mongolism. It is remarkable that the patient's general health should be satisfactory.

REFERENCES

Ford, C. E., Hamerton, J. L. (1956) The chromosomes of man. *Nature, Lond. 178*:1020.

────── Jacobs, P. A., Lajtha, L. G. (1958) Human somatic chromosomes. *ibid. 181*:1565.

Jacobs, P. A., Strong, J. A. (1959) A case of human intersexuality having a possible XXY sex-determining mechanism. *ibid. 183*:302.

Lejeune, L., Gautier, M., Turpin, R. (1959) Les chromosomes humains en culture de tissus. *C. R. Acad. Sci., Paris, 248*:602.

Mittwoch, U. (1952) The chromosome complement in a mongolian imbecile. *Ann. Eugen., Lond. 17*:37.

Tjio, J. H., Levan, A. (1956) The chromosome number of man. *Hereditas, 42*:1.

────── Puck, T. T. (1958) The somatic chromosomes in man. *Proc. Nat. Acad. Sci. 44*:1229.

5

A SEX-CHROMOSOME ANOMALY IN A CASE OF GONADAL DYSGENESIS (TURNER'S SYNDROME)

C. E. Ford, Ph.D. Lond., K. W. Jones, Ph.D. Wales, P. E. Polani, M.D. Pisa, M.R.C.P., D.C.H., J.C. de Almeida, M.D. Brazil, and J. H. Briggs, M.B. Lond., M.R.C.P.

G ONADAL dysgenesis (ovarian agenesis, gonadal dysplasia) is a clinical syndrome usually presenting as a failure of secondary sex characteristics at puberty in girls whose gonads are absent or rudimentary. It is often associated with other congenital malformations such as small stature, digital anomalies, and, more rarely, webbed neck, congenital heart-disease, renal anomalies, intellectual subnormality, and other developmental errors. The more extreme expressions are often referred to as Turner's syndrome.

A considerable proportion of patients with gonadal dysgenesis are chromatin-negative (Décourt, Sasso, Chiorboli, and Fernandes 1954, Polani, Hunter, and Lennox 1954, Wilkins, Grumbach, and Van Wyck 1954), although chromatin-negativity (Barr and Bertram 1949) is an invariable feature of normal males. One possible explanation is that gonadal dysgenesis in man is due to castration while an embryo, since the experimental castration of embryonic rabbits results in the production of animals of female phenotype irrespective of the genetic sex-constitution of the embryo (Jost 1947). However, in abnormal individuals chromatin negativity or positivity ("nuclear sexing") may not necessarily indicate true chromosomal sex (*Lancet* 1956, Polani, Lessof, and Bishop 1956). An alternative explanation for the findings in gona-

Reprinted from *The Lancet*, April 4, 1959, pp. 711-713.

We wish to thank Dr. P. M. F. Bishop for permission to study a patient under his care. We acknowledge the skilful technical assistance of Mr. G. D. Breckon, Miss P. A. Moore, and Miss S. R. Wakefield.

71

dal dysgenesis might be abnormal sex differentiation following anomalous sex determination in the zygote.

Two approaches to the problem of certainly identifying the sex chromosomes present in Turner's syndrome suggested themselves: direct cytological observation, and the study of colourblindness, which is a sex-linked recessive character and an X-chromosome marker. The results obtained by the second method agreed with the simple interpretation of the "nuclear sexing" results: chromatin-negative patients with gonadal dysgenesis seemed to have only one X chromosome (Polani et al. 1956). The presence or absence of the Y chromosome could not be determined and it was thought likely that the patients had an XY sex-chromosome constitution, although the possibility that they might be XO was also considered. Danon and Sachs (1957) also suggested that some patients with gonadal dysgenesis might have an XO sex-chromosome constitution, but that other patients might be examples of somatic mosaicism in respect of their sex-chromosome constitution. A study of the blood groups of three patients with gonadal dysgenesis (Platt and Stratton 1956) supplied evidence that these individuals were not haploid—i.e., were not XO merely because all their chromosomes were unpaired.

Technical developments have recently made it possible to obtain accurate information regarding the somatic chromosomes of human patients, either in bone-marrow cells briefly incubated in vitro (Ford, Jacobs, and Lajtha 1958) or in cells from tissue cultures (Tjio and Puck 1958). In consequence the normal number of human chromosomes and their normal morphology are now reasonably well known. The subject of this report is a chromatin-negative case of Turner's syndrome whose bone-marrow cells proved to contain 45 chromosomes only, instead of the normal number of 46, and whose sex-chromosomal constitution is determined to be XO.

CASE REPORT

The patient presented at the age of 14 with a short stature, primary amenorrhœa, and absence of secondary sex characteristics. In addition she was backward at school.

Family History. Parents healthy. Father 5 ft. 4 in., mother 5 ft.

2 in. A maternal aunt, who died at the age of 21, was dwarfed and had had only two scanty periods; she was known to have pernicious anæmia. Two brothers 6 and 10 years old and one sister aged 9 were all healthy.

Personal History. Maternal health good during pregnancy, and delivery normal. Birth weight 5 lb. 4 oz. Early development normal.

On examination, height 51 in., lower segment 25 in., arm-span 50 in. Weight 4 st. 13 lb.

There was slight facial asymmetry, low implantation of the ears, and a small chin. There was a high arched palate, a short broad neck without webbing, slight funnel deformity of the chest, cubitus valgus, pes cavus, and digital deformities. Cardiovascular system normal. Blood-pressure 110/70. Normal femoral pulses. There was no evidence of puberty.

Investigations

Examination of skin biopsy and blood smear showed a chromatin-negative pattern.

Follicle-stimulating hormone positive to 32 mouse units 17-ketosteroids 10.8 mg. per day.

Radiographically chest, heart, intravenous pyelography normal. Radiological assessment of bone age corresponded to the chronological age.

No defect in colour-vision (Ishihara) in patient or parents.

The marrow cells, obtained by a routine marrow puncture, were suspended in a mixture of glucose-saline and serum from the patient herself, and were sent to Harwell for cytological processing. After incubation the cells were exposed to colchicine for one hour, then fixed and stained by the Feulgen procedure. Squash preparations were made and the chromosomes were studied in cells arrested in the metaphase of mitosis by the action of the colchicine.

The chromosomes were counted in 102 cells of which 99 cells were found to have 45 chromosomes only. The remaining 3 cells contained fewer than 45 chromosomes and previous experience suggests that the deficiency is likely to be a consequence of damage to the cells during the making of the preparations. Fourteen cells were selected for detailed study. In every one of them 4 small acrocentric chromosomes were present, as in a normal female: in a normal male there are 5 of these chromosomes, one being the Y chromosome. All the selected cells also contained 15 me-

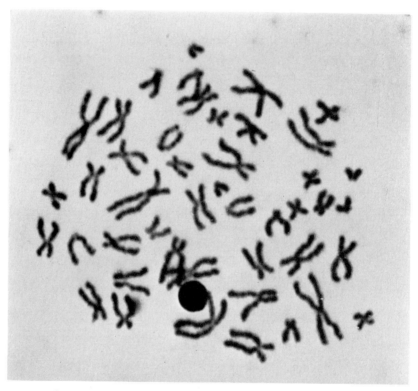

Fig. 1. Chromosomes (45) of the patient with Turner's syndrome discussed in the text. Colchicine-arrested metaphase in a bone-marrow cell. Feulgen squash preparation (×2200). The round black body is probably an oil droplet.

dium-length metacentric chromosomes, as in a normal male—a normal female having 16 which include the two X chromosomes (Ford et al. 1958). These observations of themselves strongly suggest that the chromosome constitution is XO.

The individual recognition of the X and Y chromosomes may be a matter of some difficulty. However Tjio and Puck (1958) assert that X and Y chromosomes can be recognised individually in their preparations made from tissue cultures. We agree that the Y chromosome can be distinguished in favourable cells of normal males, but we have not yet been able to identify the X chromosome (or chromosomes) unequivocally in bone-marrow preparations. Nevertheless in many of the selected cells of the present patient it was possible to make a reasonably satisfactory classification of the chromosomes into 22 pairs and one odd chromosome. A photograph of one of these cells is reproduced in fig. 1. In fig. 2 the chromosomes from the same cell are shown arranged in pairs. Suspicion that the odd chromosome is the X is inevitable, but this chromosome and the two members of pair 6 are very similar in length and arm-ratio and their true relationships remain uncertain. The probability that one of the three is X is strengthened by the good agreement of their proportions with those of undoubted X-chromosomes in X-Y bivalents at metaphase in primary spermatocytes (Ford and Hamerton 1956). Experience of numerical chromosomal abnormalities in animals and plants (Swanson 1957) suggests that it is very improbable that a human individual who has only 45 chromosomes as the result of the loss of a large or medium-sized autosome would be viable, but that an XO zygote might well develop to maturity. We therefore conclude that the sex-chromosome constitution of the patient is XO.

DISCUSSION

These observations are of interest not only with reference to Turner's syndrome. Here is an individual who is female anatomically and psychologically, whose cells are "male" as judged by nuclear sexing, and whose chromosomes are neither normally male nor normally female. However, as judged by her chromosomes she has no male component, but half a normal female component, and there seems no justification for considering her to be really male in any sense. It must therefore be accepted that chromatin negativity does not necessarily imply maleness and it would probably be best if the phrase "nuclear sexing" were dropped from the vocabulary and the more accurate if less striking terms, chromatin negativity or positivity, were always used instead. The very real clinical reasons for doing this have already been stressed.

An explanation of the origin of the sex chromosome anomaly in gonadal dysgenesis can be sought in the process of non-disjunction, best known as an abnormality of oogenesis in *Drosophila melanogaster* (Morgan, Bridges, and Sturtevant 1925). Non-disjunction of the sex-chromosomes in the female fly implies the migration of two X chromosomes to one pole of the spindle during

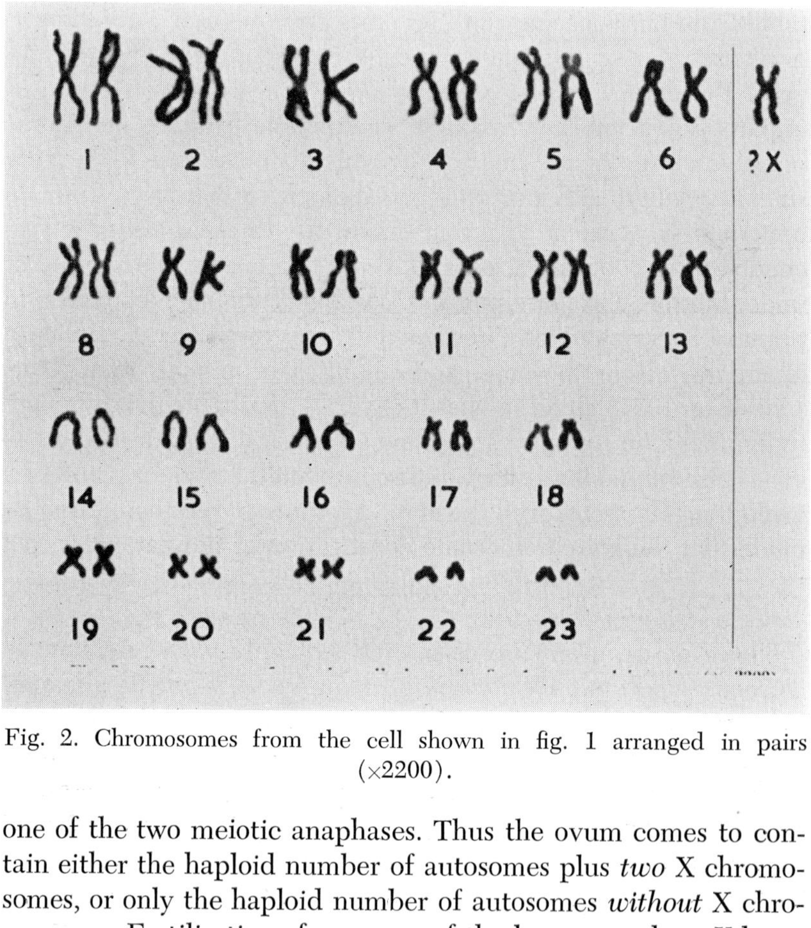

Fig. 2. Chromosomes from the cell shown in fig. 1 arranged in pairs (×2200).

one of the two meiotic anaphases. Thus the ovum comes to contain either the haploid number of autosomes plus *two* X chromosomes, or only the haploid number of autosomes *without* X chromosomes. Fertilisation of an ovum of the latter type by a Y-bearing sperm results in a non-viable YO zygote; fertilisation by an X-bearing sperm yields an XO zygote which develops into a sterile male. Our findings suggest that in man an XO zygote develops into a sterile "agonadal" individual whose phenotype is female.

Fertilisation of the other type of abnormal ovum (XX) by an X-bearing sperm gives, in drosophila, an XXX zygote with poor viability, but which occasionally survives pupation and then emerges as a fly with accentuated female secondary sexual characteristics, technically called a "super-female"; fertilisation by a Y-bearing sperm yields an XXY zygote which develops into a fertile female. In man the XXX state is as yet unknown, but evidence that the XXY individual appears as a chromatin-positive case of Klinefelter's syndrome has been presented (Ford, Polani, Briggs, and Bishop 1959, Jacobs and Strong 1959). The evidence in favour of the occurrence of non-disjunction in man is thereby strengthened.

Non-disjunction has so far been considered as occurring during oogenesis only. Family colour-vision studies in cases of gonadal dysgenesis suggest that it may also occur during spermatogenesis. If an O ovum is fertilised by an X sperm and the resultant individual has a major red-green colour-vision defect, the father should also show the colour-vision defect. But in four families where patients with gonadal dysgenesis (chromatin-negative) have a major red-green colour-vision defect this was not the case (Lenz 1957, Stewart 1958 personal communication; and two of our families, see Bishop et al. 1959). It would appear that in these patients the X-chromosome with the anomalous colour-vision gene was not of paternal origin but was derived from a heterozygous (carrier) mother. These patients have not been examined cytologically, but, if they are XO, it will follow that they developed from zygotes arising from the fertilisation of normal X-bearing ova by sperm carrying neither X nor Y. Such sperm would arise as a result of non-disjunction during spermatogenesis. Evidence that this is by no means unlikely is provided by the observation that X and Y chromosomes are sometimes unpaired at metaphase in first spermatocytes (Ford and Hamerton 1956). Both chromosomes would then be expected to migrate to the same pole in approximately 50% of the ensuing anaphases.

In conclusion it should be emphasised that the XO patient should not be referred to as an instance of "sex-reversal," as a "chromosomal male," or as a "genetic male": she is a female, with an abnormal genotype.

REFERENCES

Barr, M. L., Bertram, E. G. (1949) *Nature, Lond. 163*:676.

Bishop, P. M. F., Lessof, M. H., Polani, P. E. (1959) Memoir no. 7. Society for Endocrinology, London. Ed.: C. R. Austin (in the press).

Danon, M., Sachs, L. (1957) *Lancet, ii*:20.

Décourt, L., Sasso, W. da S., Chiorboli, E., Fernandes, J. M. (1954) *Rev. Assoc. med. Brazil, 1*:203.

Ford, C. E., Hamerton, J. L. (1956) *Nature, Lond. 178*:1020.

——— Jacobs, P. A., Lajtha, L. G. (1958) *ibid. 181*:1565.

——— Polani, P. E., Briggs, J. H., Bishop, P. M. F. (1959) *ibid.* (in the press).

Jacobs, P. A., Strong, J. A. (1959) *ibid. 183*:302.

Jost, A. (1947) *C. R. Soc. Biol., Paris, 141*:126.

Lancet (1956) 2:127.

Lenz, W. (1957) *Acta Geneticæ Medicæ et Gemellologiæ, 6*:231.

Morgan, T. H., Bridges, C. B., Sturtevant, A. H. (1925) *Bibliog. Genetica, 2*:1.

Platt, R., Stratton, F. (1956) *Lancet,* ii, 120.

Polani, P. E., Hunter, W. F., Lennox, B. (1954) *ibid.* ii, 120.

——— Lessof, M. H., Bishop, P. M. F. (1956) *ibid.* ii, 118.

Stewart, J. S. S. (1958) Personal communication.

Swanson, C. P. (1957) Cytology and Cytogenetics. (Prentice Hall, Englewood Cliffs, N. J.).

Tjio, J. H., Puck, T. T. (1958) *Proc. Nat. Acad. Sci, 12*:1229.

Wilkins, L., Grumbach, M. M., Van Wyck, J. J. (1954) *J. clin. Endocrin. 14*:1270.

6

A PRESUMPTIVE HUMAN XXY/XX MOSAIC

Dr. C. E. Ford, Dr. P. E. Polani, J. H. Briggs and Dr. P. M. F. Bishop

THE discovery of "sex chromatin" by Barr and Bertram[1] and the subsequent recognition of its regular occurrence in normal females of many mammalian species (including man) has provided a new approach to the study of human intersexual conditions, the value of which is demonstrated in the proceedings of a recent symposium.[2] Although the presence of sex chromatin is generally taken to be diagnostic of an XX individual, this is not proved, and the unequivocal determination of the sex chromosome constitution can only come from the direct study of the chromosomes themselves.

A technique for obtaining chromosome preparations from biopsy specimens of bone marrow has recently been described in outline and used in the study of one "chromatin-positive" case of Klinefelter's syndrome.[3] (Klinefelter's syndrome is a variable clinical syndrome in somatically male individuals who are sterile, generally with azoospermia, often with gynæcomastia and endocrine defects, but essentially and always with small testes after puberty.) The few cells from this first case seen in metaphase contained chromosomes indistinguishable from those of a normal female. Recently we have been able to examine the chromosomes from two further cases of this syndrome. One, chromatin-negative, had the chromosomes of a normal male. The second, chromatin-positive, gave an unexpected result and is the subject to this article.

A marrow specimen was obtained by sternal puncture at Guy's Hospital, converted into a suspension there and immediately sent to Harwell for cytological processing. The final preparations contained a satisfactory number of cells in mitotic metaphase, although many of them were unsuitable for accurate observation

Reprinted from *Nature*, Vol. 183, pp. 1030-1032, April 11, 1959.

owing to supercontraction of the chromosomes, or separation of the chromatids at the centromeres, or both. Sixty-five cells were accepted as suitable for counting, and the results are summarized in Table 1. In ten cells, including those recorded as containing 48 and 49 chromosomes, there was an uncertainty of one, or two, chromosomes. The method of counting (to minimize subjective bias) and the errors to which the recorded counts are liable have been discussed previously.[3, 4]

We have not yet succeeded in identifying the individual X and Y chromosomes, although it has been reported that Y is distinguishable from other similar chromosomes in preparations

TABLE 1

Counts of Chromosomes in 65 Cells. Klinefelter's Syndrome
(Chromatin-Positive)

No. of chromosomes	41	42	43	44	45	46	47	48	49
No. of cells	1	0	0	2	3	13	44	1	1

made from cells in tissue culture.[5] Nevertheless, it is possible to identify sex cytologically by classifying the chromosomes into four clearly defined groups:[3] (1) the shortest chromosomes have nearly terminal centromeres; there are four in the female, five in the male; (2) the next longer ones form a mixed group; there are sixteen in both sexes; (3) the medium-length chromosomes have submedian or sub-terminal centromeres; there are sixteen in the female, fifteen in the male; (4) the longest ten chromosomes are well differentiated and form five easily recognized pairs that are the same in both sexes. It follows that Y is a short chromosome with a nearly terminal centromere and that X is a medium-length chromosome with a sub-median or sub-terminal centromere. This is in accord with observations on the sex chromosomes bivalent at metaphase in first spermatocytes.[6]

Twelve of the cells with 47 chromosomes from the present case were selected for detailed analysis. All were found to contain five very short acrocentric chromosomes plus sixteen other short chromosomes (as in a male) and sixteen chromosomes in the medium-length group (as in a female). The remaining ten chromosomes were the five long pairs common to both sexes. An example is

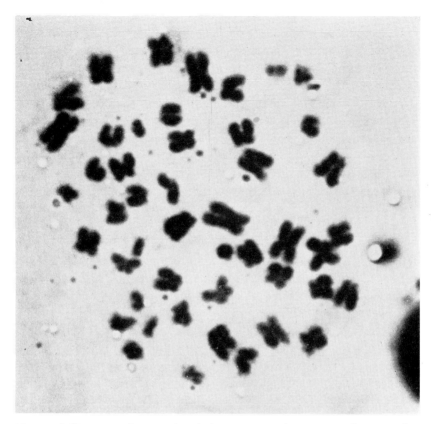

Fig. 1. Cell in metaphase with 47 chromosomes (presumptively *XXY* plus 44 autosomes) from the bone marrow of the patient with Klinefelter's syndrome (chromatin-positive). Feulgen squash after colchicine pretreatment. (×2,220)

shown in Fig. 1. The obvious interpretation is that these cells contain two *X*-chromosomes and one *Y*-chromosome, in addition to the normal 22 pairs of autosomes, although the possibility that they are basically female and trisomic for one of the small acrocentric autosomes is not excluded. In so far as the 47-chromosome cells are concerned, our case is therefore parallel to that described very recently by Jacobs and Strong.[7]

An attempt was made to classify the chromosomes in all thirteen cells with counts of 46. This was possible in eleven cells, although not all were of equal technical standard. Five of them

contained an apparently normal female set with *four* small acrocentrics, sixteen other short chromosomes, sixteen medium-length
and ten long chromosomes. There were points of uncertainty in
the remaining six cells, but at least three of them probably had
the same constitution. We therefore believe the case to be an instance of true mosaicism, notwithstanding the likelihood that
some counts of 46 may represent damaged cells that originally
contained 47 chromosomes. In the first place, there are many more
cells with a count of 46 than would be expected (in our experience) from damage alone; and secondly, the chance of loss of one
of the same group of five chromosomes from at least five, probably
eight, and possibly more of the eleven cells must be very low
indeed.

The supposition is that the 47-chromosome cells are *XXY* and the case is
a true mosaic, it is most reasonable to suppose that the 46-chromo-
some cells arose through loss of the Y-chromosome by mitotic non-
disjunction. It is known that clones of reticular cells, characterized
by one or more visible chromosome rearrangements, may appear during the regeneration of the bone marrow in irradiated
mice;[8, 9] and recent evidence has shown that in certain circumstances they may proliferate differentially even to the extent that
one clone is disseminated widely and outgrows all the rest (Ford,
C. E., Micklem, S., and Gray, S. M., unpublished work). There is
also evidence that marrow cells deficient in chromosome segments
produced by irradiation of normal animals are very rapidly eliminated (Sharman, G. B., unpublished work). Now, loss of the
Y-chromosome from an *XXY* cell would be a step in the direction
of *normality,* and such cells might therefore exhibit a small selective advantage relative to their progenitors; on the other hand,
loss of an autosome would yield a deficient cell, which, if it did
not die, would not be expected to multiply. We therefore assume
that the 46-chromosome cells contain two X-chromosomes and no
Y-chromosome, that is, contain the normal female complement.

The supposition is that the mosaic patient developed from an
XXY zygote and that this arose from fertilization of a non-disjunctional *XX* egg by a normal *Y* sperm, or of a normal *X* egg by a
non-disjunctional *XY* sperm. The occurrence of one non-disjunctional type immediately suggests that others may be found. These

could include *XXX, XO, YO,* and possibly *XYY* types; some of them have indeed been postulated to exist on various grounds. Of these, perhaps, the most likely candidate is *XO* for chromatin-negative cases of Turner's syndrome.[10] The occurrence of an individual with Klinefelter's syndrome and one with Turner's syndrome in the same sibship[11] is readily explained on such a basis, since the two syndomes would represent complementary zygotic types and could appear as a result of habitual non-disjunction of the sex chromosomes in a parent during maturation of either the ova or the sperm.

The *Drosophila* type of sex determination has been so frequently taken as a model in texts and reviews of all sorts that it is important to point out that in our case, and in the case reported by Jacobs and Strong,[7] the *XXY* individual presented an essentially male phenotype, whereas in *Drosophila* the *XXY* fly is a fertile female.[12] If these cases should prove to be the first two instances of a general rule, it would indicate that the *Y*-chromosome in man is strongly "male-determining," in contrast to the *Y*-chromosome of *D. melanogaster*, which is essentially inert in relation to the development of the sex phenotype, although necessary for male fertility.[11]

We wish to acknowledge the skilful technical assistance of Mr. G. Breckon, Miss S. R. Wakefield and Miss P. A. Moore.

Addendum. Since the draft of this communication was completed, we have, in conjunction with our colleagues, Dr. D. G. Harnden and Dr. K. W. Jones, examined the chromosomes of three more chromatin-positive cases of Klinefelter's syndrome and of one chromatin-negative case of Turner's syndrome. The former all have 47 chromosomes, show no evidence of mosaicism and are presumptively *XXY* individuals. Forty-five chromosomes were found regularly in bone marrow cells from the patient with Turner's syndrome, and analysis of the detailed chromosome morphology is consistent with the anticipated *XO* constitution. (Miss Jacobs and Dr. J. S. S. Stewart have kindly allowed us to state that they have found 45 chromosomes in a chromatin-negative case of Turner's syndrome, and that their observations are also consistent with *XO* interpretation.)

REFERENCES

1. Barr, M. L., and Bertram, E. G., *Nature, 163*:676 (1949).
2. Symposium on Nuclear Sex, edit. D. Robertson Smith and W. M. Davidson (Heinemann, London, 1958).
3. Ford, C. E., Jacobs, P. A., and Lajtha, L. G., *Nature, 181*:1565 (1958).
4. Ford, C. E., Hamerton, J. L., and Mole, R. H., *J. Cell. Comp. Physiol., 51, Supp.* 1, 235 (1958).
5. Tjio, J. H., and Puck, T. T., *J. Exp. Med., 108*:259 (1958).
6. Ford, C. E., and Hamerton, J. L., *Nature, 178*:1020 (1956).
7. Jacobs, P. A., and Strong, J. A., *Nature, 183*:302 (1959).
8. Ford, C. E., Ilbery, P., and Loutit, J. F., *J. Cell. Comp. Physiol., 50,* Supp. 1, 109 (1957).
9. Barnes, D. W. H., Ford, C. E., Gray, S. M., and Loutit, J. F., Proc. Second Int. Conf. Peaceful Uses of Atomic Energy, Geneva, 1958, Vol. 6, Biological Sciences (in the press).
10. Polani, P. E., Lessof, M. H., and Bishop, P. M. F., *Lancet,* ii, 118 (1956). Danon, M., and Sachs, L., *ibid.,* ii, 20 (1957).
11. Bassoë, H. H., *J. Clin. Endocrinol., 16*:1614 (1956).
12. Bridges, C. B., in "Sex and Internal Secretions," edit. E. Allen (Baillière, Tindall and Cox, London, 1939).

7

COLOUR-BLINDNESS IN KLINEFELTER'S SYNDROME

CURT STERN

MALES with testicular hypoplasia (Klinefelter's syndrome) are of two cytological types. A minority has sex-chromatin-negative nuclei as have normal males, whereas the majority has sex-chromatin-positive nuclei as have normal females. The demonstration of the male-determining property of the mammalian Y-chromosome, proved for man[1] and mouse,[2] had led to a clarification of the chromosomal status of sex-chromatin-positive Klinefelter individuals. They are XXY.[1, 2]

It is well known that the frequency of females homozygous for recessive genes which are located in the X-chromosome is much lower than of hemizygous affected males. Thus, X-linked red-green colour-blindness occurs among males of European ancestry in the order of 8%, whereas in females it is only about 0.5%. It has been thought that a genetic correlate of the presence of two X-chromosomes in sex-chromatin-positive Klinefelter individuals would be a very low frequency of colour-blindness, equivalent to that in females. This expectation seemed to be borne out by studies of Polani, Bishop, Lennox, Ferguson-Smith, Stewart and Prader.[3] They tested 55 sex-chromatin-positive Klinefelter patients for their colour vision and found that none was affected. Additional tests have brought the total number to 72, all with normal colour vision (Polani, R. E., personal communication). Different results, however, were reported by Nowakowski, Lenz and Parada.[4] Among 34 sex-chromatin-positive Klinefelter individuals they detected three affected persons, two of whom were deuteranomalous and one protanopic. It will be shown that the findings of the two groups of investigators are compatible with

Reprinted from *Nature*, Vol. 183, pp. 1452-1453, May 23, 1959.

each other and that they may provide new insight into the behaviour and constitution of human chromosomes.

One of the deuteranomalous men had a deuteranomalous mother and a father with normal colour vision. Assuming *XXY* constitution of the propositus, he would be expected to be deuteranomalous if he originated from a non-disjunctional egg carrying
two maternal *X*-chromosomes fertilized by a sperm carrying a
Y-chromosome. The other deuteranomalous and the protanopic
propositus both had normal fathers, and mothers who, on independent evidence, were heterozygous for an allele for defective
colour vision. How can the defective colour vision of the presumably *XXY* propositi be explained? There is a possibility, of
unknown strength, that they are manifesting heterozygotes.[5] But
in *Drosophila* and other organisms the phenomenon of homozygous
recessive offspring from heterozygous mothers mated to hemi- or
homo-zygous dominant males is well known. It occurs in consequence of crossing-over and non-disjunction. If the chromosomes
of the mother carry the alleles *A* and *a*, then at meiosis four chromatids, two carrying *A* and two *a*, will be present. If no crossing-
over occurs between the kinetochore and the locus of *A*, non-disjunction at the first meiotic division will produce an *Aa* egg; but
if within the region designated, certain types of cross-overs occur,
an "equational" non-disjunctional egg of the type *AA* or *aa* can be
formed. This apparently had occurred in the eggs which gave rise
to the two presumably homozygous Klinefelter individuals with
defective colour vision from heterozygous mothers.

The frequency of homozygosis due to crossing-over and non-
disjunction is a function of the distance between the kinetochore
and the locus concerned. With a map distance between these two
so great as to result in free recombination, the maximum of 16.7%
of recessive homozygosis is obtained (leaving out minor complications). In other words, as the result of non-disjunction of the
X-chromosomes in heterozygous females a maximum of about one-
sixth of the *XXY* sons could be homozygous recessives. Since the
frequency of women heterozygous for one of the other of the
alleles for *X*-linked colour-blindness is about 15%, maximally one-
sixth of their Klinefelter sons from non-disjunction in the mothers,
or maximally 2.5% of all Klinefelters of this origin, could be colour-

blind. In addition, approximately 0.5% of Klinefelters would be colour-blind coming from homozygous affected mothers. A further source of colour-blind Klinefelter sons could be non-disjunction of the X- and Y-chromosomes in colour-blind men married to heterozygous or homozygous affected women. Approximately 0.5% of Klinefelter individuals would be colour-blind due to this mechanism.

Depending on the relative proportion of individuals who owe their Klinefelter status to non-disjunction in the mother as compared to the father, the frequency of colour-blindness among them would vary between a maximum of 2.5 + 0.5 = 3% and 0.5%. The maximum expectation is statistically compatible with the observations of both groups of investigators, namely, 0 affected to 72 not affected, and 3 affected to 31 not affected. Combining the data results in 3 affected out of 106 individuals, or 2.8%. The statistical uncertainty of this value is, of course, great.

An alternative hypothesis to the one proposed here would be that in man equational exceptions originate without crossing-over as the result of non-disjunction at the second meiotic division. If this were the only source of colour-blind Klinefelter males, they would constitute 7.5% (from heterozygous mothers) plus 0.5% (from homozygous mothers) of all propositi.

All three colour-blind individuals originated after non-disjunction in their mothers. Their frequency of 2.8% suggests that most Klinefelter males with positive sex chromatin come from this source. Assuming that the first hypothesis proposed is correct, it suggests that the frequency of crossing-over among non-disjunctional eggs, leading to equational exceptions, is high. Furthermore, the high frequency of equational exceptions suggests that the locus for colour-blindness lies at a considerable distance from the kinetochore of the X-chromosome.

REFERENCES

1. Jacobs, P. A., and Strong, J. A., *Nature, 183*:302 (1959). Ford, C. E., Polani, P. E., Briggs, J. H., and Bishop, P. M. F., *Nature, 183*:1030 (1959).
2. Welshons, W. J., and Russell, L. B., *Proc. U. S. Nat. Acad. Sci.* (in the press). Russell, W. L., Russell, L. B., and Gower, J. S. *ibid.* (in the press).

3. Polani, P. E., Bishop, P. M. F., Lennox, B., Ferguson-Smith, A. M., Stewart, J. S. S., and Prader, A., *Nature, 182:*1092 (1958).
4. Nowakowski, H., Lenz, W., and Parada, J., *Klin. Wochenschr., 36:*683 (1958); *Acta Endocrinologia, 30:*296 (1959).
5. Walls, A.M.A. *Arch. Ophth.* (in the press).

8

MECHANISMS OF
MEIOTIC NON-DISJUNCTION IN MAN

JOHN S. S. STEWART

IT is now well known that there is an abnormal chromosome number in mongolism in chromatin-positive Klinefelter's syndrome, and in chromatin-negative Turner's syndrome. It is also known that mongolism is associated with increased maternal age, and there is some evidence that a similar association exists in chromatin-positive Klinefelter's syndrome[1, 2] and in chromatin-negative Turner's syndrome.[1] In cases of chromatin-positive Klinefelter's syndrome previously studied the available data (Table 1) provide supporting evidence that there is an association with, among other possibilities, increased maternal age. Fifty-four cases were classified with respect to position in the sibship. Four were in the centre of the sibship and of the remaining 50 cases, 17 were in the first half and 33 in the second half. This is significantly different from the expected 25 to 25 distribution.

It is generally agreed that meiotic non-disjunction is the most probable cause of these conditions. Further information about the number and origin of X chromosomes can be obtained from colour-blindness studies.[3-5] A colour-blind chromatin-positive case of Klinefelter's syndrome with colour-normal parents could be due to a defect of oogenesis. This was pointed out independently by Stewart[3] and Stern.[6] Stern considers that available data on chromatin-positive Klinefelter's syndrome suggest an abnormality of the first meiotic division but they are, in fact, equally consistent with a defect of the second meiotic division. The expected frequency of colour-blindness following a second meiotic abnormality which he quotes (8%) is correct for a locus close to the centromere but he does not consider the expected

Reprinted from *Nature*, Vol. 187, No. 4739, pp. 804-805, August 27, 1960.

Genetic Mechanisms in Human Disease

frequency for a locus sufficiently far from the centromere to give random segregation. The frequency of females homozygous for colour-blindness is 0.5%. All XX eggs from such individuals will be homozygous recessive for colour-blindness. The frequency of females heterozygous for colour-blindness is 15% and with random segregation one-sixth of their secondary oocytes will carry the gene for colour-blindness on both chromatids. Non-disjunction

TABLE 1

POSITION OF PATIENT IN SIBSHIP

		1	2	3	4	5	6	7	8	9	10	11	12	13	
	1	3													3
	2	3	10												13
	3	0	1	8											9
	4	1	2	0	2										5
	5	0	1	0	1	5									7
	6	1	0	1	1	0	1								4
Number in	7	0	0	0	0	0	0	2							2
sibship	8	0	0	0	1	0	0	0	1						2
	9	1	0	0	0	0	0	0	1	0					2
	10	0	0	1	0	0	0	0	0	1	3				5
	11	0	0	0	0	0	0	0	0	0	0	1			1
	12	0	0	0	0	0	0	0	0	0	0	0	0		0
	13	0	1	0	0	0	0	0	0	0	0	0	0	0	1
		9	15	10	5	5	1	2	2	1	3	1	0	0	54

at the second meiotic division gives exceptional XX eggs and 2.5% of these will be homozygous recessive (one-sixth × 15%). The expected frequency of colour-blindness in exceptional individuals due to a second meiotic abnormality is therefore 3% (2.5% from heterozygous mothers and 0.5% from homozygous mothers). Thus the expected limits of colour-blindness incidence in exceptional individuals following an abnormality of the second meiotic division of oogenesis are 3-8%. Collection of further data may provide information about the position of the colour-blindness locus relative to the centromere, about the relative frequency of non-disjunction in oogenesis and spermatogenesis and about the state of meiosis at which non-disjunction occurs.[5]

There is good evidence that some cases of chromatin-negative Turner's syndrome are due to a defect of spermatogenesis and that some cases of chromatin-positive Klinefelter's syndrome are due to a defect of oogenesis; and the opposite situations probably occur.[5] A defect of oogenesis may be assumed if a colour-normal case of chromatin-negative Turner's syndrome is found with a colour-blind mother and a colour-normal father, and a defect of spermatogenesis would be indicated by a colour-normal case of chromatin-positive Klinefelter's syndrome with a colour-blind mother and a colour-normal father.[5] Defects of spermatogenesis in the chromosomal intersexes may be related to the unequal size of the X and Y chromosomes with consequent failure of pairing leading to non-disjunction during meiosis. In oogenesis all chromosomes are paired, but a similar causal mechanism might operate for a chromosomal aberration such as inversion could lead to failure of pairing and non-disjunction. A chromosomal aberration of this sort might be inherited or it might be caused by environmental influences. A possible clue to the mechanism is provided in the reports that mongolism is associated with increased maternal age but not with increased paternal age,[1] and that there is little increase in the number of female germ cells after birth.[7] Environmental influences, including temperature, hormones and those such as radiation which cause genetic change, may predispose to defects of oogenesis but not to defects of spermatogenesis if old women have old eggs but old men have young sperm.

REFERENCES

1. Penrose, L. S., Symposium (in the press) (abstract, *Lancet*, ii, 448 (1959)).
2. Lenz, W., Nowackowski, H., Prader, A., and Schirren, C., *Sweiss med. Woch.*, 89:727 (1959).
3. Stewart, J. S. S., *Lancet*, ii, 833 (1959).
4. Stewart, J. S. S., *Proc. Roy. Soc. Med.*, 52:817 (1959) (abstract, *J. Endocrinol.*, 18:29 (1959).
5. Stewart, J. S. S., Symposium (in the press) (abstract, *Lancet*, ii, 448 (1959)).
6. Stern, C., *Nature*, 183:1452 (1959).
7. Zuckerman, S., Ciba Colloquium on Ageing, 2:31 (1956).

REMARKS BY CURT STERN

It is useful at this stage of human cytogenetics to keep in mind the whole spectrum of possibilities of chromosomal behaviour. In this sense Dr. Stewart's emphasis on the possibility of non-disjunction during the second meiotic division is valuable. His discussion rests on the assumption that non-disjunction is preceded by crossing-over between homologous chromosomes. In my discussion of second division non-disjunction I had specified absence of crossing-over (and, thus, made no assumption as to closeness of the locus for colour blindness to the kinetochore). According to Dr. Stewart's scheme it would follow that genes distantly located would less often become homozygous than proximal genes. This is the opposite to what is well established in *Drosophila*, although it cannot be excluded, of course, that human chromosomes may behave differently. In *Drosophila* the more frequent homozygosis for distal than proximal genes signifies that non-disjunction preceded by crossing-over occurs during the first meiotic division.

Apart from the question whether non-disjunction occurs during the first or second meiotic division, Ford's suggestion that it may also occur in early cleavage cannot be dismissed.[1] This suggestion accounts for homozygosis of the locus for colour-blindness by mitotic non-disjunction without reference to crossing-over or of gene location.

I wish to add two minor points in reference to my earlier communication: (1) The statement about a "maximum" of recessive homozygosis of 16.7% was in error; instead this frequency follows from random assortment. (2) The choice of 0.5% as the incidence of colour-blind women was made for the sake of a round number; 0.45 or 0.4% are more accurate values.

REFERENCE

1. Ford, C. A., *Amer. J. Hum. Genet.*, *12*:104 (1960).

9

GÉNÉTIQUE

Aberrations Chromosomiques et Maladies Humaines. La Polydysspondylie à 45 Chromosomes

NOTE DE MM. RAYMOND TURPIN, JÉRÔME LEJEUNE, JACQUES LAFOURCADE et MLLE MARTHE GAUTIER, présentée par M. Léon Binet

AINSI que le démontre l'anomalie chromosomique du Mongolisme (Lejeune, Gautier, Turpin),[1,2] la présence d'un autosome supplémentaire peut être compatible avec la survie et même, parfois, avec la reproduction.

La possibilité d'existence d'autres anomalies chromosomiques nous a conduits à examiner systématiquement les chromosomes d'enfants anormaux. C'est ainsi que nous avons observé la présence de 45 chromosomes seulement chez un enfant atteint de malformations vertébrocostales avec troubles du développement.

Observations clinique et radiologique.—La malformation (polydysspondylie) intéresse trois territoires rachidiens:

—cervical (pincement d l'interligne C_3-C_4 et fusion des arcs postérieurs de ces vertèbres; rachischisis de C_5);

—dorsal (pincement des interlignes D_1-D_2 et D_2-D_3, cette dernière vertèbre étant réduite à son hémicorps droit, avec absence de la troisième côte gauche; les lames et les épineuses de ces trois vertèbres sont fusionnées);

—sacré: hémi-lombalisation gauche de S_1.

Par ailleurs on note un élargissement modéré du canal rachidien dans la région cervico-dorsale et la fermeture de la selle turcique, sans doute par ossification du ligament interclinoïdien.

Reprinted from *Comptes rendus des séances de l'Académie des Sciences, t.* 248, pp. 3636-3638, séance du 22 juin 1959.

L'analyse des cellules somatiques d'un enfant atteint de malformations multiples de la colonne vertébrale révèle la présence de 45 chromosomes. L'hypothèse d'une fusion d'un grand télocentrique T_1 et du petit télocentrique v_s (manquant) est envisagée.

Comparé aux valeurs conventionnelles il existe un net retard du développement somatique: à 4 ans ½ ce garçon pèse 12,200 kg et mesure 0,92 m (au lieu des valeurs moyennes: 16 kg et 1 m). Son tour de tête est de 46,5 cm (au lieu de 49). Mais le père et la mère (normaux) mesurent respectivement 1,63 et 1,49 m; et la sœur normale elle aussi, pèse à 6 ans 16,200 kg et mesure 1,06 m seulement.

Enfin le quotient intellectuel (Q=0,89) révèle un retard léger mais réel, bien qu'il faille tenir compte des difficultés de language et de l'instabilité de l'enfant.

Examen chromosomique.—L'utilisation de la méthode de culture de fibroblastes et d'analyse chromosomique précédemment

	Comptage sur dessins			Photos et caryotype			
	44	45	46	44	45	46	*Total*
Biopsie due 15 janvier 1959 (côté gauche)	—	7	—	—	5	—	12
Biopsie du 20 mai 1959 (côté gauche)	—	5	—	—	4	—	9
Biopsie du 20 mai 1959 (côté droit)	—	6	—	—	5	—	11
		18			14		32

décrite (Lejeune, Turpin et Gautier)[4] a permis de décompter régulièrement dans les cellules de cet enfant 45 chromosomes, au lieu du nombre normal de 46. Les résultats concordants de trois biopsies différentes sont résumés ci-dessous, seules les cellules « parfaites » (Lejeune, Gautier et Turpin)[2] étant prises en considération.

Ces 33 cellules et, plus précisément, les 14 caryotypes révèlent l'absence d'un petit télocentrique du type ν_8, les groupes G, M, M_d, P et C étant morphologiquement normaux (*cf.* Lejeune, Turpin, Gautier).[3]

L'hypothése d'une absence du ν_8 par non-disjonction pourrait être envisagée si l'on ne constatait régulièrement sur l'un des télocentriques, T_1, la présence d'un petit segment fortement coloré au lieu et place des petits bras hétérochromatiques habituels (*fig.* 1, T_2 et T_3).

Ces deux constatations, absence d'un ν_8 et présence d'un segment anormal sur un T_1, évoquent un remaniement chromosomique [fusion centromérique de ces deux chromosomes (?)].

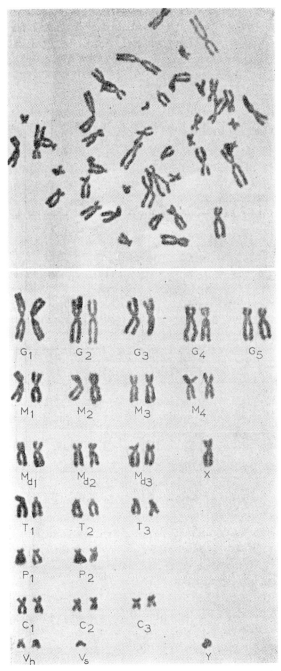

Fig. 1. Cellule et caryotype d'un cas de polydysspondylie à 45 chromosomes (remarquer le prolongement anormal du premier télocentrique T_1, et l'absence d'un v_8).

Au total, il s'agit d'une anomalie certaine (45 chromosomes au lieu de 46) résultant peut être d'un remaniement, avec ou sans perte de substance chromosomique.

Il semble plausible que l'anomalie chromosomique soit la cause du syndrome clinique, mais aucune démonstration directe de ce fait ne peut être actuellement apportée.

REFERENCES

1. J. Lejeune, Mlle M. Gautier et R. Turpin, *Comptes rendus*, 248, 1959, p. 602.
2. J. Lejeune, Mlle M. Gautier et R. Turpin, *Comptes rendus*, 248, 1959, p. 1721.
3. J. Lejeune, R. Turpin et Mlle M. Gautier, *Bull. Acad. Nat. Méd.*, 143, n°s 11 et 12, 1959, p. 256-265.
4. J. Lejeune, R. Turpin et Mlle Gautier, *Annales de Génétique*, n° 2, 1959.

10

MEDULLARY GONADAL DYSGENESIS (CHROMATIN-POSITIVE KLINEFELTER'S SYNDROME)

A Genetically Determined Condition with Eunuchoid Measurements But Early Epiphyseal Closure

JOHN S. S. STEWART, M.B. Glasg.

EUNUCHOIDISM is described as one of the features of chromatin-positive Klinefelter's syndrome, but in adults with this condition body measurements are characterised by an increased sole-to-pubis measurement with relatively normal arm span and apparently normal bone age (Stewart, Mack, Govan, Ferguson-Smith; and Lennox 1959). An adult, with typical clinical features, came to a male subfertility clinic and the findings in this case are described here. Further information about the eunuchoid measurements and their relationship to bone-age can be obtained from patients about the time of puberty; and 4 patients age 14-19 years were investigated (2 were discovered in a clinical survey of mentally retarded schoolchildren, 1 was seen in clinical surgical practice complaining of nocturnal enuresis, and 1 attended an endocrine clinic because of gynæcomastia.

Reprinted from *The Lancet*, June 6, 1959, pp. 1176-1178.

It is a pleasure to acknowledge my indebtedness to Prof. W. A. Mackey and Mr. James Jarvie for laboratory and clinical facilities, to Dr. James Ewan for permission and assistance in conducting the survey of schoolchildren, and to Mr. Arthur Jacobs, Dr. E. G. Oastler, and Mr. W. B. Stirling for permission to investigate and report patients under their care. I am grateful to Dr. D. G. Harnden and Dr. C. E. Ford for their report on the chromosomal sex in case 1 and to Dr. J. Z. Walker for his X-ray reports. I am indebted also to Dr. P. M. Peacock for the organ culture, Dr. A. D. T. Govan for f.s.h. assays, Dr. J. C. Eaton for 17-ketosteroid and biochemical estimations, Mr. P. A. D. Gardner for intelligence testing, Mr. G. Donald for the photographs, and Dr. Bernard Lennox for advice and nuclear sexing.

Chromosomal Sex

At the time of testicular biopsy in 1 patient (case 1), a small piece of testis was set up in organ culture by Dr. P. M. Peacock at Glasgow Royal Infirmary. After subculture the specimen was transferred to Harwell where Dr. D. G. Harnden and Dr. C. E. Ford obtained chromosome counts of 47. The sex chromosomal constitution appeared to be XXY.

Clinical Survey of Schoolchildren

In Glasgow mentally handicapped schoolchildren who are educable I.Q. approximately 50-70) attend school until the age of 16. Most of the older schoolboys attend three schools and the 182 boys, aged 15 or 16 years, at these schools, were examined clinically. Two boys had some clinical features of chromatin-positive Klinefelter's syndrome—testicular atrophy, tall stature, and slight gynæcomastia. The diagnosis was confirmed by nuclear sexing of oral mucosal smears. A further 18 boys in whom the diagnosis was considered to be possible but unlikely were chromatin-negative. The incidence of the syndrome was 1.1% in the small sample surveyed—a similar incidence to that found in a cytological survey of younger subjects from the same source (Ferguson-Smith 1959).

CASE REPORTS

Case 1.—Date of birth, Dec. 4, 1930. This patient (fig. 1) attended a male subfertility clinic complaining of sterility. Testes were small and body measurements were moderately eunuchoid. There was no gynæcomastia and hair distribution was normal. An oral mucosal smear was chromatin-positive and the histological appearance of the testis was typical of Klinefelter's syndrome. Urinary excretion of follicle-stimulating hormone (F.S.H.) was more than 80 mouse units per day. Bone age was adult.

Case 2.—Date of birth, March 23, 1944. This patient attended an endocrine clinic at the age of 13 years 8 months because of gynæcomastia. Testes were small and body measurements eunuchoid: span 61½ in., height 62 in., sole to pubis 32½ in. The diagnosis was confirmed by chromatin-positive buccal smear and testicular biopsy. The patient was seen again aged 14 years 11 months. Gynæcomastia was more prominent and measurements eunuchoid. The patient had grown 1½ in. in 16 months. His intelligence was normal. Bone age was in advance of chronological age. Epiphyses for the lower end of humerus had already fused and the olecranon epiphyses were fusing.

Case 3.—Date of birth, May 5, 1943. This patient (fig. 2) was discovered in the clinical survey of mentally handicapped schoolchildren. He was tall for his age, slight gynæcomastia was present,

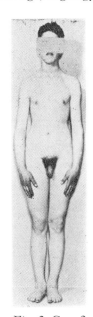
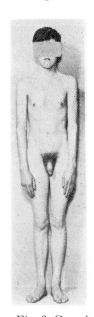

Fig. 1. Case 1.   Fig. 2. Case 3.   Fig. 3. Case 4.

and testes were small. His intelligence was low: verbal 69, performance 75, Wechsler full scale I.Q. 71, Raven's matrices 25th percentile. The diagnosis was confirmed by buccal smear and testicular biopsy. Bone-age was considerably in advance of chronological age. Fusion had begun or was complete in all femoral and tibial epiphyses.

Case 4.—Date of birth, May 13, 1942. This patient (fig. 3) was also discovered in the clinical survey. He was taller than average with eunuchoid measurements, slight gynæcomastia, and small testes. His intelligence was low: verbal 61, performance 82, Wechsler full scale I.Q. 68, Raven's matrices 25th percentile. The diagnosis was confirmed by buccal smear and testicular biopsy. Bone age was considerably in advance of chronological age. All femoral and knee epiphyses had fused and fusion of humeral and iliac crest epiphyses was beginning.

Case 5.—Date of birth, Jan. 11, 1940. This patient attended a urological clinic complaining of intermittent nocturnal enuresis. Apart from a tuberculous infection of one knee in childhood he had always been well. He was a rather inadequate and effeminate individual and his enuresis seemed to be largely psychogenic. He was a tall thin youth with eunuchoid measurements and small

TABLE 1

BODY MEASUREMENTS AND RADIOLOGICAL FINDINGS

Case No.	Body Measurements (in.)						Chronological Age		Approximate Bone Age
	ARM SPAN (1)	HEIGHT (2)	SOLE TO PUBIS (3)	CROWN TO PUBIS (4)	1-2	3-4	YEARS	MONTHS	YEARS
1	72	68	35¾	32¼	4	3½	27	11	Adult
2	63½	63½	33½	30	0	3½	14	11	15-16
3	71	69¼	35½	33¾	1¾	1½	15	2	19-20
4	72	69¼	36¾	32½	2¾	4¼	16	2	19-20
5	70½	70¼	37	33¼	¼	3¾	19	2	21-22

testes but no gynæcomastia. Bacteriological examination of urine was negative for tubercle bacilli. His intelligence was normal. Buccal smear and testicular biopsy confirmed the diagnosis of chromatin-positive Klinefelter's syndrome. Bone age was in advance of chronological age. In the limbs all epiphyses of long bones were fused and iliac crest epiphyses were fused.

The clinical and radiological findings in these cases are summarised in table 1 and the hormonal and biochemical findings are given in table 2.

DISCUSSION

Genetic Aetiology

Early genetic studies (Stewart, Ferguson-Smith, Lennox, and Mack 1958, Stewart, Izatt, Ferguson-Smith, Lennox, and Mack 1958) suggested that chromatin-positive Klinefelter's syndrome was due to a chromosomal aberration and that in some cases it could be transmitted through the paternal line as a sex-controlled dominant character which was not sex-linked. Sibship data indicated that all cases could not be familial and most appeared to be sporadic. The possibility of heteroploidy was explored by investigation of blood-groups, although at that time translocation or inversion crossover was considered to be more likely. Chromatin-positive nuclear sex suggests that two X chromosomes are present and this is confirmed by data on colour blindness (Polani, Bishop, Ferguson-Smith, Lennox, Stewart, and Prader 1958). The chromosomal sex can be determined by examination of somatic cells in mitosis. The chromosome number in man is 46 (Ford and Ham-

TABLE 2

HORMONAL AND BIOCHEMICAL FINDINGS IN YOUNGER PATIENTS
(AGES AS IN TABLE 1)

| Case No. | Daily-Urinary Excretion of | | Serum Levels of | |
	F.S.H. (MOUSE UNITS)	17-KETO-STEROIDS (MG.)	INORGANIC PHOSPHORUS (MG. PER 100 ML.)	ALKALINE PHOSPHATASE (BODANSKY UNITS)
2	>80*	6.5*	4.4	6.2
3	40-80	5.5	3.2	3.8
4	40-80	6.3	3.4	3.1
5	>80	13.2	3.1	1.2

* At age 13 years 10 months.

merton 1956) and it is convenient to use bone-marrow for determining chromosomal sex (Ford et al. 1958). It is now recognised that patients with chromatin-positive Klinefelter's syndrome have 47 chromosomes and that their sex chromosomal constitution is apparently XXY (Jacobs and Strong 1959, Ford et al. 1959). In case 1 the confirmation of the XXY constitution in tissue culture and the report of identical twins with the syndrome (Grumbach and Barr 1958) suggests that the aberration arises at meiosis or during very early development, but mosaics are possible. Although familial cases may be relatively uncommon, it does not follow (*pace Lancet* 1959) that the condition cannot be genetic. Indeed the demonstration of heteroploidy in bone-marrow cells and in fibroblasts is good evidence that the condition is genetic. Moreover, such an abnormality or the tendency to produce it could explain the familial incidence suggested by the data reported (Stewart et al. 1958).

Eunuchoidism and Advanced Bone Age

Eunuchoid measurements are usually considered to be due to delay in epiphyseal closure, but clearly this cannot be the cause in Klinefelter's syndrome. In all four young patients (table 1) bone age is considerably in advance of chronological age. Thus, early epiphyseal closure appears to be a feature of the syndrome and it is probably related in some way to the partly eunuchoid measurements found in adults (Stewart et al. 1959). Although epiphyseal closure varies with sex yet in some of these patients bone age is in advance even of that expected in females.

Growth is supposed to be largely controlled by a pituitary factor, mainly growth hormone, and a steroid factor, mainly sex hormones. At puberty the influence of the pituitary factor is decreasing and of the steroid factor increasing. Limb epiphyses are closing and those in the arms do so later than those in the legs. A growth spurt in early puberty followed by early epiphyseal closure might explain the partly eunuchoid measurements. Since F.S.H. excretion is raised in Klinefelter's syndrome it is possible that there is an increased output of other pituitary hormones. It is also a feature of the syndrome that Leydig cells are increased and morphologically abnormal so that a qualitative or quantitative abnormality of androgens might be present. Serum-inorganic-phosphorus and serum-alkaline-phosphatase levels appear to be rather high for age in case 2, the youngest patient (table 2). These might be a manifestation of increased growth-hormone activity. Total 17-ketosteroids appear to be normal. Obviously several factors may operate and no conclusion is possible at present but the problem is an interesting one.

Nomenclature

The discovery that cases of Klinefelter's syndrome are XXY chromosomal intersexes and that cases of Turner's syndrome are XO (Jacobs and Stewart 1959, Ford et al. 1959) suggests that development of the gonadal cortex is dependent on the presence of two X chromosomes but that a Y chromosome is necessary for development of the gonadal medulla. It is now necessary to revise previous attempts to correlate nomenclature with the developmental defect present in cases of gonadal dysgenesis (Stewart 1958). It would be logical to describe Turner's syndrome and its variants as examples of cortical gonadal dysgenesis and of Klinefelter's syndrome and its variants as examples of medullary gonadal dysgenesis. True hermaphroditism may prove to be XX/XY or other mosaics and could be considered as examples of corticomedullary gonadal dysgenesis. The recent discoveries emphasise that precisions in terminology is necessary, the more so because of recent publicity of "sex reversal" in the lay Press. Patients with cortical dysgenesis and medullary dysgenesis can now be reassured, without reservation, that they are female and male respectively.

SUMMARY

A case of chromatin-positive Klinefelter's syndrome had 47 chromosomes and an apparent XXY sex chromosomal constitution. Four patients aged 14-19 years with chromatin-positive Klinefelter's syndrome had eunuchoid measurements in spite of early epiphyseal closure which appears to be a feature of the syndrome. The significance of these findings is discussed and the names cortical dysgenesis and medullary dysgenesis are proposed for the syndromes of Turner and Klinefelter.

REFERENCES

Ferguson-Smith, M. A. (1959) *Lancet,* i, 219.
Ford, C. E., Hammerton, J. L. (1956) *Nature, Lond.* 178:1020.
—— Jacobs, P. A., Lajtha, L. G. (1958) *ibid.* 181:1565.
—— Polani, P. E., Briggs, J. H., Bishop, P. M. F. (1959) *ibid.* 183:1030.
Grumbach, M. M., Barr, M. L. (1958) *Recent Prog. Hormone Res.* 15:255.
Jacobs, P. A., Stewart, J. S. S. (1959) (in preparation).
—— Strong, J. A. (1959) *Nature, Lond.* 183:302.
Lancet (1959) i, 237.
Polani, P. E., Bishop, P. M. F., Ferguson-Smith, M. A., Lennox, B., Stewart, J. S. S., Prader, A. (1958) *Nature, Lond.* 182:1092.
Stewart, J. S. S. (1958) *Lancet,* i, 161.
—— Ferguson-Smith, M. A., Lennox, B. Mack, W. S. (1958) *ibid.* ii, 117.
—— Izatt, M. M., Ferguson-Smith, M. A., Lennox, B., Mack, W. S. (1958) Symposium on Nuclear Sex; p. 123, London.
—— Mack, W. S., Govan, A. D. T., Ferguson-Smith, M. A., Lennox, B. (1959) *Quart. J. Med.* (in the press).

11

SEX REVERSAL IN NEWBORN BABIES

Keith L. Moore, B.A., M.Sc., Ph.D. Western Ontario

S EX reversal may be detected in the newborn by the sex-chromatin test (Moore et al. 1953, Moore and Barr 1955). The validity of this test of chromosomal sex has been confirmed by several other investigators (Emery and McMillan 1954, Sohval et al. 1955, Lennox 1956, Segal and Nelson 1957, Silagy and Chiang 1958, and others). Sex reversal is seldom detected in the newborn because it is rarely associated with other recognisable congenital abnormalities. It is usually detected in adolescents with abnormalities of sex development. Sex reversal may be suspected in some girls at birth, or during childhood, if they show clinical characteristics of gonadal dysgenesis (Turner's syndrome and related conditions). A sex-chromatin test would reveal whether sex reversal had occurred.

Sex reversal was suspected in man before a method of detecting it was introduced (Jost 1950, Wilkins 1950). They suggested that some patients with gonadal dysgenesis, although anatomically female, might be chromosomal males. This possibility was suggested after Jost had shown that male rabbit fœtuses always developed into females when they were castrated at a sufficiently early stage of development.

Polani et al. (1954) were the first to test the chromosomal sex of patients with gonadal dysgenesis; they found that all 3 of their

Reprinted from *The Lancet*, January 31, 1959, pp. 217-219.

I am grateful to Dr. I. Maclaren Thompson, professor and head of anatomy, for his guidance, especially in statistics, and for critically reading the manuscript. I am also grateful to Dr. Harry Medovy, head of pediatrics, and his staff, for their assistance in this investigation. I want to thank Dr. Angus Wood for collecting the smears, and the many nurses who assisted him. This investigation was supported by a grant from the Committee for Research in Problems of Sex, National Academy of Sciences—National Research Council (U.S.A.).

patients were chromosomal males. However, it was soon shown
that not all patients with this disorder are chromosomal males; for
in several investigations, taken together, about 20% of them were
chromosomal females (Grumbach et al. 1955, Barr 1956). The
chromosomal males are thought to begin as male embryos, and
then develop into essentially normal-appearing girls when testes
fail to differentiate.

Apparent females with so-called "testicular feminisation" (Morris 1953) may also be thought of as instances of male-to-female
sex reversal *(Lancet* 1958). These patients are often classified as
male pseudohermaphrodites, but they differ from the latter in
some important respects. They appear normal at birth, and develop into essentially normal-appearing women (Morris 1953,
Nelson 1956). Their male chromosomal sex and gonads are usually
detected only when they present themselves with inguinal herniæ
or amenorrhœa. These patients are thought to originate as male
embryos, and then to feminise when the fœtal testes fail to secrete
the hormones or inductor substances essential for the differentiation of male accessory sex organs.

Sex reversal in apparent males is now very well known. The
observation that some patients with Klinefelter's syndrome had
chromatin-positive nuclei, the female type (Plunkett and Barr
1956, Bradbury et al. 1956), stimulated considerable interest in
this disorder *(Lancet* 1956). Originally this condition was thought
to be quite rare, but many cases were soon reported (Riis et al.
1956, Jackson et al. 1956, Nelson 1956, Grumbach et al. 1956,
Ferguson-Smith et al. 1957, Raboch 1957, Beattie 1957). These
reports showed that not all patients with this syndrome were
chromatin-positive, and that conversely many patients were chromatin-positive who did not fit the Klinefelter syndrome. Numerous names have been used to describe these patients, because
of the variation in characteristics from patient to patient. Testicular dysgenesis is the name used in the remainder of this paper;
this term is preferred because it denotes imperfect development
of testes, a characteristic feature of all such cases.

The histological structure of the testes has varied from one
patient to another, but the main defect has been fibrosis and

hyalinisation of the seminiferous tubules. Germ-cells have been absent or scarce in most cases, but complete spermatogenesis has been observed in isolated portions of some patients' tubules. Spermatozoa have never been observed in semen samples from these patients. Men with chromatin-positive nuclei and testicular dysgenesis apparently begin development as female embryos; then testes mysteriously develop which secrete the necessary hormones or inductor substances causing development of male accessory sex organs.

Attempts have been made to estimate the frequency of chromatin-positive males in the general population. Ferguson-Smith et al. (1957) suggested that at least 1 in every 10,000 males is chromatin-positive, whereas Prader et al. (1958) thought the incidence may be as high as 1 in 1,000. The incidence appears to be higher among mentally defective persons than in the general population. The results of two surveys of these patients were: 4 in 325 males (Ferguson-Smith 1958), and 8 in 336 males (Prader et al. 1958).

In the present investigation chromosomal sex of infants was tested in order to detect sex reversal in the newborn. The purpose was to determine whether there is any hitherto undescribed association between sex reversal and any evident congenital abnormality, and to determine the incidence of sex reversal in these newborns.

METHODS

Oral smears were collected over a period of twelve months from the 3,715 babies (1,911 males and 1,804 females) born at the Winnipeg General Hospital.

The smears were prepared by scraping the oral mucosa with a sterile nickel spatula, and smearing the material over a relatively small area of a clean microscope slide. Each smear was fixed immediately in equal parts of ether and 95% ethyl alcohol, the fixation extending overnight. The smears were stained with cresyl echt violet, using the staining procedure described in an earlier paper (Moore and Barr 1955).

Each smear was examined under the oil-immersion objective of a binocular microscope for the presence or absence of visible sex chromatin. The anatomical sex of the infant was unknown to the microscopist at the time of the examination. Sex-chromatin counts were not made routinely, because the chromosomal sex was usually obvious. However, at least 100 nuclei were examined from each infant before a diagnosis of sex was made. Additional smears had to be collected in some cases because the routine ones were not of sufficiently high technical quality. When the chromosomal-sex diagnosis differed from the anatomical sex of an infant, several more smears were collected. Some of these smears were stained by the Feulgen method for confirmatory observations.

The chromosomal sex was recorded on the infants' charts in all sex-reversed cases. Infants with a chromosomal sex opposite to their anatomical sex were given a special examination by the medical staff of the department of pediatrics. The parents of the sex-reversed infants were not informed of the discrepancy, and confirmatory biopsies were not done, because unnecessary attention, especially after the babies had left the hospital, might have caused some concern to the parents. Gonadal biopsies were impracticable in all cases, because clinically these babies were normal.

OBSERVATIONS

Apparent males.—In 5 of 1,911 males tested, typical female-sex chromatin was observed; the chromosomal sex was male in all the other anatomical males. Amongst the 5 chromatin-positive males, the proportion of nuclei counted exhibiting female-sex chromatin varied from 53% to 64%. Moore and Barr (1955) have found that even in people that were females both chromosomally and anatomically the proportion of nuclei showing female-sex chromatin varied from 40% to 60%.

All the pregnancies producing the 5 chromatin-positive males were uncomplicated. All were single-birth full-term infants. The only abnormal finding was the presence of female-sex chromatin in their nuclei. The external genitalia were entirely male in appearance, and normal in size for newborns. The testes had descended into the scrotum in all infants, and were normal in size and consistence on palpation.

Apparent females.—The female-sex chromatin was a conspicuous feature of many nuclei of all 1,804 females, and had the characteristics described by Moore and Barr (1955).

DISCUSSION
Incidence

The incidence of chromatin-positive males in 1911 newborn males was 0.26%. The frequency of sex reversal in anatomical males born at this hospital was calculated from table v of Mainland et al. (1956) to be between 0.06% and 0.74%. These percentages represent the lower and upper 1% confidence limits. In a further publication the incidence of sex reversal in the present series of newborn males will be compared with the incidence in male mental defectives, in whom higher frequencies have been reported. Some of the chromatin-positive males in the present series may later show mental retardation; this will be discussed in the paper under preparation.

The results of the present investigation seem to indicate that female-to-male sex reversal is commoner than male-to-female sex reversal, for no sex-reversed males were detected in the 1,804 anatomical females tested. The upper confidence limit of sex reversal in apparent females born at this hospital was calculated from table ix of Mainland et al. (1956) to be 0.29%. A larger number of observations would improve this estimate, especially if broader sampling of the general population were achieved.

Probable Future Development of Chromatin-positive Newborn Males

Most of the chromatin-positive males reported before this series have been postpubertal, and have shown clinical characteristics of testicular dysgenesis. Only a few prepubertal cases have been reported, and they have been essentially normal-appearing boys; but, after chromatin-positive oral smears, histological evidence of testicular dysgenesis has been found in 2 cases (Bunge and Bradbury 1957, Ferguson-Smith 1958). It is generally held that all chromatin-positive males have or will develop testicular dysgenesis; but this may not be so. Some chromatin-positive males may develop normally, and be indistinguishable from normal males except by their female-sex chromatin. If all 5 chromatin-positive males in the present series develop testicular dysgenesis, then the incidence of this condition must be higher than is generally thought at present.

There is some evidence to support the possibility of fertility in chromatin-positive males. Spermatogenesis has been observed in testicular biopsies from a few patients; in most of them it has been incomplete, but spermatozoa have been seen in some (Bunge and Bradbury 1956, Nelson 1956, Ferguson-Smith et al. 1957, Segal and Nelson 1957). All these patients have been sterile, but so are all patients with testicular dysgenesis whether they are sex-reversed or not. The finding of spermatogenesis in chromatin-positive males shows that fertility is possible in such males, if the testes were to develop normally. It is known that some sex-reversed fishes and amphibians have the ability to reproduce (Witschi 1939, Chang and Witschi 1956).

The offspring of a chromatin-positive male should all be chromosomal females, for such males could produce only X-type spermatozoa.* These statements are true only if the sex chromatin in his cells represents 2 X-chromosomes. The origin of sex chromatin is not definitely known, but it is generally thought to be reliable indicator of female chromosomal sex (Moore and Barr 1954, Lennox 1956, Sachs and Danon 1956, Segal and Nelson 1957). Although a fertile chromatin-positive male should produce all females, the possibility that he may produce chromatin-positive males like himself cannot be excluded.

These considerations suggest that the 5 chromatin-positive males in the present series will probably show normal sex development until puberty. Some will probably develop characteristics of testicular dysgenesis during adolescence, but others may become normal-appearing fertile males.

Aetiology of Female-to-Male Sex Reversal

The ætiology is not known, but several hypotheses have been suggested. Most of the suggestions have been concerned with chromosomal abnormalities, probably because differentiation of the gonads is generally thought to be genetically controlled. Stew-

---

* There appears to be general agreement that such males have two X chromosomes and one Y chromosome. Thus spermatoza, if produced, could be the following types: X, XX, XY, or Y. If such spermatozoa fertilized normal ova, XX, XXX, XXY, or XY zygotes could result. Persons with these sex chromosome patterns are now known to exist. The first two types should appear feminine, whereas the last two should appear masculine.

art et al. (1958) have admirably discussed the various chromosomal hypotheses, and have proposed a new one based on their
genetical studies. Stewart et al. also adduce some evidence of
familial transmission of testicular dysgenesis in chromatin-positive
males.

Early deficiency of primordial germ-cells in the gonads has
been suggested as a causative factor for sex reversal in patients
with testicular dysgenesis (Witschi 1956, Witschi et al. 1957).
These investigators have also suggested various factors which
might cause a reduction in the number of primordial germ-cells
in the gonads of man.

The following is a further contribution to speculation concerning the ætiology of female-to-male sex reversal in man. It is well
known that hormones from hyperplastic fœtal adrenals cause
masculinisation of the external genitalia of females; similar effects
have been observed in girls whose mothers have been treated with
steroids during pregnancy (Wilkins et al. 1958, Gold and Michael
1958, Nellhaus 1958). The gonads were not affected in any of the
above cases, apparently because the hormones acted after the
direction of differentiation of the gonads was determined. In some
masculinised females the source of the hormones was not detected; Wilkins et al. (1958) have suggested that in these cases
there may be an abnormal metabolism of maternal or placental
hormones during pregnancy, resulting in the formation of androgenic substances. If this were to arise early enough, these androgens might cause the indifferent gonads of female embryos to
develop as testes, eventuating in complete masculinisation of all
accessory sex organs. It is well known that partial gonadal sex
reversal in the freemartin of cattle (a chromosomal female) is
caused by fœtal testicular secretions from a male twin (Lillie
1917, Moore et al. 1957). Furthermore, androgens administered to
genetic female frogs at a critical stage in development caused
testes to differentiate instead of ovaries (Witschi 1951). Thus
hormonal imbalance may possibly cause female-to-male sex reversal in man.

Probable Prenatal Development of Chromatin-positive Males

The chromosomal sex of these infants, established at fertilisation, was female. During early gonadal differentiation some factor

caused the cortices of the indifferent gonads to degenerate; then testes differentiated from the medullary regions. The testes secreted hormones or inductor substances which caused complete differentiation of male accessory sex organs. The testes descended into the scrotum at the normal time, and the chromosomal females had the anatomical appearance of normal males.

SUMMARY

The chromosomal sex of 3,715 newborn infants (1,911 males and 1,804 females) was detected by the oral-smear technique of Moore and Barr (1955).

All except 5 of the infants had a chromosomal sex consistent with their anatomical sex. The 5 exceptions were all anatomical males; they were normal-appearing infants but had sex chromatin patterns typical of chromosomal females. They are regarded as instances of female-to-male sex reversal.

It is suggested that some of these chromatin-positive males are likely to develop characteristics of testicular dysgenesis during adolescence; some may also become mentally subnormal. The possibility of such males developing normally is also discussed.

Most writers suggest that female-to-male sex reversal is caused by chromosomal aberration; other possibilities are discussed, and a hypothesis of hormonal imbalance is offered.

REFERENCES

Barr, M. L. (1956) *Canad. med. Ass. J.* 74:419.

Beattie, L. (1957) *Canad. Serv. med. J.* 13:469.

Bradbury, J. T., Bunge, G., Boccabella, R. A. (1956) *J. clin. Endocrin.* 16:689.

Bunge, R. G., Bradbury, J. T. (1956) *J. Urol.* 76:758.

—— (1957) *ibid.* 78:775.

Chang, C. Y., Witschi, E. (1956) *Proc. Soc. exp. Biol., N.Y.* 93:140.

Emery, J. L., McMillan, M. (1954) *J. Path. Bact.* 68:17.

Ferguson-Smith, M. A. (1958) *Lancet*, i, 928.

—— Lennox, B., Mack, W. S., Stewart, J. S. S. (1957) *ibid.* ii, 167.

Gold, A. P., Michael, A. M. (1958) *J. Pediat.* 52:279.

Grumbach, M. M., Engle, E. T., Blanc, W. A., Barr, M. L. (1956) *J. Clin. Endocrin.* 16:923.

—— Van Wyk, J. J., Wilkins, L. (1955) *ibid.* 15:1161.

Jackson, W. P. U., Shapiro, B. G., Uys, C. J. (1956) *Lancet*, ii, 857.

Jost, A. (1950) *Gynéc. et Obstét.* 49:44.

Lancet (1956) ii, 877.
—— (1958) i, 89.
Lennox, B. (1956) *Scot. med. J. 1:97.*
Lillie, F. R. (1917) *J. Exp. Zool. 23:371.*
Mainland, D., Herrera, L., Sutcliffe, M. I. (1956) Tables for Use with Binomial Samples. New York University College of Medicine.
Moore, K. L., Barr, M. L. (1954) *Acta anat., Basel, 21:197.*
—— (1955) *Lancet, ii, 57.*
—— Graham, M. A., Barr, M. L. (1953) *Surg. Gynec. Obstet. 96:641.*
—— (1957) *J. exp. Zool. 135:101.*
Morris, J. M. (1953) *Amer. J. Obstet. Gynec. 65:1192.*
Nellhaus, G. (1958) *New Engl. J. Med. 258:935.*
Nelson, W. O. (1956) *Acta endocrin., Copenhagen, 23:227.*
Plunket, E. R., Barr, M. L. (1956) *Lancet, ii, 853.*
Polani, P. E., Hunter, W. F., Lennox, B. (1954) *ibid. ii, 120.*
Prader, A., Schneider, J., Francés, J. M., Züblin, W. (1958) *ibid. i, 968.*
Raboch, J. (1957) *J. Clin. Endocrin. 17:1429.*
Riis, P., Johnsen, S. G., Mosbeck, J. (1956) *Lancet, i, 962.*
Sachs, L., Danon, M. (1956) *Genetica, 28:201.*
Segal, S. J., Nelson, W. O. (1957) *J. clin. Endocrin. 17:676.*
Silagy, J. M., Chiang, C. H. (1958) *N.Y. St. J. Med. 58:2801.*
Sohval, A. R., Gaines, J. A., Gabrilove, J. L. (1955) *Amer. J. Obstet. Gynec. 70:1074.*
Stewart, J. S. S., Lennox, B., Mack, W. S. (1958) *Lancet, ii, 121.*
Wilkins, L. (1950) The Diagnosis and Treatment of Endocrine Disorders in Childhood and Adolescence. Springfield, Ill.
—— Jones, H. W., Holman, G. H., Stempfel, R. S. (1958) *J. Clin Endocrin. 18:559.*
Witschi, E. (1939) *in* Sex and Internal Secretions (edited by Allen, Danforth, and Doisy); p. 145. Baltimore.
—— (1951) *Recent Progr. Hormone Res. 6:1.*
—— (1956) *in* Transactions of Third Conference on Gestation (edited by C. Villee). Josiah Macy, Jr., Foundation, New York.
—— Nelson, W. O., Segal, S. J. (1957) *J. clin. Endocrin. 17:737.*

12

HOW COMMON IS SEX REVERSAL?
Leading Article

S INCE so many patients with so many different syndromes
have been proved in the past few years to have nuclear sex
at variance with their apparent sex, and estimates of the frequency of such sex reversal have been steadily rising, it has become an obvious necessity to determine the true incidence by
nuclear-sexing a large random sample of apparently normal people. Obvious, but daunting: even by the oral mucosal smear
method[1] the labour involved in a large survey is very great.
Nevertheless, Dr. Keith Moore, whose article appears on p. 104
of this issue, has now completed a survey of all the 3,715 babies
born in Winnipeg General Hospital in one year, and has found
this sufficient to produce most significant results. All the 1,804
apparent females were confirmed as genetic females. Of the 1,911
apparent males, however, 5 proved to have female nuclear sex.
Apparently, therefore (as had been suspected), sex reversal is not
symmetrical—that is to say, female-to-masculine sex reversal is
much commoner that male-to-feminine—and incidentally the difference is enough to account for a small but significant fraction
of the differential sex ratio at birth. While completely feminised
males (Turner's syndrome and related gonadal dysgeneses, and
testicular feminisation) are rare enough to be completely absent
from Moore's series, completely masculinised genetic females are
almost common, forming something like 1 in 400 of the masculine
population.

Nearly all such cases must be examples of chromatin-positive
Klinefelter's syndrome. Since the first cases were described less
than three years ago,[2] substantial series of cases have been reported from several centres.[3-7] High incidences of the condition
have been demonstrated in patients attending male infertility
clinics[8, 9] and in mental defectives.[10, 11] As Dr. Ferguson-Smith

Reprinted from *The Lancet*, i:237-239, 1959.

points out this week (p. 219) combination of the various surveys made in Glasgow shows that the incidence in that city cannot be less than 1 in 3,000, and it is probably a good deal higher. Prader et al.[11] believed that the incidence in Zürich was at least 1 in 1,000. It is possible to deduce an estimate very near Moore's from other sources. Combination of Campbell's[12] estimate that 12% of married couples are infertile with Davidson's[13] that the husband is azoospermic in 8% of such couples investigated suggests that some 1% of men produce no spermatozoa. The figures of Ferguson-Smith et al.[9] indicate that 17% of azoospermics are chromatin-positive. This is 0.17% (or 1 in 600) of all men; and if we allow for the undetermined (but not negligible) number who produce some spermatozoa, we end up with something not much less than Moore's 1 in 400. This is a remarkable finding, even if it is only approximately correct. There must be one or two genetic females in every battalion of the British Army, and a few such cases on nearly every general practitioner's list.

We may have to abandon some attractive hypotheses of the origin of sex-reversed Klinefelter's syndrome. Most people will be loth to forgo the idea of some kind of genetic background. A very few pairs of affected brothers have been recorded, and some indirect evidence for a familial incidence has been noted by Stewart et al.[5] But if there were any kind of ordinary genetic transmission, convincing pedigrees would by now have been reported in substantial numbers. Possibly a few cases, especially those with associated disorders, are familial; but this does not affect the conclusion that the majority of cases must be sporadic—just as the familial incidence of colonic cancer associated with polyposis, or of œsophageal cancer associated with tylosis, does not affect the general conclusion that the majority of cancers at these sites are essentially non-genetic. Whatever produces the condition probably acts between fertilisation and the time of differentiation of the gonads: it may concern the mechanism of fertilisation or the development of either of the individual gametes that take part in fertilisation, but it seems most unlikely to be any more remote than this. Moore's suggestion that hormonal balance at the crucial pregonadal stage of fœtal development is at fault is as good a hypothesis as any—indeed, something similar was once put forward in these columns[14]—but it rests on no solid evidence.

Dr. Ferguson-Smith's paper, besides consolidating the evidence for a high incidence in mental defectives, describes a unique series of prepubertal cases. He has established that in the tests at this stage the only recognisable lesion, and very probably the essential lesion, is a conspicuously low content of germ-cells. This makes it worth while reconsidering a hypothesis advanced by Witschi.[15] Witschi showed that in amphibia the number of germ-cells reaching the gonad profoundly affected the development of the gonad. If none reached it, no formed gonad would develop; if a normal complement reached it, the gonad would develop normally into ovary or testis according to the genetic sex of the embryo; but if an intermediate number reached it, the gonad tended constantly towards the male type, even in genetic females. He explained both Turner's syndrome and Klinefelter's syndrome on this basis: in Turner's syndrome no germ-cells reach the gonad anlage, which thus does not develop at all (so secondary sex characters develop in the neutral feminoid type); in Klinefelter's syndrome the germ-cells are deficient in numbers, so a male gonad is produced even in genetic females. This is a considerable simplification of Witschi's hypothesis, but it probably represents the useful bones of it. Ferguson-Smith's argument that a similar deficiency of germ-cells is found in the testes in some other conditions (notably in undescended testes, where the observation is an important one) is not altogether relevant; for these are all genetic males, and it is the possible effect of germ-cell deficiency in genetic females which chiefly concerns us. Witschi produced his germ-cell deficiencies in amphibian larvæ by allowing ova to become over-ripe before fertilisation; one shudders at the difficulties involved in any attempt to prove or disprove the influence of the age of the maternal ovum at fertilisation on the occurrence of Klinefelter's syndrome. It is in fact when one comes down to details a most unsatisfactory hypothesis in many ways; but it can certainly be credited with being more exactly in accordance with Dr. Ferguson-Smith's new findings than any other.

Dr. Ferguson-Smith's suggestion that the clumsy and now inaccurate name "Klinefelter's syndrome" be replaced by "micro-orchidism" will repel those who believe that there is already enough confusion of names in this field. Yet the suggested name is neater and hardly less precise than seminiferous-tubule dysgenesis (the current transatlantic favourite, with several inferior variants) or hyperplastic medullary gonadal dysgenesis.[16] Eponyms are still being coined for the testicular feminisation syndrome.[17] Perhaps opinions in this field are still too fluid for successful attempts to codify nomenclature; but confusion will grow if some agreement is not reached soon.

REFERENCES

1. Moore, K., Barr, M. L. *Lancet*, 1955, ii, 67.
2. Plunkett, E. R., Barr, M. L. *ibid*. 1956, ii, 853. Bradbury, J. T., Bunge, R. G., Boccabella, R. A. *J. clin. Endocrin*. 1956, *16*:689.
3. Segal, S. J., Nelson, W. O. *J. clin. Endocrin*. 1957, *17*:676.
4. Grumbach, M. M., Blanc, W. A., Engle, E. T. *ibid*. p. 703.
5. Stewart, J. S. S., Ferguson-Smith, M. A., Lennox, B., Mack, W. S. *Lancet*, 1958, ii, 117.
6. Polani, P. E., Bishop, P. M. F., Lennox, B., Ferguson-Smith, M. A., Stewart, J. S. S., Prader, A. *Nature, Lond*. 1958, *182*:1092.
7. Wiedemann, H-R., Romatowski, H., Tolksdorf, M. *Artzl. Wschr*. 1957, *12*:857.
8. Grumbach, M. M., Barr, M. L. *Rec. Progr. Horm. Res*. 1959, *14*:255.
9. Ferguson-Smith, M. A., Lennox, B., Mack, W. S., Stewart, J. S. S. *Lancet*, 1957, ii, 167.
10. Ferguson-Smith, M. A. *ibid*. 1958, i, 928.
11. Prader, A., Schneider, J., Zubtin, W., Frances, J. M., Ruedi, K. *Schweiz. med. Wschr*. 1958, 88:917; *Lancet*, 1958, i, 968.
12. Campbell, H. *Brit. med. J*. 1958, i, 429.
13. Davidson, H. A. *ibid*. 1949, ii, 1328.
14. *Lancet*, 1956, ii, 127.
15. Witschi, E., Nelson, W. O., Segal, S. J. *J. clin. Endocrin*. 1957, *17*:737.

13

DYSGENESIS OF THE SEMINIFEROUS TUBULES*

MURRAY L. BARR, M.Sc., M.D.

THE cytological tests of chromosomal sex are now well established as diagnostic aids in gonadal dysgenesis, formerly called "ovarian agenesis," and hermaphroditism (Davidson and Smith, 1956; Lennox, 1956; Nelson, 1956). About 80% of patients with gonadal dysgenesis have male nuclei, which suggests that they developed in the female direction when deprived of the masculinising hormone or inductor of embryonal testes (Grumbach *et al.*, 1955). In hermaphroditism the tests assist in distinguishing male pseudohermaphrodites who have male nuclei from female pseudohermaphrodites who have female nuclei (Barr, 1956).

It has recently been shown that a proportion of sterile males with hyalinisation and fibrosis of the seminiferous tubules have female nuclei. They appear, therefore, to represent an almost complete female——→male sex reversal from an early stage in embryonal development. This finding will be of particular interest to the genito-urinary specialist because of its bearing on male sterility.

CYTOLOGICAL TESTS OF CHROMOSOMAL SEX

The tests of chromosomal sex are based on the presence of a mass of sex chromatin in cell nuclei of normal females that is absent or insignificant in nuclei of normal males. The sex chromatin is about 1 μ in diameter and is typically located against the inner surface of the nuclear membrane. All information presently available indicates that the sex chromatin is formed by "heterochromatic" regions of the two X-chromosomes that adhere to each other (Sachs and Danon, 1956).

Reprinted from *British Journal of Urology*, Vol. XXIX, No. 3, September 1957.

* Read at the combined meeting of the Canadian Urological Association and the British Association of Urological Surgeons at Montreal, May 1957.

This study was supported by a grant from the National Research Council of Canada and the D. H. McDermid Medical Research Fund.

117

Fig. 1.   Fig. 2.

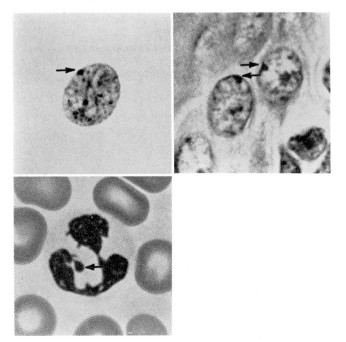

Fig. 3.

Fig. 1. Nucleus in an oral mucosal smear from a chromosomal female. (Cresyl echt violet.) ×2,000.

Fig. 2. Cells of the spinous layer in a skin biopsy specimen from a chromosomal female. (H. & E.) ×2,000.

Fig. 3. Neutrophil in a blood film from a chromosomal female. (Giemsa.) ×2,000.

Three procedures are now available for detecting the nature of the sex chromosome complex (XX or XY) in anomalies of sex development.

1. Oral Smear Method.—This procedure was described simultaneously by Marberger *et al.* (1955) and Moore and Barr (1955). Over 40% of healthy, well-preserved nuclei in mucosal smears from chromosomal females contain the sex chromatin (Fig. 1), which is lacking in smears from chromosomal males. The simplicity of this procedure makes it the method of choice.

2. Skin Biopsy Method.—Nuclei in the spinous layer of the epidermis are studied in sections of high technical quality (Moore *et al.*, 1953). A clearly defined mass of sex chromatin is present only in the cells of chromosomal females, where it can be identified in over 50% of nuclei (Fig. 2).

3. Neutrophil Method.—In chromosomal females an average of 2 to 3% of neutrophil leucocytes have a small, accessory nuclear lobule that presumably contains the sex chromatin (Davidson and Smith, 1954) (Fig. 3). This particular nuclear lobule does not occur in neutrophil leucocytes of chromosomal males.

The practicality of each of the three methods has been verified by a number of investigators.

The terms "female nuclei" and "male nuclei" are used in this report. However, it is advisable to use the less stigmatising terms "chromatin-positive" and "chromatin-negative" for female and male nuclei respectively when discussing cases of sex reversal in clinical surroundings and when recording the findings of cytological tests on hospital charts.

THE CLINICAL PICTURE OF DYSGENESIS OF THE SEMINIFEROUS TUBULES WITH FEMALE NUCLEI

The following generalised account is based on the writer's study of five cases in collaboration with Dr. E. R. Plunkett and Dr. Lillian M. Beattie, on twenty-two additional cases for whom cytological tests were done in this department, and on reports that have appearerd in the recent literature (Bradbury *et al.*, 1956; Jackson *et al.*, 1956; Nelson, 1956; Plunkett and Barr, 1956; Riis *et al.*, 1956; Sohval *et al.*, 1956; Witschi, 1956). Earlier reports of patients with hyalinisation of the seminiferous tubules were also consulted in this connection since, in retrospect, it is certain that female nuclei would have been demonstrable in many of the patients if tests of chromosomal sex had been available (*e.g.*, Klinefelter *et al.*, 1942; Heller and Nelson, 1945, *a* and *b*; Nelson and Heller, 1945; de la Balze *et al.*, 1952).

1. Testes.—The testes are small (about 1½ by 1 by 1 cm.) and of variable consistence. Many of the seminiferous tubules are represented by hyaline masses that are considerably smaller than normal tubules (Fig. 4). The hyalinised tubules may have small lumina, but they contain none of the cells that characterise the normal epithelium of seminiferous tubules. In other tubules there are varying degrees of fibrotic thickening of the tunica propria (Fig. 5). The epithelial cells cannot be equated, as a rule, with either germinal or Sertoli cells when fibrosis is well advanced. Sertoli cells are recognisable in tubules with less severe fibrosis.

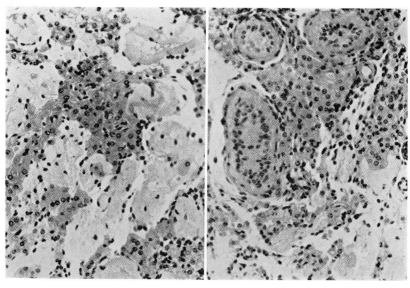

Fig. 4.   Fig. 5.

Areas of the same testis biopsy specimen from a patient with dysgenesis of the seminiferous tubules and female nuclei. (H. & E.) ×200.

Germinal epithelium is usually absent but sometimes the earlier stages of spermatogenesis are in evidence, even to the spermatid stage. Spermiogenesis has not been encountered. Varying degrees of tubular abnormality may occur in the same specimen. Spermatozoa are absent from the semen as a consequence of the tubular pathology.

There are many Leydig cells in a microscopic field, but in view of the small size of the testes the total number is probably not excessive. The Leydig cells occur in clumps, which are sometimes quite large, scattered among the abnormal tubules. There is frequently vacuolation and a deficiency of refractile granules in the cytoplasm, which are indications of some degree of functional failure. Pathological changes, therefore, involve all elements of the testis, but the principal defect lies in the seminiferous tubules. The remainder of the reproductive system has an essentially normal male morphology and female elements have not been noted.

2. Physical Findings.—There is frequently evidence of androgen deficiency during the puberal and adolescent periods. This may take the form of a eunuchoid stature, sparse growth of hair on face, pubes, in the axilla and on the body generally, with lack of recession of the hairline at the temples, pre-puberal pitch of voice, poor muscular development, and small penis. However, it has to be emphasised that clinical signs of androgen deficiency may be entirely lacking, especially in the younger adults. In general, the Leydig cells tend to fail earlier than usual, as indicated by an early onset of the male climacteric. There may be varying degrees of gynæcomastia, which tends to be progressive for several years following puberty.

3. Endocrine Findings.—The urinary excretion of 17-ketosteroids is usually in the low normal or subnormal range, an observation that may be correlated with the frequent clinical and cytological evidence of mild to moderate androgen deficiency. The urinary excretion of pituitary gonadotrophins is likely to be elevated, as the result of a lack of inhibition of the gonadotrophin-producing cells. This has been variously attributed to hypofunction of the Leydig cells or the absence of a second testicular hormone that is normally elaborated by the tubular epithelium.

The condition just summarised is similar, if not identical, to the Klinefelter syndrome as described by Klinefelter *et al.* (1942) and modified by Heller and Nelson (1945 *a*).

DYSGENESIS OF THE SEMINIFEROUS TUBULES WITH MALE NUCLEI

A similar condition is encountered in patients with male nuclei and their relation to those with female nuclei is not understood. In general, the tubular abnormalities are less pronounced when the nuclei are male, but it would require considerable experience to distinguish the two types in all instances on the basis of testis structure alone. The exact proportion of patients with dysgenesis of the seminiferous tubules who have female nuclei or male nuclei is not known. However, a good indication of this is given by Nelson (1956), who found that of eighty-eight patients with Klinefelter's syndrome, seventy had female nuclei and eighteen had male nuclei. The proportions that are found in various series will

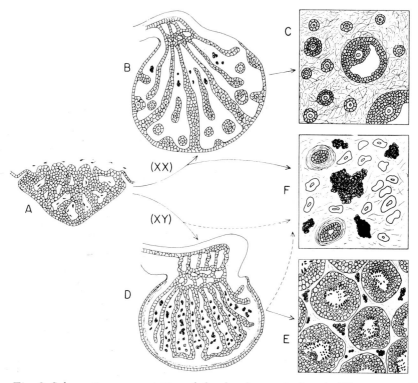

Fig. 6. Schematic representation of the development of an indifferent gonad (A) into an ovary (B and C), a testis (D and E), or a testis-like gonad with dysgenesis of the seminiferous tubules (F).

no doubt vary according to the criteria of selection of the individual cases.

Aetiology—Although the ultimate factors that cause an embryo bearing the XX-sex chromosome complex to develop into a male with abnormal testes are not known, certain aspects of faulty embryogenesis can be visualised (Fig. 6).

In embryos whose cells bear the XX-sex chromosome complex, differentiation of the ovary begins through genetic influences early in the third month of gestation. The ovarian cortex develops largely from ingrowths of the germinal epithelium, while the primary sex cords of the medullary region that form seminiferous tubules in the male gradually atrophy (Fig. 6, A, B, and C). In subjects with dysgenesis of the seminiferous tubules and female nuclei, some influence apparently inhibits cortical maturation entirely and prompts the medullary sex cords to develop into ab-

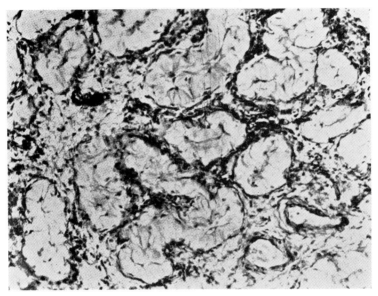

Fig. 7. Testis biopsy specimen from a 15-year-old patient with dysgenesis of the seminiferous tubules and female nuclei. (Masson.) ×200. (By courtesy of Dr. F. W. Wiglesworth, the Montreal Children's Hospital.)

normal seminiferous tubules. At the same time Leydig cells develop freely and function throughout the fœtal period as they would in a normal testis (Fig. 6, A and F).

Since clinical signs of tubular dysgenesis are not manifest until puberty or afterwards, biopsy specimens of the gonads have not been studied in early life. Prior to the demonstration of female nuclei in these patients, it was thought that the testes underwent degenerative or involutional changes during the puberal period. It now seems more likely that the gonads are abnormal from early embryonal life and that the process is basically one of dysgenesis of gonadal elements, although degenerative and involutional changes may contribute to the final structure of these abnormal gonads. The likelihood of an early onset of gonadal pathology is supported by the structure of the gonad illustrated in Fig. 7. Although the patient was only 15 years of age, almost all of the tubules in the biopsy specimen were completely hyalinised.

An accumulation of experimental evidence by many workers (*e.g.*, Jost, 1950) indicates that a masculinising hormone or inductor elaborated by Leydig cells of the fœtal testis is required to overcome the inherent tendency of an embryo to feminise. In normal ovarian development the few Leydig cells in the medullary region do not interfere with feminisation. In normal fœtal testes and the testis-like gonads of the patients under consideration, the secretion of the abundant Leydig cells guides the maturation of the internal and external genitalia in the male direction. Since the condition appears to be a female——→male sex reversal, Nelson (1956) is technically correct in suggesting that it be designated as "female pseudo-hermaphroditism with gonadal dysgenesis." But in the practical situation the patients are clearly males, and a terminology that suggests otherwise is best avoided.

Differentiation of the testis begins during the latter part of the second month of embryonal life. The germinal epithelium is isolated from the main mass of the gonad at an early stage by the tunica albuginea and the primary sex cords gradually develop into seminiferous tubules (Fig. 6, A, D, and E). The structure of the gonads in patients with male nuclei is a less radical departure from normal gonadal structure, compared with gonads of patients who should have ovaries according to their chromosomal sex. Consequently, the gonadal abnormality may be initiated at a later stage of development in chromosomal males (Fig. 6, A and F or A, D, and F).

Subjects with ovarian tissue only and male nuclei have not been described.* This may be related to the fact that the embryonal

---

* In an earlier report the writer listed a case of female pseudohermaphroditism, not caused by adrenal hyperplasia, with male nuclei (Barr, 1954). Later investigation showed that the diagnosis of female pseudohermaphroditism was probably incorrect. A right ovary was found on laparotomy but no gonad was identified on the left side. This patient may have been a true hermaphrodite with a right testis or ovotestis that could not be located.

testis surrenders the potentiality of cortical development very early through the appearance of a tunica albuginea. The medullary zone of the ovary regresses slowly so that potentialities for the development of testis-like tissue are retained for a considerable time.

The factors responsible for the production of a testis-like gonad in an embryo with the XX-sex chromosome complex are entirely unknown, but certain theoretical possibilities may be considered. There may be a genetical error, since the development of ovaries or testes from the indifferent gonads is controlled by the balance between female-determining genes and male-determining genes in the chromosome complement. The influence of an androgenic hormone on the gonads in the critical period of ovarian differentiation has to be considered, but a freemartin type of anomaly is exceedingly unlikely since the condition is not associated with twinning. On the basis of experiments using frog's eggs, Witschi (1956) offers the interesting suggestion that the tubular dysgenesis type of patient might result from fertilisation of an over-ripe ovum by a sperm that bears an X-chromosome. In the human, as in the frog, over-ripeness of the ovum may cause a deficiency in the primordial germ cells that normally migrate into the indifferent gonad from the extra-embryonic endoderm. The resulting cortical under-development might allow the medullary component to form a testis-like gonad that masculinises the embryo. The cause of the somewhat similar tubular abnormality in patients with male nuclei is equally obscure.

SOME PRACTICAL CONSIDERATIONS

Hypogonadal males characterised by tubular dysgenesis and female nuclei probably occur more frequently than is generally realised. According to Heller and Nelson (1948) the Klinefelter syndrome is the most common form of male hypogonadism, and Nelson (1956) reported that about 80% of the patients with Klinefelter's syndrome studied by him had female nuclei. The finding of female nuclei by one of the cytological tests of chromosomal sex will therefore often point the way to the correct diagnosis in cases of male hypogonadism. It is suggested that the simple oral smear method be used whenever the signs noted in the foregoing account are present. The method will at times be especially useful in establishing the cause of sterility in an infertile couple. The beneficial results from testosterone therapy are a further encouragement to the recognition of these patients. With androgen substitution therapy there is usually improvement of the psyche and muscle development, relief from symptoms of the male climacteric and correction of such sexual infantilism as may be present (Heller and Nelson, 1945 *b*). There is no expectation, of course, that the basic defect in the gonads can be corrected by androgen therapy.

SUMMARY

Certain patients with male hypogonadism characterised by hyalinisation and fibrosis of the seminiferous tubules have female nuclei. They appear to be instances of an almost complete sex reversal that dates from an early stage of embryonal development. The indifferent gonads apparently develop as imperfect testes, rather than ovaries, and the androgenic activity of the embryonal testis-like gonads directs sexual development in the male direction. It is important to recognise these patients in order to establish the cause of sterility when this problem is under investigation, and to take advantage of the benefits that accrue from androgen substitution therapy.

REFERENCES

Barr, M. L. (1954). *Surg. Gynec. Obstet.*, 99:184.
—— (1956). *Canad. med. Ass. J.*, 74:419.
Bradbury, J. T., Bunge, R. G., and Boccabella, R. A. (1956). *J. clin. Endocrin.*, 16:689.
Davidson, W. M., and Smith, D. R. (1954). *Brit. med. J.*, 2:6.
—— (1956). *Post. Grad. med. J.*, 32:578.
de la Balze, F. A., Arrillaga, F. C., Irazu, J., and Mancini, R. E. (1952). *J. clin. Endocrin.*, 12:1426.
Grumbach, M. M., Van Wyk, J. J., and Wilkins, L. (1955). *J. clin. Endocrin.*, 15:1161.
Heller, C. G., and Nelson, W. O. (1945 *a*). *J. clin. Endocrin.*, 5:1.
—— (1945 *b*). *J. clin. Endocrin.*, 5:27.
—— (1948). *J. clin Endocrin.*, 8:345.
Jackson, W. P. U., Shapiro, B. G., Uys, C. J., and Hoffenberg, R. (1956). *Lancet*, 2:857.
Jost, A. (1950). *Arch. Anat. micr. Morph. exp.*, 39:577.

Klinefelter, jun., H. F., Reifenstein, jun., E. C., and Albright, F. (1942). *J. clin. Endocrin.*, 2:615.

Lennox, B. (1956). *Scot. med. J.*, 1:97.

Marberger, E., Boccabella, R. A., and Nelson, W. O. (1955). *Proc. Soc. exp. Biol., N. Y.*, 89:488.

Moore, K. L., and Barr, M. L. (1955). *Lancet*, 2:57.

Moore, K. L., Graham, M. A., and Barr, M. L. (1953). *Surg. Gynec. Obstet.*, 96:641.

Nelson, W. O. (1956). *Acta endocr., Copenhagen*, 23:227.

Nelson, W. O., and Heller, C. G. (1945). *J. clin. Endocrin.*, 5:13.

Plunkett, E. R., and Barr, M. L. (1956). *Lancet*, 2:853.

Riis, P., Johnsen, S. G., and Mosbech, J. (1956). *Lancet*, 1:962.

Sachs, L., and Danon, M. (1956). *Genetica*, 28:201.

Sohval, A. R., Gabrilove, J. L., Gaines, J. A., and Soffer, L. J. (1956). *J. Mt. Sinai Hosp.*, 23:647.

Witschi, E. (1956). In "Gestation," ed. by C. A. Villee, p. 119. (New York: Josiah Macy, Jr. Foundation.)

14

SEX CHROMATIN AND PHENOTYPE IN MAN

Disagreement Between Nuclear Sex and Phenotype Raises Questions About the Cause of Sex Anomalies

Murray L. Barr, M.Sc., M.D.

IT is now firmly established that there is a sexual dimorphism in the structure of intermitotic nuclei of man and certain other mammals. The difference between the sexes is that a special mass of chromatin or chromocenter, the sex chromatin, is clearly visible in nuclei of normal females but not in those of normal males. In normal individuals, at any rate, the presence or absence of sex chromatin is probably related to the XX sex chromosome complex of females and the XY sex chromosome complex of males.

A discrepancy between nuclear structure and the more obvious sexual features of the phenotype is found in certain developmental sex anomalies in man. For example, the phenotype is predominantly female in the Ullrich-Turner syndrome (gonadal dysgenesis), although the nuclei are usually indistinguishable from those of normal males. Similarly, the nuclei have a male structure in the syndrome of testicular feminization, but the external anatomy is strikingly feminine. Conversely, many phenotypical males with the Klinefelter syndrome (seminiferous tubule dysgenesis) have nuclei that are indistinguishable from those of normal females.

The sexual dimorphism of intermitotic nuclei has become a useful diagnostic aid, even when used empirically, in dealing with the sex anomalies.[1] But the ultimate aim is an understanding of the biology of the sex anomalies as a prelude to preventive measures. This requires information from the study of abnormal sex development in subhuman forms[2] and from the study of human chromosomes in dividing cells, through recently developed techniques.[3, 4]

Reprinted from *Science,* September 18, 1959, Vol. 130, No. 3377, pages 679-685.

This article represents an attempt to summarize current concepts of the pathogenesis of some syndromes encountered in clinical medicine, and to point out the many gaps in our knowledge that have to be filled before etiological factors can be fully understood.

NORMAL GONADAL DIFFERENTIATION

Gonadal ridges appear in the human embryo at about the fourth week of gestation. Their structure is identical in male and female

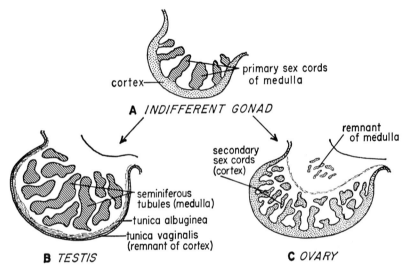

Fig. 1. Diagrammatic representation of development of a testis from the medullary component, and an ovary from the cortical component, of the indifferent gonad of an early embryo. [Modified from Grumbach and Barr, *Recent Progr. in Hormone Research (26)*, courtesy Academic Press, New York.]

embryos until the seventh week (Fig. 1, A). The cellular cortex of the indifferent gonad has the potentiality of developing into an ovary. The medulla, consisting of primary sex cords in a mesenchymal stroma, has the potentiality of developing into a testis.[5] Primordial germ cells can be identified in cortex and primary sex cords from the sixth week onward, having migrated into the gonad from the region of the extra-embryonal entoderm.

The fate of the indifferent gonad is established by the balance between male-determiners and female-determiners in the genotype.[6] When the sex chromosome complex is XY, male-determining genes on autosomes predominate over female-determining genes on autosomes predominate over female-determining genes on the single X chromosome. The medulla begins to develop, and genes on the single X chromosome. The medulla begins to develop, and the cortex to regress, at the seventh week. The primary sex cords become seminiferous tubules, and intestitial cells appear between them, while the cortex becomes the thin visceral layer of the *tunica vaginalis* that adheres to the *tunical albuginea* (Fig. 1, *B*). It is noteworthy that the endocrine component of the testis, consisting of interstitial or Leydig cells, is well developed in the embryonal testis and again after puberty but is inconspicuous in the intervening period.

When the sex chromosome complex is XX, female-determiners on the two X chromosomes outweigh male-determiners on autosomes.[7] Beginning at the ninth week, the cortex develops into an ovary through the ingrowth of secondary sex cords, and the medulla regresses (Fig. 1, *C*). Interference with this crucial step of differentiation of bipotential gonads into testes or ovaries, at about the end of the second month of embryonic development, appears to be the point of departure for most sex anomalies in man. The genetic balance between male-determiners and female-determiners may be altered by a mutant gene or by an abnormality of one or more of the chromosomes that bear these determiners. But experimental evidence testifies to the frequent adverse effects of various nongenetic factors on gonadal differentiation. Evidence for possible genetic or nongenetic factors that might interfere with normal gonadal differentiation has to be sought for each type of sex anomaly.

NORMAL DIFFERENTIATION OF INTERNAL AND EXTERNAL GENITALIA

Wolffian ducts (primordia of epididymides, *vasa deferentia*, and seminal vesicles) and Müllerian ducts (primordia of Fallopian tubes, uterus, and vagina) are both present when gonadal differentiation begins, and the external genitalia are also in a bipotential state. Much experimental work bears on the factors responsible for development of internal and external genitalia in a direction which is consistent with the male or female character of the gonads. Treating embryos with androgens or estrogens, transplanting an embryonal gonad into an embryo of the opposite sex, and depriving an embryo of the influence of embryonal gonads have all yielded pertinent results. The consequences of surgical removal of gonads in rabbit and rat embryos and the destruction of gonads by x-rays in mouse embryos form the basis of current hypotheses concerning the pathogenesis of sex anomalies in man.[8-10]

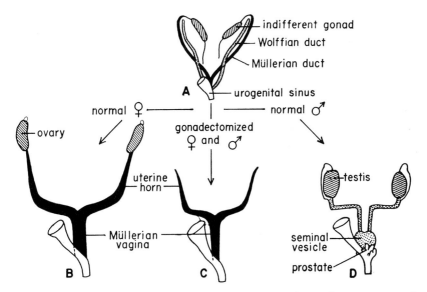

Fig. 2. Schematic representation of development of sex ducts in normal and gonadectomized rabbit embryos. [After Jost, "Sex Differentiation and Development" *(51),* courtesy Cambridge Univ. Press, London.]

The outstanding work of Jost on rabbit embryos illustrates the results obtained in such experiments (Fig. 2).

Gonadal differentiation into testes or ovaries begins on the 15th day in the rabbit, while differentiation of the duct system begins on the 20th day and is virtually complete by the 28th day, which is about two days before birth (Fig. 2, *A-B* and *A-D).* Gonadectomy of female embryos at any stage or of male embryos at about the 20th day is followed by maturation of the duct system and the external genitalia in a female direction, although the uterus is rather smaller than normal (Fig. 2, *A-C*). There is normal maturation of the male genitalia if removal of the testes is delayed beyond the 24th day. These observations indicate that ovaries are not essential for female development, but that the action of an inductor or evocator from the interstitial cells of the embryonal testes is necessary during a critical period for male development. Although much remains to be learned of the factors controlling embryogenesis of the reproductive system, the requirement of a masculinizing evocator of testicular origin to counteract a tenden-

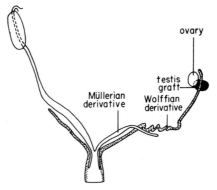

Fig. 3. Genital tract of a 28-day-old female rabbit embryo in which a testicular graft from a 21-day-old embryo had been implanted adjacent to an ovary on the 20th day of development. [After Jost, *Arch. anat. microscop. morphol. exptl. (9)*, courtesy Masson, Paris.]

cy of all embryos to feminize is a keystone in current concepts of the pathogenesis of congenital errors of sex development.

The masculinizing evocator appears to have a local action on adjacent tissues, since a unilateral graft of embryonal testis into a female embryo stimulates the Wolffian duct and suppresses the Müllerian duct on the side of the transplant preferentially[9,10] (Fig. 3). A similar asymmetry follows unilateral gonadectomy of male embryos between the 20th and 24th day and occurs in human true hermaphrodites when there is testicular tissue on one side only. The substance seems to act in the manner of embryonal evocators generally, which is consistent with experimental evidence that the evocator substance differs in its physiological effects, and probably in chemical composition, from testosterone and other androgenic hormones.

The Müllerian ducts of rat embryos in the early undifferentiated stage persist and grow in vitro, and the Wolffian ducts regress, regardless of the sex of the donor.[9,10] This suggests that the inherent tendency of embryos to feminize is genetically controlled, rather than the result of an exogenous factor such as maternal estrogens. There is little information relating to genetic mechanisms that may operate in this connection. The genes involved must be other than the male-determiners and female-determiners whose balance controls gonadal differentiation, since female differentiation can occur whether the sex-chromosome complex is XX or XY.

SEXUAL DIMORPHISM OF INTERMITOTIC NUCLEI

Chromosomal, gonadal, and phenotypical sex are normally in agreement. But the sex-chromosome complement may be incon-

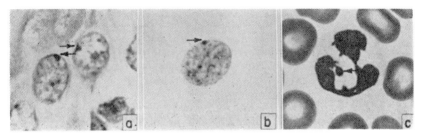

Fig. 4.

sistent with the main features of the phenotype when there has been an error in gonadal differentiation. Consequently, the "tests of chromosomal sex," having as their basis a sexual dimorphism in the structure of intermitotic nuclei, are useful diagnostic aids in clinical practice and raise new problems in connection with the etiology of sex anomalies.

The sex chromatin that characterizes nuclei of females is usually adherent to the inner surface of the nuclear membrane and is often so closely related to the membrane as to have a planoconvex outline (Fig. 4, *a* and *b*).[11] It is about 1 micron in diameter and can be resolved frequently into two components of equal size. The sex chromatin shares with the rest of the chromatin an affinity for basic dyes and, like the rest of the chromatin, reacts positively to tests for deoxyribonucleic acid, staining readily with the Feulgen technique and with methyl green. In particularly favorable circumstances, as in the study of whole mounts of thin membranes, the sex chromatin can be identified in virtually every nucleus. In sections of tissues 5 microns in thickness, sex chromatin can be identified in 60 to 80% of the nuclei, depending on the technical quality of the preparations and such factors as the size of the nuclei and the coarseness of the general chromatin particles. A chromatin mass larger than other chromatin particles of the nucleus is encountered in up to 10% of the cells in sections of tissues from males. This particular mass of chromatin is seldom as large as the sex chromatin of females, and its significance is uncertain.

Neutrophils have a different kind of sexual dimorphism (Fig. 4, c).[12] In a small proportion of neutrophils of females (1 to 10%, average about 3%), there is an accessory nuclear lobule; such a lobule is encountered with the greatest rarity, if at all, in neutrophils of males. The relation of the accessory nuclear lobule to the sex chromatin is not known.

Nuclei have been examined for sex chromatin in 24 mammalian representatives, more extensively in some than in others (Table 1).[13] In man and monkey, the imprint of sex on nuclear structure is present in the various tissues and organs, cells with small pyknotic nuclei excepted. This is also true of those carnivores that have been studied extensively and probably holds for carnivores generally. Nerve-cell nuclei bear a clear imprint of sex in the few representatives of the order Artiodactyla that have been studied, but the nuclear chromatin is too coarse in nonnervous tissues to allow identification of the sex. In the Virginia opossum, the only marsupial that has been examined, sex chromatin is present in nuclei of both sexes, but the size is significantly larger in females. There are multiple large particles of chromatin in nuclei of the rabbit and of rodents, so these animals are unsuitable for work that depends on the sex characteristics of intermitotic nuclei. But there are exceptions, for the sex chromatin can be identified in motor neurons of female rats and hamsters and in ameloblasts of newborn rats, and the sex-identifying variant that occurs in neutrophils of man is also present in those of the rabbit. Representatives of an order appear to have similar nuclear characteristics with respect to the coarseness of the chromatin particles and the clarity of the sex chromatin of females.

Nuclear dimorphism according to sex is lacking in the very early stages of embryonic development. In the cat, for example, this feature could not be detected in the morula stage and was

TABLE 1
SEXUAL DIMORPHISM IN CELL NUCLEI OF MAMMALS

Representatives	Dimorphism Present?
Primates	
Man	Yes
Monkey	Yes
Carnivora	
Cat	Yes
Dog	Yes
Mink	Yes
Marten	Yes
Ferret	Yes
Racoon	Yes
Skunk	Yes
Coyote	Yes
Wolf	Yes
Bear	Yes
Fox	Yes
Artiodactyla	
Goat	Yes
Deer	Yes
Swine	Yes
Cattle	Yes
Marsupialia	
Opossum	Yes
Lagomorpha	
Rabbit	No
Rodentia	
Rat	No
Hamster	No
Mouse	No
Guinea pig	No
Ground hog	No

seldom seen in blastocysts. Neither has sex chromatin been described in ova of primary follicles. But nuclear dimorphism is clearly established in embryos of the cat well before gonadal differentiation, and the imprint of sex is visible in resting nuclei of human and macaque embryos from the 12th to the 19th day onward.[14]

Since the sex chromatin is a Feulgen-positive chromocenter, it presumably represents positively heterochromatic regions of chromosomes—that is, regions that are dense and prominent when the euchromatic regions are indistinct. The fine details of the sex chromatin, especially its bipartite structure and its connection with a delicate thread that may also be double, as well as the multiple masses of sex chromatin that are present in polyploid nuclei, suggests that it is formed from heterochromatic regions of a pair of homologous chromosomes.[15] Although an alternative interpretation has been suggested,[16] the weight of evidence favors the view that the bipartite sex chromatin of females is formed by heterochromatic regions of the two X chromosomes, and that a definite chromocenter is not formed by the nonhomologous sex chromosomes of the heterogametic sex.[17] This interpretation implies somatic pairing, for the X chromosomes at any rate.[18] Somatic association of heterochromatic X chromosomes has, indeed, been described in ovarian follicular cells of the mouse.[19]

The sex chromosomes vary in their heterochromaticity in different cell types, depending, possibly, on differences in the immediate environment of the chromosomes. As mentioned above, sex chromatin has not been described in ova and is lacking in the very early stages of embryonic development, while the XX complex forms a definite chromocenter throughout the rest of the life span of females. Conversely, the XY complex is strongly heterochromatic in prophase of meiosis but seldom produces a recognizable chromocenter in somatic cells. Other variants are on record. For example, the X and Y chromosomes form separate chromocenters of the same size in somatic cells of the ground vole, so that nuclei of males and females cannot be distinguished from each other; the multiple X chromosomes of certain insects form individual chromocenters, the sexes being divergent with respect to the number of these chromocenters that are formed; and the XY, rather than the XX, complex forms a distinctive chromocenter in somatic cells of the silkworm and the spruce budworm, in which the female is the heterogametic sex.[20, 21]

TESTS OF CHROMOSOMAL SEX IN CLINICAL MEDICINE

Application of the principle of nuclear sexual dimorphism to the study of patients with sex anomalies requires only an easily obtainable source of cells.[12, 22] A skin biopsy specimen may be

studied, since the sex characteristics of the nuclei are well defined
in the mature spinous cells of thc epidermis and in the large spherical nuclei of hair follicles (Fig. 4, *a*). A smear preparation of oral
epithelium is particularly easy to obtain and is the favored procedure on that account (Fig. 4, *b*). Although whole nuclei are
present in oral smears, the incidence of nuclei with unequivocal
sex chromatin is low (30 to 60%) in chromosomal females, and in
an occasional preparation the sex chromatin is less conspicuous
than usual because of being much flattened against the nuclear
membrane. However, these factors do not seriously lessen the use-
fulness of the oral-smear method, because chromocenters at the
nuclear membrane that could be interpreted as sex chromatin occur with the greatest rarity in smears from chromosomal males.
The neutrophil method (Fig. 4, *c*) gives the same information as
is derived from the more conventional skin-biopsy and oral-smear
techniques. Preparations of high technical quality are required for
each of the tests. The preferred technical procedures are given
elsewhere.[23]

A correlation between the presence of sex chromatin and XX
sex chromosomes or the absence of sex chromatin and XY sex
chromosomes, can logically be assumed for normal individuals.
But the interpretation is not necessarily so straightforward in the
sex anomalies.[24] The possibility of a chromosomal abnormality
need not be considered when the congenital error clearly does not
involve the genetic sex determiners. For example, the sex chromatin indicates the XX complex in the adrenogenital syndrome,
where the fetal adrenal cortex is at fault, and when there is partial masculinization of the external genitalia in a female newborn
whose mother received progestins during pregnancy.[25] In addition, a chromosomal abnormality, other than sex chromosomes
that are inconsistent with the phenotype, need not be suspected
if the congenital error can be clearly attributed to a mutant gene
or genes among the sex-determiners.

If the foregoing conditions are not fulfilled, the presence of sex
chromatin in the "tests of chromosomal sex" means only that the
nuclei contain heterochromatic regions of two X chromosomes.
One of these chromosomes may be defective in its euchromatic
region, there may be an unusual sex chromosome complex (such

as XXY), or the autosomes that bear male-determiners may be in some way abnormal. Conversely, absence of sex chromatin in the "tests of chromosomal sex" indicates that two normal X chromosomes are not present. The sex chromosome constitution could, in theory, be XO, or there could be an abnormality of the autosomes carrying male-determiners. Awareness of the possibility of chromosomal abnormalities as a basis for some genetic sex anomalies should stimulate study of whole-chromosome complements by techniques that are now available.

CONGENITAL ERRORS OF SEX DEVELOPMENT IN MAN

The hermaphrodite group was the main center of interest until recently. Hermaphrodites were known in ancient times and have always attracted attention because of the bizarre intersexual morphology of the external genitalia. There are three main varieties. Both testicular and ovarian tissues are present in true *hermaphrodites.* The nuclei have a female chromatin pattern in some patients and a male chromatin pattern in others. *Male pseudohermaphrodites* have testes, and the nuclei are always male. The internal and external genitalia have an intersexual morphology in true hermaphrodites and male pseudohermaphrodites, but the details vary widely from one subject to another. Through some physiological deficiency, the evocator produced by the embryonal testes has failed to bring about full masculinization of the reproductive system in the male pseudohermaphrodite.

Female pseudohermaphrodites have ovaries and essentially normal female internal genitalia. But there is persistence of the fetal urogenital sinus, clitoral hypertrophy, and at times partial fusion of the labioscrotal folds to produce intersexual external genitalia. With few exceptions, the condition is the result of hyperplasia of the fetal adrenal cortex and elaboration of androgenic steroids in excessive amounts. The sex chromosome complement is always XX. The hermaphrodite group is described in detail in the classical book by Young, and the discussion is brought up to date in recent publications.[16, 26, 27] The following account is limited to errors of sex development in which there is an extreme divergence between the phenotype and the nuclear chromatin pattern.

GONADAL DYSGENESIS

Gonadal dysgenesis (or virtual agenesis) is encountered as a component of the Ullrich-Turner syndrome. The individual has a female phenotype, with essentially normal external genitalia, vagina, uterus, and tubes. The principal defect is in the gonads, which are represented by slender streaks of connective tissue,

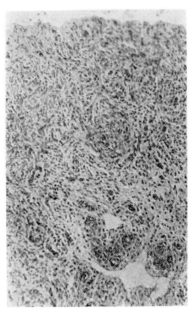

Fig. 5. Gonad consisting entirely of connective tissue that simulates ovarian stroma, in a 4-year-old girl with gonadal dysgenesis and a male chromatin pattern. (Hematoxylin-eosin.) (×125) [Courtesy Melvin M. Grumbach.]

simulating ovarian stroma, attached to the broad ligaments (Fig. 5). Derivatives of mesonephric ducts may be present, but there is rarely any evidence of ovarian follicles or seminiferous tubules in the typical syndrome, except possibly during the neonatal period.[28] Various congenital abnormalities are associated with gonadal dysgenesis. Shortness of stature is almost the rule, and there are often cutaneous folds at the sides of the neck. Less frequently, there may be a variety of skeletal or vascular anomalies and a number of other defects. Urinary excretion of pituitary gonadatropins is elevated after the age of 10 years, and secondary sex characteristics fail to develop naturally at puberty.

Both Jost and Wilkins suggested that a proportion of individuals with gonadal dysgenesis might be chromosomal males, the embryos having feminized in the absence of the masculinizing evocator of testicular origin.[9, 10, 29] This prediction was verified promptly[30] when tests of chromosomal sex became available, at least to the extent that 80% of subjects with gonadal dysgenesis are now known to have a male chromatin pattern, while the remainder have a female chromatin pattern.[31, 32]

But the etiological factor responsible for failure of gonadal development and for the associated anomalies remains obscure. A maternal factor is a possibility, although none has yet been demonstrated.[28, 31] Or an adverse nongenetic factor may originate in the zygote, following, for example, the fertilization of an overripe ovum.[33] If the etiology of the Ullrich-Turner syndrome proves to be nongenetic or if a mutant gene with pleiotropic manifestations is responsible, the sex chromosome complement would be XY or XX, in accordance with the structure of the intermitotic nuclei. Tests of color vision indicate that those with sex chromatin bear the XX complex and that those without sex chromatin bear the XY (or XO) sex chromosome complex.[34] Other methods of study, especially the examination of entire chromosome complements at metaphase, are needed to investigate the possibility of chromosomal anomalies that would not be visible in intermitotic nuclei.[21, 35]

Whatever the etiology of the virtual agenesis of the gonads proves to be, embryological development proceeds along female lines in accordance with the principle that an evocator of testicular origin is required for masculinization.

TESTICULAR FEMINIZATION

The syndrome of feminizing testes is another condition in which the phenotype is predominantly female, although the intermitotic nuclei have a male chromatin pattern and probably contain the XY sex chromosome complex.[26, 36] The syndrome is in some respects an extreme form of male pseudohermaphroditism, but there are unique features that justify its consideration as a distinct entity.

The external genitalia are normally female in the typical syndrome, but pubic hair is often lacking. The vagina is a blind pouch, uterus and tubes being usually absent. Testes are present bilaterally in the pelvis or inguinal regions, accompanied by epididymides and proximal portions of *vasa deferentia*. The semi-

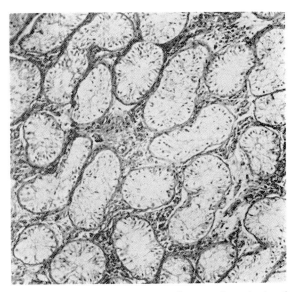

Fig. 6. Testis from a subject with the syndrome of testicular feminization. There are adequate Leydig cells, but the seminiferous tubules show the inhibition of spermatogenesis that occurs in undescended testes. (Hematoxylin-eosin.) (×85)

niferous tubules are immature (Fig. 6) because of the undescended position of the testes. Leydig cells are present in normal numbers. There is a normal female habitus, and the breasts develop well at puberty. The secondary sex characteristics are, in fact, strikingly feminine, and primary amenorrhoea may be the only overt indication of an abnormality of the reproductive system.

The syndrome is a hereditary anomaly that is transmitted by normal mothers. In families that include these subjects, there is a normal sex ratio if those with testicular feminization are added to normal males. The anomaly is probably caused by a mutant gene, but examination of the chromosome complement at metaphase is required to rule out a chromosomal abnormality consistent with male-type intermitotic nuclei. A quantitative or qualitative defect in the production of the evocator by interstitial cells is probably responsible for failure of male development in those parts of the reproductive system that are farthest from the testes. The interstitial cells clearly have a perverse metabolism, as shown by the development of feminine secondary sex characteristics at puberty and by the onset of menopausal symptoms if the testes are removed.

SEMINIFEROUS TUBULE DYSGENESIS (KLINEFELTER'S SYNDROME)

The Klinefelter syndrome includes subjects in whom there is a discrepancy between the phenotype and nuclear structure which is the reverse of that found in most individuals with gonadal agenesis and in those with the syndrome of feminizing testes.

The reproductive system has undergone normal male development, except that the testes are small and sperms are lacking from the semen. Eunuchoid traits may be present, and there is gynecomastia occasionally. Increased urinary excretion of pituitary gonadotropins is almost the rule, and the level of urinary 17-ketosteroids may be decreased.[37] There was no reason to suspect a discrepancy between nuclear structure and the phenotype in any of these subjects, and the discrepancy was noted in the routine application of tests of chromosomal sex to various types of disorder of the reproductive system.[38] The proportion of subjects who satisfy the clinical requirements for inclusion in the syndrome and who have a female chromatin pattern is not known exactly; three out of four may be a reasonable assumption.

The unusual histological structure of the testes is the most significant finding, and it differs to some extent, depending on whether the nuclei are female or male. The seminiferous tubules are highly abnormal when the nuclei are female. They are commonly represented by hyaline masses (Fig. 7, *a*), or there may be small tubules, with a thickened *lamina propria,* that contain Sertoli cells or epithelial-like cells of a type difficult to identify (Fig. 7, *b*). Spermatogonia or even more mature germ cells are present in a few tubules of some individuals. Spermatogenesis to the stage of mature sperms is encountered only rarely but is compatible with a female chromatin pattern in the somatic cells. The appear-

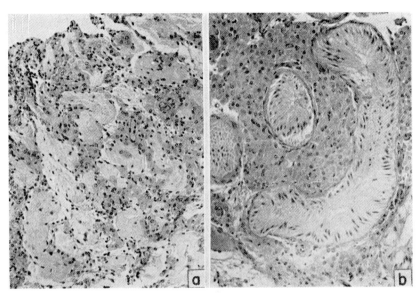

Fig. 7. Photomicrographs illustrating gonadal structure in seminiferous tubule dysgenesis (Klinefelter's syndrome) in a subject with a female chromatin pattern. The tubules may be reduced to hyalinized masses (*a*), or they may have thickened fibrous tunics and grossly defective epithelia (*b*). The Leydig cells are in large aggregates. (Hematoxylin-eosin.) (×125)

ance of Leydig cells in large clumps contrasts with their scattered arrangement in normal testes. When the nuclei are male, the tubular defects are less severe and the Leydig cells are in smaller aggregates.

The results of family studies suggest a genetic etiology of the Klinefelter syndrome.[39] If a mutant gene among the sex-determiners is responsible, the sex-chromosome complex would be XX or XY according to the chromatin pattern. Tests of color vision have yielded conflicting results.[40] However there may be an XXY complex or a deficiency in the euchromatic portion of an

X chromosome when the nuclei are female, or there may be an abnormality of the autosomes that bear male-determiners whether the nuclei are female or male. In this condition, probably even more than in the other sex anomalies, it will be necessary to study the entire chromosome complement in metaphase. A beginning in this direction has been made.[4, 41]

Whatever the precise etiological factor may be, testis-like gonads develop from the indifferent gonads of the early embryo regardless of whether the nuclei have female or male characteristics. Although there is severe dysgenesis of the seminiferous tubules, the abundant intestitial cells produce the evocator that masculinizes the embryo, resulting in an individual who has a male phenotype. A full understanding of the syndrome of seminiferous tubule dysgenesis is particularly desirable because of its association, in many instances, with some degree of mental retardation.[42]

CONCLUDING REMARKS

The principle of sexual dimorphism in the structure of intermitotic nuclei is well established and forms the basis of the tests of chromosomal sex that are valuable adjuncts to diagnosis in clinical medicine. An attempt has been made to point out deficiencies in our knowledge that may attract the attention and interest of biologists. The etiology of the sex anomalies is in need of clarification, and a study of entire chromosome complements would be especially helpful. Other lines of investigation are suggested by the problems discussed during the Symposium on Nuclear Sex that was held in London, England, in September 1957.[43]

ADDENDUM

Several reports that have an intimate bearing on this subject appeared after submission of the manuscript.

At the time of preparation of the paper, there were two reports that dealt with the sex chromosome complex in a sex anomaly, as determined by the new cytological techniques, but they were in disagreement.[4, 41] Ford *et al.*[44] have now described an XX/XXY mosaicism in a patient with the Klinefelter syndrome and a female chromatin pattern, which approaches the description of an XXY complex in a similar patient by Jacobs and Strong.[41] I understand that the presence of an XXY complex in such subjects has been confirmed by unpublished work in several laboratories. On the basis of this finding, Stern[45] was able to resolve the seemingly divergent results that had been recorded in connection with tests of color vision in patients with the Klinefelter syndrome.[40]

The presence of an extra chromosome, which is one of the smallest autosomes, has been demonstrated in mongolism.[46] A somatic cell chromosome number of 48, rather than the normal 46, has been found in a unique individual with both mongolism and the Klinefelter syndrome.[47] One of the extra chromosomes was the small autosome that occurs in mongolism; the other was contributed by the unusual XXY sex chromosome complex of the Klinefelter syndrome. Important observations are also being made on the sex chromosome complement in cases of gonadal dysgenesis or Turner's syndrome, in which a single X chromosome, unpaired with either another X chromosome or a Y chromosome, has been described.[48]

These observations necessitate a revision of the currently accepted hypothesis of genetic sex-determining mechanisms in man, which are based on cytogenetic studies in *Drosophila*. It now appears that the Y chromosome, far from having a passive role in sex determination, contains potent male-determining genes. In fact, the gonads have a nearly normal testicular structure in an XXY chromosome-bearing individual until the age of puberty, when the testicular pathology that is characteristic of the Klinefelter syndrome develops rapidly.[49] The Y chromosome of the mouse has also been shown to bear male-determining factors.[50] But the details differ in the two species, for the XO sex chromosome arrangement results in a fertile female in the mouse and an infertile female in man.

The view that the sex chromatin is an XX chromosome marker is consistent with an XXY-complex for patients with Klinefelter's syndrome and a female chromatin pattern, and with an XO arrangement for patients with Turner's syndrome and a male chromatin pattern. But the important significance of the recent observations on chromosomal abnormalities is the clear demonstration of aneuploidy as a cause of some developmental errors in man. The next few years are certain to bring developments of the first importance in the field of human cytogenetics and in the application of cytogenetics to certain aspects of clinical medicine.

REFERENCES AND NOTES

1. Our work on cell nuclei and sex anomalies was supported by the National Research Council, National Cancer Institute, National Health Grants, D. H. McDermid Medical Research Fund, and J. P. Bickell Foundation (all of Canada). This article is based in part on the Lecture in Medicine, which was delivered before the annual meeting of the Royal College of Physicians and Surgeons of Canada, Vancouver, B. C., 23-24 Jan. 1959.

2. E. Witschi, in *Sex and Internal Secretions* (Williams and Wilkins, Baltimore, 1939); L. V. Domm, *ibid.*

3. T. C. Hsu, *J. Heredity* 43:167 (1952); J. H. Tjio and A. Levan, *Hereditas* 42:1 (1956).

4. C. E. Ford, P. A. Jacobs, L. G. Lajtha, *Nature* 181, 1565 (1958).

5. R. K. Burns, *Proc. Natl. Acad. Sci. U. S.* 41:669 (1955).

6. C. B. Bridges, in *Sex and Internal Secretions* (Williams and Wilkins, Baltimore, 1939).

7. The Y chromosome is assumed to be inert, as the genetic balance theory of sex determination is usually stated. But the Y chromosome is almost universally present in the male, in mammals, and it may yet be shown to contain significant male-determining genes.

8. A. Raynaul and M. Frilley, *Ann. endocrinol. (Paris)* 8:400 (1957); L. J. Wells and R. L. Fralick, *Am. J. Anat.* 89:63 (1951).

9. A. Jost, *Arch. anat. microscop. morphol. exptl.* 39:577 (1950).

10. ———, *Recent Progr. in Hormone Research* 8:379 (1953).

11. K. L. Moore and M. L. Barr, *Acta Anat.* 21:197 (1954).

12. W. M. Davidson and D. R. Smith, *Brit. Med. J.* 2:6 (1954).

13. M. A. Graham and M. L. Barr, *Anat. Record* 112:709 (1952); K. L. Moore and M. L. Barr, *J. Comp. Neurol.* 98:213 (1953); R. H. Prince, M. A. Graham, M. L. Barr, *Anat. Record* 122:153 (1955); T. Lüers, *Blutstudien* 2:81 (1956); P. J. Carpentier, L. A. M. Stolte, M. J. Dobbelaar, *Nature* 180:554 (1957); K. L. Moore, M. A. Graham, M. L. Barr, *J. Exptl. Zool.* 135:101 (1957); K. L. Moore and A. O. Aiyede, *Anat. Record* 130:431 (1958); M. A. Graham and M. L. Barr, *Arch. anat. microscop. morphol. exptl.*, in press.

14. M. A. Graham, *Anat. Record* 119:469 (1954); C. R. Austin and E. C. Amoroso, *Exptl. Cell Research* 13:419 (1957); W. W. Park, *J. Anat.* 91:369 (1957).

15. J. Reitalu, *Acta Genet. Med. et Gemellol.* 6: 393 (1957); H. P. Klinger, *Exptl. Cell Research* 14:207 (1958); ——— and H. G. Schwarzacher,

Nature 181:1150 (1958); D. M. Serr, M. A. Ferguson-Smith, B. Lennox, J. Paul, *ibid. 182*:124 (1958).

16. S. J. Segal and W. O. Nelson, *J. Clin. Endocrinol. and Metabolism 17*:676 (1957).

17. M. A. Graham and M. L. Barr, *Anat. Record 112*:709 (1952).

18. M. L. Barr and K. L. Moore, *Proc. Can. Cancer Research Conf. 1956* (1957), vol. 2, p. 3.

19. S. Ohno, W. D. Kaplan, R. Kinosita, *Exptl. Cell Research 15*:616 (1958).

20. L. Geitler, *Z. Zellforsch. u. mikroskop. Anat. 26*:641 (1937); S. G. Smith, *McGill Med. J. 13*:451 (1944).

21. L. Sachs and M. Danon, *Genetica 28*:201 (1956).

22. K. L. Moore, M. A. Graham, M. L. Barr, *Surg. Gynecol. Obstet. 96*:641 (1953); K. L. Moore and M. L. Barr, *Lancet 2*:57 (1955); E. Marberger, R. A. Boccabella, W. O. Nelson, *Proc. Soc. Exptl. Biol. Med. 89:* 488 (1955).

23. M. L. Barr, in *Recent Advances in Clinical Pathology* (Churchill, London), vol. 3, in press.

24. ———, *Lancet, 1*:47 (1956).

25. L. Wilkins and H. W. Jones, Jr., *Obstet. and Gynecol. 11*:355 (1958).

26. M. M. Grumbach and M. L. Barr, *Recent Progr. in Hormone Research 14*:255 (1958).

27. H. H. Young, *Genital Abnormalities, Hermaphroditism, and Related Adrenal Diseases* (Williams and Wilkins, Baltimore, 1937); L. Wilkins, M. M. Grumbach, J. J. Van Wyk, T. H. Shepard, C. Papadatos, *Pediatrics 16*:287 (1955); B. Lennox, *Scot. Med. J. 1*:97 (1956); H. W. Jones, Jr., and W. W. Scott, *Hermaphroditism, Genital Anomalies and Related Endocrine Disorders* (Williams and Wilkins, Baltimore, 1958).

28. R. Richart and K. Benirschke, *New Eng. J. Med. 258*:974 (1958).

29. A. Jost, *Compt. rend. assoc. anat. 34*:255 (1947); L. Wilkins, The Diagnosis and Treatment of Endocrine Disorders in Childhood and Adolescence (Thomas, Springfield, Ill., 1950).

30. L. Decourt, W. da S. Sasso, E. Chiorboli, J. M. Fernandes, *Rev. assoc. med. brasil. 1*:203 (1954); P. E. Polani, W. F. Hunter, B. Lennox, *Lancet 2*:120 (1954); L. Wilkins, M. M. Grumbach, J. J. Van Wyk, *J. Clin. Endocrinol. and Metabolism 14*:1270 (1954).

31. M. M. Grumbach, J. J. Van Wyk, L. Wilkins, *ibid. 15*:1161 (1955).

32. W. Ehrengut, *Z. Kinderheilk. 77*:322 (1955); E. Witschi, W. O. Nelson, S. J. Segal, *J. Clin. Endocrinol. and Metabolism 16*:922 (1956); W. M. Davidson and D. R. Smith, *Postgraduate Med. J. 32*:578 (1956). P. Riis, F. Fuchs, S. G. Johnsen, J. Mosbech, C. E. Pilgaard, *Acta Genet. et Statist. Med. 6*:256 (1956); W. O. Nelson, *Acta Endocrinol. 23*:227 (1956).

33. E. Witschi, in *Gestation* (Josiah Macy, Jr. Foundation, New York, 1956).

34. P. E. Polani, M. H. Lessof, P. M. F. Bishop, *Lancet* 2:118 (1956).

35. M. Danon and L. Sachs, *ibid.* 2:20 (1957).

36. J. McL. Morris, *Am. J. Obstet. and Gynecol.* 65:1192 (1953).

37. H. F. Klinefelter, Jr., E. C. Reifenstein, Jr., F. Albright, *J. Clin. Endocrinol.* 2:615 (1942); C. G. Heller and W. O. Nelson, *ibid.* 5:1 (1945); ———, *ibid.* 5:27 (1945); ———, *ibid.* 8:345 (1948); W. O. Nelson and C. G. Heller, *ibid.* 5:13 (1945); F. A. de la Balze, F. C. Arrillaga, J. Irazu, R. E. Mancini, *J. Clin. Endocrinol. and Metabolism* 12:1426 (1952).

38. J. T. Bradbury, R. G. Bunge, R. A. Boccabella, *ibid.* 16:689 (1956); W. P. U. Jackson, B. G. Shapiro, C. J. Uys, R. Hoffenberg, *Lancet* 2:857 (1956); E. R. Plunkett and M. L. Barr, *ibid.* 2:853 (1956); P. Riis, S. G. Johnsen, J. Mosbech, *ibid.* 1:962 (1956); M. M. Grumbach, W. A. Blanc, E. T. Engle, *J. Clin. Endocrinol. and Metabolism* 17:703 (1957); W. O. Nelson, *Fertility and Sterility* 8:527 (1957); M. A. Ferguson-Smith, B. Lennox, W. S. Mack, J. S. S. Stewart, *Lancet* 2:167 (1957).

39. J. S. S. Stewart, M. A. Ferguson-Smith, B. Lennox, W. S. Mack, *ibid.* 2:117 (1958).

40. P. E. Polani, P. M. F. Bishop, B. Lennox, M. A. Ferguson-Smith, J. S. S. Stewart, A. Prader, *Nature* 182:1092 (1958); H. Nowakowski, W. Lenz, J. Parada, *Acta Endocrinol.* 30:296 (1959).

41. P. A. Jacobs and J. A. Strong, *Nature* 183:302 (1959).

42. R. Q. Pasqualini, G. Vidal, G. E. Bur, *Lancet* 2:164 (1957); M. A. Ferguson-Smith, *ibid.* 1:928 (1958); A. Prader, J. Schneider, J. M. Francés, W. Züblin, *ibid.* 1:968 (1958); A. Prader, J. Schneider, W. Züblin, J. M. Francés, K. Rüedi, *Schweiz. med. Wochschr.* 88:917 (1958); M. L. Barr, E. L. Shaver, D. H. Carr, E. R. Plunkett, in preparation.

43. D. Robertson Smith and W. M. Davidson, Eds., *Symposium on Nuclear Sex* (Heinemann, London, England, 1958).

44. C. E. Ford, P. E. Polani, J. H. Briggs, P. M. F. Bishop, *Nature* 183:1030 (1959).

45. C. Stern, *ibid.* 183:1452 (1959).

46. J. Lejeune, M. Gauthier, R. Turpin, *Compt. rend.* 248:602 (1959); P. A. Jacobs, A. G. Baikie, W. M. Court Brown, J. A. Strong, *Lancet* 1:710 (1959).

47. C. E. Ford, K. W. Jones, O. J. Miller, U. Mittwoch, L. S. Penrose, M. Ridler, A. Shapiro, *ibid.* 1:709 (1959).

48. C. E. Ford, K. W. Jones, P. E. Polani, J. C. de Almeida, J. H. Briggs, *ibid.* 1:711 (1959).

49. M. A. Ferguson-Smith, *ibid.* 1:219 (1959).

50. W. L. Russell, L. B. Russell, J. S. Gower, *Proc. Natl. Acad. Sci. U. S.*

45:554 (1959); W. J. Welshons and L. B. Russell, *ibid.* 45:560 (1959).

51. A. Jost, in "Sex Differentiation and Development," *Society for Endocrinology Memoir No. 7*, C. R. Austin, Ed. (Cambridge Univ. Press, London, 1959).

52. M. L. Barr, *Brit. J. Urol.* 29:251 (1957).

15

SEX CHROMATIN

Murray L. Barr

IN a recent article,[1] I favored the view that the sex chromatin represents heterochromatic regions of the two X chromosomes of female cells. The assumption of somatic pairing of the X chromosomes is an unsatisfactory aspect of this hypothesis. Somatic pairing of chromosomes is well known in many species of insects and has been described in the newt and frog.[2] But evidence for such a relationship between the X chromosomes or other homologous chromosomes in somatic cells of mammals is admittedly scanty and inconclusive. For example, Ohno et al.[3] found evidence in the mouse for somatic association of the X chromosomes in epithelial cells of ovarian follicles and the mammary gland, but not in other types of cells that were examined. A possible way out of the dilemma is suggested by two important observations that have come to my attention. They demonstrate, at any rate, that the precise relationship between the sex chromatin and chromosomes is an unsolved problem that challenges the resources of cytologists.

Kosin and Ishizaki[4] showed that the presence of sex chromatin in somatic-cell nuclei is a female characteristic in the domestic chicken. Since the female is here the heterogametic sex, the sex chromatin cannot in this instance be a derivative of homologous sex chromosomes. Further, it is stated that the sex-chromatin complex for the female chicken is ZO.[5] It seems, on this basis, that the sex chromatin in fowl is a derivative of the single Z chromosome, unless it bears no direct relationship to the sex-chromosome complex.

Related to the foregoing observation is the study by Ohno et al.[6] on nuclei of regenerating liver in the rat. A distinctive chromocenter was seen in interphase nuclei of females but not of

Reprinted from *Science*, November 13, 1959, Vol. 130, No. 3385, page 1302.

males. In prophase nuclei, neither the X nor the Y chromosome of the male seemed to demonstrate positive heteropycnosis. But in prophase nuclei of females the surprising observation was made that one X chromosome was positively heteropycnotic while the other X chromosome was isopycnotic with respect to the autosomes. Ohno and his collaborators suggest that the positively heterochromatic X chromosome may be of paternal origin. It was folded back on itself in early prophase nuclei; this could explain the occasional clearly bipartite appearance of the sex chromatin Ishizaki[7] states that a bipartite structure has also been detected in the sex chromatin of the chicken.

Confirmation of this work, and particularly its extension to the nuclei of man, would be of first importance in interpretation of the chromatin pattern and sex-chromosome constitution of patients with anomalies of sex development. Exact knowledge of the basis of nuclear sexual dimorphism is also needed for an explanation of the female chromatin pattern that is found in some teratomas in male hosts.[8] We are now passing from the descriptive to the more difficult analytical phase in the study of the sex chromatin. The work of cytogeneticists and students of chromosome morphology is likely to play a decisive role in establishing the basis of sexual dimorphism in interphase nuclei.

REFERENCES AND NOTES

1. M. L. Barr, *Science 130*:679 (1959).
2. J. M. N. Boss, *Texas Repts. Biol. and Med. 13*:213 (1955).
3. S. Ohno, W. D. Kaplan, R. Kinosita, *Exptl. Cell Research 15*:616 (1959); S. Ohno, E. T. Kovacs, R. Kinosita, *ibid. 16*:462 (1959).
4. I. L. Kosin and H. Ishizaki, *Science 130*:43 (1959).
5. R. A. Miller, *Anat. Record 70*:155 (1958); E. Witschi, *Science 130*:372 (1959).
6. S. Ohno, W. D. Kaplan, R. Kinosita, *Exptl. Cell Research*, in press.
7. H. Ishizaki, personal communication.
8. L. M. Myers, *J. Pathol. Bacteriol. 78*:43 (1959).

16

SEXUAL DIMORPHISM IN INTERPHASE NUCLEI*

Murray L. Barr, M.Sc., M.D.

T HE subject of sexual dimorphism in interphase nuclei has only a tenuous relationship with genetics, since the presence or absence of sex chromatin yields no information concerning the autosomes and, in certain sex anomalies, may give incomplete information as to the nature of the sex chromosome complex. Such interest as the subject may have in this symposium arises from three sources. Nuclear sexual dimorphism is the basis for relatively simple tests that are useful diagnostic aids when dealing with errors of sex development in man; the tests have drawn attention to the possibility of unusual sex chromosome complexes in two syndromes; and the basis of nuclear sexual dimorphism, in terms of chromosome morphology and behaviour, is a challenging problem to the cytologist and cytogeneticist.

THE SEX CHROMATIN

There are recent accounts of the structure of interphase nuclei according to sex (Grumbach and Barr, 1958; Barr, 1959), and only the main observations are recalled at this time. The imprint of sex is found in a special chromocenter, the sex chromatin, that is distinctive of the female in certain mammals. Like chromocenters generally, the sex chromatin is basophilic and Feulgen-positive. But it is larger than the other chromatin particles and is usually located against the inner surface of the nuclear membrane

Reprinted from *American Journal of Human Genetics.* March 1, 1960, Vol. 12, No. 1, pp. 118-127.

° Part of a Symposium on Cytology in Human Genetics held on Sept. 2, 1959, under the joint sponsorship of the American Society of Human Genetics and the Genetics Society of America during the meetings of the American Institute of Biological Sciences at Pennsylvania State University, August 30 to Sept. 3, 1959.

Studies on which this report is based were supported by the National Research Council and National Health Grants of Canada, the J. P. Bickell Foundation and the D. H. McDermid Medical Research Fund.

(Fig. 1, a & b). The sex chromatin is studied to best advantage in the large, vesicular nuclei of neurones, although in some animals (e.g., cat) it lies against the large nucleolus of this particular type of cell. Sexual dimorphism of the nuclei is present from early stages of embryonic development and has been described in cells cultured *in vitro*.

A characteristic chromatin pattern for male and female occurs

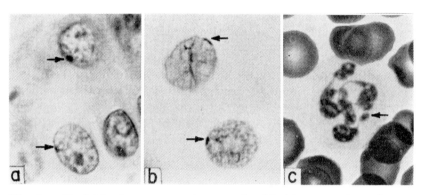

Fig. 1. a. Nuclei in the stratum spinosum of a skin biopsy specimen from a normal female. Hematoxylin and eosin stain. b. Nuclei in an oral smear preparation from a normal female. Thionin stain. c. Neutrophil leucocyte in a blood film from a normal female. Giemsa stain. 1800×.

in most types of cells in man, monkey and carnivores. In the order Artiodactyla, which is comprised of some of the hoofed animals, the sex chromatin is visible in neuronal nuclei of females but not of males, while the nuclear chromatin is too coarse in most other types of cells for satisfactory demonstration of this detail. With the exception of a few cell types, the nuclei of rodents and the rabbit (a lagomorph) contain numerous large masses of chromatin and are not well suited to the study of sexual dimorphism. Nuclei of the Virginia opossum are unusual in that a definite chromocenter is present in the nuclei of both sexes, but it is significantly larger in females than in males.

DERIVATION OF THE FEMALE-SPECIFIC CHROMOCENTER

The fact of nuclear sexual dimorphism has been firmly established by many independent studies, but the derivation of the sex chromatin remains an unsolved problem. The following considerations bear on this important and vexatious question.

The sex chromatin, if it has a basis in common with other chromocenters, is probably derived from heterochromatic regions of chromosomes. The concept of a chromosomal origin is supported by the finding of two or more masses of sex chromatin in nuclei that are known to be hyperdiploid. Examples are malignant cells (Moore and Barr, 1954 a) and cells of amniotic epithelium (Klinger and Schwarzacher, 1958). Chromosomes that bear sex-determining genes are likely to be involved and the sex chromosomes are the obvious candidates, since they alone are distinctly different in the two sexes.

An alternative hypothesis was put forward by Segal and Nelson (1957), who suggested that the sex chromatin may be derived from a pair of autosomes that bears male-determiners. It was postulated that these autosomes, or regions of them, might be positively heteropycnotic and genetically inert in females, but isopycnotic and genetically active in males. This intriguing hypothesis is based on the genetic balance theory of sex determination, which states that the autosomes carry the male-determiners and implies that the Y chromosome has a passive role in sex determination. But this theory must be reassessed for mammals in the light of recent evidence that the Y chromosome bears male-determining genes in the mouse (Russell, Russell and Gower, 1959; Welshons and Russell, 1959) and in man (Jacobs and Strong, 1959; Ford *et al.*, 1959 b).

Reverting to a possible relationship between sex chromatin and sex chromosomes, Graham and Barr (1952) and Moore and Barr (1953) suggested that the sex chromatin may represent heterochromatic regions of homologous X chromosomes in somatic pairing. It was implied that the property of heterochromaticity was less well developed in the XY complex of somatic cells, compared with the XX complex, or that the XY complex failed to form a conspicuous chromocenter because of the small size of the Y chromosome. This suggestion found some support in the bipartite appearance of the sex chromatin (Klinger, 1958) and from other detailed studies of interphase nuclei. For example, Reitalu (1957) described details in hepatic cell nuclei of human embryos that were compatible with somatic pairing of the X chromosomes. The heterochromatic portions of these chromosomes seemed to form the bipartite sex chromatin, while the euchromatic portions were visible as delicate threads attached to the nucleolus. In cells of male embryos, the single X chromosome formed a small chromocenter but identification of the Y chromosome was difficult. These structures were duplicated in tetraploid nuclei of both sexes. Reitalu also noted that the two X chromosomes present in tetraploid nuclei of males were not associated in somatic pairing. This observation may be related to the finding of Moore and Barr (1954 a) that the frequency of nuclei with a sex chromatin-like mass conformed to normal values in malignant tumours in males, while nuclei with two, or even three, masses of sex chromatin occurred in malignant tumours in females. Reitalu's observations were confirmed on several points by Serr *et al.* (1958), who studied human thyroid epithelial cells cultured *in vitro*. The presence of an XXY complex in patients with the Klinefelter syndrome and female-type nuclei (Jacobs and Strong, 1959; Ford *et al.*, 1959 b) and of an XO arrangement in patients with Turner's syndrome and male-type nuclei (Ford *et al.*, 1959 a: Tjio, Puck and Robinson, 1959) is compatible with the view that the sex chromatin is an XX chromosome derivative, but does not constitute proof that this is so.

Perhaps the principal weakness of the foregoing hypothesis is the necessity of invoking somatic pairing of the X chromosomes. While pairing of homologous chromosomes in somatic cells is well known in many insects and has been described for the newt and frog (Boss, 1955), there seems to be little evidence of a conclusive nature that bears on this matter so far as mammals are concerned. For example somatic association of the X chromosomes has been recorded in epithelial cells of ovarian follicles and mmary gland in the mouse, but could not be detected in other types of cells that were examined (Ohno, Kaplan and Kinosita, 1959 a; Ohno, Kovacs and Kinosita, 1959). Recent studies suggest a possible way out of the impasse that one would not have predicted. Ohno, Kaplan and Kinosita (1959 b) made the surprising observation that only one of the X chromosomes of female rat liver cells was positively heteropycnotic, while both X and Y chromosomes in similar cells of males were isopycnotic with respect to the autosomes. The positively heteropycnotic X chromosome, which may be of paternal origin, appeared to be folded back on itself in early prophase. Ohno and his collaborators point out that the sex chromatin may be derived from a single X chromosome and that the configuration of this chromosome may explain the bipartite appearance of the sex chromatin.

The observations of Kosin and Ishizaki (1959) on nuclei of the domestic chicken are consistent with a derivation of the sex chromatin from a single chromosome. They found the characteristic sexual dimorphism that has been described for mammals, the sex chromatin being present in the female. Since the female of the domestic chicken is said to possess a ZO sex chromosome constitution (Miller, 1938; Newcomer, 1957; Witschi, 1959), it follows that the sex chromatin, if related to the sex chromosomes at all, is a derivative of the single Z chromosome of the female in this species.

Extension of these recent observations to those mammals whose nuclei have a well defined sexual dimorphism, and particularly to man, will be of the greatest interest in interpretation of chromatin pattern and sex chromosome constitution of patients with the syndromes of Turner and Klinefelter. It is gratifying to find cytologists with experience in the study of chromosomes taking an interest in this problem.

APPLICATION OF NUCLEAR SEXUAL DIMORPHISM TO HUMAN SEX ANOMALIES

(a) Tests in Current Use

The *skin biopsy method* was the first to be introduced (Moore, Graham and Barr, 1953), and it has been largely replaced by methods that avoid any surgical procedure. Various staining methods can be used (Moore and Barr, 1954 b; Klinger and Ludwig, 1957), but the preparations must be of high technical quality. Cells in the stratum spinosum and hair follicles are the most satisfactory. Sex chromatin can be identified in from 60 to 80% of their nuclei in normal females (Fig. 1 a), while in normal males a rather smaller chromocenter, of unknown significance, is encountered in less than 10% of nuclei. The procedures used for preparing sections of skin for this purpose are applicable to other tissues that may be obtained at operation or post mortem.

The *oral smear method* is used extensively, mainly because of its simplicity (Moore and Barr, 1955; Marberger, Boccabella and Nelson, 1955). A variety of staining methods may be used, provided that other technical requirements are satisfied. The method of Klinger and Ludwig (1957) has the advantage of eliminating the staining of bacteria. This method includes hydrolysis of the preparation in N HCl at 56°C for *not more* than 5 min., prior to staining with thionin. The details are recorded elsewhere (Barr, in press). Some prefer to stain the smears with cresyl echt violet or another basic dye, without prior treatment other than the usual fixation.

Smear preparations of the oral mucosa are so easy to obtain that they are likely to be studied from large numbers of persons. So a word of caution may be advisable. In general, the nuclei in oral smears display the same sexual dimorphism that is found in nuclei of tissues generally (Fig. 1 b). But the tendency of the female sex chromosome complex (or part of it) to form a distinctive chromocenter is not as pronounced in nuclei of oral epithelium as it is in nuclei at other sites. Consequently, the proportion of healthy-appearing nuclei that contain recognizable sex chromatin may be as low as 25 or 30% in oral smears from normal females, although higher figures, even up to 80%, are often obtained. Further, the sex chromatin is smaller than usual in some preparations from normal females and may be greatly flattened against the nuclear membrane (Fig. 1 b, upper nucleus). On the credit side, a chromocenter that could be confused with the sex chromatin is very rarely present in oral smear preparations from normal males.

In some preparations from both sexes, many nuclei contain a spherical chromocenter that lies well away from the nuclear membrane. The position of this chromocenter is such that it should cause no difficulty in the interpretation of the preparation. As an unusual occurrence, satisfactory oral smears cannot be obtained, probably because of an unhealthy condition of the oral mucosa, and one of the other methods must then be used. The oral smear test has proved reliable, in our hands, in a study of about 3,000 individuals. Anyone who proposes to apply this method to problems of sexual differentiation should first acquire technical and observational experience from the study of a series of preparations from normal males and females.

The sex chromatin is more prominent in nuclei of vaginal smears than it is in those of oral smears (Carpentier, Stolte and Visschers, 1956; Guard, 1959). Vaginal smears could be obtained from patients with suspected gonadal dysgenesis (Turner's syndrome) or testicular feminization.

The *neutrophil test,* which is based on a type of sexual dimorphism peculiar to polymorphonuclear leucocytes, was discovered by Davidson and Smith (1954) and has received abundant confirmation (e.g., Kosenow and Scupin, 1956; Briggs, 1958; Wiedemann, Tolksdorf and Romatowski, 1958). In normal females, a small proportion of neutrophils (1 to 10%, average about 3%) have an accessory nuclear lobule with a filamentous attachment to a lobe of the nucleus (Fig. 1 c). The accessory lobule has average dimensions of $1.2\ \mu \times 1.6\ \mu$ and it occurs more frequently with increasing nuclear lobulation. This configuration occurs with the greatest rarity, if at all, in neutrophils of normal males. The relation of the female-specific nuclear lobule to the sex chromatin is not known, but results of the oral smear and neutrophil tests have the same significance as diagnostic aids in the sex anomalies.

In normal males, there are frequently nuclear projections that, while they are smaller, have the same shape as the accessory lobule of females. Occasionally, "the small clubs" of the male are sufficiently large as to make interpretation difficult, unless one has had considerable experience in studying the many variants of nuclear morphology in neutrophil leucocytes.

(b) Application of the Tests to Sex Anomalies in Man

The foregoing cytological tests have a diagnostic value and a theoretical bearing on errors of sex development.

(i) **Female Pseudohermaphroditism.** In most subjects with female gonads and internal genitalia, but with intersexual external genitalia, the anomaly is caused by fetal adrenocortical hyperplasia and excessive elaboration of androgenic steroids during the third trimester (the adrenogenital syndrome in females). A similar abnormality may result from the administration of progestins to the mother during pregnancy (Wilkins and Jones, 1958). The genetic sex determining mechanism is not involved in either instance and the nuclei always have a female chromatin pattern, as expected. The external genitalia are not necessarily distinctive of female pseudohermaphroditism, as compared with male pseudohermaphroditism, and the main value of the tests is as an aid in distinguishing between the two conditions.

(ii) **Male Pseudohermaphroditism.** Subjects with male gonads and an intersexual development of the remainder of the reproductive system appear to arise through a defective evocator action on the part of the embryonal testes (Jost, 1953). Although family studies suggest that there is a genetic etiological factor, there is no particular reason for suspecting an unusual sex chromosome complex. In any event, the nuclear chromatin pattern is always male.

(iii) **Testicular Feminization.** This special form of male pseudohermaphroditism is characterized by normally female external genitalia and good development of female secondary sex characteristics at puberty. The anomaly follows a maternal inheritance pattern and is probably based on a defect at the gene level. The nuclear chromatin pattern is consistently male.

(iv) **True Hermaphroditism.** Subjects with both ovarian and testicular tissue and intersexual development of the reproductive tract may have either a female or a male chromatin pattern, more frequently the former. Hungerford *et al.* (1959) reported the presence of an XX complex in a true hermaphrodite whose nuclei contained sex chromatin. But chromosome studies need to be done on additional patients to explore the possibility of an abnormal sex chromosome complex, such as XXY in some true hermaphrodites with female-type interphase nuclei.

(v) **Gonadal Dysgenesis (Turner's syndrome)** (Fig. 2). In patients with gonadal dysgenesis (called Turner's syndrome when there are certain added congenital defects), the "gonads" consist of slender streaks of connective tissue. The rest of the reproductive system has a female morphology. Shortness of stature is almost the rule and other anomalies, of the skeletal and cardiovascular systems especially, occur in a proportion of subjects. Urinary

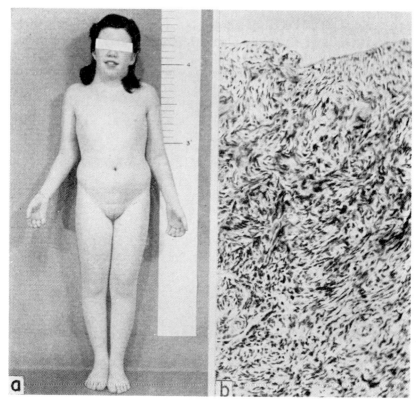

Fig. 2. a. 16-year-old patient with syndrome of gonadal dysgenesis (Turner's syndrome) and a male chromatin pattern. Courtesy of Dr. J. C. Rathbun, Professor of Pediatrics, University of Western Ontario. b. Histological structure of typical "streak gonad" in the syndrome of gonadal dysgenesis. Hematoxylin and eosin stain. 280×. Courtesy of Dr. M. M. Grumbach, Columbia-Presbyterian Medical Center.

excretion of pituitary gonadotrophins is elevated after the age of 10 years and secondary sex characteristics fail to develop at puberty.

The nuclei have a male chromatin pattern in 80% of patients with the syndrome of gonadal dysgenesis (Grumbach, Van Wyk and Wilkins, 1955; Grumbach and Barr, 1958). It has now been shown that the male chromatin pattern is correlated with the presence of an XO sex chromosome complex or, in some patients, with an XX/XO mosaicism (Ford *et al.*, 1959 a; Tjio, Puck and

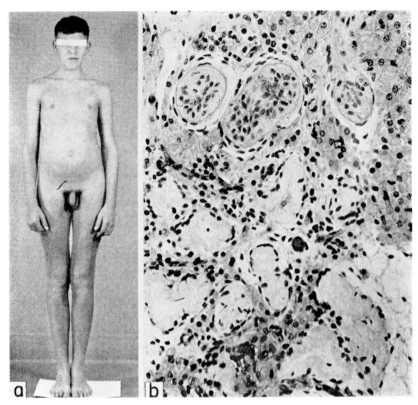

Fig. 3. a. 15-year-old patient with seminiferous tubule dysgenesis (Klinefelter's syndrome) and a female chromatin pattern. b. Testicular histopathology in Klinefelter's syndrome. Some of the tubules are entirely hyalinized, others contain only Sertoli cells. The Leydig cells are in large aggregates. Hematoxylin and eosin stain. 125×.

Robinson, 1959; Ford, this Symposium; Fraccaro, this Symposium). It appears, therefore, that XO and XY complexes are not equivalent in the genetic sex determining mechanism of man, but rather that the Y chromosome is an important carrier of male-determiners. The XO complex is incomplete for either sex and definitive gonads fail to develop from the undifferentiated embryonal gonads. The development of a female reproductive tract is probably the result of an inherent tendency of all embryos to feminize in the absence of a masculinizing inductor of testicular origin (Jost, 1953).

(vi) **Seminiferous Tubule Dysgenesis (Klinefelter's syndrome)** (Fig. 3). Phenotypic males with the syndrome of seminiferous tubule dysgenesis or Klinefelter's syndrome have small testes with varying degrees of fibrosis and hyalinization of the seminiferous tubules. Spermatogenesis is scanty if it occurs at all. The legs are usually long in relation to the length of the trunk and eunuchoid traits, such as poor growth of facial hair, are frequently seen. Urinary excretion of pituitary gonadotrophins is usually elevated after puberty.

The nuclei have a female chromatin pattern in about three-fourths of subjects who qualify on clinical grounds for inclusion in the Klinefelter syndrome (Nelson, 1957; Raboch, 1957). The finding of female-type nuclei in these phenotypic males is related to the presence of an XXY sex chromosome complex or and XX/XXY mosaicism (Jacobs and Strong, 1959; Ford *et al.*, 1959b). The gonads have a nearly normal testicular structure before puberty (Siebenmann and Prader, 1958; Ferguson-Smith, 1959). It appears, therefore, that the male-determining factors carried by the Y chromosome, together with such male-determiners as there may be on autosomes, almost entirely override the female-determiners on the two X chromosomes. But there is an abnormal response of the seminiferous tubules to the hormonal changes of puberty and they rapidly undergo regressive changes.

SUMMARY

The presence of a distinctive chromocenter, the sex chromatin, in interphase nuclei is a female characteristic in man and some other mammals. This nuclear detail provides a useful diagnostic aid in several errors of sex development in man. Absence of sex chromatin has been correlated with an XO complex or an XX/XO mosaicism in the syndrome of gonadal dysgenesis. Presence of sex chromatin has been correlated with an XXY complex or an XX/XXY mosaicism in the syndrome of seminiferous tubule dysgenesis.

Critical and analytical work by students of chromosome morphology and behaviour is needed to establish the basis for the sexual dimorphism of interphase nuclei.

REFERENCES

Barr, M. L. 1959. Sex chromatin and phenotype in man. *Science 130*:679-685.

Barr, M. L. Cytological tests of chromosomal sex. *Recent Advances Clin. Path.* (Churchill, London), vol. 3 (in press).

Boss, J. M. N. 1955. The pairing of somatic chromosomes: a survey. *Texas Rep. Biol. M. 13*:213-221.

Briggs, D. K. 1958. The individuality of nuclear chromatin with particular reference to polymorphonuclear neutrophil leucocytes. *Blood 13*:986-1000.

Carpentier, P. J., Stolte, L. A. M., and Visschers, G. P. 1956. Determination of genetic sex by the vaginal smear. *J. Clin. Endocr. Metab. 16*:155-160.

Davidson, W. M., and Smith, D. R. 1954. A morphological sex difference in the polymorphonuclear neutrophil leucocytes. *Brit. M. J. ii*:6-7.

Ferguson-Smith, M. A. 1959. The prepubertal testicular lesion in chromatin-positive Klinefelter's syndrome (primary micro-orchidism) as seen in mentally handicapped children. *Lancet i*:219-222.

Ford, C. E., Jones, K. W., Polani, P. E., de Almeida, J. C., and Briggs, J. H. 1959 a. A sex-chromosome anomaly in a case of gonadal dysgenesis (Turner's syndrome). *Lancet i*:711-713.

Ford, C. E., Polani, P. E., Briggs, J. H., and Bishop, P. M. F. 1959 b. A presumptive human XXY/XX mosaic. *Nature 183*:1030-1032.

Graham, M. A., and Barr, M. L. 1952. A sex difference in the morphology of metabolic nuclei in somatic cells of the cat. *Anat. Rec. 112*:709-723.

Grumbach, M. M., and Barr, M. L. 1958. Cytologic tests of chromosomal sex in relation to sexual anomalies in man. *Recent Progr. Hormone Res. 14*:255-324.

Grumbach, M. M., Van Wyk, J. J., and Wilkins, L. 1955. Chromosomal sex in gonadal dysgenesis (ovarian agenesis): relationship to male pseudo-hermaphrodism and theories of human sex differentiation. *J. Clin. Endocr. Metab. 15*:1161-1193.

Guard, H. R. 1959. A new technic for differential staining of the sex chromatin, and the determination of its incidence in exfoliated vaginal epithelial cells. *Am. J. Clin. Path. 32*:145-151.

Hungerford, D. A., Donnelly, A. J., Nowell, P. C., and Beck, S. 1959. The chromosome constitution of a human phenotypic intersex. *Am. J. Human Genet. 11*:215-236.

Jacobs, P. A., and Strong, J. A. 1959. A case of human intersexuality having a possible XXY sex-determining mechanism. *Nature 183*:302-303.

Jost, A. 1953. Problems of fetal endocrinology: the gonadal and hypophyseal hormones. *Recent Progr. Hormone Res. 8*:379-413.

Klinger, H. P. 1958. The fine structure of the sex chromatin body. *Exp. Cell. Res. 14*:207-211.

Klinger, H. P., and Ludwig, K. S. 1957. A universal stain for the sex chromatin body. *Stain Techn.* 32:235-244.

Klinger, H. P., and Schwarzacher, H. G. 1958. Sex chromatin in polyploid nuclei of human amnion epithelium. *Nature 181:*1150-1152.

Kosenow, W., and Scupin, R. 1956. Die Bestimmung des Geschlechts mit Hilfe einer Kernanhangsformel der Leukocyten. *Acta haemat.* 15:349-363.

Kosin, I. L., and Ishizaki, H. 1959. Incidence of sex chromatin in Gallus domesticus. *Science 130:*43-44.

Marberger, E., Boccabella, R. A., and Nelson, W. O. 1955. Oral smear as a method of chromosomal sex detection. *Proc. Soc. Exp. Biol.* 89:488-489.

Miller, R. A. 1938. Spermatogenesis in a sex-reversed female and in normal males of the domestic fowl, *Gallus domesticus. Anat. Rec.* 70:155-189.

Moore, K. L., and Barr, M. L. 1953. Morphology of the nerve cell nucleus in mammals, with special reference to the sex chromatin. *J. Comp. Neur.* 98:213-231.

Moore, K. L., and Barr, M. L. 1954 a. The sex chromatin in human malignant tissues. *Brit. J. Cancer 11:*384-390.

Moore, K. L., and Barr, M. L. 1954 b. Nuclear morphology, according to sex, in human tissues. *Acta anat.* 21:197-208.

Moore, K. L., and Barr, M. L. 1955. Smears from the oral mucosa in the detection of chromosomal sex. *Lancet ii:*57-58.

Moore, K. L., Graham, M. A., and Barr, M. L. 1953. The detection of chromosomal sex in hermaphrodites from a skin biopsy. *Surg. Gyn. Obst.* 96:641-648.

Nelson, W. O. 1957. The "Klinefelter syndrome." *Fertil. & Steril.* 8:527-536.

Newcomer, E. H. 1957. The mitotic chromosomes of the domestic fowl. *J. Hered.* 48:227-234.

Ohno, S., Kaplan, W. D., and Kinosita, R. 1959 a. Somatic association of the positively heteropycnotic X-chromosomes in female mice *(Mus musculus). Exp. Cell Res.* 15:616-618.

Ohno, S., Kaplan, W. D., and Kinosita, R. 1959 b. Formation of the sex chromatin by a single X-chromosome in liver cells of *Rattus norvegicus. Exp. Cell Res.* 18:415-418.

Ohno, S., Kovacs, E. T., and Kinosita, R. 1959. On the X-chromosomes of mouse mammary carcinoma cells. *Exp. Cell Res.* 16:462-465.

Raboch, J. 1957. Thirty-one men with female sex chromatin. *J. Clin. Endocr. Metab.* 17:1429-1439.

Reitalu, J. 1957. Observations on the so-called sex chromatin in man. *Acta genet. med. gemell.* 6:393-402.

Russell, W. L., Russell, L. B., and Gower, J. S. 1959. Exceptional inheritance of a sex-linked gene in the mouse explained on the basis that the X/O sex chromosome constitution is female. *Proc. Nat. Acad. Sc.* 45:544-560.

Segal, S. J., and Nelson, W. O. 1957. Developmental aspects of human hermaphrodism: the significance of sex chromatin patterns. *J. Clin. Endocr. Metab.* 17:676-692.

Serr, D. M., Ferguson-Smith, M. A., Lennox, B., and Paul, J. 1958. Representation of the X-chromosome in intermitotic nuclei in man. *Nature* 182:124.

Siebenmann, R., and Prader, A. 1958. Das echte Klinefelter-Syndrom vor der Pubertät. *Schweiz. med. Wschr.* 88:607-610.

Tjio, J. H., Puck, T. T., and Robinson, A. 1959. The somatic chromosomal constitution of some human subjects with genetic defects. *Proc. Nat. Acad. Sc.* 45:1008-1016.

Welshons, W. J., and Russell, L. B. 1959. The Y-chromosome as the bearer of male determining factors in the mouse. *Proc. Nat. Acad. Sc.* 45:560-566.

Wiedemann, H. R., Tolksdorf, M., and Romatowski, H. 1958. Über das Kerngeschlecht der weissen Blutzellen und den Wert der Diagnose des chromosomalen Geschlechts aus dem Blut, verglichen mit anderen Methoden. *Med. Mschr.* 12:665-668.

Wilkins, L., and Jones, H. W. 1958. Masculinization of the female fetus. *Obst. Gyn.* 11:355.

Witschi, E. 1959. Age of sex-determining mechanisms in vertebrates. *Science* 130:372-375.

17

NUCLEAR SEX AND GENITAL MALFORMATION IN 48 CASES OF RENAL AGENESIS, WITH ESPECIAL REFERENCE TO NONSPECIFIC FEMALE PSEUDOHERMAPHRODITISM*

Peter J. Carpentier, M.D.,** and Edith L. Potter, M.D.

A LARGE proportion of all individuals with malformations of the genital system exhibit abnormalities of other organs. The latter sometimes so dominate the clinical picture that genital or gonadal abnormalities are not noticed, or excite little interest, and it seems probable that in this way many abnormalities in sexual development have escaped detection in the past. As a consequence, careful examination of the genital system and the different sex characteristics might yield rewarding information if done systematically in all individuals with any variety of malformation. This seems particularly true when, as in renal agenesis, there is much greater frequency in one sex, and the organs involved have a close ontogenetic relationship to the genital system. For this reason a study has been made of the different sex criteria and the associated genital malformations of 48 infants with complete bilateral renal agenesis on whom autopsy examinations were performed at the Chicago Lying-in Hospital. These findings have also been correlated with other observations on maldevelopment of the genitals, especially those found in female pseudohermaphrodites.

A sex characteristic which has proved very reliable and is re-

Reprinted from *American Journal of Obstetrics and Gynecology*, St. Louis. Vol. 78, No. 2, pages 235-258, August 1959.

* Supported in part by United States Public Health Service Grant for Medical Research 3166.

** Present address: 78 Belgielei St., Antwerp, Belgium.

We wish to thank Dr. W. P. Plate, professor at the Department of Gynecology and Obstetrics of the University of Utrecht in the Netherlands for permission to include data from studies done by Dr. Peter J. Carpentier in his institute.

ferred to in this paper as nuclear sex was discovered by Barr.[1] He described a small chromatin body, about one micron in diameter, in the cell nuclei of human females and females of several animal species, which he was unable to detect in the cells of males. Although direct proof is still lacking, much indirect evidence justifies the opinion that this chromatin body, the so-called sex chromatin, is derived from heterochromatic portions of the XX chromosome complex and consequently is indicative of true genetic sex. This discovery has been responsible for important advances in the clinical investigation of certain syndromes associated with aberrations in sexual development.[2-8] Methods have also been developed for identification of nuclear sex by the study of polymorphonuclear leukocytes in blood smears[9, 10] and squamous cell nuclei in oral,[11] vaginal, and urogenital[12] smears. Valuable retrospective studies have also proved possible since sex chromatin can be identified in tissue sections or vaginal smears that have been on file for many years.

One variety of malformation which, because of its uneven sex distribution, has been subjected to investigation of nuclear sex pattern is anencephaly. Approximately 90% of such infants appear to be females and abnormalities of the gonads or reproductive system are rare. Polani and Claireaux[13] examined tissue cells from 4 male and 8 female anencephalic fetuses and found complete agreement between the chromatin pattern of the nuclei and the sex as indicated by the form of external and internal organs. Perrin and Benirschke[14] reported similar results in 27 female and 8 male anencephalic fetuses and included a description of the gonads in 27 cases. One of us (P. J. C.) in an unpublished series of 10 female anencephalic fetuses found a uniformly female-type nuclear pattern in oral and vulvovaginal smears.

Bilateral renal agenesis is another malformation in which one sex predominates, with about three-fourths appearing to be males. The only record of a comparison of sex determined by nuclear pattern and that resulting from inspection of the gonads and genital system in infants with this malformation is from Davidson and Ross[15] who found complete agreement in 4 males and one female. In view of these considerations it seemed worthwhile to extend this investigation to a larger series of cases.

The number of infants with bilateral renal agenesis who have been encountered on the autopsy service of the Chicago Lying-in Hospital is the largest group ever collected. Among almost 11,000 autopsies performed from 1935 to the present time on fetuses and newborn infants, 48 were on infants or fetuses who had no renal tissue. Twenty were observed before 1944 and were described in 1946[16, 17] and 10 more were added to this group in 1952.[18] The remainder were observed in the intervening years with none found in 1957 or 1958.

The present study is based on gross examinations of these infants as recorded at the time of autopsy and on microscopic study of tissue sections. Eighteen of the group were stillborn, half of them with variable degrees of maceration which at times rendered adequate postmortem examination and histologic investigation difficult or impossible. In addition, 5 of the 24 infants who were not born in this institution were dissected elsewhere and only tissue samples and a report of clinical and autopsy data were received for study.

In only 41 cases were tissue sections available for systematic investigation of the nuclear sex type, 2 having been lost and 5 being unsatisfactory because of maceration. From 2 to 10 sections were available in each case. All sections were carefully examined under a 40 and 60 mm. objective with a ×15 ocular giving a magnification of 600-900. Only well-outlined vesicular nuclei with homogeneously distributed chromatin were selected for study. The most satisfactory nuclei were found in young fibroblasts, in cells from skeletal, smooth and cardiac muscle, in adrenal cortex, and in basal layers of stratified epithelium. Cells of other organs, including the liver, were generally not satisfactory for this purpose. No attempt was made to determine the exact percentage of cell nuclei containing a sex chromatin body. Since in all tissues the majority of cells are unsuitable, counting the frequency with which the sex chromatin body can be recognized becomes relatively meaningless. Instead, it seems better to examine very critically the chromatin pattern of some 20 entirely satisfactory cells and to base one's opinion on these. Moreover, experience has led us to believe that a true sex chromatin body occurs exclusively in the female. Chromatin agglomerations, which cannot be distinguished from it even by an experienced observer, may occasionally be found in the male, but very rarely in suitable nuclei. Provided that the examiner has sufficient critical sense and has had adequate experience, essentially qualitative criteria are preferable to empirical, quantitative limits. In extensive material from sexually normal and abnormal patients, studied by one of us (P. J. C.) during the last 3 years, in which conclusions were almost always reached before the state of the patient was known, this method of approach has never given rise to confusion.

Among the 41 cases with suitable tissue sections, 10 presented female-type and 31 male-type nuclei. In every infant possessing male-type nuclei, the diagnosis of nuclear sex agreed with the reported genital and gonadal findings. Among the subjects with female-type nuclei, however, one (Case 4) had been registered as a male. In the remaining 9 females, internal genital organs, gonads, and nuclear chromatin pattern were concordant.

DIAGNOSIS OF SEX

Generally speaking, sex can be diagnosed in normal individuals from any characteristic present in one sex and absent in the other. This is ordinarily done at birth by simple inspection of the external genitals. However, in individuals in whom the possibility of sexual maldevelopment is suspected the different components of the sex pattern should be studied separately as their normal interrelationship may be lost.

It is now generally agreed that the nuclear chromatin pattern has replaced the gonads as the most important criterion of sex. However, it is important that all criteria for diagnosis of sex be included in any study of sexual abnormality. Inspection of the external genitals at birth, the gross and microscopic exploration of the gonads and other sex organs at operation or autopsy, and a study of the nuclear chromatin pattern in any available cells or tissues should be part of every investigation and chromosome count.

In our material the following correlations were made:

External Genital Organs.—In 33 infants, 25 males and 8 females, the external genitals were sufficiently normal for sex to be correctly diagnosed on *external examination*. In 11 others the ex-

TABLE 1

Infants and Fetuses in Whom the Correct Diagnosis of Sex by External Examination Was Difficult or Impossible

| Number | Weight (in Grams) | Genital Organs | | Gonads | Nu-clear Sex | Major Associated Mal-Formations* |
		EXTERNAL	INTERNAL			
41608	1180	Absent	Male type	Testes anterior to symphysis	M	Sirenomelus, imperforate anus Type III, duodenal stenosis, absent descending colon, intraventricular septal defect
56151	1310	Absent	Male type	Abdominal testes	M	Sirenomelus, imperforate anus Type III, hypoplastic colon, single umbilical artery
52413	995	Absent	Male type	Abdominal testes	M	Sirenomelus, imperforate anus Type III, absent sigmoid and rectum, tetralogy of Fallot
54118	1040	Penis absent, scrotum present	Male type	Abdominal testes, bilateral hydrocele	M	Sirenomelus, imperforate anus Type III, tracheoesophageal fistula, absent aortic arch, second of twins
46271	1790	Posterior tail-like penis and scrotum	Male type	Abdominal testes	M	Sirenomelus, imperforate anus Type III
47417	360	Absent	No tubes, uterus, or vagina	Abdominal gonads, probably testes	—	Sirenomelus, imperforate anus Type III

		External genitalia	Type	Gonads	Sex	Diagnosis
38482	1645	Penis absent, scrotum present	Male type	Testes in scrotum	M	Imperforate anus Type III, absent sigmoid and rectum
52176	1230	Penis absent, half scrotum absent	Male type	Abdominal testes	M	Anorectal malformation Type I
545	1480	Penis normal, scrotum absent	Male type	Abdominal testes	M	Imperforate anus Type III
53132	1190	Rudimentary structure possibly a clitoris	Rudimentary tubes and uterus, closed vagina	Normal ovaries	—	Imperforate anus Type III, colon terminating in vagina
491409	225	Hyperplastic clitoris or small penis	Normal tubes, no uterus or vagina	Normal ovaries	—	Imperforate anus Type III, sigmoid and rectum absent
47357	1290	Normal penis and empty scrotum	Normal tubes, no uterus or vagina	Normal ovaries	F	Pseudohermaphrodite, imperforate anus Type III, colon terminating a bladder (Case 1)
54120	1110	Normal penis and empty scrotum	Normal tubes, no uterus or vagina	Normal ovaries	F	Pseudohermaphrodite, imperforate anus Type III, colon terminating in bladder (Case 2)
51245	1580	Penis with abnormal labia or scrotum	Hypoplastic tubes, no uterus or vagina	Small ovaries	F	Pseudohermaphrodite, sirenomelus, imperforate anus Type III, absent sigmoid and rectum (Case 3)
42258	1015	Hypoplastic penis and scrotum	No tubes, uterus, or vagina	Abdominal "testes"	F	Pseudohermaphrodite, imperforate anus Type III, absent sigmoid and rectum, malformed hands and arms (Case 4)

* The lungs were hypoplastic and the feet and legs were abnormal in position in all instances except where otherwise noted.

ternal genitals were absent or abnormal and a positive diagnosis
was impossible, and in 4 instances female pseudohermaphrodites
(see case reports) were incorrectly diagnosed as males because of
a penile urethra (Table 1).

Seven of the 15 infants with abnormal external genitals showed

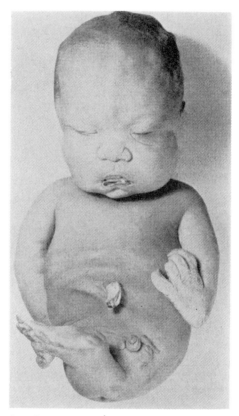

Fig. 1. The only female infant with sirenomelus deformity. Note the penile
structure with glans and terminal urethra, flanked by two skin folds.

the sirenomelus deformity, characterized by a single lower extremity resulting from fusion of the lower limbs. Six of these were
males; 4 had no external genital structures, one had a taillike appendage arising posteriorly from the lower end of the sacrum
which proved to be a penis, and in another the penis was absent
but an empty scrotum was present. Five possessed testes and

male-type nuclei and one was an extremely macerated small fetus of 360 grams in which no uterus or Fallopian tubes could be found and which was consequently assumed to be male. The seventh infant in the sirenomelus series had a penile structure flanked by small folds (Fig. 1) which could be interpreted equally as rudimentary labia or an abnormal bifid scrotum. It proved to be female (Case 3) although before postmortem examination it was thought probably to be a male because of the penile urethra.

Of the remaining 8 infants with marked abnormalities of the external genitals the gonads and the sex chromatin pattern agreed in indicating that 3 were male and 5 female. In 2 of the males the penis was absent: one had a normal scrotum, the other had what appeared to be a half scrotum in the right groin. In the third male the penis was normal but the scrotum was absent. Of the 5 females, 3 were considered males with undescended testes on external examination because of a penis with a central urethra and absence of anything resembling a vagina (Cases 1, 2, and 4). The fourth lacked external genitals, although a small structure thought possibly to be a rudimentary clitoris was present in one groin with a tiny depression 2 mm. deep lying beneath it. The fifth female was a 225 gram macerated fetus with a structure described as a small penis. This fetus was not included with the 4 pseudohermaphrodites because of the inability to determine unequivocally the character of this structure.

Gonads.—A gross description of the gonads was available in 43 of the infants. In 12 they were described as ovaries, in 30 as testes, and in one they were assumed to be testes, although a positive statement was impossible because of extreme maceration. Except for the one case described in Case 4 the gonads in every instance were in accord with the independently determined nuclear sex type.

A definite description of the gonads was not available in 5 but the infants were all stated to be male. In 3 of these the autopsy report did not specifically mention the gonads but all 3 had male-type nuclei. One original protocol and 2 sets of tissue sections could not be found.

Histologic sections of the gonads were available for study in

18 cases. In 6 they were ovaries and in 12 testes. The testes appeared normal in all except 2 instances where the testicular tubules were slightly hypoplastic. One of these was a sirenomelus with no external genitals and a malformed heart; the other was a twin with a long and angulated penis and multiple other anomalies, including imperforate anus, absent sacral and lumbar spine, extreme hypoplasia of the lungs, and webbing of the neck and knees. The ovaries were normal in all 6 cases.

MALFORMATIONS OF GENITAL ORGANS IN THE TWO SEXES

Males

External Genital Organs: In addition to the 9 males with severe malformations described in Table I, 4 others had less marked disturbances in development of the external genitals. Three had a variable degree of elongation and angulation of the penis accompanied by anorectal anomalies and one had a slight hypospadias but the testes were in the scrotum and the anus and rectum were normal. The external genital development of the remaining 22 males appeared to be normal.

Internal Genital Organs: The location of the testes was specifically described in 25 of the total 35 males. In 12 both testes were located in the abdominal cavity, in one both were at the pelvic brim, and in another they were high in the usual location of the kidneys. In 5 they were incompletely descended and in 8 both were in the scrotum.

Although the description of the male genital ducts was often somewhat incomplete several essential facts emerge from the available data. A grossly normal or slightly hypoplastic epididymis and ductus deferens were present but the seminal vesicles were frequently lacking. Whenever the prostrate could not be definitely identified grossly, microscopic evidence indicating at least a rudimentary development could generally be found in sections of the bladder neck region.

Females

External Genital Organs: In addition to the 6 females described in Table I there were 7 others with malformations since no female had an entirely normal genital system. Excluding the one de-

scribed in Table I which was thought to be a male with undescended testes, the following statements can be made, based on all
12 cases. The clitoris was small and rudimentary in one case,
normal or presumably normal in 7, and hyperplastic in one. In the
only female sirenomelus (Case 3) it had a penile appearance
and in 2 others (Cases 1 and 2) it looked like a completely normal
penis, with a patent urethra and was accompanied by a normal-
looking empty scrotum.

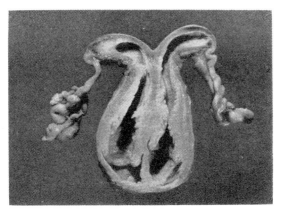

Fig. 2. Uterus bicornis duplex with double closed vagina.

A female-type urethral opening was present and patent in 7,
hypoplastic in 2, and replaced by a penile urethra in 3.

Internal Genital Organs: A normal vagina with a normal orifice
was present in only 2 infants but in one of these it ended blindly,
due to the absence of the uterus; in the other it communicated
with a double uterus. In 8 infants no trace of vagina could be
found. In the 2 remaining females the vagina had no external
opening: in one it consisted of a small pouch containing the two
cervices of the uterus bicornis duplex (Figs. 2 and 3) and in the
other it was moderately dilated and filled with meconium because
of a small communication with a blind-ending colon; the uterus
was absent.

A uterus was missing in 8 infants, in 2 it consisted of two un-
fused, rudimentary tissue knobs, and in 2 others of a uterus bicornis duplex.

The Fallopian tubes were more frequently normal than any

other part of the female genital tract; this was the case in 8 of the 12 infants. In 3 they were hypoplastic, in another the right tube was normal and attached to the homolateral, knoblike uterine half while the left was an isolated structure ending free in the inguinal canal.

In 9 of the 12 recognized females the ovaries were normal. In 2 they were hypoplastic, flat, thin, and tapelike. In another they were large and elongated, had a combined weight of 2 grams, and contained many grossly visible follicles.

CASE REPORTS

The following cases are those in which a female child was erroneously thought to be male on external examination because of a penile urethra.

Fig. 3. From the same infant as in Fig. 2 showing organs in situ. The appearance of the adrenal glands is typical of renal agenesis.

Case 1—47357. A stillborn Negro fetus weighing 1,290 grams and measuring 39.5 cm. in length, the fifth child of a 26-year-old woman who had had no prenatal care, was delivered precipitously from a breech position in the thirty-third week of pregnancy after unattended labor of less than one hour. External examination re-

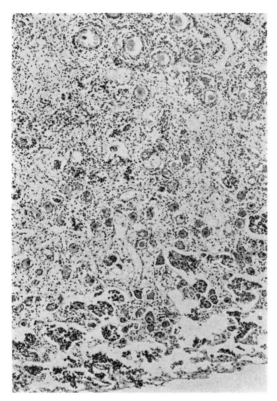

Fig. 4. Section of normal ovary from infant with penile urethra shown in Figs. 5 and 6 (Case 1). (×130; reduced ⅘.)

vealed a face characteristic of renal agenesis with prominent epicanthic folds and ears low set at an angle and containing little cartilage, bilateral calcaneovalgus, an imperforate anus, and external genitals resembling those of a normal male with undescended testes.

The organs were normal except for the lungs which were hypoplastic, the kidneys and ureters which were both absent, and the colon which terminated in the sigmoid portion. This communicated with the bladder through an extremely small opening. The bladder contained meconium which could be expressed from the penile urethra. The anus was imperforate. The vagina and uterus were absent although both Fallopian tubes and both ovaries were present. The lower ends of the tubes merged with the surrounding tissue and were not attached to each other or to anything that resembled a uterus.

The ovaries contained normal ova and early Graafian follicles (Fig. 4). The penile structure contained a urethra surrounded by erectile tissue (Figs. 5 and 6), and the base of the bladder had a few small glandlike structures suggestive of rudimentary prostate glands. The lungs were moderately hypoplastic and hemorrhage was present in the interstitial tissue. The chromatin pattern of nuclei in all sections was of the female type.

Case 2—54120. A white fetus weighing 1,110 grams, measuring 38.0 cm. in length, was born in the thirtieth week of pregnancy by breech extraction with manual aid. The mother was 20 years old and had had 3 previous pregnancies, the first ending in a stillbirth, the second in neonatal death, the third in a healthy surviving child. No untoward symptoms were present during pregnancy, labor, or delivery. The infant was alive at birth but respiration could not be established and the heart stopped beating after 21 minutes.

External examination of the body revealed a facies typical of renal agenesis with a prominent epicanthic fold and large soft ears lacking cartilage, set in a low oblique position. The feet were in a valgus position. The infant was accepted as a male because of a structure thought to be a penis and the absence of labia or vaginal orifice. When the pelvic and abdominal organs were investigated the gonads were found to be ovaries and were adjacent to normal-appearing Fallopian tubes. The lower end of one tube frayed out into surrounding tissues and the other end was attached to a small nodule adjacent to the bladder (Fig. 7). Both kidneys and ureters were absent. The anus was imperforate and the terminal portion of the sigmoid colon communicated with the bladder. Meconium-stained material could be expressed from the patent urethra. The vagina could not be identified but microscopic examination of a small mass above the bladder revealed several small masses of squamous epithelium with minute central lumina which probably represented an abortive attempt at formation of a vagina.

The penile structure had a central urethra surrounded by erectile tissue typical of the corpus cavernosum urethrae with well,

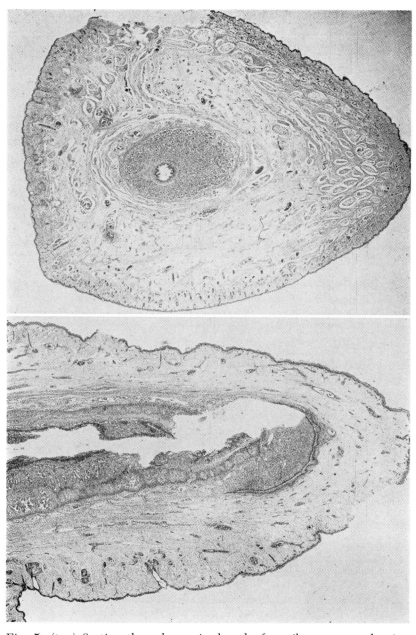

Fig. 5. *(top)* Section through proximal end of penile structure showing urethra surrounded by corpus spongiosum. (×10; reduced ½.)

Fig. 6. *(bottom)* Longitudinal section through penile structure showing glans, preputial fold, urethra, corpus spongiosum, and corpus cavernosum. (×20; reduced ½.)

179

but somewhat irregularly, developed corpera cavernosa penis. The ovaries contained numerous primordial follicles and were normal for a premature fetus. The lungs were extremely hypoplastic and almost no alveoli had developed. Nuclear chromatin was of the female type.

 Case 3—51245. A white fetus with a typical sirenomelus de-

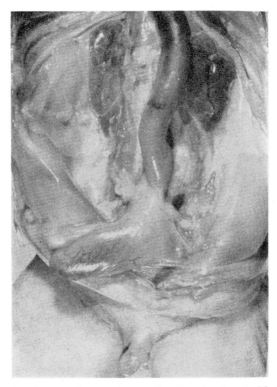

Fig. 7. View showing penile structure, colon terminating in bladder, normal adrenal glands, Fallopian tubes, and ovaries. Uterus absent except for rudiment attached to left tube (Case 2).

formity (Fig. 1) weighed 1,580 grams and measured 33 cm. in length. No clinical history was available. External examination revealed a facies typical of complete renal agenesis with prominent epicanthic folds and large low-set ears lacking cartilage. Skeletal malformations included absence of the left radius and thumb, absence of one finger of the right hand, extreme hypoplasia and fusion of bones, and soft tissues of lower extremities.

Anus and vagina were absent. To the left of the midline on the lower abdominal wall was a structure 2 cm. in length resembling a penis with glans, prepuce, and central urethra and flanked on both sides by small folds, suggesting rudimentary labia or a hypoplastic bifid scrotum. Examination of the body cavities revealed hypoplasia of the lungs, bilateral absence of kidneys and ureters, and absence of bladder, uterus, and vagina. The sigmoid colon and rectum were absent. The ovaries and Fallopian tubes appeared normal. The lower ends of the Fallopian tubes frayed out into suprapubic fat.

Microscopically the tubes and ovaries were normal. The ovaries contained normal primitive germ cells, primordial follicles, and one follicle with luteinization of the theca interna. The nuclei in all sections were of the female type.

Case 4—42258. A white fetus weighing 1,005 grams, measuring 32 cm. in length was delivered as the first of twins in the first pregnancy of a 22-year-old woman. The first twin was considered male, the second female. The placenta was fused and had 2 amnions and 2 chorions. Both twins were stillborn. The second twin weighed 1,230 grams and was a normally formed female who appeared to have died of intracranial hemorrhage.

The first twin had multiple skeletal malformations including shortening of the ulna and bilateral absence of the radius and thumb producing typical clubhands. The right tibia and fibula were absent and a six-toed foot was joined at the knee. The left foot was in an equinovalgus position with incomplete separation of the first two toes. The spine was scoliotic producing a concavity of the left chest and convexity of the right. There was no indication of an anus. The external genitals were stated to be rudimentary but were not further described.

The organs in the body cavities were normal except that the colon terminated in a blind pouch in the region of the mid-descending colon, and the kidneys, ureters, and bladder were absent. Testes were stated to be in the abdomen, one attached near the diaphragm. Unfortunately they were not examined microscopically.

This autopsy was performed in another institution and tissues and protocol sent to the Chicago Lying-in Hospital as part of a routine procedure. The fetus was accepted as a male until the present investigation led to the discovery of a female nuclear chromatin pattern. It is very unfortunate that the gonads were not examined microscopically for if they were ovaries this case would be similar to the preceding three cases, while if they were actually testes it would be the first case of Klinefelter's syndrome to be described in a newborn infant.

This case illustrates very graphically, however, the mistakes in designation of sex that can follow superficial and incomplete examinations.

SEXUAL MALDEVELOPMENT ASSOCIATED WITH OTHER CONGENITAL ABNORMALITIES

Malformations of the sex organs have been described in association with malformations of all kinds in all parts of the body and in some instances investigation of individuals with nongenital abnormalities has contributed a great deal to our knowledge of disturbances in formation of the genital system. In fact, the intelligent observation of sex linkage in certain congenital malformations led to a major discovery in the field of developmental pathology. Whereas the Turner-Albright syndrome of "rudimentary ovaries" associated with infantilism, dwarfism, and other congenital anomalies[19-21] is found almost exclusively in females, coarctation of the aorta occurs predominantly in males. Observing the combination of these conditions in 3 patients assumed to be female, Polani, Hunter, and Lennox[2] investigated their nuclear chromatin pattern and found it to be male. This surprising discovery caused a great sensation but it was soon widely confirmed[3, 4, 12] and the majority of patients with the Turner-Albright syndrome have been shown to possess male-type nuclei. The experimental work of Jost[22, 23] showed that sexual development along a female pattern follows early intrauterine castration of male rabbit embryos and it is now generally believed that a similar situation occurs in the human in the Turner-Albright syndrome—that some unknown factor destroys the embryonic male gonad and that this is responsible for development of a female genital tract. The same or a related damaging factor is thought to cause the associated anomalies of other organs generally found in these patients. In related conditions of male pseudohermaphroditism ascribed to a lesser degree of embryonic testicular damage, associated congenital anomalies are also observed.[3, 4]

Recently, a similar correlation has become apparent in an entirely different condition, Klinefelter's syndrome. This was originally regarded as an endocrinologic and morphologic testicular disorder, accompanied by azoospermia and eventual gynecomastia. In 1956 it was discovered simultaneously by different investigators,[5-8] that a large number of these patients, who present a male habitus and entirely normal male genitals, have female-type nuclei. As a consequence this condition seems to constitute the opposite of the Turner-Albright syndrome in relation to genital development and nuclear sex.

Pasqualini and co-workers[24] in 1957 stressed the high incidence of mental deficiency in patients with Klinefelter's syndrome. This prompted the investigation of nuclear sex in mentally retarded patients by Ferguson-Smith[25] and by Prader and associates.[26] Both studies led to the discovery of an unsuspected number of patients with chromatin-positive nuclei and a testicular disorder characteristic of Klinefelter's syndrome.

That malformations of the genital organs are frequently found in association with renal agenesis has been recognized by many investigators.[15, 27] This association has been observed not only in dead infants with bilateral absence of the kidneys, but also in patients with less marked or unilateral urologic abnormalities which have not directly interfered with survival.[28-30] The frequency with which urinary tract deformities occur in conjunction with a malformed vagina or uterus is well known to gynecologists.[31-35]

From our series and from some of the pertinent literature, the impression is gained that, in the male, malformations of the internal genital organs are less frequent and less pronounced. Definite data as to their real incidence and extent, however, could be provided only by a sufficiently large number of suitable cases studied in detail as was done by Davidson and Ross.[15] As pointed out by Guizetti and Pariset[36] internal genital malformation in adults is considerably more difficult to detect in the male than in the female. Especially careful scrutiny is all the more necessary to exclude such anomalies in male fetuses and newborn infants.

None of the female infants in our series possessed a completely normal genital tract. The least severe malformation was a double uterus with a complete septum and two separate cervices with the remainder of the genital tract normal. Internal genital anomalies in females with bilateral renal agenesis are extremely common and the presence of an entirely normal genital tract in such females must be a very rare occurrence, although such a case was recently described by Duxbury.[37] *

Absence or malformation of the external genitals has been reported[27] but possible marked or complete masculinization in female subjects seems not to have been widely recognized.

The presence of a major anorectal malformation of the same type in all 4 of our female pseudohermaphrodites with penile urethras is striking. Moreover, the incidence of such anal abnormalities is high in the whole series, being approximately 40%.

Ladd and Gross[38, 39] have proposed a valuable classification for congenital anorectal malformations that has become widely used. In Type I the rectum is constricted a few centimeters above the anal level. In Type II the anus is imperforate, but perineum and rectum are in coaptation, unlike Type III where they are separated by a distance of several centimeters. In Type IV the bowel is interrupted at a level higher than the perineum and consequently is accompanied by a blind anal pouch.

Anorectal abnormalities were present in 20 of the 48 cases in our series. Fifteen resembled Type III except that the malformations were generally more extensive than those described in living patients and both rectum and sigmoid were frequently absent. In some an even larger portion of the colon was missing.

Twelve of the anorectal malformations occurred in males, 10 of them being Type III and the others Types I and II.

Eight of the anorectal malformations occurred in females, 6 of them being Type III. In the 2 others the anal orifice was abnormally located. In one of them the rectum opened between the labia, while the bladder opened into the rectum—a cloaca-like anomaly that has also been described by Sieber and Klein[40] in two cases of "nonadrenal" female pseudohermaphroditism. In the

---

* After this paper had been accepted for publication an infant was born at the Chicago Lying-in Hospital with bilateral renal agenesis but with normal ovaries, Fallopian tubes, uterine corpus, cervix, and vagina.

other the location of the anus was more posterior than normal, probably related to the absence of the sacrum. Two of the Type III anomalies (Cases 1 and 2) were complicated by the presence of a communication between the rectum and bladder, so that meconium could be expressed through the urethra. In another female of the same category there was a communication between the rectum and a closed vaginal pouch which was distended with meconium.

Anorectal malformations were present in our series more often in females than in males; in the former they were found in two-thirds of the cases, in the latter in only one-third of the cases.

It is remarkable and probably of significance that in 19 of the 20 infants whose external genitals were abnormal an anorectal malformation was present. The only one with a normal anus and rectum was a male with a slight degree of hypospadias, unaccompanied by cryptorchidism. Among the 28 cases without external genital malformation, only one minor anorectal anomaly, a more sacral location of the anus, was found.

Seven infants in the series presented the fused-limb or sirenomelus malformation. Five were definitely male, one was presumably male and only one was female. All had absent or malformed external genitals. All had an extensive Type III abnormality of the lower intestine. In one infant the urethra was absent and the external genitals, although recognizable, were of a strange shape and abnormally located, forming a taillike appendage at the base of the spine.[41] The only reference to such taillike appendages in association with sirenomelus that we have discovered is by Ballantyne[42] who found several such cases in the literature, but in none was there evidence that the true significance of this structure was appreciated.

The correlation between anorectal anomalies and abnormalities of the urinary and the genital system is also evident in the literature.[38, 39, 43-46] Norris and co-workers[47] noted that the anomalies most often associated with an imperforate anus were genitourinary and that this association occurred predominantly in males.

Moore and Lawrence[48, 49] analyzed the clinical features and the correlated anomalies in 120 cases of congenital anorectal malformation. The danger to life of this lesion is apparent from the fact that half of their patients were less than 5 days of age and only 11% were more than 2 years old. Four patients were stated to be of questionable sex but, unfortunately, no further details were given. The over-all incidence of associated abnormalities was 72% but in the cases examined at autopsy this figure rose to 97%. One-third of the patients presented malformations of the urinary tract with megaloureter, absence of one kidney, or aplasia of one kidney being the most frequent. One-fifth of the female patients had malformation of the internal genital organs. Twelve patients were mentally deficient. Also present were hypospadias, bifid scrotum, rudimentary penis, and complete absence of the external genitals. One cannot but wonder how rewarding a screening of the nuclear sex type in this series would have been.

VARIETIES OF FEMALE PSEUDOHERMAPHRODITISM

Through the years different classifications have been proposed for the many varieties of sexual maldevelopment, but recently, because of considerable advance in knowledge in this field, they have become more adequate than they were formerly.[8, 50-53] In these attempts at classification, however, little attention has been paid to the possible existence of other malformations. This is rather surprising, for when associated malformations are present in one case and not another it seems very probable that there may be a fundamental difference in the causative factors. For this reason it seems to us appropriate, when studying sexual maldevelopment, to make a distinction between the cases with and those without concurrent extragenital anomalies.

Such a distinction has the advantage, especially in female pseudohermaphroditism, of coinciding fairly well with the dividing line between what is known with reasonable certainty and what is not—between cases tending to depend in their etiology upon a single, specific agent and those governed by as yet unrecognized dysontogenetic factors.

Coexisting anomalies may profoundly alter prognosis and management in any given case and consequently an attempt should invariably be made to determine their presence or absence since the findings may be important in making a differential diagnosis.

Because of these observed differences, we propose to attribute the term "specific" to the cases of female pseudohermaphroditism which show a disturbance in the genital system only, and "nonspecific" to those showing additional malformations in other organ systems.

Specific and nonspecific gonadogenital aberrations seem to occur in both sexes, but the distinction is especially clear-cut in female pseudohermaphrodites. Thus it is possible in our present

TABLE 2

CLASSIFICATION OF DIFFERENT FORMS OF FEMALE PSEUDOHERMAPHRODITISM

I. *Specific Female Pseudohermaphroiditism Without Associated Malformations.*—
   A. Fetal androgenic influence
      1. Adrenogenital syndrome
   B. Maternal androgenic influence
      1. Treatment during pregnancy with androgenic or progestogenic compounds ("artificial" or "iatrogenic" female pseudohermaphroditism)
      2. Virilizing tumor during pregnancy (arrhenoblastoma)
      3. Functional deviation of steroid metabolism (?)
   C. Other forms of specific female pseudohermaphroditism (unapparent fetal or maternal androgenic factors? undetected congenital anomalies?)
II. *Nonspecific Female Pseudohermaphroditism With Associated Malformations.*—
   "Group 2" of Gross and Meeker, "special group" of Jones, cases reported and quoted here, etc.

---

state of knowledge to propose a simple classification of female pseudohermaphroditism, based on etiological and clinical factors (Table 2).

SPECIFIC FEMALE PSEUDOHERMAPHRODITISM

In specific female pseudohermaphroditism, according to the definition, there are no accompanying malformations of nongenital organs. At present several etiological subgroups may be distinguished.

The largest and best known subgroup (Table 2, I, A) is made up of cases of so-called adrenogenital syndrome, in the study and treatment of which Wilkins and co-workers[21, 54] have made such important advances. In these cases the source of the androgens masculinizing the female fetus is the fetal adrenal gland itself. Clinically there is evidence in these infants of hyper- and dysfunction of the adrenal gland at birth, resulting in a marked increase in the output of 17-ketosteroids and sometimes in a typical disorder, the so-called salt-losing syndrome, which is characterized by a marked loss of salt and water through vomiting, diarrhea, and other pathways. In surviving untreated subjects, early appearance of sexual hair, advanced bone growth, and a stocky muscular build are noted. The adrenal gland is stated to show marked enlargement and to weigh, in the newborn, as much as 8 grams. In microscopic sections the zona reticularis and the zona fascicularis are described as greatly widened. Biochemically, the syndrome is characterized by the inability of the adrenal cortex to achieve certain steps in the biosynthesis of vital glucocorticoids. This results in the accumulation of intermediate androgenic steroids and their metabolites and in an increased ACTH production by the pituitary as the latter is not inhibited by a sufficiently high glucocorticoid blood level. The synthesis of androgenic steroids is thereby even more stimulated and morphologic hyperplasia of the adrenal gland is enhanced. The only known way of breaking this vicious cycle is by the administration of cortisone or a substitute which provides the vitally needed glucocorticoid and inhibits excessive ACTH production by the pituitary. As a rule the results of this therapy are striking. There is considerable evidence to favor the view that the fundamental fault lies in a deficiency of one or more enzymes essential for the biosynthesis of cortisol.[55] This syndrome, which frequently occurs in siblings, may therefore be considered as a specific biochemical anomaly, due to an inborn error of steroid metabolism.[56]

None of the infants of our series showed definite gross or microscopic hyperplasia of the adrenals. Their shape was flat and round, as is usual when the kidney is absent[18, 57] (Fig. 2), except in one infant where they were fused in the midline. The size was proportionate to the size of the infant in most cases and their combined weight generally close to 0.25% of the total body weight of the infant. In a very few of the more severely malformed fetuses the adrenals were slightly hypoplastic or moderately enlarged. The zona fascicularis and the zona reticularis were generally well developed but not abnormally widened.

A second subgroup of specific female pseudohermaphroditism is caused by the presence in the maternal blood of abnormal steroids which are responsible for virilization of the female fetus. Several forms of this subgroup may be differentiated according to the origin of these steroids.

In the first form (Table 2, I, B, 1) the source of the responsible steroids is exogenous to the maternal organism and provided by the oral and parenteral administration of androgens or progestational agents to the pregnant woman in an attempt to prevent abortion or to provide treatment for some concurrent condition. This form of specific female pseudohermaphroditism may be called "artificial" or even "iatrogenic." Whereas in the beginning only a few isolated observations were reported, the number of cases being published is now increasing at a disquieting rate, especially since the introduction of progestational agents that are effective when given orally and which have been proved to possess marked androgenic properties. Thus far, cases of genital virilization in the female fetus have been reported after the administration during pregnancy of recognized androgens such as intramuscular testosterone,[58-60] oral methyltestosterone,[58, 59, 61-64] intramuscular methylandrostenediol,[65] and of new orally administered progestational compounds such as 17-ethinyltestosterone (synonyms: ethisterone, pregneninolone, anhydrohydroxyprogesterone),[63] 17-ethinyl, 19-nortestosterone (synonym: norethisterone),[66] and 17-methyl, 19-nortestosterone (synonym: normethandrolone, methylestrenolone).[67]

The degree of virilization of the external genitals of the infant is dependent on the androgenic potency of the compound, the dosage and duration of the therapy, and especially on the stage of embryologic development at the time medication is started. In the cases of iatrogenic pseudohermaphroditism so far reported, the only abnormality that has been observed is virilization of the external genitals, and this at times has been extreme. The internal genital organs have been found normal in all instances where an exploratory laparotomy or autopsy was performed. In this variety of pseudohermaphroditism signs of abnormal adrenal secretion are lacking, the 17-ketosteroid excretion is within normal limits, and the clinical course is generally uneventful. Therapy is ordinarily not indicated, except for plastic surgery of the external genitals at a suitable age in the cases of marked masculinization.

This unintentional human experiment strikingly demonstrates the sensitivity of the female fetus to circulating androgenic steroids. In contrast, the male fetus, as indicated by the observations of Davis and Potter,[68] does not seem to sustain any adverse morphogenic effect on its genital system by the daily administration of high doses of oral diethylstilbestrol or intramuscular testosteronepropionate to the mother in the course of the second trimester. Thus far no complications resulting from administration of any steroids to the mother during pregnancy have been described in the male fetus or newborn.

A second, but evidently very rare, form of specific female pseudohermaphroditism caused by androgens in the maternal circulation is due to the existence of an androgen-producing tumor in the mother during pregnancy (Table 2, I, B, 2). A remarkable case was described by Brentnall[69] in which an arrhenoblastoma of the ovary complicated pregnancy. At birth the infant presented a urethral opening at the base of an enlarged clitoris, the labia minora were fused, the labia majora were corrugated and separated by a raphe. Clinical examination disclosed no other congenital abnormality. Another such case was described by Xavier and De Abreu Junquiera,[70] cited by Javert and Finn.[71] In this instance the virilization of the female fetus was less marked and consisted only of an enlargement of the clitoris, the remainder of the external genitals being normal.

One would be justified in supposing that other virilizing tumors in the mother, such as adrenal adenomas or carcinomas, might equally well masculinize the female fetus. It is possible, however, that the presence of such a tumor interferes with the establishment of a pregnancy and that this is the reason such an association has not been described. The time of onset and rate of tumor growth are probably also important in this respect. Again, it is interesting to note that under such circumstances only the female fetus is affected and the male fetus seems immune to genital malformation. In 3 cases of pregnancy complicated by an arrhenoblastoma, quoted by Javert and Finn,[71] 2 ended with the delivery of normal male infants while the third (of unknown sex) terminated in an abortion.

In this subgroup caused by the influence of maternal androgens, a third form (Table 2, I, B, 3) of specific female pseudohermaphroditism, due to a functional deviation of maternal steroid metabolism during pregnancy, might be postulated. Although its existence as an entity still has to be established, rather sparse but somewhat suggestive evidence is available.

Recently, Wilkins and co-workers[63] reported the case of a patient (A-66969) whose picture had been published earlier in his textbook[21] under the heading of nonadrenal female pseudohermaphroditism. But for some interesting features of the maternal history, which subsequently came to light, this case might have been considered a genuine example of female pseudohermaphroditism occurring in the absence of fetal and maternal androgenic influence. The patient was born of a first pregnancy during which the mother, although she received no hormone treatment, had shown a marked increase in weight (74 pounds), a deepening of the voice, coarsening of the features, and an increased amount of facial hair. After the birth of the patient the mother had had seven pregnancies all associated with some swelling of the face and all ending in miscarriage. Three fetuses were identified as male. In the four others identification of sex was impossible. The ninth pregnancy was unaccompanied by untoward symptoms and resulted in the birth of a normal girl.

In another case of nonadrenal female pseudohermaphroditism (N. H., B34604) reported by Wilkins and co-workers[63] and also by Jones[72] and Jones and Scott,[73] the mother received no hormone treatment during pregnancy, but was troubled with severe acne on the skin of the back, shoulders, and face and thought, herself, that she had some enlargement of the clitoris. Acne and facial hair disappeared after delivery.

These observations would seem to be of the utmost importance and may occur less rarely than appears to be the case from the few published reports. It is not impossible that in early pregnancy functional disturbances in maternal steroid metabolism may alter the development of the external genitals of an otherwise normal female fetus. At the present time, more data are needed and it would be extremely worth while to investigate history, clinical symptoms, and steroid metabolism of all mothers who have borne a female child with nonadrenal pseudohermaphroditism as well as those who have presented symptoms during pregnancy suggestive of the two cases reported by Wilkins, Jones, and Jones and Scott.

It is interesting that in spite of its widespread use in early pregnancy progesterone has so far been implicated in only a few instances of virilization of the female fetus.[63] Wilkins has postulated that the mothers of these children must differ from others in some unknown way pertaining to the diffusion or metabolization of the administered steroid. This may be equally true for other steroids and in this relation the case of Vandekerckhove[74] is noteworthy. From the beginning of the pregnancy he administered methylandrostenediol orally in increasing amounts so that by the time of delivery a total of 6.85 Gm. had been given. A female infant was born who had normal external genitals. This contrasts with the findings of Zander and Mueller[65] who administered less than half this dose of methylandrostenediol by intramuscular injection twice weekly and started treatment only after the sixth month of pregnancy yet noted marked virilization of the female infant at birth. The explanation of this difference may lie in the mode of administering or in a markedly different sensitivity in the 2 women. In either case it must be assumed the metabolism of the compound was different.

In our series of sexual malformations accompanying renal agenesis the maternal history was irrelevant in practically every case. Hormone treatment was not given and the few recorded abnormalities in the mother before or during pregnancy seemed not to be more frequent than would be expected in a random sample of mothers who bore normal children.

In a last subgroup of specific female pseudohermaphroditism (Table 2, I, C) those cases may be placed in which neither a fetal nor a maternal androgenic influence seems responsible for the virilization observed in the infant's external genitals at birth but which, according to the definition "specific," lack associated abnormalities of the extragenital organs. Cases fitting into this subgroup have been described by Chanis,[75] Cotte[76] (2 cases), Jones,[72] Jones and Scott[73] (Patient C. L., A-90431), and Haynes and associates.[77] Unfortunately, prenatal data are lacking in all these cases since 4 of the 5 were adults when first seen.

It is to be noted, however, that without the valuable information about the maternal symptoms during pregnancy, the cases of Wilkins (A66969), Jones,[72] and Jones and Scott[73] (N. H., B34604), which have been previously mentioned, would also have been placed in this subgroup. It is also remarkable how similar the cases of Chanis[75] and Cotte[76] are to Case A66969 of Wilkins. All lacked clinical evidence of adrenal hyperplasia, all had a female habitus and hair distribution, and, most important, all had the spontaneous onset of breast development and menstruation at a normal age. Moreover, the pregnancies subsequent to corrective surgery of the external genitals in both of the patients described by Cotte are striking proof of the normal procreative possibilities of such women.

It is our feeling that with improvement in clinical investigation the cases in which fetal and maternal androgenic influence as well as associated anomalies are reportedly absent will become more and more exceptional. While temporarily a dumping ground for cases of nonadrenal female pseudohermaphroditism in which essential data relating to maternal history, fetal adrenal, and associated extragenital anomalies are lacking, this subgroup may well disappear. This disappearance would also depend to some extent on an advancement of our knowledge concerning steroid metabolism in mother and fetus during pregnancy. It seems very probable that the production of specific female pseudohermaphroditism is entirely dependent on an androgenic influence, be it from a fetal or a maternal source or from a combination of both.

NONSPECIFIC FEMALE PSEUDOHERMAPHRODITISM

Under this heading all cases of female pseudohermaphroditism may be included which, in addition to varying degrees of masculinization of the external genitals, show congenital malformations of other organs. The latter most commonly involve the urinary and internal genital system and the lower intestine. Very often, in a given case, two or more of these systems are affected and the viability of the subject will depend on the extent of these malformations. As a result, such abnormalities may be observed in nonsurviving fetuses and infants even more often than in adult patients.

The cases we have reported with renal agenesis, imperforate anus, and male-type external genitals clearly belong to this category. Since 4 of our female infants, including the originally misdiagnosed male infant with female-type nuclei, presented this kind of anomaly, it is surprising that it has not been noted before. The only similar case we have been able to find in the literature is one described by Leffler.[57] Marked hypertrophy of the clitoris and the absence of a visible vagina suggested male genitals with hypospadias. Both kidneys and ureters were absent. The adrenals were flat oval discs weighing 6.5 grams. Fallopian tubes and cystic ovaries were present but no uterus could be recognized.

As is readily apparent from a study of the current literature, nonspecific female pseudohermaphroditism, though showing a remarkable correlation with bilateral renal agenesis, is by no means confined to it. Various malformations of the urogenital and intestinal tract and of other organ systems may occur in combination with "nonandrogenic" female pseudohermaphroditism. One example is a case described by Siegel[78] which, but for the presence of a single hydronephrotic kidney and ureter, had many features in common with our cases. The child died of acute pyelonephritis 21 days after birth and autopsy disclosed a markedly hypertrophied clitoris, a hypospadic urethra, an imperforate and distended vagina, an imperforate anus, a urethrosigmoid fistula, and a uterus didelphys.

Cases characterized by the combination of masculinization of the external genitals and urogenital abnormalities occurring in the absence of a recognized exposure to androgens have been collected by Jones[72] and Jones and Scott[73] into a "special group." Included were an unpublished case reported by Douglas and a number of cases, reported by Atkinson and Masson[79] (Case 3), by Howard and Hinman[80] (Cases 1 and 2), and by Perloff and associates[81] (Case 2). Most of the affected individuals were seen at a very young age and often a narrow phallic urethra, a urethrovaginal fistula, a grossly distended bladder, and a urine-filled vagina were complicated by life-endangering urinary infection. Kidney and urethral anomalies were frequent but not invariable, and in no instance was there evidence of adrenal hyperplasia or dysfunction. Two additional cases of female pseudohermaphroditism with urinary tract malformations reported by Papadatos and Klein[82] should also be included in this category.

Gross and Meeker[50] studied 75 patients with abnormal sexual development and classified them into 6 different groups, the first 2 being female pseudohermaphrodites. In their Group I were 28 cases of adrenogenital syndrome; in Group II were 9 cases of so-called "nonadrenal female pseudohermaphroditism." The majority of the cases in Group II had malformations of the internal genital organs. In one the left kidney was absent and in 2 the anus was imperforate. None of the 9 patients had adrenal dysfunction, advanced bone growth, or excessive urinary 17-ketosteroid excretion.

Three similar cases, 2 of them with renal anomalies, were described by Reilly and co-workers[60] and 2 others with a special type of communication between bladder, vagina, and rectum, complicated by urinary infection, were reported by Sieber and Klein.[40]

Wilkins and associates[63] commenting on "nonadrenal" female pseudohermaphrodites, felt that it was impossible to explain all these malformations on a simple hormonal basis and concluded that a study of a possible hormonal etiology would be of most interest in "nonadrenal" cases without congenital anomalies.

The etiological background of nonspecific female pseudohermaphroditism as well as the interrelationship of its different features is still obscure. It is impossible to tell at the present time whether the masculinization of the external genitals is a coincidental and local developmental abnormality or is due to a general and as yet unrecognized androgenic influence.

That masculinization associated with other malformations cannot be explained by a single maternal factor seems supported by what has been observed in twin pregnancies. In Case 2, reported by Perloff and co-workers,[81] the twin sibling was a normal female. The same is true for our Case 4 where, except for reportedly large adrenal glands, the female twin was entirely normal. However, in another infant in our series (54118 of Table 2) presenting a sirenomelus syndrome and partial absence of the genitals, the other twin, a male, also had multiple major malformations, including hypoplastic kidneys and an imperforate anus. He had, however, no genital abnormalities and the cell nuclei were of the male type.

The occurrence in a female of a well-formed penis, with glans, prepuce, corpora cavernosa, corpus spongiosum, and complete phallic urethra, remains poorly understood. Although exact figures cannot be obtained, this feature seems more frequently associated with nonspecific than with specific hermaphroditism. According to Prader[83] it is extremely rare to find a completely penile urethra in the adrenogenital syndrome of the female although two remarkable examples of this have been described by Bentinck and associates[84] and by Matheson and Ward.[85]

It is noteworthy that in practically every instance of complete penile urethra in a female, doubt as to sex does not arise immediately after birth and the child is assumed to be a male.

The evidence available from experimental and human embryology indicates that the growth and differentiation of a penis with a central urethra in normal males and in most female pseudohermaphrodites are governed by androgens. However, in nonspecific female pseudohermaphroditism evidence of androgenic factors has never been obtained. Reilly and co-workers[60] have suggested that the masculinization of the genitals should be considered part of a general effect producing a blighted embryo. This view seems to be supported by the close correlation we have observed between absence or malformation of the external genitals and abnormalities of the internal genital organs and the lower intestinal tract. Nevertheless it is difficult to imagine how the genital tubercle would be stimulated to develop into a near-perfect replica of the male organ by the usual teratologic factors.

Perhaps the lack of more valid arguments in favor of an androgenic influence may be due to the rarity of the syndrome or to the limitations of our investigative procedures. In any case, several possibilities might be considered to account for the observed facts. In order to explain the greater frequency of a complete penile urethra in cases where other internal malformations are present, it seems necessary to assume that the responsible agent must exert an influence earlier in pregnancy than does the fetal adrenal hyperplasia associated with the adrenogenital syndrome. It must then also be assumed that this influence is temporary or has other features preventing its detection at birth. It might have its origin in some as yet undetectable disturbance in the mother or possibly in some intrinsic change in placental structure or function. Whatever the real explanation, the possibility that malformations and disturbances in steroid metabolism may be interrelated or may, in some way, even be related to a common factor, cannot be dismissed.

The 12 cases of nonspecific female pseudohermaphroditism cited by Wilkins together with the ones reported and quoted here make a total of 23. This syndrome, however, is probably not as rare as was formerly thought, although its frequency cannot yet be accurately estimated. If the entire literature on anorectal, genital, and renal malformations were carefully investigated, many more cases of a similar nature would doubtlessly be found. Determination of the sex chromatin pattern in smears or histologic sections from patients with these conditions, would be of the utmost interest. Our study was limited to cases of complete bilateral renal agenesis yet, in this series alone, 4 nonspecific female pseudohermaphrodites were found, one of them not recognized as female until the chromatin pattern was studied. As already stressed, it should be realized that the associated malformations may compromise viability to such an extent that survival is unusual. In relation to the problems considered here this is unimportant, provided the same interest is shown in fetal and neonatal pathology as in living patients. If not, the real incidence of many congenital disturbances will be greatly underestimated.

CONCLUSION

In our present state of knowledge, a sharp distinction can be made between "specific" female pseudohermaphroditism due to a fetal or maternal androgenic influence and not complicated by congenital anomalies, and "nonspecific" female pseudohermaphroditism in which no androgenic influence can be demonstrated but which is accompanied by malformations of other organs. The existence of these two distinct types is doubtless related to the chronology and mechanism of the etiological factors involved.

If we are to learn more about the etiology of sexual malformation in the human, the gonads, genital organs, and nuclear sex should be systematically studied in every fetus and in every new-born whether alive or dead, whenever congenital malformations are discovered. As is readily apparent from our findings, even the most macerated fetus is worthy of careful investigation.

The desirability of thorough inspection of the perineum in every newborn cannot be overemphasized. The passage of meconium through the urethra in the absence of an anal opening is an indication that a rectovesical fistula is present. It should be kept in mind that in such infants as well as in those with urethrovaginal fistulas, urinary infection is a frequent and dangerous complication. As pointed out by Papadatos and Klein,[82] the differential diagnosis between nonspecific pseudohermaphroditism and adrenogenital syndrome may be difficult. Genital malformation, vomiting, and dehydration occur in both, but in the adrenogenital syndrome associated malformations are lacking. Consequently, when such symptoms are present a careful search must always be made for the possible presence of other malformations. The finding of a complete penile urethra in an individual with female chromatin pattern is highly suggestive of a nonspecific type of female pseudohermaphroditism.

Invariably, the nuclear sex and the urinary, genital, and intestinal tracts should all be investigated as soon as a disturbance in any one of these is observed. No clinical study of a female pseudohermaphrodite should be considered complete without an excretory urogram.

The steroid metabolism and endocrinologic background of any woman presenting signs of virilization during pregnancy or any giving birth to a female pseudohermaphrodite should also be investigated.

SUMMARY

In view of the frequent association of genital malformations and malformations of certain other organ systems, the discovery of one should invariably lead to an investigation of the possible presence of the other.

Because of the close relationship of the urinary and genital systems in embryologic development and the marked preponderance of males among infants with complete bilateral renal agenesis, genital development and nuclear sex were studied in 48 fetuses and infants presenting this abnormality.

The nuclear sex type was concordant with the external genital sex recorded at birth except in 4 cases which presented a special type of pseudohermaphroditism and were reported in detail. The final result of this study indicated that 13 infants were female, and 35 were male.

The external genitals were often absent, malformed, or, in some females, markedly masculinized. In the female infants the internal genitals were invariably malformed.

Twenty infants in the series presented anorectal malformations, 15 of them having an imperforate anus and an absence of the terminal portion of the intestine. The correlation with external genital malformation was striking.

Seven of the 20 presented a sirenomelus malformation.

A sharp distinction can be drawn between female pseudohermaphroditism with and without associated malformations. For the latter, apparently due to a single hormonal factor, the term "specific" is suggested, and for the former, apparently having a more complex etiology, the term "nonspecific" is proposed, This terminology has the advantage of stressing important clinical and theoretical differences.

The cases of nonspecific pseudohermaphroditism found in the literature together with 4 cases reported here make a total of 23. However, the syndrome is probably much more frequent than this would indicate. To appreciate its real incidence and its clinical variations, further study is needed.

REFERENCES

1. Barr, M. L., *Modern Trends in Obstetrics and Gynecology* (Second Series), London, 1955, Butterworth & Co., Ltd., p. 117.
2. Polani, P. E., Hunter, W. F., and Lennox, B., *Lancet* 2:120, 1954.
3. Gordon, G. S., Overstreet, E. W., Traut, H. F., and Winch, G. A., *J. Clin. Endocrinol.* 15:1, 1955.
4. Grumbach, M. M., van Wijck, J. J., and Wilkins, L., *J. Clin. Endocrinol.* 15:1161, 1955.
5. Nelson, W. O., *Acta endocrinol.* 23:227, 1956.
6. Plunkett, E. R., and Barr, M. L., *Lancet* 2:853, 1956.

7. Bradbury, J. T., Bunge, R. G., and Bocabella, R. A., *J. Clin. Endocrinol.* 16:689, 1956.
8. Grumbach, M. M., Blanc, W. A., and Engle, E. T., *J. Clin. Endocrinol.* 17:703, 1957.
9. Davidson, W. M., and Smith, D. R., *Brit. M. J.* 2:6, 1954.
10. Briggs, D. K., and Kupperman, H. S., *J. Clin. Endocrinol.* 16:1163, 1956.
11. Moore, K. L., and Barr, M. L., *Lancet* 2:57, 1955.
12. Carpentier, P. J., Stolte, L. A. M., and Visschers, G. P., *J. Clin. Endocrinol.* 16:155, 1955.
13. Polani, P. E., and Claireaux, A. E., *Lancet* 2:599, 1957.
14. Perrin, E. V., and Benirschke, K., *J. Clin. Endocrinol.* 18:327, 1958.
15. Davidson, W. M., and Ross, G. I. M., *J. Path. & Bact.* 58:459, 1954.
16. Potter, E. L., *J. Pediat.* 29:68, 1946.
17. Potter, E. L., *Am. J. Obst. & Gynec.* 51:885, 1946.
18. Potter, E. L., *Pathology of the Fetus and the Newborn*, Chicago, 1952, The Year Book Publishers, Inc.
19. Lisser, H., Curtis, L. E., Escamilla, R. F., and Goldberg, M. B., *J. Clin. Endocrinol.* 7:665, 1947.
20. Del Castillo, E. B., De la Baize, F. A., and Argonz, J., *J. Clin. Endocrinol.* 7:385, 1947.
21. Wilkins, L., *The Diagnosis and Treatment of Endocrine Disorders in Childhood and Adolescence*, Springfield, Ill., 1950, Charles C Thomas, Publisher.
22. Jost, A., *Gynéc. et obst.* 49:44, 1950.
23. Jost, A., In Pincus, G., editor, *Recent Progress in Hormone Research*, New York, 1953, Academic Press, Inc., vol. 7, p. 379.
24. Pasqualini, R. Q., Vidal, G., and Bur, G. E., *Lancet* 2:164, 1957.
25. Ferguson-Smith, M. A., *Lancet* 1:928, 1958.
26. Prader, A., Schneider, J., Frances, J. M., and Zublin, W., *Lancet* 1:968, 1958.
27. Amolsch, A. L., *J. Urol.* 38:360, 1937.
28. Shumacker, H. B., Jr., *Arch. Surg.* 37:586, 1938.
29. Nalle, B. C., Crowell, J. A., and Lynch, K. M., *J. Urol.* 61:862, 1949.
30. Frost, I. F., *Am. J. Obst. & Gynec.* 75:210, 1958.
31. Woolf, R. B., and Allen, W. M., *Obst. & Gynec.* 2:236, 1953.
32. Phelan, J. T., Counseller, V. S., and Greene, L. F., *Surg. Gynec. & Obst.* 97:1, 1953.
33. Miller, N. F., and Stout, W., *Obst. & Gynec.* 9:48, 1957.
34. Jones, W. S., *Obst. & Gynec.* 10:113, 1957.
35. Thomson, J. D., Wharton, L. R., Sr., and Te Linde, R. W., *Am. J. Obst. & Gynec.* 74:397, 1957.
36. Guizetti, P., and Pariset, F., *Virchows Arch. path. Anat.* 204:372, 1911.
37. Duxbury, J. H., *Canad. M. A. J.* 78:123, 1958.

38. Ladd, W. E., and Gross, R. E., *Am. J. Surg.* 23:167, 1934.
39. Ladd, W. E., and Gross, R. E., *Abdominal Surgery of Infancy and Childhood*, Philadelphia and London, 1941, W. B. Saunders Company, chap. XIII.
40. Sieber, W. K., and Klein, R., *Pediatrics* 22:472, 1958.
41. Potter, E. L., *Pathology of the Fetus and the Newborn*, Chicago, 1952, The Year Book Publishers, fig. 527.
42. Ballantyne, J. W., *Manual of Antenatal Pathology and Hygiene—The Embryo*, Edinburgh, 1904, William Green & Sons, p. 325.
43. Mayo, C. W., and Rice, R. G., *Surgery* 27:485, 1950.
44. Spence, H. M., *J. Urol.* 71:453, 1954.
45. Berman, J. K., *Surg. Gynec. & Obst.* 66:11, 1938.
46. Orloff, M. J., *J. Pediat.* 45:316, 1954.
47. Norris, W. J., Brophy, T. W., and Brayton, D., *Surg. Gynec. & Obst.* 88:623, 1949.
48. Moore, T. C., and Lawrence, E. A., *Surgery* 32:352, 1952.
49. Moore, T. C., and Lawrence, E. A., *Surg. Gynec. & Obst.* 95:281, 1952.
50. Gross, R. E., and Meeker, I. A., *Pediatrics* 16:303, 1955.
51. Hoffenberg, R., and Jackson, W. P. U., *J. Clin. Endocrinol.* 17:454, 1957.
52. Segal, S. J., and Nelson, W. O., *J. Clin. Endocrinol.* 17:676, 1957.
53. Witchi, E., Nelson, W. O., and Segal, S. J., *J. Clin. Endocrinol.* 17:737, 1957.
54. Bierich, J., *Ergebn. inn. Med. u. Kinderh.* 9:510, 1958.
55. Bongiovanni, A. M., and Eberlein, W. R., *Pediatrics* 16:628, 1955.
56. Eberlein, W. R., and Bongiovanni, A. M., *Helvet. paediat. acta* 11:105, 1956.
57. Leffler, R. J., *Am. J. Clin. Path.* 21:752, 1951.
58. Hoffmann, F., Overzier, C., and Uhde, G., *Geburtsh. u. Frauenh.* 15:1061, 1955.
59. Grunwaldt, E., and Bates, T., *Pediatrics* 20:503, 1957.
60. Reilly, W. A., Hinman, F., Pickering, D. E., and Crane, J. T., *A. M. A. J. Dis. Child.* 95:9, 1958.
61. Hayles, A. B., and Nolan, R. B., *Proc. Staff Meet. Mayo Clin.* 32:41, 1957.
62. Gold, A. P., and Michael, A. M., *J. Pediat.* 52:279, 1958.
63. Wilkins, L., Jones, H. W., Holman, G. H., and Stempfel, R. S., *J. Clin. Endocrinol.* 18:559, 1958.
64. Nellhaus, G., *New England J. Med.* 258:935, 1958.
65. Zander, J., and Mueller, H. A., *Geburtsh. u. Frauenh.* 13:216, 1953.
66. Grumbach, M. M., Quoted by Wilkins.[63]
67. Carpentier, P. J., *Bull. Soc. roy. belge. gynéc. et obst.* 28:137, 1958.
68. Davis, M. E., and Potter, E. L., *Endocrinology* 42:370, 1948.
69. Brentnall, C. P., *J. Obst. & Gynaec. Brit. Emp.* 52:235, 1945.

70. Xavier, F. P., and De Abreu Junquiera, M., *Rev. gynec. e obst. 1:*356, 1938.
71. Javert, C. T., and Finn, W. F., *Cancer 4:*60, 1951.
72. Jones, H. W., *Obst. & Gynec. Surv. 12:*433, 1957.
73. Jones, H. W., and Scott, W. W., *Hermaphrodism, Genital Anomalies and Related Endocrine Disorders,* Baltimore, 1958, The Williams & Wilkins Co.
74. Vandekerckhove, D., *Ann. endocrinol. 15:*513, 1954.
75. Chanis, D., Jr., *J. Urol. 47:*508, 1942.
76. Cotte, G., *J. Mt. Sinai Hosp. New York 14:*170, 1947.
77. Haynes, E., Thomas, H. P., and Wheeler, M. S., *M. Rec. 154:*307, 1941.
78. Siegel, I., *Am. J. Obst. & Gynec. 47:*705, 1944.
79. Atkinson, W., and Masson, J. C., *S. Clin. North America 14:*571, 1934.
80. Howard, F. S., and Hinman, F., Jr., *J. Urol. 65:*439, 1951.
81. Perloff, W. H., Conger, K. B., and Levy, L. M., *J. Clin. Endocrinol. 13:*783, 1953.
82. Papadatos, C., and Klein, R., *J. Pediat. 45:*662, 1954.
83. Prader, A., *Helvet. paediat. acta 9:*231, 1954.
84. Bentinck, R. C., Lisser, H., and Reilly, W. A., *J. Clin. Endocrinol. 16:*412, 1956.
85. Matheson, W. J., and Ward, E. M., *Arch. Dis. Childhood 29:*22, 1954.

18

GENES ON THE Y CHROMOSOME INFLUENCING RATE OF MATURATION IN MAN

Skeletal Age Studies in Children With Klinefelter's (XXY) and Turner's (XO) Syndromes

J. M. Tanner, M.D., D.Sc., Lond., A. Prader, M.D., H. Habich, M.D. and M. A. Ferguson-Smith, M.B., Glasg.

IT has long been known that girls are physically more mature than boys at all ages from birth to adulthood. In skeletal maturity, judged by the appearance and progressive development of ossification centres, girls at birth are advanced by a matter of weeks, at primary-school age by months, and at adolescence by the two years which separate the sexes in their growth spurts and in the age at which they reach adult height. This sex difference begins early in intrauterine life; the centre for the talus, for example, appears an average of 2 weeks earlier in girls (22-29 weeks) than in boys (24-32 weeks). The chimpanzee, the rhesus monkey, and, apparently, the rat, have a similar sex dimorphism. Other indicators of developmental age, such as the dentition and the velocity of growth in physical measurements, show the same distinction. Each permanent tooth erupts earlier in girls and in female apes and monkeys. The pattern of velocity and acceleration in the average girl's growth curve of stature is at a given chronological age similar to that shown by the average boy's curve somewhat later (see Tanner 1955, p. 51).

The cause of this striking difference is quite unknown. The recent demonstration by Ford, Jacobs, and others (Jacobs and Strong 1959, Ford, Jones et al. 1959) that most patients with Klinefelter's syndrome have the chromosomal formula XXY and

Reprinted from *The Lancet*, August 22, 1959, pp. 141-144.

We wish heartily to thank Prof. Alan Moncrieff for his critical encouragement of these studies, and Mr. R. H. Whitehouse for his skilled assistance.

those with gonadal dysgenesis XO now makes it possible to find out whether genes on the Y chromosome are responsible. We are in a position to see whether XXY individuals follow the development-rate of boys (XY) or of girls (XX), and whether the lack of the second X chromosome accentuates or retards the rate of development of XO individuals.

MATERIAL AND METHODS

We have investigated the skeletal age of 27 individuals between the ages of 6 and 18 with Klinefelter's syndrome. Nineteen of

RATIO OF SKELETAL AGE (GREULICH-PYLE) TO CHRONOLOGICAL AGE IN CONTROLS AND PATIENTS: KLINEFELTER'S SYNDROME CASES RATED ACCORDING TO BOYS' STANDARDS, TURNER'S SYNDROME CASES RATED ACCORDING TO GIRLS' STANDARDS

	Controls		Klinefelter's Syndrome			Turner's Syndrome		
	ZURICH	KIL-MAR-NOCK	ZURICH	GLAS-GOW	ZURICH	LON-DON	BALTI-MORE[*]	PHILA-DEL-PHIA[†]
No.	47	21	19	8	8	8	19	5
Age (yr.) ..	6-17	7-12	6-23	7-12	7-15	1-14	1-17	1-17
Range	0.70-1.07	0.63-1.04	0.66-1.10	0.65-0.90	0.69-0.95	0.72-1.00	0.73-1.67	
Mean	0.93	0.88	0.90	0.82	0.79	0.82	0.95	0.87
S.E. mean ..	0.01	0.03	0.02	0.03	0.04	0.04	0.04	

[*] Grumbach et al. 1955.   [†] Mellman et al. 1958.

these came from Zurich and 8 from Glasgow. The characteristics of a number of them have been reported previously (Prader et al. 1958, Ferguson-Smith 1958, 1959). It should be remembered that all were mental defectives.

The skeletal ages, taken from the hand and wrist, were assessed by reference to the Greulich-Pyle Atlas (Greulich and Pyle 1950), and since we had no guarantee that normal Zurich and Glasgow children agreed with these American norms we assessed also, as controls, 47 normal boys and girls of matched age distribution in Zurich and 21 boys drawn at random from a large sample of normal children in Kilmarnock, close by Glasgow, whose X-rays were taken in a study providing the basis of new, but as yet incomplete, standards of skeletal age (J. M. Tanner, M. J. R. Healy, and R. H. Whitehouse, unpublished).

Measurements of height and weight were available for most of these patients and for 9 of their normal brothers. The percentile status and height and weight age were assessed for the Zurich children by reference to Heimendinger's (1958) standards for Basle children, and for Glasgow children by Cheeseman and Walby's (1954) standards for Belfast children, which latter probably approach the Glasgow norm better than Provis and Ellis's (1955) standards for Edinburgh children, and certainly much better than Tanner's (1958) standards for English children.

We have investigated also 9 children from Zurich with untreated Turner's syndrome, aged 7-18, 8 with known male nuclear sex, 1 untested. In addition, hand X-rays were available for 8 cases of Turner's syndrome aged 1-14, in the files of The Hospital for Sick Children, Great Ormond Street, London. We are indebted to Dr. L. G. Blair, Dr. R. E. Bonham-Carter, Dr. P. R. Evans, Dr. A. P. Norman, Dr. B. E. Schlesinger, and Sir Wilfrid Sheldon for permission to study these last patients and their X-rays.

RESULTS

The results are summarised in the accompanying table.

Skeletal Age

The skeletal ages of the Klinefelter's syndrome patients were estimated by reference to the *male* standards, for reasons shortly to become apparent. The majority of these patients are slightly retarded over the Greulich-Pyle norms: the skeletal-age/chronological-age ratio covers a range of 0.66 to 1.10 in the Zurich cases, and 0.65 to 0.90 in the Glasgow ones. The means are 0.90 ± 0.02 for Zurich and 0.82 ± 0.03 for Glasgow. The Greulich-Pyle standards, however, are taken from an economically superior group of American children, and some retardation in relation to them is probably to be expected. In fact, the 47 control Zurich children have a mean ratio of 0.93 ± 0.01 with a range of 0.70 to 1.07. This degree of retardation is the same for both sexes and at all ages. Allowing additionally for the fact that mentally subnormal children are in general slightly retarded compared to bright children we see that the Zurich Klinefelter's syndrome cases fit the pattern of the normal *male* very closely. The same is true of the Glasgow cases: the 21 Kilmarnock control boys have a mean ratio of 0.88 ± 0.03 with a range of 0.63 to 1.04. The Glasgow Klinefelter's syndrome mean is slightly, but insignificantly, less.

If the Klinefelter's syndrome patients had been compared to the normal female standards, however, the retardation would have been very large. Since a boy is normally about 0.80 times the skeletal age of a girl of the same chronological age the Klinefelter's syndrome patients would have averaged only 0.72 in Zurich and 0.66 in Glasgow, whereas the control figures would, of course, be unchanged. Thus it is clear that *XXY leads to the same skeletal age as XY, at least throughout the age range 6-18.*

Patients with Turner's syndrome, on the other hand, are usually said in published reports to have a normal or only slightly re-tarded bone age, and this by reference to *female* standards. The 8 cases we have studied in London uphold this belief; related to the female standards their average ratio is 0.82 ± 0.04, with a range of 0.72 to 1.00. This is perhaps slightly retarded compared with what we would expect normal girls of similar locality and social background to be, but only slightly. Related to male stand-ards the London Turner's syndrome average would be 1.00, which is distinctly in advance of our normal children. The Zurich patients under the age of 18, however, had an average skeletal-age/chronological-age ratio of 0.79 ± 0.04 with a range of 0.68 to 0.95. This is distinctly below the expected normal average of 0.93 at Zurich. Relative to *male* standards, however, these children would be about as much advanced as they are retarded relative to female ones. There is also an additional fact pointing to their equivalence with females rather than with males. The Turner's syndrome cases, unlike the Klinefelter's, show a greater degree of asymmetry of development amongst the various epiphyses than is normal. In this they seem to resemble hypopituitary dwarfs. It looks as though there is some added defect over and above any simple action on general rate of development. The presence of such a defect, would, of course, harmonise with the reduction of height growth in Turner's syndrome and with the frequent pres-ence of other skeletal anomalies. The 19 cases between 1 and 17 years of age reported by Grumbach et al. (1955) give an average

ratio of 0.95 ± 0.04, and the 5 cases of the same age range reported by Mellman et al. (1959) an average of 0.87. Both these
groups of investigators used an appearance-fusion system for bone
age, which may be less sensitive to pathological defects of shape
and developmental asymmetry than the Greulich-Pyle method.

We may conclude, therefore, that, though in Turner's syndrome
there is probably some slight retardation compared with the girl's
standards, together with abnormal asymmetry of development, in
general *XO leads to approximately the same skeletal age as XX.*

Height, Weight, and Body Build

The Zurich Klinefelter's syndrome patients are mostly tall for
their age despite their mental deficiency, which is usually associated with reduced stature. The range of their percentile status
is from 20 to 95, with an average figure of 67 based on 20 cases.
There is no difference between those who have reached adult or
near-adult height and those who have not; the average percentile
for the 12 cases less than 15 years of age is 64. Nine brothers of 7
patients were measured; and 7 had a lower percentile for height,
1 the same percentile, and only 1 a higher percentile. The excess
height of Klinefelter's syndrome patients is in each instance due to
abnormally long legs. The pubis-head measurement is normal for
boys of the same chronological age, but the pubis-heel measurement is excessive. This is equally true before puberty as during
and after it. The span, though difficult to evaluate because of lack
of adequate standards and techniques, may be somewhat increased also, though less than the leg length. Raboch and Maly's
(1957) 5 adult patients had a normal forearm length, together
with long legs, slightly reduced trunk length, and much reduced
shoulder width.

The Glasgow patients were less tall, with an average percentile
of 38 and a range of 10 to 60.

In each instance weights keep pace, more or less, with heights.
The Zurich children have an average percentile status of 60, with
those under 15 years averaging 62. The Glasgow children average
27. The explanation for the discrepancy between the two series is
probably that the Glasgow children's intelligence quotients (I.Q.s)

ranged from 45 to 85, whereas the Zurich children's were all between 75 and 85. Children with a really low i.q. are frequently very small.

Besides their long legs, the Klinefelter's syndrome children have other features of a feminine—or, perhaps more accurately, eunuchoid—bodily appearance. We have not made the detailed studies which alone could establish the degree to which the feminine or eunuchoid physique is approached, but frontal view photographs of 18 patients certainly suggest a striking lack of mesomorphy, together with a somewhat greater similarity of appearance than one would expect in 18 boys chosen at random.

The Turner's syndrome cases, as is well known, are small in stature at all ages, even compared with girls' standards. Most of the Zurich cases are below the first percentile for height, and, with two notable exceptions (90th and 75th percentiles), for weight.

DISCUSSION

Maturity

XXY individuals have a rate of skeletal maturation corresponding to XY, and XO individuals a rate corresponding to XX. Thus, Y produces retardation in the presence of either one or two Xs, and without Y neither one nor two Xs produce this effect. It follows that genes on the Y chromosome are the cause of the normal sex difference in rate of development. Though until recently the Y chromosome in man was thought to be inert, it is now clear that genes upon it are the cause of the differentiation of the primary gonad into a testis rather than an ovary. The further differentiation of the external genitalia into penis and scrotum is believed to be due to the action of androgens produced by the fœtal testis rather than to direct action of the Y chromosome genes in the tissues concerned.

The male delay in maturation might be brought about by either of these mechanisms—that is, directly or by the fœtal-testicular hormones. A direct action seems more likely, however, since androgens in all other instances cause an advance, not a delay, in maturation. The differentiation of the testis occurs at about the 7th intrauterine week. We do not know at exactly what stage of fœtal life the male retardation of development begins, but there is reason to think it may be just about this time. At 20 weeks the male is about 2 weeks retarded (Pryor 1923), at 40 weeks about 4 weeks retarded; at 10 weeks he might well be 1 week retarded, and this would denote action of the Y chromosome at 7 weeks or earlier. It is tempting to think that the factors causing retardation and those causing gonadal differentiation may be closely related.

The mechanism whereby the male maintains his relative retardation throughout the growing period is totally obscure. The only hormone that might be implicated, on present information, is the thyroid. In young rats administration of thyroid hormone accelerates skeletal development, tooth eruption, and eyelid opening (Walker 1957), though the effect diminishes under experimental conditions as the time of administration is prolonged. In man clinical hypothyroidism causes a delay in all phases of development and hyperthyroidism an advance. The same is true in monkeys (see Tanner 1955, p. 124). The very meagre data on thyroid function in normal boys and girls, however, gives no indication of any sex difference. The figures of Martman et al. (1956), for example, on the ^{131}I uptake of prematures a day after birth give identical averages for boys and girls of 1,500-2,500 g, as do those of Oliner et al. (1957) from birth to 18.

There seems to be some mechanism in the tissues themselves, on the other hand, for controlling their speed of development. It is very striking how after a period of disease or malnutrition causing retardation of growth and development a "catch-up" phase follows during which the velocity may exceed greatly the normal rate of growth and maturation. But this "catch-up" rate slows down to normal as the child reaches its previously established growth curve. This suggests that the control of maturation is based on signals from the tissues themselves, even if these signals act by affecting the release of a hormone centrally.

Body-build

The effect of genes on the Y chromosome in controlling body build is at present not clear. It is worth noting, however, that long before puberty a sex dimorphism is present, boys being more muscular, or more generally mesomorphic in shape, than girls (see Tanner 1955, p. 43). This, however, is clearly *not* simply due to the presence of the Y chromosome, since XXY children in general do *not* resemble XY children in build.

The 16 chromatin-positive Klinefelter's syndrome adult patients studied by Stewart et al. (1959) showed a significantly greater length of leg than either controls from the same infertility clinic or chromatin-negative Klinefelter's syndrome adults. As in our children, lengths of trunk were similar in all groups. Our data extend this finding down to prepubescent ages, and show clearly that the abnormally great leg length is not due to delayed epiphyseal closure, but to a greater growth-rate from an early age. Just how early it begins is a question full of interest. There are a number of finely regulated growth gradients during development, so that, for instance, the head end of the organism is at any time nearer final completion than the base of the spine, the hands than the forearm and upper arm, and the feet than the calf and thigh. The legs bring up the rear in this procession; they are laid down last and are least developed at birth. A very small variation from normality at the time of establishment of the initial gradient would result, one might suppose, in a continuously increased or diminished growth velocity subsequently. An example is provided by the normal sex difference in length of forearm relative to upper arm, which results from the boys' relative velocity of forearm being just slightly more than the girls' throughout the whole growth period (see Tanner 1955, p. 37).

Since in respect of leg length XXY children resemble XX even less than XY we cannot ascribe the long legs to the action of X chromosomes either. It seems more likely to be due either to an early imbalance in differentiation or else to a lack of secretion of some "male" hormone. This must occur, however, at some stage *after* the time at which the external genitalia and genital ducts are laid down, since their normality in XXY persons argues a near-normal secretion during early foetal life.

The lack of mesomorphy in the XXY individuals, if it can be established more firmly in future cases, would be an important result, since it would show that differentiation of muscle is also not primarily dependent on the Y chromosome, either directly or through the secretion of foetal-testicular androgens. In this characteristic the XXY *does* resemble the XX. Too few studies of physique in Turner's syndrome have been made for us to know what the complementary situation, of XO, leads to so far as mesomorphy is concerned. We do have the general impression that XO children are frequently as mesomorphic as the XXY.

As a working hypothesis then, we suggest that it is the double dose of X which chiefly inhibits the development of muscular differentiation and the mesomorphic body build. That a few Klinefelter's syndrome patients are fairly well muscled as adults does not necessarily disprove this hypothesis, since they have been subjected to the action of male androgens at puberty, as women are not. Our theory would only demand that they should not exceed in mesomorphy the level reachable by women appropriately treated with androgens. Disproof would, however, follow the finding of a Klinefelter's syndrome patient who was *highly* mesomorphic, but we have not seen one to date. Klinefelter's syndrome children, considered as males, seem in many ways to be at the opposite pole to the extreme mesomorph, who is advanced relative to other boys in bone age (Dupertius and Michael 1953), short for his age, relatively short-legged, and "masculine" in appearance.

SUMMARY

Girls are ahead of boys in skeletal development and other signs of physical maturity from before birth to adulthood. Light has been thrown on the mechanism of this sex dimorphism by the assessment of skeletal age in 27 individuals between the ages of 6 and 18 with Klinefelter's syndrome, and in 16 individuals with Turner's syndrome. The former children, with chromosomal formula XXY, have a skeletal age equivalent to normal males XY; the latter, of formula XO, a skeletal age approximately equivalent to normal females XX.

It is concluded that genes on the Y chromosome are responsible for the sex dimorphism in rate of development in man and other primates. The action of the Y chromosome in causing differentiation of the primitive gonad into a testis is evident at about 7 intrauterine weeks, and the retardation of development in the male probably begins at about this time also. There is a possibility that the two actions are closely related.

The Klinefelter's syndrome children have longer legs than is normal at all ages studied, though their trunk length is quite usual. Since this characteristic appears before puberty it is due, not to delay in epiphyseal fusion, but to a fundamental difference in growth-rate. Besides this our impression is that the great majority are somewhat feminine or eunuchoid in appearance and distinctly lacking in mesomorphy or degree of muscularity. If this impression is substantiated it would follow that the sex dimorphism in mesomorphy, which is certainly present before puberty is due primarily, *not* to the action of the Y chromosome, but to a double dose of X-inhibiting muscular differentiation and development.

REFERENCES

Cheeseman, E. A., Walby, A. L. (1954) *Ulster med. J.* 23, suppl. 3.

Dupertius, C. W., Michael, N. B. (1953) *Child Developm.* 24:203.

Ferguson-Smith, M. A. (1958) *Lancet, i:*928.

———— (1959) *ibid. i:*219.

Ford, C. E., Jones, K. W., Polani, P. E., de Almeida, J. C. C., Briggs, J. H. (1959) *ibid. i:*711.

Greulich, W. W., Pyle, S. I. (1950) *Radiographic Atlas of Skeletal Development of the Hand and Wrist.* London.

Grumbach, M. M., van Wyk, J. J., Wilkins, L. (1955) *J. clin. Endocrin.* 15:1161.

Heimendinger, J. (1958) *Helv. pædiat. Acta,* 13:471.

Jacobs, P. A., Strong, J. A. (1959) *Nature, Lond.* 183:302.

Martman, E. E., Corrigan, K. E., Charbeneau, H. P., Smith, A. (1956) *Pediatrics,* 17:503.

Mellman, W. J., Bongiovanni, A. M., Hope, J. W. (1959) *ibid.* 23:530.

Oliner, L., Kohlenbrener, R. M., Fields, T., Kunstadter, R. (1957) *J. clin. Endocr.* 17:61.

Prader, A., Schneider, J., Zublin, W., Frances, J. M., Ruedi, K. (1958) *Schweiz. med. Wschr.* 88:917.

Provis, H. S., Ellis, R. W. B. (1959) *Arch. Dis. Childh.* 30:328.

Pryor, J. W. (1923) *Anat. Rec.* 25:252.

Raboch, J., Maly, V. (1957) *Endokrinologie,* 34:315.

Stewart, J. S. S., Mack, W. S., Goven, A. D. T., Ferguson-Smith, M. A., Lennox, B. (1959) *Quart. J. Med.* (in the press).

Tanner, J. M. (1955) *Growth at Adolescence.* Oxford.

———— (1958) in *Modern Trends in Pædiatrics* (second series) (edited by A. Holzel and J. P. M. Tizard). London.

Walker, D. G. (1957) *Bull. Johns Hopk. Hosp.* 101:101.

19

HAEMOPHILIA A IN A "GIRL" WITH MALE SEX-CHROMATIN PATTERN

Inga Marie Nilsson, M.D., Lund, S. Bergman, M.D., Lund,
J. Reitalu, Ph.cand., Lund, and J. Waldenstrom, M.D., Lund

CLASSICAL hæmophilia (antihæmophilic globulin deficiency) is transmitted by a sex-linked recessive gene and is therefore very rare in females. The homozygous hæmophilic state in the female can result from the marriage of a hæmophilic man to a woman who is a carrier of the disease. Four such cases of true hæmophilia in the female have been reported (Merskey 1951, Israëls, Lempert, and Gilbertson 1951, Pola and Svojitka 1957). Also Brinkhous and Graham (1950) have shown the occurrence of hæmophilia in the homozygous female dog.

Quick and Hussey (1958) have reported the case of an 11-year-old girl with a coagulation defect indistinguishable from classical hæmophilia A, except that the family history was negative. A case of hæmophilia A has also been described by Choremis et al. (1956) in a 2-year-old girl with unknown family history. These seeming exceptions to strict sex linkage in hæmophilia have not been explained, and Quick and Hussey suggested that their patient's condition was caused by mutation.

We report here a case of severe hæmophilia A in a girl, in which chromosome studies have explained the apparent exception from sex-linked inheritance. The child, who had female external genital characteristics, was shown to have a male sex-chromatin pattern.

THE CASE

The patient, a child aged 16 months, had always bruised readily. At 12 months a trivial trauma of the thigh gave rise to a large

Reprinted from *The Lancet*, September 5, 1959, pp. 264-266.

This investigation was supported by grants from the Swedish Medical Research Council and from the Swedish Cancer Society.

hæmatoma, for which she was admitted to hospital. A prolonged coagulation-time was then observed. On a later occasion a large hæmatoma followed lumbar puncture. The hæmoglobin fell from 11.2 g. per 100 ml. to 4.6 g.; and she received repeated blood-traufusions. She had had long episodes of nose-bleeding. There had been no bleeding into joints, but the child had not yet learnt to walk.

Family History

Fig. 1 shows the pedigree. One of the patient's brothers had died soon after birth, with bleeding. There was no consanguinity

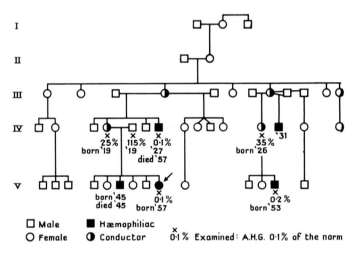

Fig. 1. The pedigree.

between the parents. None of the paternal ancestors had any known bleeding tendency and the father's coagulation-time, bleeding-time, and plasma anti-hæmophilic globulin (A.H.G.) were normal. The patient's mother (IV: 4) belonged to a hæmo-philic family (Sköld 1944, fam. 22). Two (IV: 6 and V: 13) of the hæmophiliacs in that family had been investigated by us and had been found to have severe hæmophilia A with A.H.G. activities of 0.1% and 0.2%. The patient's mother (IV: 4), and her maternal cousin (IV: 11) with a hæmophilic boy, had A.H.G. activities of 25% and 35%. The only coagulation defect found in the carriers and bleeders in that family was a low A.H.G. value.

None of the maternal or paternal ancestors had had any other known congenital malformations. The mother's blood was group A Rh-negative and the father's group A Rh-positive.

Examination and Investigations

The girl was of normal size for her age (fig. 2). She had several hæmatomas but no petechiæ. No congenital malformations such as digital anomalies or webbed neck were observed. Physical and radiological examination did not reveal any signs of congen-

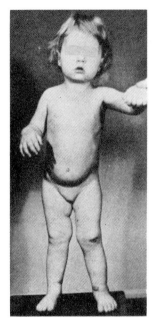

Fig. 2. The patient.

ital heart-disease. The external genital characteristics were of female appearance though the labia minora were small and the clitoris somewhat large for the child's age; no uterus could be palpated per rectum, and the hymen appeared to be imperforate (Prof. S. Genell).

The patient belonged to blood-group A Rh-positive.

Coagulation studies were performed by previously reported methods (Nilsson et al. 1957) and gave the following results: coagulation-time 120 min. (normal value 4-8 min.); bleeding-time 4-5 min.; platelet count 320,000 per c.mm.; prothrombin consumption 118%; fibrinogen 0.34 g. per 100 ml. The one-stage prothrombin-time was normal; the prothrombin and proconvertin (Owren's P & P) value was 112%, the factor V value was 120%. The plasma A.H.G. activity, as determined by the recalcification method on hæmophilia-A plasma, was 0.1%. The hæmophilia-B-factor content of the plasma was 60%. The prolonged recalcification-time of the patient's plasma was corrected by the addition of normal plasma, $BaSO_4$-adsorbed plasma, hæmophilia-B plasma, and human fraction I-O containing A.H.G. (Blombäck and Nilsson 1958). On the other hand, addition of hæmophilia-A plasma, had no effect. No anticoagulants could be detected to explain the delayed coagulation. There was no fibrinolysis.

Thus the laboratory findings in this patient were identical with those obtainable in severe hæmophilia A in males.

Genetic Studies

Sex determination on blood-films was performed by the method of Kosenow (1956). Among 500 neutrophil polymorphs 1 leucocyte with an appendage of type A or drumstick was found, 3 with the appendages of type B, and 68 with appendages of type C. This result was thought to indicate a male chromosomal pattern.

Studies of resting cells from skin specimens by the method of Reitalu (1957) also indicated a male sex pattern.

Skin biopsy was performed twice for culture and cytological study. Because of the bleeding tendency attempts were made to remove the specimens from the epidermis only (left elbow fold and right thigh).

The bits of skin were cultured by the method of Reitalu and Bergman (1959). The medium was changed every third day. Epithelium-like cells gradually grew out, and after 3 months the yield in two Carrel flasks was sufficient for investigation. The contents of the two Carrel flasks were transferred to slides (Bergman 1959).

The mitotic frequency was low. A few of the cells divided on the fourth day after transfer to the slides. These cells were exposed to colchicine, fixed, and stained in the manner described by Bergman et al. (1959). In fig. 3 the chromosomes from a cell are shown after arrangement in pairs. The cells in the metaphase had 46 chromosomes, 5 of which were small and acrocentric. Of these, 3 were similar and 1 of them was presumed to be the Y chromosome. It was not possible, however, to exclude the possibility that 1 of the 2 small autosomal pairs was trisomic (fig. 3). One of the large subterminal chromosomes had no partner and ranked in size between the 5th and 6th pairs. The quotient between the length of the long arm and the short arm of this chromosome was 1.90—i.e., close to that given by Tjio and Puck (1958) and by Chu and Giles (1959) for the X chromosome.

DISCUSSION

Three possibilities were considered: (1) the child might be a homozygous hæmophilic female by inheritance or mutation; (2)

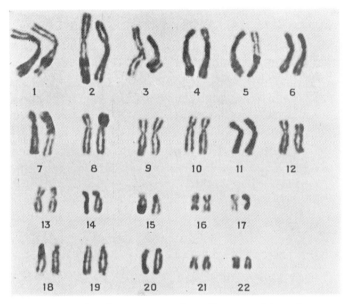

Fig. 3. The chromosomes of a cell arranged in pairs.

the child might be a heterozygous female (carrier) with unusual bleeding tendency; or, (3) the child might have a male chromosomal pattern.

Heterozygous inheritance of the hæmophilic gene was possible, since the mother was a true carrier of hæmophilia A; but homozygous inheritance was unlikely since the father was not affected and nothing suggested that the child was not his offspring. Moderately decreased A.H.G. values have been found in females who are heterozygous for the hæmophilic gene (Nilsson et al. 1959), but as a rule these females do not bleed more readily than normal. There are only a few reports of heterozygous females with increased bleeding (Fantl and Margolis 1955, Douglas and Cook 1957, Taylor and Biggs 1957, McGovern and Steinberg 1958). These females belong to families with mild hæmophilia A and had symptoms similar to those seen in males with mild hæmophilia. Our patient, however, had symptoms of severe hæmophilia A with an A.H.G. activity of only 0.1%. The results of the coagulation investigation of the patient were also the same as those found for the hæmophilic male relatives in her family. The female carriers in the family, on the other hand, had A.H.G. values of 25% and 35% and no bleeding symptoms. To explain the coagulation disorder of this child by the assumption that she was a female carrier of hæmophilia with unusually low A.H.G., therefore appeared unsatisfactory.

The occurrence of hæmophilia in this girl, who might be heterozygous for the hæmophilic gene, could be due to a mutation of the other X chromosome, resulting in a homozygous female. This possibility was eliminated by chromosome studies which showed that the patient did not have a XX chromosomal constitution (fig. 3).

The chromosome studies showing a male sex-chromatin pattern offered the explanation. Hæmatological sex determination by the method of Kosenow (1956) indicated that the nuclear sex was male. Tissue culture of skin specimens and cytological studies showed 46 chromosomes and a probable XY sex chromosomal constitution (fig. 3).

Our knowledge of the morphology of the sex chromosomes is as yet not sufficient to permit identification with certainty. Even their position in regard to size among the autosomes is uncertain and shows variation. According to Tjio and Puck (1958) the Y chromosome lies between the 20th and 21st pair according to size and is one of the largest among the 5 small acrocentric chromosomes. Chu and Giles (1959) place the Y chromosome after the 22nd pair, which implies that it is the smallest. The X chromosome according to Tjio and Puck should be placed between the 4th and 5th, according to Chu and Giles the 5th and 6th pairs, and according to Ford et al. (1959a) it is believed to be the 7th in order of length.

In our patient two possible genetic constitutions must be con-sidered—XY or XO. According to the first alternative the patient is a chromosomal male. According to the second the patient could be a female with an abnormal genotype as described by Ford et al. (1959b) in a chromatin-negative case of Turner's syndrome in which the bone-marrow cells proved to contain 45 chromosomes and in which the sex chromosomal constitution was determined as XO. But our patient had no congenital malformations such as digital anomalies, webbed neck, or evidence of heart-disease which are common in Turner's syndrome. The child's age made an exact sex determination impossible and the possibility that she is a hermaphrodite cannot be determined until she has reached sexual maturity.

It appears probable that the sex chromosomal constitution of the patient was XY. Such an interpretation also agrees with the results of the hæmatological sex determination and the studies of resting cells.

We may ask ourselves whether similar observations might have been published without complete clarification. It is possible that the two instances of hæmophilia A in girls (Quick and Hussey 1958, Choremis et al. 1956) mentioned earlier are similar to the present case. However, nothing is known about the pedigree in these patients, and determination of cytological sex was not at-tempted. There is one observation in the literature which strongly indicates a chromosomal situation like that described by us. Wal-ton (1956) in a study of sex-linked muscular dystrophy of the Duchenne type observed one affected girl along with seven males in the same family. The girl's mother was obviously the conductor. The leucocyte sex was of male type.

Our case demonstrates that seeming exceptions from sex-linked inheritance may in reality conform to the genetic pattern that would be expected. It also confirms the correctness of leucocyte sex determinations and chromosome maps, since the single X chro-mosome found was marked by a sex-linked genetic trait.

REFERENCES

Bergman, S. (1959) *Acta path. microbiol. scand.* (in the press).
——— Reitalu, J., Lenz, W., Nowakowski, H. (1959) *Ann. hum. Genet.* (in the press).

Blombäck, M., Nilsson, I. M. (1958) *Acta med. scand. 161*:301.

Brinkhous, K. M., Graham, J. B. (1950) *Science, 111*:723.

Choremis, K. B., Zervos, N., Tsevrenis, H., Apostolopoulou, E., Mandalaki, T. (1956) *Helv. pædiat. acta, 3*:305.

Chu, E. H. Y., Giles, N. H. (1959) *Amer. J. hum. Genet. 11*:63.

Douglas, A. S., Cook, I. A. (1957) *Lancet, ii*:616.

Fantl, P., Margolis, J. (1955) *Brit. med. J. i*:640.

Ford, C. E., Jones, K. W., Miller, O. J., Mittwoch, U., Penrose, L. S., Ridler, M., Shapiro, A. (1959a) *Lancet, i*:709.

―――― Polani, P. E., de Almeida, J. C., Briggs, J. H. (1959b) *ibid.* p. 711.

Israëls, M. C. G., Lempert, H., Gilbertson, E. (1951) *ibid. i*:1375.

Kosenow, W. (1956) *Triangle, 2*:321.

McGovern, J. J., Steinberg, A. G. (1958) *J. Lab. clin. Med. 51*:386.

Merskey, C. (1951) *Quart. J. Med. 20*:299.

Nilsson, I. M., Blombäck, M., v. Francken, I. (1957) *Acta med. scand. 159*:35.

―――― Thilén, A., v. Francken, I. (1959) *ibid.* (in the press).

Pola, V., Svojitka, J. (1957) *Folia haemat. Lpz. 75*:43.

Quick, A. J., Hussey, C. V. (1958) *Lancet, i*:1294.

Reitalu, J. (1957) *Acta Genet. med. (Roma), 6*:393.

―――― Bergman, S. (1959) *Acta path. microbiol. scand.* (in the press).

Sköld, E. (1944) *Acta med. scand.* suppl. *150.*

Taylor, K., Biggs, R. (1957) *Brit. med. J. i*:1494.

Tjio, J. H., Puck, T. T. (1958) *J. exp. Med. 108*:259.

Walton, J. N. (1956) *Ann. hum. Genet. 21*:40.

20

EVIDENCE FOR THE EXISTENCE OF
THE HUMAN "SUPER FEMALE"

Patricia A. Jacobs, B.Sc. St. And., A. G. Baikie, M.B. Glasg.,
M.R.C.P.E., W. M. Court Brown, M.B., B.Sc. St. And., F.F.R.,
T. N. MacGregor, M.D. Edin., F.R.C.S.E., F.R.C.O.G., N. Maclean,
M.B., Edin., M.R.C.P.E., and D. G. Harnden, Ph.D. Edin.

THREE groups of human beings with abnormal chromosome numbers have now been described. One of these, the mongols, has been shown to have 47 chromosomes, the additional chromosome being a small acrocentric autosome (Lejeune, Gauthier, and Turpin 1959, Jacobs, Baikie, Court Brown, and Strong 1959). In the other two groups there are abnormalities of the number of the sex chromosomes. In the chromatin-positive form of Klinefelter's syndrome, a chromosome number of 47 has been found and a chromosomal sex of XXY (Jacobs and Strong 1959); while in the second group, consisting of apparent females with Turner's syndrome who are chromatin-negative on nuclear sex determination, the chromosomal number is 45 and the chromosomal sex is XO (Ford, Jones, Polani, Almeida, and Briggs 1959).

This present report concerns a third type of sex-chromosome anomaly—namely, the "super-female," characterised by a chromosomal number of 47 and a chromosomal sex of XXX.

CASE AND INVESTIGATION
Clinical Data

The patient, born in 1924, is the youngest of a sibship of three girls. At the time of the parent's conception her mother was 41 years of age and her father was probably 40. As far as is known she is the product of a full-term normal pregnancy.

Reprinted from *The Lancet*, September 26, 1959, pp. 423-425.

We are grateful to Miss M. Brunton, Miss C. M. Scammell, and Mr. A. Ross for technical assistance.

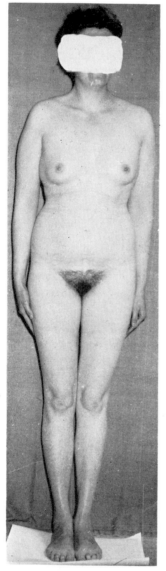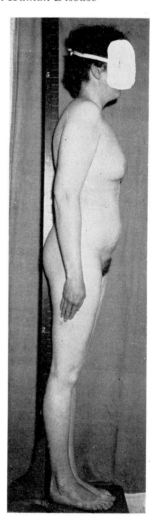

Fig. 1. Present appearance of patient.

She was first seen by one of us (T. N. M.) in 1946 because of secondary amenorrhœa. Menstruation is thought to have begun in 1938, at the age of 14, and from the onset it was irregular, occurring every 2-3 months and lasting about 3 days. The last spontaneous menstruation was in 1943, and the cessation was accompanied by lassitude and occasional flushes.

She was of average height (176 cm.) and weight (58.2 kg.). Her breasts were underdeveloped and her external genitalia infantile. The vagina was small and the uterocervical canal measured 6 cm. The urinary gonadotrophin excretion was persistently high and the basal temperature recording was monophasic.

Œstrogen therapy caused some development of the breasts

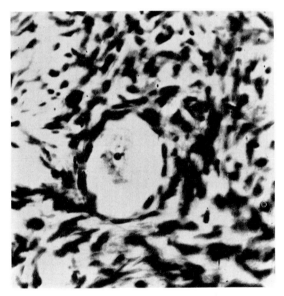

Fig. 2. Section of ovary showing primordial follicle.

and of the external genitalia, and also of the vagina and uterus, with slight uterine bleeding. But œstradiol implants of as much as 50 mg. induced only a limited response. The present appearance of the patient is shown in fig. 1.

At laparotomy in 1952 the ovaries looked postmenopausal. Biopsy provided a wedge measuring 1 × 0.5 cm. in cross-section. On examination, the stroma appeared normal and contained only one primordial follicle (fig. 2); a later follicle with a granulose-cell layer was also seen, but no corpora albicantia were obvious. If this biopsy material is representative of the ovarian tissue as a whole, follicle formation has been deficient.

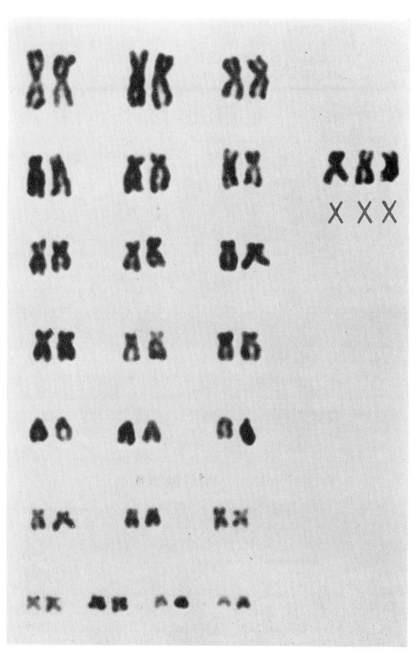

Fig. 3. Representative marrow cell and idiogram showing 47 chromosomes and the presumptive X chromosomes.

Chromosome Analysis

Sternal marrow was cultured and treated in the way described by Ford, Jacobs, and Lajtha (1958). The chromosomes of sixty-three cells were counted (see table).

The great majority of the cells contained 47 chromosomes, and departures from this number are attributed to artefacts arising during preparation. A detailed analysis was made of the chromosomes of thirteen cells of suitable quality. All were found to have an additional chromosome in the medium-size range where the X chromosome is to be found (fig. 3). It is presumed, therefore, that this patient has an XXX sex-chromosome constitution, and this presumption is supported by the findings on nuclear sex determination on buccal smears (see below) and by the fact that her abnormalities seem to be confined to the genital tract. The alternative explanation that the additional chromosome is an autosome is unlikely; for in mongolism, the only condition in which an additional autosome is known to occur, there are widespread abnormalities.

The skin was cultured by one of us (D. G. H.), and the chromosomes studied in forty-seven cells (Harnden 1959). Of these, forty-three contained 47 chromosomes, two had 46 and two had 48. Deviations from 47 are thought to have occurred during culture or the preparation of the material for microscopy. Analysis of the chromosomes confirmed the bone-marrow findings.

Examination of the bone-marrow chromosomes of the mother showed a normal diploid number of 46 with a chromosomal sex of XX.

MARROW CHROMOSOME COUNTS

		Chromosome Number				
	44	45	46	47	48	Polyploids	Total
Cells counted	1	1	5	51	2	3	63

Nuclear Sex Analysis

Buccal smears were stained with cresyl echt violet (Moore and Barr 1955) and with thionin (Klinger and Ludwig 1957). By both methods sex-chromatin bodies were demonstrated in a high proportion of cells. In the smears stained with cresyl echt violet 57% of the nuclei contained a single chromatin body and 14% contained two chromatin bodies. In these latter cells there was some variation in the appearances of the bodies and in their positions on the nuclear membranes; in the majority the bodies were clearly separated (fig. 4A-C). Where a cell contained two chromatin bodies they did not differ significantly in size. In one cell, however, one of the bodies appeared in a "diplococcal" form (fig. 4C).

The proportion of cells containing chromatin bodies (71%) was greater than that found in buccal smears from normal women stained with the same preparation of cresyl echt violet. Twenty-five smears were obtained from 20 normal women, and in each smear a hundred cells were examined. The percentage of chromatin-positive cells varied from 36 to 51, the mean value being 40.8

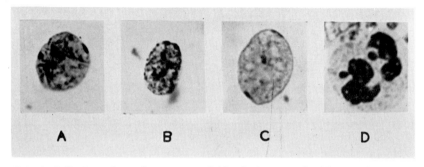

Fig. 4. Cells from buccal mucosa and blood showing double sex-chromatin bodies.

and the standard deviation 3.4. In none of these control preparations was a cell seen containing two chromatin bodies.

Female nuclear appendages were seen in the blood-films: 8 "drumsticks" (Davidson and Smith 1954) were present in five hundred neutrophil polymorphs, and 22 appendages—types A and B (Kosenow and Scupin 1956)—were observed in a further thousand neutrophils. The nuclear sex was clearly female, but the proportion of cells containing appendages was not in excess of that in normal women. Only one cell was found to contain 2 drumsticks (fig. 4D).

Sections of ovarian tissue were also stained with cresyl echt violet and with thionin, and in some of the stromal cells 2 chromatin bodies were seen.

DISCUSSION

It is now apparent that the condition can exist in man in which the chromosome number is 47, composed of 44 autosomes and 3

X chromosomes. This condition is analogous to the super-female found in *Drosophila melanogaster*. In this organism primary non-disjunction of the X chromosome occurs with a frequency of about 1/2,000 (Waddington 1950), and eggs containing an XX pair when fertilised by X-bearing sperms give rise to super-females. In drosophila such super-females are often inviable. Our case suggests that in man the condition may affect only the genital tract.

Our finding that some of the cells of the buccal mucosa contain a second sex-chromatin body raises the possibility that the hetero-chromatic mass of the third X chromosome may be visible. This, however, seems unlikely; for, if it were so, the heterochromatic mass of the single X chromosome of the male should also be visible. The fact that the single X chromosome in the male is not visible suggests that the additional X chromosome in our case may contain an unusual amount of heterochromatic material. Only a more detailed study of further examples of this condition will decide whether this is the correct interpretation.

A further anomaly is the finding that the proportion of drum-sticks in the polymorphonuclear leucocytes was no higher than in normal females. The significance of this observation, too, is not clear; but it does raise the possibility the polymorphonuclear appendages are not such a direct indication of the presence of two X chromosomes as is the presence of a nuclear sex-chromatin body in buccal mucosal cells.

If it can be shown in further cases that the proportion of cells containing two chromatin bodies is associated with an XX chromosomal sex, determination of the nuclear sex chromatin on buccal mucosal cells may be a valuable screening procedure in looking for the "super-female."

REFERENCES

Davidson, W. M., Smith, D. R. (1954) *Brit. med. J. ii*:6.
Ford, C. E., Jacobs, P. A., Lajtha, L. G. (1958) *Nature, Lond. 181*:1565.
——— Jones, K. W., Polani, P. E., Almeida, J. C., Briggs, J. H. (1959) *Lancet, i*:711.
Harnden, D. G. (1959) *Brit. J. exp. Path.* (in the press).
Jacobs, P. A., Baikie, A. G., Court Brown, W. M., Strong, J. A. (1959) *Lancet, i*:710.

————— Strong, J. A. (1959) *Nature, Lond. 183:*302.

Klinger, H. P., Ludwig, K. S. (1957) *Stain Tech. 32:*235.

Kosenow, W., Scupin, (1956) *Klin. Wschr. 34:*51.

Lejeune, J., Gauthier, M., Turpin, R. (1959) *C.R. Acad. Sci., Paris, 248:*602.

Moore, K. L., Barr, M. L. (1955) *Lancet, ii:*57.

Waddington, C. H. (1950) An Introduction to Modern Genetics. London.

21

CHROMOSOME STUDIES IN HUMAN LEUKAEMIA

A. G. Baikie, M.B. Glasg., M.R.C.P.E., W. M. Court Brown, M.B.,
B.Sc. St. And., F.F.R., Patricia A. Jacobs, B.Sc. St. And., and
J. S. Milne, M.B., B.Sc. Edin.

THE occurrence in neoplastic cells of chromosome abnormalities, both of number and form, is now well established, although their frequency and significance in relation to carcinogenesis remains uncertain (Levan 1956, Koller 1957). Recent technical advances have facilitated more accurate observations on human chromosomes, particularly those of marrow cells, and the karyotype has been studied in a number of cases of leukæmia. Previously Ford, Jacobs, and Lajtha (1958) had reported their findings in twelve cases of human leukæmia, in only three of which, however, was a complete analysis possible; in one of these, a blast-cell leukæmia, the karyotype was abnormal, but in the other two the chromosomes were normal in number and appearance. The need for further studies has been emphasised by the discovery that mongols are trisomic for one of the smallest acrocentric autosomes (Lejeune, Gauthier, and Turpin 1959, Jacobs, Baikie, Court Brown, and Strong 1959), and by the reported association between their particular trisomic state and a raised mortality from childhood leukæmia (Carter 1956, Krivit and Good 1956, Stewart, Webb, and Hewitt 1958). Furthermore, leukæmia

Reprinted from *The Lancet*, September 26, 1959, pp. 425-428.

We are grateful to Prof. L. J. Davis, Dr. E. B. French, Dr. James Innes, Dr. J. G. Macleod, Prof. R. McWhirter and his staff, Dr. J. K. Slater, Dr. J. A. Strong, and Dr. R. W. D. Turner for referring cases to us or allowing us to study patients under their care.

Acknowledgement is due to Dr. D. G. Harnden, of the M.R.C. Radiobiological Unit, for culturing and examining the skin-biopsy material, and Dr. Alexander Gordon of the Western General Hospital, Edinburgh, for the necropsy findings.

We are also grateful to Miss M. Brunton, Mrs. E. M. Gillis, and Miss M. D. Robertson for technical assistance.

provides a special opportunity for serial chromosomal studies which may permit correlation of chromosomal abnormalities with the clinical type and behaviour of the disease, and may also shed light on the reasons for the variable response to treatment and for relapses after an initial response to chemotherapy.

We are now able to report the results of such serial chromosome studies in a case of acute leukæmia during the 8 months which elapsed between diagnosis and death. More limited observations have been made in eleven other cases of leukæmia and in two cases of myelomatosis.

MATERIAL AND METHODS

Bone-marrow samples for chromosome analysis and for smear preparations were obtained by aspiration through a Salah needle. The chromosome studies on marrow material were carried out by the method described by Ford et al. (1958), and on the skin-biopsy material by the method of Harnden (1959). The hæmatological methods used were essentially those described by Dacie (1956), but bone-marrow was examined in smear preparations (Davidson, Davis, and Innes 1943) and defibrinated blood was used for buffy-coat films.

CASE REPORTS

In this section data are presented on cases 1-11 of leukæmia, and cases 12-13 of myelomatosis. Both the clinical and chromosomal data are presented in full for case 1, and are summarised (table II) for the remaining cases.

Case 1.—A woman, aged 56, was admitted to hospital in August, 1958. For 4 weeks she had been unduly tired, and she had had a severe epistaxis. There were no notable features in her medical history, and at no time before her final illness was she exposed to artificial radiation. She was pale, and had a few retinal hæmorrhages. Clinically there was no enlargement of liver, spleen, or lymph-nodes.

Her blood and marrow were examined on Sept. 3, at which time marrow chromosome studies were also undertaken. The blood findings were: Hb 4.6 g. per 100 ml.; packed-cell volume 15%; platelets 78,000 per c.mm.; reticulocytes 0.6%, white-cell count 1,700 per c.mm. (polymorphs 35%, lymphocytes 50%, abnormal mononuclears 15%).

The abnormal mononuclear cells varied in size and apparent maturity, but most had the characteristics of primitive cells. Similar mononuclear cells predominated throughout the bone-marrow, and here they were generally larger and more immature. Erythropoiesis was normoblastic and few megakaryocytes were seen. A diagnosis of acute aleukæmic leukæmia was made, and the leukæmic cells were thought to be of the myelomonocytic variety.

Course of Illness

Treatment was by initial blood-transfusion and prednisolone 60 mg. daily, which was reduced to 40 mg. daily before her discharge from hospital on Sept. 19. On this regime the white-cell count rose and was maintained between 8,000 and 10,000 per c.mm., the differential count remaining unchanged. The platelet-count varied between 90,000 and 120,000, but the hæmoglobin level declined slowly and the patient was readmitted for a further blood-transfusion on Dec. 8. The dose of prednisolone was increased to 60 mg. daily, and thereafter the hæmoglobin level was maintained without further transfusion. On Oct. 15, and again on Jan. 5, 1959, the bone-marrow biopsy was repeated for routine hæmatology and for chromosome counts.

In February, 1959, a rib fractured. There was no evidence of a generalised osteoporosis, but other steroid side-effects were by now conspicuous. She felt less well and purpuric spots appeared frequently, although both platelet and hæmoglobin levels were maintained at the previous improved figures (Hb 11.4 g. per 100 ml., platelets 110,000 per c.mm.), and the white-cell count was essentially unchanged (7,600 per c.mm.).

She was readmitted to hospital in March, so that the dose of prednisolone might be reduced under observation. Radiography showed two more rib fractures. Although the dose of prednisolone was slowly reduced and corticotrophin was substituted, the levels of hæmoglobin, platelets, and white cells fell rapidly. This hæmatological deterioration continued, and 2 days after the last dose of corticotrophin the patient had hæmaturia and rectal bleeding. Steriod therapy was resumed, using dexamethasone 6 mg. daily, and thereafter the hæmoglobin, platelet-counts, and white-cell counts all rose to their previous levels and the patient became fit to return home. Bone-marrow biopsy was repeated on April 2, and although the appearance of the smears was substantially unaltered there now was a marked change in the chromosome constitution of the cells.

On April 7 the patient was readmitted for the last time. She complained of severe back pain, and there was radiological evidence of erosion of the bodies of L1-3 but no evidence of generalised decalcification. The bone lesions were thought to be due to leukæmic infiltration, and palliative radiotherapy was given to the lumbar vertebræ. A single surface dose of 1,000 rads was given to a 15 × 10 cm. field centred posteriorly over the spinous process of L2. After this, there was a slight fall in her blood-levels to Hb 9 g. per 100 ml., platelets 83,000 per c.mm., and white cells 4,400 per c.mm. On April 20 she collapsed suddenly with signs of massive gastrointestinal-tract hæmorrhage, and died despite blood-transfusion. Immediately after death, bone-marrow was aspirated from the sternum, iliac crest, and the spinous process of the first lumbar vertebra. These marrow samples were used for further examination of the marrow-cell chromosomes as well as for conventional smear preparations.

Postmortem Findings

The histological appearances on the bone-marrow accorded with those of these smear preparations. There was no leukæmic infiltration, other than a few cells in the spleen and in a mesenteric lymph-node. The bone lesions noted in life were seen to be due to osteoporosis and not to leukæmic infiltration. The adrenal cortex showed marked atrophy, and there was severe fatty change in the liver.

Comment

Apart from the abnormality of the bone-marrow chromosomes, other notable features of this case of acute myelomonocytic leukæmia were persistence of the relatively aleukæmic peripheral blood-picture, and the small amount of infiltration of other organs compared with the bone-marrow. The evidence of leukæmia in marrow and peripheral blood was unaltered by steroid therapy. In this case steroids apparently helped by sustaining production and survival of red cells and by maintaining hæmostasis.

TABLE 1

CHROMOSOME COUNTS IN CASE 1

Marrow Sample	Date	Site	Chromosome Number													Cells Counted
			<43	43	44	45	46	47	48	49	50	>50	4N	8N	>8N	
A	Sept. 3, 1958	Sternum	2	..	3	2	24(8)*	45	75	27	6	..	..	..	..	184
B	Oct. 15, 1958	Sternum	..	1	1	1	12(5)	25	28	9	1	..	1	..	1	80
C	Jan. 5, 1959	Sternum	..	1	..	2	9(2)	25	46	15	4	1	1	..	..	104
D	April 2, 1959	Sternum	..	..	1	2	9(7)	34	22	12	1	..	2	1	..	84
E	April 20, 1959	Sternum	..	1	..	2	7(4)	36	25	15	8	1	5	..	..	1C0
F	April 20, 1959	Lumbar spine	..	..	1	1	4(1)	7	9	13	3	1	..	..	..	39
G	April 20, 1959	Iliac crest	..	..	..	3	5(2)	18	20	6	1	7	2	1	..	63

* Numbers in parentheses indicate the number of cells with a diploid number of 46 in which no morphological abnormalities could be seen. X^2 tests.—For this purpose the polyploid cells were ignored and the remaining numbers were grouped as follows: $\leq 46, 47, 48, 49, \leq 50$

Results: comparison of B with A, $X^2 = 2.20$; $p > 0.50 < 0.70$; C with A + B, $X^2 = 3.42$, $p > 0.30 < 0.50$; D with A + B + C, $X^2 = 9.58$; $p > 0.02 < 0.05$; D + E with A + B + C, $X^2 = 16.64$, $p < 0.01$; F and E, $X^2 = 8.18$, $p < 0.05 > 0.10$.

TABLE 2

DETAILS OF PATIENTS STUDIED

Case	Age	Diagnosis	Date (1959)	Whether Treated	NO.	Chromosomes STRUCTURAL ABNORMALITIES
2	64	Acute leukemia	May 14	Untreated	46-50	None seen
3	41	Acute leukemia	June 2	Treated	46-50	None seen
			Jan. 5	Treated	46	Probable translocation
			Jan. 19	Treated	46	Probable translocation
			Feb. 10	Treated	46	Probable translocation
4	48	Acute leukemia	May 8	Untreated	46	Probable translocation
			May 26	Treated	46	None
5	70	Acute leukemia, polycythaemia vera	...	Treated	46	None
6	50	Chronic myeloid leukaemia	...	Treated	46	None
7	76	Chronic myeloid leukaemia	...	Untreated	46	None
8	61	Chronic myeloid leukaemia	...	Untreated	46	None
9	72	Chronic myeloid leukaemia	...	Treated	46	None
10	51	Chronic myeloid leukaemia	...	Treated	46	None
11	76	Chronic lymphatic leukaemia	...	Treated	46	None
12	58	Myelomatosis	...	Untreated	46	None
13	55	Myelomatosis	...	Untreated	46	None

CHROMOSOME STUDIES

The chromosome-counts done on sternal marrow obtained from case 1 on five times in eight months were all abnormal (table 1). On the first three occasions they ranged from 46 to 50, with a well-defined modal number of 48, and there were ring chromosomes

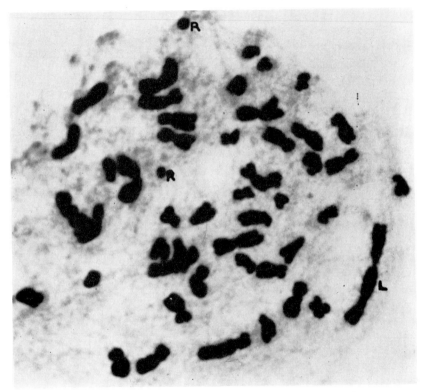

Cell from bone-marrow showing 50 chromosomes. R, ring chromosome. L, large submetacentric chromosome.

(often positively heteropyknotic) and chromosome fragments. In the sternal marrow taken eighteen days before death and immediately after death the modal chromosome number had changed to 47. Ring chromosomes and fragments were still present, and in addition an abnormally large submetacentric chromosome was seen in three cells (see figure). The marrow from the lumbar vertebra, which had been irradiated 5 days before death, contained considerably fewer cells in mitosis than did the sternal marrow removed at the same time; and the modal number was 49 in contrast to that of the unirradiated sternal marrow. In all marrow specimens there was a small proportion of cells having 46 chromosomes, but most of these contained chromosomes with structural abnormalities and cannot therefore be regarded as normal marrow cells.

To ascertain whether or not this patient had an inherent chromosome abnormality a skin biopsy was performed on April 7. The specimen of skin was cultured (Harnden 1959), and the chromosomes were examined. In thirty-six of the thirty-seven cells analysed the chromosome number was 46 and there were no morphological abnormalities. Variation from this number was attributed to the culture technique.

Preliminary results of chromosome studies of the bone-marrow cells from ten further cases of leukæmia are shown in table 2. In cases 5-11 the chromosomes numbered 46 and their morphology appeared normal. The material from case 2 yielded very few dividing cells, but in the twenty-one cells examined the chromosome number ranged from 46 to 50. In cases 3 and 4 the chromosome number was 46, but in both instances an abnormal chromosome was seen in a high proportion of the cells, the appearances of this chromosome suggesting that a translocation had given rise to an aberrant cell line.

DISCUSSION

The finding of chromosomal abnormalities in four out of five cases of acute leukæmia, and the apparent absence of such changes in six cases of chronic leukæmia and two of myelomatosis raises two interdependent problems. What is the relation of these chromosome changes to the pathogenesis of acute leukæmia, and does their absence in chronic leukæmia denote an essential difference between the acute and chronic forms, either in their mechanisms of induction or in their pathogenesis? Three possibilities may be considered. Firstly the chromosome changes may arise as epiphenomena in a grossly disordered bone-marrow; secondly the visible chromosome changes may include the fundamental change which has conferred neoplastic qualities on the marrow cells; and thirdly it is possible that the chromosome changes are the consequences—perhaps the remote consequences—of a more subtle alteration in the genetic constitution of the leukæmic cell. This last interpretation seems the most likely.

If the chromosome changes arise merely as a result of a gross disorder of the bone-marrow, it is difficult to understand why none have been found in the chronic leukæmias, in which the marrow was at least as disordered as in many instances of acute leukæmia, and perhaps more so than in cases 1 and 3. It is possible that translocations, such as would account for the findings in cases 3 and 4, were also present in cases 1 and 2 but were obscured by the more gross changes present; and it could be that such translocations represent the fundamental structural change which induces leukæmia. On the other hand it may well be that the gross and varied chromosome changes found in four of our cases, and in the single case of Ford et al. (1958), arose as the consequence of a more subtle genetic change which is not demonstrable by current techniques.

Thus our observations appear to strengthen the concept that acute leukæmias are the result of changes in the genetic material in the cell. On the other hand they throw no further light on the induction mechanisms of the chronic leukæmias. Possibly separate mechanisms of induction and of development exist for chronic myeloid and chronic lymphatic leukæmia. Thus the incidence of chronic lymphatic leukæmia is apparently unaffected by radiation exposure, whereas that of chronic myeloid leukæmia is raised, along with the incidence of the acute forms of leukæmia. Furthermore, from an analysis of death-certificate data, Court Brown and Doll (1959) have inferred that chronic lymphatic leukæmia may have a separate ætiology from the other two types. As only one case of chronic lymphatic leukæmia has been examined by us, the remainder of this discussion relates only to the acute leukæmias and to chronic myeloid leukæmia.

Armitage and Doll (1957) have suggested that cancer induction is a staged process, and that the first stage consists of a change in the genetic structure of the cell. The nature of the later stages remains obscure, but possibly further genetic changes occur in a random fashion, and an autonomous state ultimately develops. On this hypothesis our findings may imply that in chronic myeloid leukæmia the fundamental change allows the affected cell series to escape from the usual factors which regulate cell replacement; at the same time cell differentiation continues along roughly normal lines, and genetic changes are limited. The converse may be true of acute leukæmia, where the rate of cell replacement may be little affected, but where departures from normal cell differentiation are marked, and progressive chromosomal aberrations are possible. Certainly the heterogeneity of chromosome number and form in the bone-marrow of case 1, and their progressive changes, provide a rationale for the natural history of acute leukæmia and its response to treatment. Moreover on this basis both the escape of acute leukæmia from the control of initially effective treatment, and the failure of some cases to respond at all, can be understood.

In case 1 it is noteworthy that the limited effects of steroids produced no change in the chromosome constitution and little or none in the hæmatological evidence of leukæmia. It is also of interest that the bone-marrow taken after death from the lumbar vertebra, which had been directly irradiated, showed a different modal chromosome number—although this difference is only on the borderline of statistical significance. This suggests that the cell line with a chromosome number of 47, which had become predominant, may have been especially radiosensitive. Whether this interpretation is justified or not, it is obvious that these methods provide an opportunity for the examination of the chromosome constitution of leukæmic cells—an opportunity which may be expected to give new insight into the natural history of the disease, whether treated or untreated, and perhaps into its fundamental nature.

SUMMARY

A case of acute leukæmia is described in which the bone-marrow cells had a modal chromosome number of 48, as well as abnormalities of chromosome form. Serial observations showed that during treatment with steroids all these abnormalities persisted until seven months after diagnosis when the modal chromosome number changed to 47.

The bone-marrow chromosomes of four other cases of acute

leukæmia were examined: one had an abnormality of chromosome number and two had morphological abnormalities alone. In contrast, no chromosomal abnormalities were found in six cases of chronic leukæmia, or in two cases of myelomatosis.

These findings are discussed in relation to the pathogenesis of leukæmia; and in relation to the natural history of acute leukæmia and the effects of treatment.

REFERENCES

Armitage, P., Doll, R. (1957) *Brit. J. Cancer, 11*:161.

Carter, C. O. (1956) *Brit. med. J.* ii:993.

Court Brown, W. M., Doll, R. (1959) *ibid. i:1063.*

Dacie, J. V. (1956) Practical Hæmatology. London.

Davidson, L. S. P., Davis, L. J., Innes, J. (1943) *Edinb. med. J. 50*:226.

Ford, C. E., Jacobs, P. A., Lajtha, L. G. (1958) *Nature, Lond. 181*:1565.

Harnden, D. G. (1959) *Brit. J. exp. Path.* (in the press).

Jacobs, P. A., Baikie, A. G., Court Brown, W. M., Strong, J. A. (1959) *Lancet, i*:710.

Koller, P. C. (1957) in *Cancer* (edited by R. W. Raven); vol. 1. London.

Krivit, W., Good, R. A. (1956) *Amer. J. Dis. Child. 91*:218.

Lejeune, J., Gauthier, M., Turpin, R. (1959) *C. R. Acad. Sci., Paris, 248*:602.

Levan, A. (1956) *Trans. N. Y. Acad. Sci. 63*:774.

Stewart, A., Webb, J., Hewitt, D. (1958) *Brit. med. J.* ii:1495.

22

THE CHROMOSOME CONSTITUTION OF A HUMAN PHENOTYPIC INTERSEX

David A. Hungerford,[*] A. J. Donnelly, Peter C. Nowell,[**] and Sidney Beck

INTRODUCTION

SHORTLY after the original description of sex chromatin (Barr and Bertram, 1949, see also Graham and Barr, 1952), application was made of the technique to the sexing of human hermaphrodites (Moore, Graham, and Barr, 1953). A great number of papers on this and similar subjects has appeared subsequently, in which the utility of the sex chromatin technique in diagnosing the genetic sex of many cell types has been demonstrated. To date, however, there have been very few investigations of human intersexes in which analysis of metaphase chromosomes has confirmed the results derived from sex chromatin determinations (Ford et al., 1953; Jacobs and Strong, 1959; Chu and Giles, 1959).

Recently, a case of this type in a twelve-year-old individual has been investigated. As a result of clinical observations to be described below, it was believed that analysis of the chromosome complement of this individual might be valuable.

For the purposes of an investigation of another kind, a technique for the karyotype analysis of human peripheral leukocytes had been developed (Nowell et al., 1958). Normally, mitosis is

Reprinted from *American Journal of Human Genetics*, Vol. 11, No. 3, September, 1959, pp. 215-236.

[*] Supported by a research grant from the American Cancer Society to Dr. Jack Schultz.

[**] Supported in part by Senior Research Fellowship SF-4 from the U. S. Public Health Service, and in part by grant C-3562 from the National Cancer Institute of the National Institutes of Health, U. S. Public Health Service.

The authors wish to express their appreciation to Miss Sarah Reifsnyder, Miss Rose Shapiro, and Miss Elizabeth Yoast for expert technical assistance.

We are indebted to Dr. A. E. Rakoff for the assay studies done in the Endocrinology Laboratory, Jefferson Medical College and Hospital, Philadelphia.

not observed in such cells *in vivo*. However, in our modification of the gradient culture method of Osgood and his colleagues (1955), high frequencies of mitosis had been observed. Results from the application of this technique as well as from observations on sex chromatin in the individual mentioned above will be described in this paper.

Case Report

Patient J. G., a Negro, was 12⅓ years old when first seen. The chief complaint was a swelling in the left breast, first noticed 3

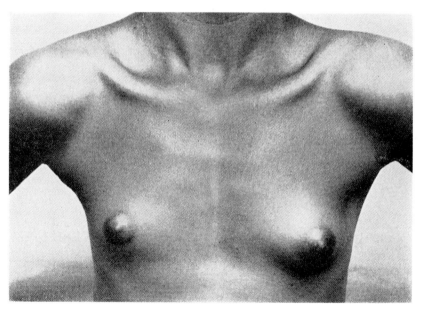

Fig. 1. Preoperative gynecomastia, pronounced on left side.

or 4 days after the breast had been struck by a baseball approximately 4 months before the patient was first seen. Two months after the injury enlargement of the right breast was noticed (Fig. 1). No pain was associated with these mammary changes.

The past medical history did not seem relevant to the chief complaint, and the history of symptoms relating to specific systems did not suggest any irregularities. The family history was unobtainable, since the child had been abandoned by his parents and later adopted by foster parents.

The youth was a slender but well developed and well nourished

individual. No abnormalities could be discovered except those relating to the breasts and to the contents of the right scrotum. The
left breast was uniformly soft and enlarged to about 6 cm. in diameter with a central depth of approximately 3 cm. The right
breast had a similar consistency, but the size approximated 3 cm.
in diameter with a central depth of 2 cm. (Fig. 1). A clinical diag-

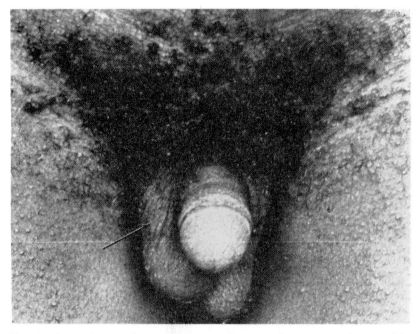

Fig. 2. External genitalia, preoperative. Arrow indicates site of tumor-like
irregularity (see text).

nosis of gynecomastia was made, and the possibility of a right
testicular lesion noted. The penis was small, although within the
normal size range and configuration for a male in early adolescence (Fig. 2). Hypospadias was not evident. The right scrotum
contained a palpable ovoid mass, presumably testicle, with a tumor-
like irregularity at the superior pole (Fig. 2, arrow). The nodule
measured approximately 2 x 1 x 1 cm. The left scrotum contained
a somewhat smaller ovoid structure judged to be testicle. The
median raphe joining the scrotal sacs was complete and without
suggestion of vaginal indentation (Fig. 6). The escutcheon was

equivocally female. A small mass, possibly prostate gland, was palpated by rectal examination.

A left subcutaneous mastectomy was performed under general anaesthesia (Fig. 3). At the same time a biopsy specimen was taken from the mass presumed to be testicle in the right scrotal sac. Histopathological study of the left breast tissue resulted in a diagnosis of gynecomastia with duct hyperplasia and cyst forma-

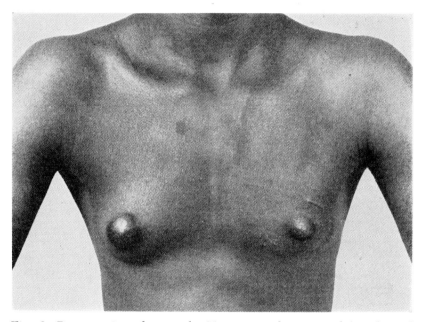

Fig. 3. Postoperative photograph. Note surgical scar on left side and development of gynecomastia on right side.

tion. No acini were found in the breast tissue, however, the duct epithelium presented in some areas a minimal papillary cellular hyperplasia. The small biopsy specimen from the contents of the right scrotum was recognized as *ovarian* tissue, with many primary follicles scattered in a typical ovarian stroma (Fig. 4).

Subsequently, investigations were made of the sex chromatin pattern in the peripheral blood neutrophils and in nuclei of various other cell types. The pattern in each instance was female. Most of the laboratory studies on the patient fell within normal limits.

Roentgenographic studies of the chest and osseous development brought to light no abnormalities. Studies of the sella turcica demonstrated a relatively small but otherwise normal structure. The intravenous urogram was normal.

Permission to perform a laparotomy could not be obtained from the foster parents, but their cooperation was gained in allowing the removal of the abnormal contents of the scrotal sacs. When

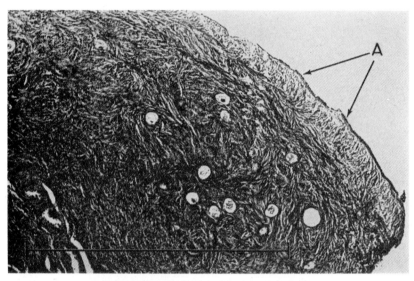

Fig. 4. Low power photomicrograph of biopsy specimen from mass originally presumed to be testicle in right scrotal sac. Note typical ovarian tissue with germinal epithelium (A), and scattered primary follicles in ovarian stroma. Hematoxylin-eosin. Scale indicates one millimeter.

the right scrotum was opened an almond shaped body measuring 3 x 2 x 1.5 cm. was found in the lower portion normally occupied by the testicle (Fig. 5, A). This structure was cystic and attached on one side by soft fibrotic tissue to a convoluted tubular structure 5 cm. long in its unextended state and 0.5 to 0.7 cm. in diameter (Fig. 5, B). That part of the tube associated with the ovoid cystic body resembled a fimbriated end. The opposite extremity was intimately attached to a resilient tissue of irregular outline (Fig. 5, C). This region of tissue included one more or less solid mass (about 1.5 cm. in its greatest dimension), occupying the superior part of the scrotal sac just below the right external inguinal ring. The impression gained from the gross appearance was that the tissues represented ovary, fallopian tube and rudimentary uterine tissue.

On the basis of the patient's male anatomical characteristics, rearing and psychological orientation, all of the right scrotal contents were removed, after it had been determined that the left scrotum contained a well formed but small testicle and epididymis. Biopsy specimens were taken from these structures (Fig. 5, D).

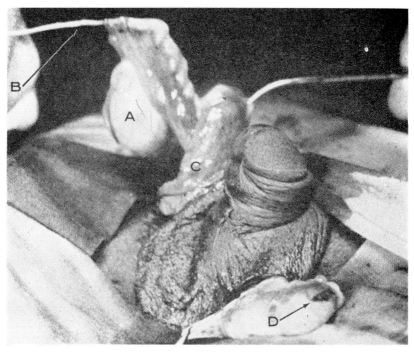

Fig. 5. Contents of scrotal sacs exposed surgically. Right sac: (A) ovotestis, (B) probe inserted in distal end of fallopian tube, (C) mass containing uterine structures. Left sac: (D) site of excision of biopsy specimen from testis.

Histological studies of the tissues confirmed the impressions given by the gross surgical anatomy. The ovarian tissue (Fig. 4) contained primordial follicles, follicular cysts, corpora albicantes and ovarian stroma. The ovarian stroma also contained structures resembling testicular tissue, including atrophic seminiferous tubules and interstitial cells (Leydig cells), the presence of which indicated that this gonad was an ovotestis. Other structures were

quite evidently epididymis (Fig. 7) and a tubule with villi, judged
to represent a fallopian tube, although in the latter some resemblance to a fetal vas deferens must be admitted. The resilient tissue at the upper end of the convoluted tube in the superior part of
the right scrotum was histologically uterine, with a glandular
mucosa suggesting endometrium. The endometrial stroma was not

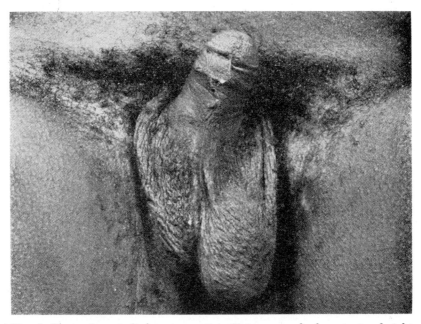

Fig. 6. External genitalia, postoperative. Note removal of contents of right
scrotal sac. Note also that there is no evidence of hypospadias, and no
suggestion of vaginal indentation of the median raphe.

well represented. Biopsy specimens from the structures in the left
scrotal sac proved them to be testicle with atrophic or hypoplastic
seminiferous tubules (Fig. 8) and an associated epididymis. There
was no evidence of spermatogenesis. These observations, made
from hematoxylin-eosin stained sections of formalin-fixed tissues,
established the diagnosis of phenotypic intersex.

Hormonal assays made on the patient's urine, preoperatively and
postoperatively, proved to be significant. Before the removal of
the ovotestis and related tissues from the right scrotal sac, the
FSH urine gonadotropins were less than 6 mouse units per 24
hours, whereas a level of 96 mouse units per 24 hours was

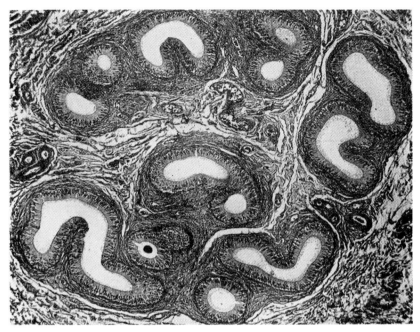

Fig. 7. Low power photomicrograph of typical epididymal tubules present in contents of right scrotal sac, adjacent to ovarian structures of right ovotestis. Hematoxylin-eosin. Same magnification as Fig. 4.

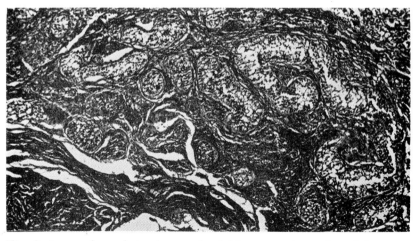

Fig. 8. Low power photomicrograph of biopsy specimen from left testis. Note atrophic seminiferous tubules. Hematoxylin-eosin. Same magnification as Fig. 4.

reached following the removal. This increase in pituitary activity was to be expected with a decrease in female gonadal tissue. The urine estrogens were first assayed at a level of 24 mouse units per 24 hours, but following the operation the level fell to 12 mouse units per 24 hours. This change is readily understandable,

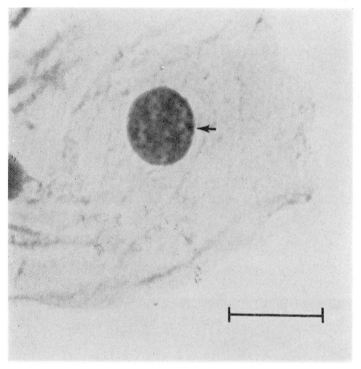

Fig. 9. Squamous epithelial cells in smear from buccal mucosa. Arrow indicates sex chromatin. Feulgen-fast green, 44× dry objective. Scale 10 μ.

since the surgery deleted much estrogen elaborating tissue (evidenced by the sections, which included ovarian follicles, corpus luteum and stroma as well as other structures of female internal genitalia). The urine 17-ketosteroids were 6.3 mg/24 hours preoperatively and 8.5 mg/24 hours postoperatively.

CYTOLOGICAL STUDIES

Sex chromatin: Preparations for this purpose were of three types. Smears of cells scraped from the buccal mucosa were fixed in ether-alcohol (1:1) and stained by the Feulgen-fast green method (Fig. 9). Peripheral blood smears used for observations of "drumsticks" in polymorphonuclear leukocytes (Davidson and Smith, 1954) were stained with Wright's stain (Fig. 10). Sections from formalin-fixed tissue were prepared specifically for investi-

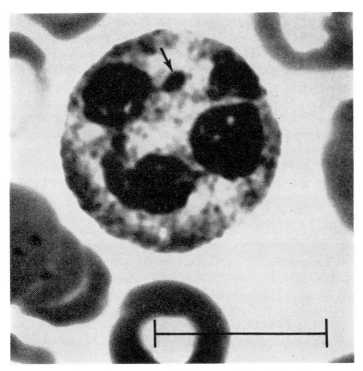

Fig. 10. Polymorphonuclear neutrophil from peripheral blood smear. Arrow indicates typical "drumstick," characteristic of females. Wright's strain, 90× oil immersion objective. Scale 10 μ.

gation of sex chromatin by the Feulgen method with fast-green counterstaining (Figs. 11-17).

Preparation of mitotic cells: Our modification of the method of Osgood and his colleagues (1955) for the culturing of human leukocytes consisted in the following. To a volume of 15 to 30 ml. of heparinized venous blood there was added phytohemagglutinin (Difco) in the proportion of 5 to 6 drops per 10 ml. of blood. This mixture was allowed to stand in ice water for 30 to 60 minutes,

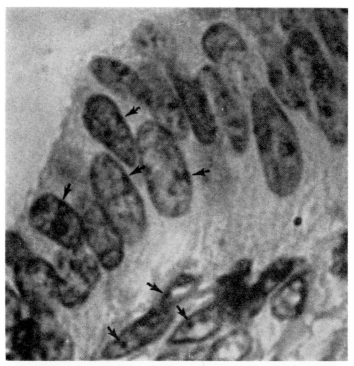

Fig. 12. Portion of endometrial epithelium with subepithelial fibrocytes. Arrows indicate sex chromatin. Feulgen-fast green, 44× dry objective. Same magnification as Fig. 9.

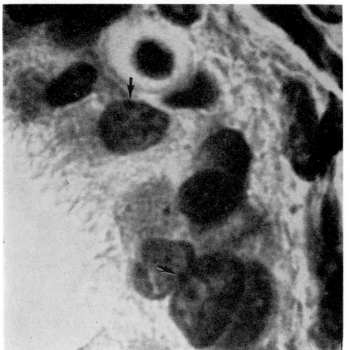

Fig. 11. Portion of ciliated epithelial lining of fallopian tube. Arrows indicate sex chromatin. Feulgen-fast green, 44× dry objective. Same magnification as Fig. 9.

Fig. 14. Cells within atrophic seminiferous tubule of left testis. Note pycnotic character of the nuclei. Arrows indicate sex chromatin. Feulgen-fast green, 44× objective. Same magnification as Fig. 9.

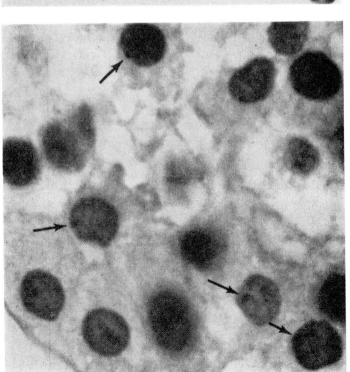

Fig. 13. Portion of corpus luteum from ovotestis. Arrows indicate sex chromatin. Feulgen-fast green, 44× dry objective. Same magnification as Fig. 9.

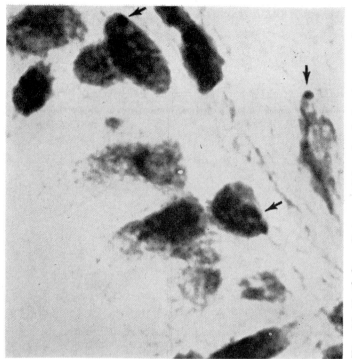

Fig. 16. Epithelium lining epididymal tubule. Arrows indicate sex chromatin. Note also sex chromatin in fibrocyte of supporting connective tissue (arrow nearest to lower right corner of the figure). Feulgen-fast green, 44× dry objective. Same magnification as Fig. 9.

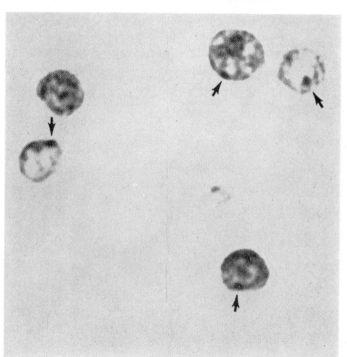

Fig. 15. Interstitial cells of left testis. Arrows indicate sex chromatin. Feulgen-fast green, 44× dry objective. Same magnification as Fig. 9.

after which sedimentation of erythrocytes was accomplished by centrifugation at 350 rpm for 10 minutes at 5°C. The supernatant, containing the leukocytes, was then pipetted off and the concentration of cells determined. The leukocyte suspension was then centrifuged at 2,000 rpm for 3 minutes and the cells resuspended

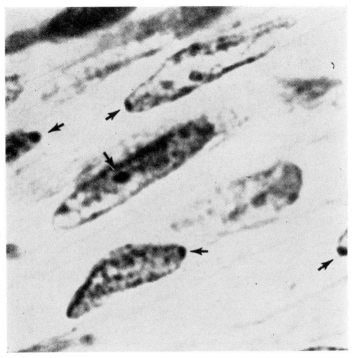

Fig. 17. Smooth muscle of fallopian tube. Arrows indicate sex chromatin. Feulgen-fast green, 44× dry objective. Same magnification as Fig. 9.

in a medium consisting of 10 to 20% normal human plasma in TC-199 (Difco) to which penicillin and streptomycin had been added. The initial concentration of cells was 1 to $2 \times 10^{(6)}$/ml. of culture. Culture volumes varied from 10 to 30 ml. and were planted in bottles of dimensions such that the depth of each culture was 3 to 4 cm. In all cases, one or two small glass slides were placed in the culture at an angle of approximately 60° from the vertical. Cells originally in suspension settled out and grew on the slides as well as on the sides and bottom of the culture bottles.

The dividing leukocytes are thought to be of monocytic and possibly lymphocytic origin in cultures of cells from individuals not having demonstrable blood anomalies. Our reasons for this statement are as follows. First, the dividing cells in our culture are morphologically too undifferentiated for classification; how-

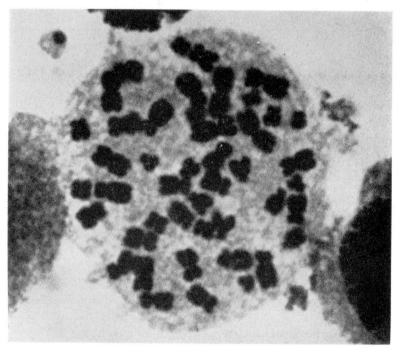

Fig. 18. Diploid metaphase plate ($2n = 46$) from peripheral leukocyte in short-term culture. Acetic orcein squash preparation, 90× oil immersion objective.

ever, when periodic addition of fresh serum is stopped and mitosis ceases, the entire population differentiates into monocytes, macrophages, and multinucleated giant cells. No cells resembling mature granulocytes or small lymphocytes are formed. Secondly, autoradiographic studies on the incorporation of tritium labeled thymidine into human peripheral leukocytes *in vitro* (Bond *et al.*, 1958) indicate that DNA synthesis occurs only in monocytes or large and medium-sized lymphocytes. Such observations support the interpretations of earlier workers in the field, who agreed gen-

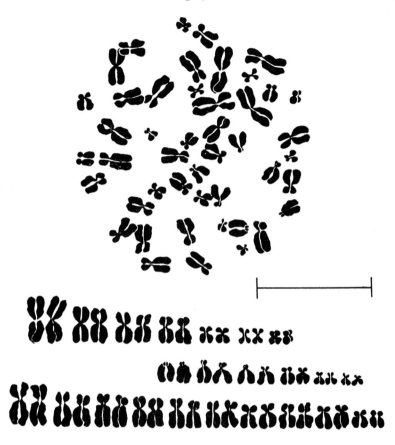

Fig. 19. Chromosome analysis of metaphase plate shown in Fig. 18. Scale represents 10 μ. The absence of a heteromorphic sex chromosome pair in the idiogram characterizes the chromosome constitution of the human female.

erally that the non-granular leukocytes (*i.e.*, monocytes and perhaps lymphocytes) were the only cell types capable of surviving for more than a few days in culture (see references cited by Bloom, 1938).

Examination of cells growing on the slides has shown that, in the case of normal human beings, optimal mitotic activity can be expected after 3 to 4 days at 37°C. For the purposes of chromosome cytology, the cultures were terminated at this time. To accumulate large numbers of cells at metaphase, colchicine was added in a $1 \times 10^{(-7)}$ M concentration at an interval of from 17 to

19 hours prior to termination. Cells were harvested from the culture bottles by shaking and decanting into centrifuge tubes, after which they were concentrated by centrifugal sedimentation, washed once with Earle's solution (Difco), and pretreated by incubation for 20 minutes at 37°C. in modified Niu-Twitty solu-

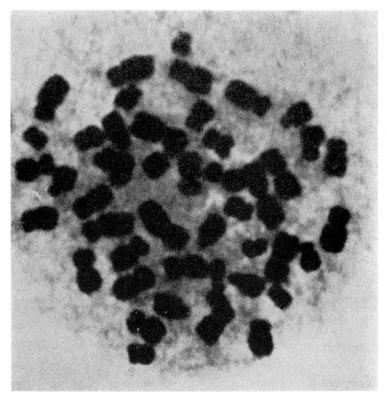

Fig. 20. Another diploid metaphase plate ($2n = 46$) from peripheral leukocyte in short-term culture. Acetic orcein squash preparation, 90× oil immersion objective.

tion (Hungerford and DiBerardino, 1958), which is hypotonic for mammalian cells. Fixation and staining in 60% acetic orcein followed pretreatment. Squash preparations were made on unsiliconed slides with siliconed coverslips, and made permanent by the dry ice method.

Cytological analysis of metaphase chromosomes: Metaphase plates judged not to have been broken during squashing (Hungerford, 1955) were recorded by means of high resolution photo-micrographs. Prints of these were made at 5320× magnification. Although approximately ¾ of this represents empty magnification, it provides a convenient size for subsequent steps in the method. Tracings of prints were checked and corrected by direct micro-scopic observation. A second tracing was made from the finished analysis of the metaphase plate and from this an idiogram was constructed. Usually, homologous pairs of chromosomes could be matched by means of two set of observations: (1) characteristic chromosome morphology, and (2) a degree of loose association of homologues which persist in pretreated metaphases, providing that the organization of the spindle has not been too drastically disoriented. A study of the latter phenomenon has been under way at the Institute for Cancer Research for some years, and it is intended that details be reported elsewhere.

The chromosomes have been classified (Figs. 19, 21) into three groups, according to centromere position: median (top row, seven pairs), subterminal (middle row, six pairs), and submedian (bot-tom row, ten pairs). Within each group, the pairs have been ar-ranged according to length. Comparison of Fig. 19 with Fig 20 indicates that the order within groups of chromosome pairs ar-ranged by this method is not always the same; *e.g.*, the second and third pairs of chromosomes with submedian centromeres are in opposite sequence. Relatively different degrees of chromosome condensation or the effects of squashing may be responsible.

RESULTS

Chromosome counts from well-spread, intact metaphases are given in Table 1. Each count was made from a free-hand sketch. Only those which could be counted to within an accuracy of plus or minus one chromosome, and which fell within the diploid range, or the range of endoreduplicated (Levan and Hauschka, 1953) tetraploids are included. Two metaphases which were not accurately countable, but were approximately tetraploid and did not show quadruplochromosomes, are not included in the table. In addition to these metaphases, there were present in low fre-quency hypoploid metaphases, which in all respects (Hungerford, 1955) appeared intact. Counts of 6, 10 (in three cells), 12, 13 ± 1,

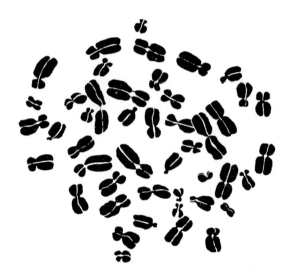

Fig. 21. Chromosome analysis of metaphase plate shown in Fig. 20. Scale represents 10 μ. Note again the absence of a heteromorphic sex chromosome pair.

15, 15 ± 1, 16 and 18 chromosomes were obtained; in addition there were several cells, not accurately countable, estimated counts from which ranged into the thirties. Whether such cells actually exist *in vivo* or represent an artifact of the culturing and/or preparative techniques is not at present known. Similar observations of metaphases with low chromosome numbers have been made in two other cases, a normal male and a normal female.

It is stressed that the counts in Table 1 are not to be interpreted as representative frequencies, since analyzable metaphases are not known to constitute a random sample of the metaphase population.

Chromosome analyses (Figs. 19, 21) of diploid metaphases (Figs. 18, 20) in this case are apparently identical with those from normal females. In no metaphase so analyzed (a total of five) was any indication of a heteromorphic sex-chromosome pair observed. Thus, the chromosomal sex of this cell type is female.

A list of the cell and tissue types in which the female sex chromatin pattern was observed is given in Table 2. All observations were made on Feulgen-fast green sections, except for those on the "drumsticks" (Davidson and Smith, 1954) in polymorphonu-

TABLE 1

Metaphase Chromosome Counts from Leukocytes in Short-Term Culture

Chromosome number	45 ±1	46	46 ±1	47	47 ±1	46 ER	47 ER
Number of metaphases	3	34	4	1	6	2	1

Only counts accurate to within ±1 chromosome are included. ER denotes endoreduplication. See text for further details.

TABLE 2

Cell and Tissue Types in Which Female Sex Chromatin Pattern Was Observed

1) Neutrophilic granulocytes in peripheral blood (Fig. 10)	Smear	Wright's stain
2) Buccal squamous epithelium (Fig. 9)	Smear	Feulgen-fast green
3) Epithelial cells of fallopian tube mucosa (Fig. 11)	Section	Feulgen-fast green
4) Epithelial cells of glands in endometrium (Fig. 12)	Section	Feulgen-fast green
5) Lutein cells of corpus luteum from ovotestis (Fig. 13)	Section	Feulgen-fast green
6) Cells in cumulus oophorus of follicular cysts	Section	Feulgen-fast green
7) Glandular epithelium of breast	Section	Feulgen-fast green
8) Cells within seminiferous tubules (Fig. 14)	Section	Feulgen-fast green
9) Interstitial cell of testis (Leydig cells) (Fig. 15)	Section	Feulgen-fast green
10) Epithelial cells of epididymal mucosa (Fig. 16)	Section	Feulgen-fast green
11) Smooth muscle cells (Fig. 17)	Section	Feulgen-fast green
12) Supporting connective tissue cells (fibrocytes) (Figs. 12, 16)	Section	Feulgen-fast green

clear neutrophil, which were from smears stained with Wright's stain. The proportion of nuclei of interstitial cells of the left testis which were observed to have sex chromatin was 38% (in 6 μ sections). Sex-chromatin frequency was estimated to be approximately the same in other cell types. Thus, the diagnosis of chromatin sex in all of the tissues examined agreed with the sex determined by chromosome analysis.

An observation which seems noteworthy was made with regard to the sex chromatin in the nuclei of smooth muscle cells. In such nuclei, there is an obvious preferential localization of the sex chromatin at one or the other tip (Fig. 17). This phenomenon has to our knowledge not been described previously, and is under further investigation.

DISCUSSION

The classification of various types of abnormal sex differentiation, along with possible etiologies, has been thoroughly discussed by Danon and Sachs (1957 and Grumbach and Barr (1958), among others. Our case would seem to fit the clinical diagnosis of "true hermaphrodite," on the basis of both male and female gonadal tissue having been histologically identified.

Cases of human intersexuality for which chromosome analyses have been reported thus far in the literature number three. The first (Ford *et al.*, 1958), clinically a case of Klinefelter's syndrome (and having a female sex chromatin pattern), was diagnosed as female on the basis of five metaphases classified as female and one as probably female. The second case (Jacobs and Strong, 1959) was an apparent male with ". . . gonadal dysgenesis with gynaecomastia and small testes associated with poor facial hair-growth and a high pitched voice." The individual's modal chromosome number proved to be 47, and on the basis of analysis of chromosome morphology in eight cells the possibility of an XXY sex-determining mechanism was proposed. The individual's sex-chromatin pattern was female. The third case (Chu and Giles, 1959) was a male pseudohermaphrodite, having a male sex-chromatin pattern. Chromosome determinations from nine cells, derived from thyroid biopsy material grown *in vitro*, showed 8 to have 46 chromosomes and one to have 47. The individual was XY.

It is not possible from the data at hand to resolve the genetic possibilities which might be involved in the case which has been described here. However, several such possibilities definitely may be ruled out. From the karyotype analyses of peripheral leukocytes and the sex chromatin constitution of several cell types, it may be stated that this individual is neither XY nor XO with regard to sex chromosome constitution. The karyotype analyses also indicate that the individual is not XXY.

Of the three most probable types of mosaic condition which might have been expected, *viz.*, XX-XXY, XX-XY, and XX-XO, the latter two can almost certainly be ruled out in all of the tissues examined on the basis of the observed relatively high frequencies of nuclei with sex chromatin present (indicating the presence of two X chromosomes in such nuclei (Reitalu, 1957)). The first possibility, XX-XXY, was not resolved in our study, although Sachs and Danon (1956) have stated that a chromocenter attributable to the Y chromosome can be recognized in certain epidermal nuclei and Reitalu (1957) has observed Y heterochromatin in fetal liver nuclei. Indeed, such mosaicism need not have been present in the single cell type from which karyotype analyses were made. Another possibility is that a mosaic condition might have been obscured by selective effects exerted by the *in vitro* environment.

Unfortunately, since our investigation was begun subsequent to the removal of the abnormal contents of the scrotal sacs, it was necessary to make sex chromatin determinations from those tissues fixed for routine histopathological diagnosis. Thus, it was not possible for us to make use of the method of Sachs and Danon (1956), which is reported to allow discrimination between X and Y chromocenters.

At least two other possible interpretations cannot be ruled out in this case. One is the strong likelihood of a genetic reversal of sex somewhat similar to that effected by the autosomal recessive gene mutation, "transformer," described in *Drosophila melanogaster* by Sturtevant (1945). The phenotype of female flies homozygous for this gene is male; it has not effect on genetic males. Interrogation of the presumed mother of this individual revealed it to be an adopted child, and it was not possible to obtain information relevant to the establishment of a pedigree.

The second possibility which we were unable to evaluate is that of a hormonal or other metabolic influence exerted on the fetus *in utero*. It is not unlikely that information of this kind might have been obtained from the real mother of the individual or her medical records, had they been available.

Regardless of the obscure nature of the very early embryological events in this case, it is virtually certain that the male gross anatomy of the patient is due to the presence of testicular tissue during virtually the entire course of fetal development. It has been well established, on the basis of fetal castration experiments in mammals (summarized by Jost, 1953), that the presence of a male gonad is required during fetal life for the differentiation of male genitalia. Castration of female fetuses does not suppress the differentiation of female genitalia. However, male fetuses castrated early develop as females, and those males castrated at progressively later times develop as intersexes with progressively increasing degrees of maleness. The case of the freemartin supports such evidence: the presence of a male gonad in the male member of dizygotic twins of opposite sex, sharing a common blood supply, affects the phenotype of the female member such that it acquires male characteristics, although its sex chromatin pattern (Moore, Graham, and Barr, 1957), and presumably its sex chromosome constitution, remain unchanged.

SUMMARY

The chromosome constitution and the sex chromatin pattern of cells from a human phenotypic intersex have been investigated. A case report is given which includes a description of the individual's gross anatomy, as well as endocrine studies, pre- and postoperative histological diagnoses, and surgical therapy. Although the external anatomy, including genitalia, was that of a male, histological examination revealed the presence of ovarian tissue, fallopian tube and endometrium, as well as testis. The modal chromosome number in metaphases of leukocytes derived from peripheral blood and after short-term culture was found to be diploid (2n = 46) and the sex chromosome constitution to be female (XX). The sex chromatin pattern of various other cell types was consistent with a genetic sex diagnosis of female. Convenient methods for the short-term *in vitro* cultivation of leukocytes from peripheral blood and for the analysis of their metaphase chromosomes are described. Some of the genetic and embryological factors which may be involved in this case are discussed briefly.

ADDENDUM

Since the present paper was submitted for publication, several papers have appeared relating defects in sex differentiation to chromosomal changes. One of these deals with a case of gonadal dysgenesis (Turner's syndrome), in which the majority of metaphases were observed to have 45 chromosomes and the sex chromosome constitution was interpreted as XO (Ford *et al.*, 1959b— see also Fraccaro *et al.*, 1959). The individual was sex chromatin negative. Another deals with a sex chromatin positive case showing both mongolism and the Klinefelter syndrome (Ford *et al.*, 1959a). In this case 48 chromosomes were present in all cells counted; the sex chromosome constitution was interpreted as XXY, and an additional small autosome was present, which is believed to be characteristic of mongolism (see also Jacobs *et al.*, 1959, Lejeune *et al.*, 1959a and b).

The demonstration of a presumptive human XXY-XX mosaic, who exhibited a sex-chromatin positive case of Klinefelter's syndrome (Ford *et al.*, 1959 c), is of particular interest with regard to the observations presented here. In their paper, 44 of the 65 cells counted had 47 chromosomes interpreted as XXY, or possibly XY and trisomic for one autosome) and 13 had 46 chromosomes (interpreted as XX). These observations, combined with those of Jacobs and Strong (1959) (see Discussion, above), are interpreted by Ford *et al.* 1959 c), as indicating that the Y chromosome in man is strongly male determining. The convincing demonstration by Welshons and Russell (1959) that mice with an XO sex chromosome constitution are fertile females, and thus that the mouse Y chromosome is male determining, lends strong support to this argument.

With this information in mind an attempt was made to analyze the two metaphases shown in Table 1 as having been counted at exactly 47 chromosomes. These two cells are not considered ideal for this purpose, and the origin of the extra chromosome remains

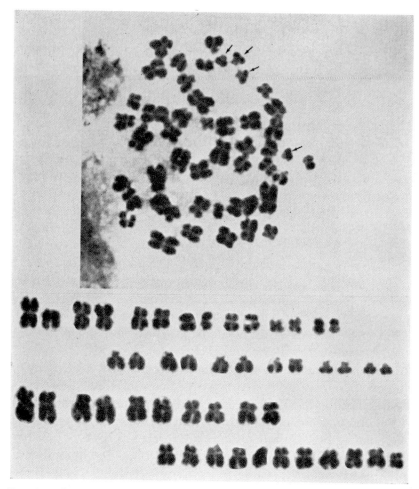

Fig. 22. Chromosome analysis of metaphase interpreted as having 47 chromosomes. Acetic orcein squash preparation, 90× oil immersion objective. Same magnification as Figs. 20 and 21. See text of Addendum for further details.

obscure. However, the analyses were sufficiently accurate to rule out an unaltered Y chromosome as the additional one (Fig. 22). The normal Y in man has been described as being in the size range of the smallest acrocentric autosomes (arrows, Fig. 22) and as being acrocentric or telocentric—see Chu and Giles (1959), Tjio and Puck (1958), and Ford *et al.* (1958). Thus, barring the remote possibility that the Y is present in a translocation configuration, sex chromosome mosaicism is not present in this cell type, although as mentioned in the Discussion above it might exist elsewhere in the individual.

REFERENCES

Barr, M. L., and Bertram, E. G. 1949. A morphological distinction between neurones of the male and female, and the behavior of the nucleolar satellite during accelerated nucleoprotein synthesis. *Nature 163:*676-677.

Bloom, W. 1938. Tissue cultures of blood and blood-forming tissues. *Handbook of Hematology,* ed. by H. Downey. New York: P. B. Hoeber, Inc. Section XX, pp. 1471-1585.

Bond, V. P., Cronkhite, E. P. Fliedner, T. M., and Schork, P. 1958. Deoxyribonucleic acid synthesizing cells in peripheral blood of normal human beings. *Science 128:*202-203.

Chu, E. H. Y., and Giles, N. H. 1959. Human chromosome complements in normal somatic cells in culture. *Am. J. Human Genet. 11:*63-79.

Davidson, W. M., and Smith, D. R. 1954. A morphological sex difference in the polymorphonuclear neutrophil leukocytes. *Brit. M. J. ii:*6-7.

Danon, M., and Sachs, L. 1957. Sex chromosomes and human sexual development. *Lancet ii:*20-25.

Ford, C. E., Jacobs, P. A., and Lajtha, L. G. 1958. Human somatic chromosomes. *Nature 181:*1565-1568.

Ford, C. E., Jones, K. W., Miller, O. J., Mittwoch, U., Penrose, L. S., Ridler, M., and Shapiro, A. 1959a. The chromosomes in a patient showing both mongolism and the Klinefelter syndrome. *Lancet i:*709-710.

Ford, C. E., Jones, K. W., Polani, P. E., de Almeida, J. C., and Briggs, J. H. 1959b. A sex-chromosome anomaly in a case of gonadal dysgenesis (Turner's syndrome). *Lancet i:*711-713.

Ford, C. E., Polani, P. E., Briggs, J. H., and Bishop, P. M. F. 1959c. A presumptive human XXY/XX mosaic. *Nature 183:*1030-1032.

Fraccaro, M., Kaijser, K., and Lindsten, J. 1959. Chromosome complement in gonadal dysgenesis (Turner's syndrome). *Lancet i:*886 (letter to the editor).

Graham, M. A., and Barr, M. L. 1952. A sex difference in the morphology of metabolic nuclei in somatic cells of the cat. *Anat. Rec. 112:*709-723.

Grumbach, M. M., and Barr, M. L. 1958. Cytologic tests of chromosomal sex in relation to sexual anomalies in man. *Recent Prog. in Hormone Res. XIV:*255-324.

Hungerford, D. A. 1955. Chromosome numbers of ten-day fetal mouse cells. *J. Morph. 97:*497-509.

Hungerford, D. A., and di Berardino, M. 1958. Cytological effects of prefixation treatment. *J. Biophys. Biochem. Cytol. 4:*391-400.

Jacobs, P. A., Baikie, A. G., Court Brown, W. M., and Strong, J. A. 1959. The somatic chromosomes in mongolism. *Lancet i:*710.

Jacobs, P. A., and Strong, J. A. 1959. A case of human intersexuality having a possible XXY sex-determining mechanism. *Nature 183:*302-303.

Jost, A. 1953. Problems of fetal endocrinology: The gonadal and hypophyseal hormones. *Recent Prog. in Hormone Res. VIII:*379-413.

Lejeune, J., Gautier, M., and Turpin, R. 1959a. Les chromosomes humains en culture de tissus. *C. R. Acad. Sci., Paris 248:*602-603.

Lejeune, J., Gautier, M., and Turpin, R. 1959b. Étude des chromosomes somatiques de neuf enfants mongoliens. *C. R. Acad. Sci., Paris 248:*1721-1722.

Levan, A., and Hauschka, T. S. 1953. Endomitotic reduplication mechanisms in ascites tumors of the mouse. *J. Nat. Cancer Inst. 14:*1-43.

Moore, K. L., Graham, M. A., and Barr, M. L. 1953. The detection of chromosomal sex in hermaphrodites from a skin biopsy. *Surg. Gyn. Obst. 96:*641-648.

Moore, K. L., Graham, M. A., and Barr, M. L. 1957. The sex chromatin of the bovine freemartin. *J. Exp. Zool. 135:*101-125.

Nowell, P. C., Hungerford, D. A., and Brooks, C. D. 1958. Chromosomal characteristics of normal and leukemic human leukocytes after short-term tissue culture. *Proc. Am. Ass. Cancer Res. 2:*331-332 (abstr.).

Osgood, E. E., and Brooke, J. H. 1955. Continuous tissue culture of leukocytes from human leukemic bloods by application of "gradient" principles. *Blood X:*1010-1022.

Osgood, E. E., and Krippaehne, M. L. 1955. The gradient tissue culture method. *Exp. Cell Res. 9:*116-127.

Reitalu, J. 1957. Observations on the so-called sex chromatin in man. *Acta Gen. Med. et Gem. 6:*393-402.

Sachs, L., and Danon, M. 1956. The diagnosis of the sex chromosomes in human tissues. *Genetica 28:*201-216.

Sturtevant, A. H. 1945. A gene in *Drosophila melanogaster* that transforms females into males. *Genetics 30:*297-299.

Tjio, J. H., and Puck, T. T. 1959. The somatic chromosomes of man. *Proc. Nat. Acad. Sc. 44:*1229-1237.

Welshons, W. J., and Russell, L. B. 1959. The Y-chromosome as the bearer of male determining factors in the mouse. *Proc. Nat. Acad. Sc. 45:*560-566.

23

A CASE OF HUMAN INTERSEX WITH
MOSAICISM OF TYPE XY/XO*

Kurt Hirschhorn, M.D., Wayne H. Decker, M.D., and
Herbert L. Cooper, M.D.

During the past year a number of reports have appeared in the literature concerning chromosomal aberrations discovered in human pathological states.[1-10] Most of these reports deal with conditions in which the chromosome number of the somatic cells has deviated from the normal human diploid number of 46. Thus, in mongolism a chromosome number of 47 with trisomy for one of the smallest acrocentric autosomes has been reported by several authors.[1, 2] In Klinefelter's syndrome, a chromosome number of 47 has also been found,[3] the abnormal number being due to the presence of an XXY sex chromosome constitution. In cases of mongolism where Klinefelter's syndrome also occurs coincidentally, a chromosome number of 48 has been found, representing both trisomy for the small autosome and the XXY sex chromosome constitution.[4, 11] In Turner's syndrome (gonadal dysgenesis) a chromosome number of 45 has been found[5a, b] due to the presence of only a single sex determining chromosome, resulting in an XO sex chromosome constitution. As predicted by the theory that non-disjunction at meiosis is the origin of such sex chromosome abnormalities, a patient with XXX constitution and a chromosome number of 47 was found. This patient exhibited secondary amenorrhea and sexual infantilism.[6]

Reprinted from the *New England Journal of Medicine*, 263:1044-1048, 1960.

From the Departments of Medicine and Obstetrics and Gynecology, New York University Medical Center.

We are grateful for the technical assistance of Mr. Orlando Rendon.

* This work was supported in part by grants from the American Heart Association, Inc. and the National Heart Institute of the U. S. Public Health Service (Grant No. H-2202) and was done during the tenure of an Advanced Research Fellowship of the American Heart Association of one of the authors (K. H.).

Other reports have dealt with abnormalities of chromosome morphology, such as the translocation found by Turpin *et al.*[7] in a case with multiple congenital skeletal abnormalities. Atypical chromosomes have also been found in some cases of acute leukemia.[8] Another group of abnormalities found in chromosomal analyses are cases where a normal chromosome pattern that does not agree with the phenotypic sex of the patient is found. Thus, Harnden and Stewart[9] have reported a case of pure gonadal dysgenesis in a female with primary amenorrhea who had ovarian hypoplasia but none of the other features of the Turner's syndrome. A sex chromosome pattern of XY was found despite the presence of uterus, fallopian tubes and vagina.

Several cases of another type of chromosomal anomaly, that of mosaicism, have been described in the literature.[10, 12, 13] Ford *et al.* found a case of Klinefelter's syndrome where two types of cells were found in the bone marrow: some with XXY, and others with XX sex chromosome constitution.[10] In addition, Ford has described some cases of Turner's syndrome with mosaicism, where the cells showed a mixture of types with XX and XO chromosome constitutions.[12] Fraccaro *et al.*[13] have reported another such case.

It is the purpose of this paper to present an example of a hitherto unreported type of mosaicism, where bone marrow cells showed a mixture of XY and XO sex chromosome constitutions. In addition, this case is of interest because it may represent the first demonstration of mosaicism in a true hermaphrodite.

CASE REPORT

On 8 August, 1959, baby M. S. was delivered at 40 weeks gestation after an uneventful pregnancy and labor. The mother had been given no hormone therapy and had had no radiation exposure immediately prior to or during her pregnancy. She had five previous pregnancies. These five children are all living and well except for one boy who is said to have a moderate hypospadias.

At delivery M. S. was noted to have abnormal external genitalia. There was a phallus the size of a penis of the average newborn male. The foreskin was lacking and an external urethral meatus could not be identified. A vaginal orifice was present and normally

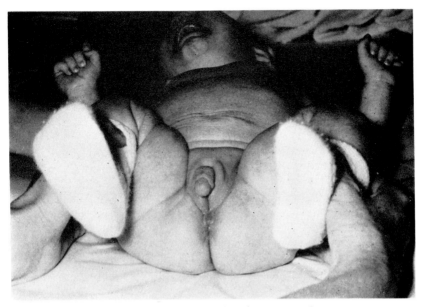

Fig. 1. External genitalia of patient M.S.

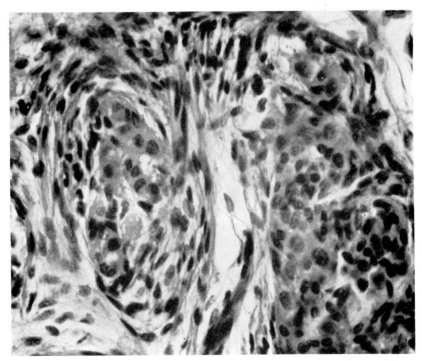

Fig. 2. Photomicrograph of histological section of gonadal biopsy from patient M.S. showing area with nest of cuboid cells.

located and the labia majora were sufficiently enlarged to simu-
late scrota. They did not contain testes, nor could these be identified inguinally (Fig. 1).

A urologist was able to locate the urethral orifice beneath the
base of the phallus. Intravenous pyelography showed a normal
urinary system. Vaginograms demonstrated a vaginal canal with

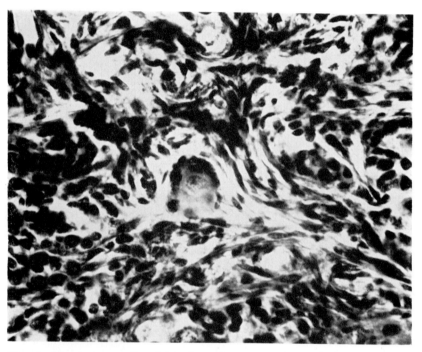

Fig. 3. Photomicrograph of histological section of gonadal biopsy from
patient M.S. showing ovarian follicle.

a small projection from its upper end. This was interpreted as
possibly representing partial filling of the uterus.

Other studies included routine blood count, urinalysis and blood
chemistries, all of which were normal. Urinary 17-ketosteroid
excretion was normal for a newborn child (av. 1.9 mg/24 hrs.).
No urinary pregnanetriol excretion was detectable. Long bone
roentgenograms revealed normal maturation.

Sex chromatin studies on both skin biopsy and buccal mucosa
showed a chromatin negative pattern. No "drumsticks" were found
in polymorphonuclear leukocytes in a smear of peripheral blood.

The child is under the care of one of the authors (W. H. D.) who performed a laparotomy when the patient was four and one-half months old. Surgery revealed an apparently normal uterus, tubes and two gonads in size and position identical to ovaries. A portion of the right gonad was removed for biopsy. Histological examination of this tissue[14] showed the presence of dense fibrous

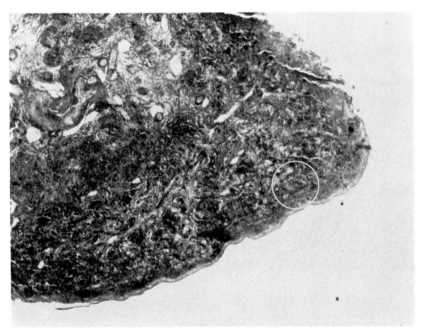

Fig. 4. Photomicrograph of histological section of gonadal biopsy from patient M.S. showing tubular structures near cortex.

stroma, such as that found in ovarian tissue. In the hilar area there were nests of cuboid cells which were interpreted as rete-like structures (Fig. 2). On careful search two areas were found which were identified as ovarian follicles with ova (Fig. 3). Near the cortex there were also tubular structures interpreted by some pathologists as early seminiferous tubules (Fig. 4).

Chromosome Examination

A specimen of bone marrow was aspirated from the iliac crest and cultured according to a modification of the method of Fraccaro *ea al.*,[15] described in detail elsewhere.[16] After five days in

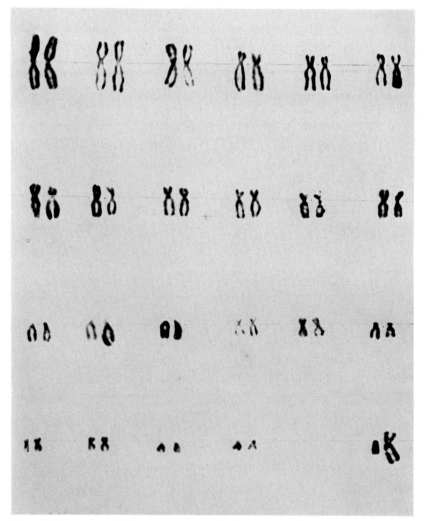

Fig. 5. Karyotype of bone marrow cell showing 46 chromosomes and XY
sex chromosome constitution.

culture, a monolayer of cells had been grown on a cover slip and
these were examined according to the method previously mentioned. Colchicine was not used. Twenty mitotic figures in metaphase were found that were felt to be clear enough for exact
chromosome counts, which were made independently by two investigators. Of these twenty cells, 12 were found to contain 45
chromosomes, which on matching revealed an XO sex chromosome

constitution. The remaining eight cells were found to contain 46 chromosomes and on matching showed a typical male chromosome constitution (XY) (Figs. 5 and 6). It is therefore inferred that two cell types are present in the marrow of this patient, one type with the XO chromosome constitution and the other with the XY constitution.

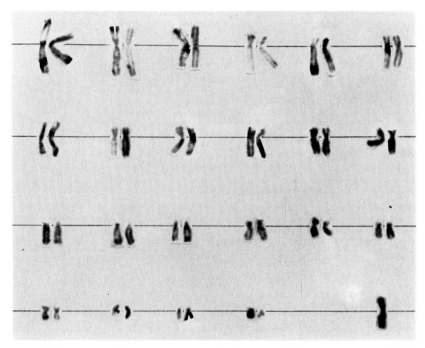

Fig. 6. Karyotype of bone marrow cell showing 45 chromosomes and XO sex chromosome constitution.

It is noted that the chromosome thought to be the Y is somewhat longer than the Y chromosome usually found in the normal male. According to Chu and Giles[17] the Y chromosome is generally the smallest of the five small acrocentrics. However, in our experience, the Y chromosome has been more variable in size than the other chromosomes. A similar observation has been made by others.[21]

DISCUSSION

While it is not yet proved, the physical findings and the interpretation of the gonadal biopsy in this case suggest that the patient may be a true hermaphrodite. Chromosomal examination of a true hermaphrodite has been reported twice previously in the literature.[18, 19] In both cases an XX pattern was demonstrated without any evidence of the presence of mosaicism. However, the possibility that mosaicism existed was discussed.[18] In our case there is evidence that mosaicism is present, with part of the cells carrying the XY karyotype and part carrying the XO karyotype. Our results showed 60% of the XO type. The 95% binomial confidence limits for our results, allowing a 10% frequency of technical error of one chromosome at each count, indicate that our sample came from a population that had some true mean value from 36 to 82% XO cells.

Court Brown *et al.*[22] suggest three criteria which should be met before making a diagnosis of mosaicism on the basis of chromosome analysis:

1. "The number of cells with counts different from the modal number must be more than can reasonably be attributed to chance."

2. "The excess of atypical cells must be demonstrable in two or more separate bone marrow examinations and preferably in two or more tissues."

3. The cells with the non-modal chromosome number should all have the same karyotype. (Our paraphrase.)

In the case under consideration, the first and third criteria are well satisfied. The second criterion is not as precisely fulfilled. While we did not perform more than one bone marrow aspiration on our patient, we did set up several separate intermediate term cell cultures from the original specimen and they were examined independently, giving similar results in each case. As indicated below, and as pointed out by Court Brown *et al.*,[22] the necessity for demonstrating mosaicism in more than one tissue is doubtful, since in the same patient bone marrow may exhibit mosaicism while skin may not. On the basis of these considerations, we feel that the diagnosis of mosaicism in our patient is justified.

The mosaicism is most probably due to the accidental loss of the Y chromosome, during anaphase, from one of the products of mitosis early in the course of embryonic development. This would result in a normal XY cell and an XO cell, both of which might continue to develop, forming parts of the resultant individual. If the loss of the Y chromosome occurred at the very first division of the zygote, one would expect at most 50% of the individual to consist of abnormal cells. The 95% confidence interval for our results includes the possibility that our sample came from a population with 50% XO cells. However, this does not mean that the cell population from which our sample was drawn (bone marrow) was equivalent to the population of cells comprising the entire individual. In fact it is unlikely from the point of view of probability that the mitotic accident occurred at the first cell division and that the entire body of our patient is a 50-50 mosaic of XY and XO cells. It is more probable that the error occurred during the development of the embryonic mesoderm, from which the blood cells are thought to be developed.[20] Only a small portion of this primitive tissue may have been affected, but it may have involved a large proportion of the cells which ultimately developed into the blood elements of the infant. This last proportion could easily have been any value within our confidence interval.

In view of the clinical picture and biopsy findings in our case, we may hypothesize that the genitalia and gonads were also involved to a great extent by the mosaicism. These structures are also mesodermal in origin[20] and may well have sprung from a mixture of cell types similar to the bone marrow predecessors. It is unfortunate that no genital or gonadal tissue was set aside for tissue culture at laparotomy, as chromosomal analysis of such material would be exceedingly enlightening. However, plastic surgery is contemplated for the patient at some time in the future, and at that time genital tissue will be secured.

SUMMARY

A case of intersexuality discovered at birth is presented. Clinical and histological evidence suggests that the patient may be a true hermaphrodite. Examination of the chromosomes of bone marrow cells indicates the presence of a mosaicism of cells with XY and XO sex chromosome constitutions.

ADDENDUM

We have recently learned that through the courtesy of Dr. Melvin Grumbach of Columbia University College of Physicians and

Surgeons, samples of bone marrow and skin from this patient were sent to Dr. Ernest H. Y. Chu at Oak Ridge National Laboratory. Dr. Chu and one of the authors (K. H.) examined the chromosomes of this material. The bone marrow again demonstrated mosaicism of cells with XY and XO sex chromosome constitution, thereby satisfying Court Brown's second criterion for mosaicism. The cells of the skin all had 46 chromosomes with XY sex chromosome constitution. This appears to confirm our hypothesis of the loss of the Y chromosome during the development of the mesoderm.

REFERENCES

1. Lejeune, J., Gautier, M., Turpin, R., Les chromosomes humains en culture de tissus. *Compte Rend. Acad. Sci. (Paris)*, *248*:602, 1959.
2. Jacobs, P. A., Baikie, A. G., Court Brown, W. M., Strong, J. A., The Somatic Chromosomes in Mongolism, *Lancet 1*:710, 1959.
3. Jacobs, P. A., and Strong, J. A., A Case of Human Intersexuality having a possible XXY sex-determining mechanism, *Nature 183*:302, 1959.
4. Ford, C. E., Jones, K. W., Miller, O. J., Mittwoch, U., Penrose, L. S., Rider, M., and Shapiro, A., Chromosomes in a patient showing both mongolism and the Klinefelter's syndrome. *Lancet 1*:709, 1959.
5a. Ford, C. E., Jones, K. W., Polani, P. E., Almeida, J. C. de, Briggs, J. H., A sex-chromosome anomaly in a case of gonadal dysgenesis (Turner's syndrome). *Lancet 1*:711, 1959.
5b. Fraccaro, M., Kaijser, K., Lindsten, J., Chromosome complement in gonadal dysgenesis (Turner's syndrome). *Lancet 1*:886, 1959. (Letter to the editor.)
6. Jacobs, P. A., Baikie, A. G., Court Brown, W. M., MacGregor, T. N., Maclean, N., and Harnden, D. G., Evidence for the existence of the human "Super Female." *Lancet 2*:423, 1959.
7. Turpin, R., Lejeune, J., Lafourcade, J., Gautier, M., Aberrations chromosomiques et maladies humaines. La polydysspondylie a 45 chromosomes. *C. R. Acad. des Sci. (Paris)*, *248*:3636, 1959.
8. Baikie, A. G., Court Brown, W. M. Jacobs, P. A., and Milne, J. S., Chromosome studies in human leukemia, *Lancet 2*:425, 1959.
9. Harnden, D. G., and Stewart, J. S. S., The chromosomes in a case of pure gonadal dysgenesis, *Brit. Med. J. 5162*:1285, 1959.
10. Ford, C. E., Polani, P. E., Briggs, J. H., and Bishop, P. M. F., A Presumptive Human XXY/XX Mosaic. *Nature 183*:1030, 1959.
11. Lanman, J., Sklarin, B. S., Cooper, H. L., and Hirschhorn, K., Klinefelter's syndrome in a ten-month-old mongolian idiot: report of a case with chromosome analysis. *New Eng. J. Med. 263*:887, 1960.

12. Ford, C. E., Human Cytogenetics: Its present place and future possibilities. *Am. J. Hum. Gen. 12*:104, 1960.

13. Fraccaro, M., Gemzell, C. A., Lindsten, J., Plasma level of growth hormone and chromosome complement in four patients with gonadal dysgenesis. *Acta Endocr.*, 1960. (In press.)

14. We are grateful to Dr. Warren Nelson of the Rockefeller Institute and to Drs. M. Kuschner, R. Dische, and L. P. Shea of the Dept. of Pathology of N.Y.U. Medical Center for their assistance.

15. Fraccaro, M., Kaijser, K., Lindsten, J., Somatic chromosome complement in continuously cultured cells of two individuals with gonadal dysgenesis. *Ann. Human Gen. 24*:45, 1960.

16. Hirschhorn, K., and Cooper, H. L., Chromosomal Aberrations in Human Disease: A review of the present status of cytogenetics in medicine. This volume pp. 00-00.

17. Chu, E. H. Y., and Giles, N. H., Human chromosome complements in normal somatic cells in culture, *Am. J. Human Genetics 11*:63, 1959.

18. Hungerford, D. A., Donnelly, A. J., Nowell, P. C., and Beck, S., The Chromosome Constitution of a Human Phenotypic Intersex, *Amer. J. Human Genetics 11*:3, 1959.

19. Harnden, D. G., and Armstrong, C. M., The chromosomes of a true hermaphrodite, *Brit. Med. J. 5162*:1287, 1959.

20. Brash, J. C., Introduction to Human Embryology in *Cunningham's Textbook of Anatomy*, 9th Ed., Oxford University Press, 1956, pp. 17-104.

21. Fraccaro, M., Personal communication.

22. Court Brown, W. M., Jacobs, P. A., Doll, R., Interpretation of chromosome counts made on bone marrow cells. *Lancet 1*:160, 1960.

24

CHROMOSOMAL SEX IN THE SYNDROME
OF TESTICULAR FEMINISATION

Patricia A. Jacobs, B.Sc. St. And., A. G. Baikie, M.B. Glasg.,
M.R.C.P.E., W. M. Court Brown, M.B., B.Sc. St. And., F.F.R.,
Hugh Forrest, M.B. Glasg., J. R. Roy, M.B. Glasg., F.R.F.P.S.,
M.R.C.P.E., D.P.M., John S. S. Stewart, M.B. Glasg., and
Bernard Lennox, M.D. Durh., Ph.D. Lond., F.R.F.P.S., M.R.C.P.

A MONG the various groups of human sexual anomalies there
are three in which the nuclear sex is at variance with the
phenotypic sex. These are (1) the chromatin-positive cases of
Klinefelter's syndrome, (2) the chromatin-negative cases of Turner's syndrome and gonadal dysgenesis in apparent females, and
(3) apparent females who are chromatin-negative on nuclear
sexing and who have the features of the testicular feminisation
syndrome. It has recently been shown that the first anomaly is
due to the presence of an extra sex chromosome, so that these
patients are XXY (Jacobs and Strong 1959, Ford, Jones, Miller,
Mittwoch, Penrose, Ridler, and Shapiro 1959; Ford, Polani,
Briggs, and Bishop 1959), and that the second anomaly depends
on the absence of one sex chromosome, so that these patients are
XO (Ford, Jones, Polani, Almeida, and Briggs 1959). We report
here the determination of chromosomal sex in four instances of
the third anomaly—testicular feminisation.

In the complete expression of this syndrome the external genitalia are female, pubic and axillary hair are absent or scanty, the
habitus at puberty is typically female, and there is primary amenorrhoea. Testes can be found either within the abdomen, or in
the inguinal canals, or in the labia majora, and as a rule the vagina

Reprinted from *The Lancet*, October 17, 1959, pp. 591-592.

Our thanks are due to Mr. W. M. Dennison, Prof. T. Ferguson Rodger, and to
Dr. E. G. Oastler for permitting us to examine their cases. We are also grateful
to Miss M. Brunton for technical assistance.

278

is incompletely developed. An epididymis and vas deferens are commonly present on both sides, and there may be a rudimentary uterus and fallopian tubes. The condition is familial and is transmitted through the maternal line (Grumbach and Barr 1958).

CASES AND INVESTIGATION

Case 1, born in 1949, was admitted to hospital in February, 1958, for repair of inguinal herniæ. The vagina was about 2 cm. long, terminated in a blind pouch. During the repair of the herniæ a recognisable testis was found in each inguinal canal. At laparotomy last May the testes were seen to be in the position normally occupied by the ovaries, and there were neither uterus nor fallopian tubes. Histologically the left gonad showed the features of a prepubertal undescended testis. The patient's mental development was normal for her age. The nuclear sex, as determined from skin biopsy material and buccal smears, was chromatin-negative. Colour-vision was normal.

Case 2, born in 1957, was admitted in May, 1958, for the repair of inguinal herniæ. The right inguinal canal contained a small testis, with the same histological features as in case 1. A vagina 1-2 cm. long was present, but there was no evidence of a cervix and no uterus was palpable. In view of the child's age tests of intelligence and of colour-vision were not undertaken. The nuclear sex (skin biopsy and buccal smear) was chromatin-negative.

Case 3, born in 1926, has been admitted to hospital three times for mental depression. She has primary amenorrhoea, and in 1947 she was told that she had no uterus. On examination in 1958 little pudendal hair was present and no pubic or axillary hair. Breast development was normal, but the vagina was only about 5 cm. in length and there was no evidence of a uterus. The patient was of less than average intelligence, and was found to be colour-blind. The nuclear sex of a skin biopsy was a chromatin-negative.

Case 4, born in 1936 was admitted in March, 1951, because of bilateral inguinal swellings and primary amenorrhoea. Breast development was normal, but pubic and axillary hair were absent. At laparotomy neither uterus nor fallopian tubes were found. Histological examination of material from the gonads showed testicular tissue. The nuclear sex (skin biopsy and buccal smears) was chromatin-negative. The patient had normal colour-vision, but a similarly affected sister and a normal brother were colour-blind.

Chromosome Examination

Sternal marrow from cases 1, 2, and 4, and iliac-crest marrow from case 3, were cultured and treated as described by Ford, Jacobs, and Lajtha (1958). The chromosome-counts are shown in the table.

CHROMOSOME-COUNTS ON MARROW CELLS: DISTRIBUTION OF
CHROMOSOME NUMBERS IN EACH CASE

Chromosome Number	42	43	44	45	46	47	48	4n	8n	8n<
No. Case 1	1	0	2	3	32	2	2	0	1	1
of Case 2	1	0	0	2	11	0	0	0	0	0
Cells Case 3	1	0	1	2	28	1	0	0	0	0
Counted Case 4	0	0	0	2	21	0	0	0	0	0

In all four marrows the great majority of cells had a normal diploid content of 46 chromosomes. There is no evidence that, in these four marrows, departures from this number are due to any cause other than artefacts produced during the preparation of the material.

Only one cell in case 1 was suitable for detailed analysis, but several suitable cells were available from cases 2 and 3, and many from case 4. In all the cells analysed in detail there were 5 small acrocentric chromosomes and 15 medium-sized metacentric chromosomes, indicating that the normal male complement of one X chromosome and one Y chromosome was present (see figure).

DISCUSSION

The observation that these patients with the testicular feminization syndrome have a normal diploid number of chromosomes and an XY chromosomal sex is consistent with the observation that they are chromatin-negative, and excludes an aberration of chromosome number as the cause of the disorder. The latter explanation, which would imply an XXY constitution in these cases, has been discussed by several authors (Petterson and Bonnier 1937, Beatty 1957, Danon and Sachs 1957). Nucleolar chromocentre anomalies were described by Danon and Sachs who regarded these as evidence of the presence of three sex chromosomes; but such an interpretation of nucleolar chromocentre ap-

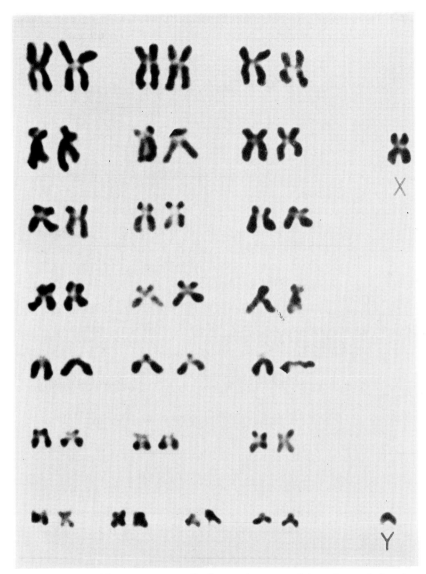

Chromosomes of bone-marrow cell of case 4, arranged in pairs and showing the presumptive X and Y.

pearances is probably not reliable (Lennox, Serr, and Ferguson-Smith 1959). Of the skin biopsies taken in these cases, though all were sufficient for recognition of sex chromatin, only two were of the very high quality needed for studies of nucleolar chromocentres. Neither of these showed any unusual frequency of nuclei with three such chromocentres. Furthermore, the colour blind state of case 3 and of the sister of case 4 makes it very improbable that two X chromosomes are present (Stewart 1959).

Our findings support the suggestion of Grumbach and Barr (1958) that testicular feminisation is associated with either a sex-linked recessive gene or a sex-limited autosomal dominant gene. Apparent females with testicular feminization are sex-reversed males. This is consistent with the results of analysis of the familial cases, which shows that the ratio of females to the sum of the affected males and normal males does not significantly differ from an expected ratio of 1 to 1 (Grumbach and Barr 1958).

REFERENCES

Beatty, R. A. (1957) Parthenogenesis and Polyploidy in Mammalian Development; p. 54. London.

Danon, M., Sachs, L. (1957) *Lancet ii*:20.

Ford, C. E., Jacobs, P. A., Lajtha, L. G. (1958) *Nature, Lond. 181*:1565.

——— Jones, K. W., Miller, O. J., Mittwoch, U., Penrose, L. S., Ridler, M., Shapiro, A. (1959) *Lancet i*:709.

——— Polani, P. E., Almeida, J. C. de, Briggs, J. H. (1959) *ibid.* p. 711.

——— Polani, P. E., Briggs, J. H., Bishop, P. M. F. (1959) *Nature, Lond. 183*:1030.

Grumbach, M. M., Barr, M. L. (1958) *Recent Prog. Hormone Res. 14*:255.

Jacobs, P. A., Strong, J. A. (1959) *Nature, Lond. 183*:302.

Lennox, B., Serr, D. M., Ferguson-Smith, M. A. (1959) *J. Endocrin.* (in the press).

Petterson, G., Bonnier, G. (1937) *Hereditas 23*:49.

Stewart, J. S. S. (1959) *Lancet ii*:592.

25

UNUSUAL CASE OF GONADAL DYSGENESIS (TURNER'S SYNDROME)

A. W. SPENCE, M.A., M.D., F.R.C.P., AND
C. W. H. HAVARD, M.A., D.M., M.R.C.P.

TURNER'S (1938) syndrome is characterized by infantilism, shortness of stature, webbing of the neck, and cubitus valgus, but numerous other congenital abnormalities have been described. Turner made no mention of the condition of the gonads. Varney, Kenyon, and Koch (1942) and Albright, Smith, and Fraser (1942) demonstrated in this disorder a high urinary excretion of gonadotrophin, and from this concluded that the infantilism was due to primary ovarian insufficiency. Previous authors, tabulated by Wilkins and Fleischmann (1944), had described similar cases in which rudimentary ovaries had been found at laparotomy or at necropsy. Wilkins and Fleischmann (1944), observing that the "ovary" consisted only of a primitive genital ridge composed of stroma-like cells and showing no proliferation of the epithelium nor primordial germ cells, proposed the term "ovarian agenesis" for this condition.

Subsequently Grumbach, Van Wyk, and Wilkins (1955) showed that most of their patients with this disturbance had a male chromatin sex pattern, and considered that the condition exemplified an extreme form of male pseudohermaphroditism. On this account Wilkins (1957) applied the term "gonadal aplasia" for this disorder, using the wider term "gonadal dysgenesis" for the entire

Reprinted from the *British Medical Journal,* December 12, 1959, Vol. ii, pp. 1288-1291.

We are indebted to Dr. E. Sanders, of Salisbury, Southern Rhodesia, for referring this patient to one of us (A. W. S.). Our thanks are due to Drs. R. D. Bulbrook and F. C. Greenwood, of the Clinico-Pathological Laboratories, Royal College of Surgeons of England, for their estimation of the urinary oestrogens, pregnanediol, and gonadotrophins, and to the members of the pathological and radiological departments, St. Bartholomew's Hospital, for the other investigations.

group of defects in the development of the gonads. Ford *et al.* (1959), however, subsequently found that a patient with gonadal dysgenesis and chromatin negative possessed 45 chromosomes instead of the normal 46. They concluded that the sex-chromosome constitution of the patient was XO, and emphasized that such a person should not be referred to as a chromosomal male, as she was a female with an abnormal genotype.

Four cases of gonadal dysgenesis have been reported by Sellheim (1924), Pela (1935), Pich (1937), and Tronci (1938) in which ovarian development had proceeded to a varying degree before arrest took place. In Pela's case, that of a woman aged 36 and 74 in. (188 cm.) in height, the ovaries were "the size of orange seeds," and on histological examination no primordial follicles were seen. In Tronci's case, that of a woman aged 20 and 61 in. (155 cm.) in height, the ovaries measured 6 by 2.5 mm. in diameter; microscopically, germinal epithelium was noted, but there were no primordial follicles. Pich described the case of a woman aged 29 with infantilism, absence of pubic and axillary hair, coarctation of the aorta, and normal stature, whose ovaries measured 28 by 5 by 3 mm. and 30 by 4 by 2 mm.; histological examination revealed proliferative germinal epithelium and fairly numerous primordial follicles. In Sellheim's case, a woman, aged 21 and also of normal stature, the ovaries measured 7.5 by 2.5 mm., and numerous primordial follicles were present. Since the urinary gonadotrophins were not estimated in any of these cases it is impossible to say whether the hormonal deficiency was primarily ovarian or primarily pituitary.

It is the purpose of this paper to record the case of a patient with infantilism, several of the congenital abnormalities of Turner's syndrome, and greatly increased urinary gonadotrophin associated with ovaries which, though of normal size, contained a diminished number of follicles showing no evidence of maturation.

CASE REPORT

A girl aged 17 was admitted to St. Bartholomew's Hospital complaining of amenorrhoea, shortness of stature, and deformity of the spine. Her birth weight was only 4 lb. (1.8 kg.), though the pregnancy had run to full term; delivery was normal. She walked and talked at the usual stages, and at school she was considered to have been above the average intelligence for her age. She had always been small, and for several years her weight has remained unchanged. For many years her parents had observed a deformity of her back. In 1956 she attended a poliomyelitis clinic in Salis-

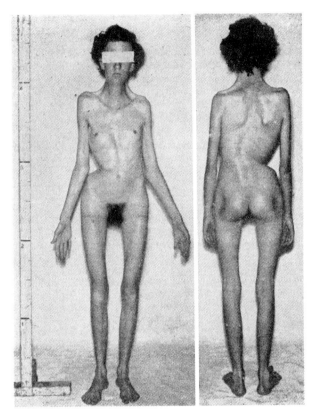

Fig. 1. Photographs of the patient.

bury, Southern Rhodesia, where she lived, but there was a difference of opinion on whether the spinal deformity was due to poliomyelitis: her mother did not know whether she had had poliomyelitis, though there were numerous cases of this disease in Salisbury at the time. She claimed to have menstruated for three days in December, 1957, but apart from this occasion there has been complete amenorrhoea.

During her childhood she contracted chicken-pox and whooping-cough, but had never suffered from mumps. During the two years before her admission to hospital she had recurrent attacks of abdominal colic localized in the right iliac fossa. Her parents and her two brothers are normal and healthy.

Physical Examination (Fig. 1).—She was an intelligent girl with a high-pitched piping voice. Weight 54 lbs. (24.5 kg.); height 57 in. (144.7 cm.), span 56½ in. (143.5 cm.), symphysis pubis to the ground 29½ in. (74.9 cm.), symphysis pubis to the vertex 27½ in. (69.8 cm.). (The limb proportions are approximately normal when due account is taken of her severe kyphoscoliosis.)

Musculo-skeletal System.—She was very thin and the musculature was poorly developed. Both deltoid muscles were greatly wasted and she was unable to lift her arms above her head. There was marked webbing of the neck, and the scapulae were winged owing to wasting of the trapezii. The mandible as poorly developed, the hard palate was high-arched and narrow, and the teeth were crowded. The clavicles were increased in length, and the manubrium sterni was at a lower level than normal so that the clavicles had a marked downward inclination medially. There was bilateral cubitus valgus. The spine showed severe kyphoscoliosis, which had resulted in tilting of the pelvis with apparent shortening of the left leg.

Skin and Hair-growth.—Her colour was somewhat sallow, but there was no abnormal pigmentation. The texture of the skin was normal. The growth of the axillary and the pubic hair was normal, and there was a moderate growth of downy hair over the limbs. The scalp hair and hair-line were normal.

Breasts and Genitalia.—There was very slight development of the breasts, and the nipples were small but pigmented. The vulva was infantile. The clitoris was normal.

Other Systems.—The cardiovascular, respiratory, and nervous systems were normal; pulse rate 80; blood-pressure 105/70. There was marked tenderness in the right iliac fossa. The urine contained no albumin and no sugar, and the deposit was normal. In a water-load-excretion test over 80% was excreted within four hours. Laryngoscopic examination (Mr. J. C. Hogg) revealed an infantile type of larynx. The visual fields were full, colour-vision was normal, and there were no lenticular opacities.

Radiological Examinations.—Radiological examination of the skull showed a minor degree of turricephaly and evidence of premature closure of the coronal and sagittal suture. In the hands there was evidence of early closure of the epiphyses; all the primary epiphyses had united. The secondary epiphyses for the ischium and ilium had appeared. There was no evidence of osteoporosis of the pelvis. The vertebral column showed gross spinal curvature; no vertebral defect was demonstrated, and there was no evidence of osteoporosis. An intravenous pyelogram was normal.

Laboratory Findings.—Blood count: haemoglobin, 92% (13.6 g./100 ml.); white cells, 3,700/c.mm. (neutrophils 52%, eosinophils

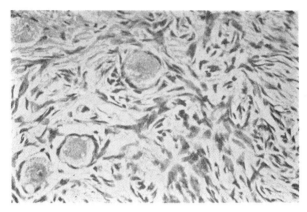

Fig. 2. Section of ovary (×310).

5%, basophils 2%, lymphocytes 30%, monocytes 11%). Erythrocyte sedimentation rate, 3 mm. in first hour (Westergren). Blood group AB, rhesus-positive. Blood urea. 18 mg./100 ml. Chromatography of urinary amino-acids; normal pattern. Serum calcium, 10.4 mg./100 ml.; serum inorganic phosphate, 4.5 mg./100 ml.; serum alkaline phosphatase, 4 King-Armstrong units/100 ml. Serum cholesterol, 258 mg./100 ml. Basal metabolic rate, minus 9%. Glucose-tolerance test: fasting level, 100 mg./100 ml. rising to 145 mg. and falling to 100 mg./100 ml. in one and a half hours. Urinary 17-ketosteroids (M.R.C. method), 3.7 and 6.6 mg. per 24 hours. Urinary 17-hydroxycorticosteroids (Norymberski), 8.4 mg. per 24 hours. Urinary 17-ketogenic steroids (Norymberski), 3.26 mg. per 24 hours. Urinary oestrogens (method of Brown, Bulbrook, and Greenwood, 1957): oestrone, 0.7 μg. per 24 hours; oestriol, 0.8 μg. per 24 hours; oestradiol-17β, nil. Urinary pregnanediol, 0.13 μg.

per 24 hours. Urinary gonadotrophins, more than 150 units of H.M.G. 20* per 24 hours—a very high figure (normal, about 10 units of H.M.G. 20 per 24 hours; post-menopause, about 60 units of H.M.G. 20 per 24 hours). Vaginal smear showed moderate oestrogenic activity. Nuclear sex of leucocytes: 6 of 312 neutrophil polymorphonuclear leucocytes examined in three blood smears showed nuclear drumsticks—female pattern (Dr. P. Storey). Nuclear sex of skin cells: moderate numbers of female cells were seen in the epidermis (Dr. W. J. Hanbury).

Laparotomy.—During her stay in hospital the patient suffered from an attack of appendicitis and an acutely inflamed appendix was removed (Mr. N. A. Green). At operation the gonads were inspected, and two ovaries were found that were normal in appearance, measuring 4.5 by 3 cm. in diameter. The uterus measured 3.75 by 3.75 cm. The hymen admitted a little finger.

Histology of Ovaries (Fig. 2).—Dr. W. J. Hanbury reported as follows: "The section shows part of an ovary in which the follicles are diminished in number and show no evidence of maturation into Graafian follicles or corpora albicantia. The tunica albuginea and cortical stroma show normal appearances."

DISCUSSION

The vagaries of the features of gonadal agenesis and dysgenesis have been fully discussed by Hoffenberg and Jackson (1957a, 1957b). We confirm their statements by the following observations: (1) Patients with rudimentary gonads are not always short in stature: for instance, the patient reported by Meyer (1931) was 66.7 in. (169.4 cm.) in height, by Schneider and McCullagh (1943) 62 in. (157.4 cm.), by Greenblatt, Carmona, and Higdon (1956) 70 in. (178.3 cm.), and by Hoffenberg and Jackson (1957a) 66.6 in. (169 cm.). (2) They may have no congenital abnormalities and may present only with amenorrhoea and infantilism (del Castillo, de la Balze, and Argonz, 1947; Greenblatt *et al.*, 1956; Hoffenberg and Jackson, 1957b; Natoli and de Pedrini, 1957). (3) The breasts may be normal (Hoffenberg, Jackson, and Muller, 1957). (4) Even menstruation may occur (Hoffenberg *et al.*, 1957).

---

* H.M.G. 20 = Human menopausal gonadotrophin, batch 20 (Organon).

We have not seen any report in the literature of a case of Turner's syndrome in which the ovaries had reached their normal size. The very high urinary excretion of gonadotrophins demonstrated that the ovarian failure was primary and not the result of anterior pituitary deficiency, which may be the cause in some cases in which the urinary gonadotrophins are low. It has been stated by previous authors that an increased excretion of gonadotrophins in the presence of the congenital abnormalities of Turner's syndrome is evidence of rudimentary gonads, but the degree of development of the ovaries in the present case demonstrates that this conclusion is not necessarily true. The ovarian failure probably occurred at the time when puberty should normally have begun; the cause of the failure is unknown. This late ovarian failure, however, was associated with the following congenital stigmata of Turner's syndrome: shortness of stature, webbing of the neck, high-arched palate, poorly developed mandible, elongation of the clavicles, and cubitus valgus.

We consider that the atrophy of the deltoid muscles, limiting the movements of the upper extremities, and the winged scapulae due to paresis of the trapezius muscles are the result of scapulo-humeral muscular dystrophy of the Erb juvenile type. There is no real evidence that the patient had had poliomyelitis; furthermore, it is unusual in poliomyelitis for the muscular wasting to be as symmetrical as in our patient. In the literature on the subject only two cases of muscular dystrophy in hypogonadism have been recorded—namely, those of Bassöe (1956). These patients were a woman with gonadal agenesis and her brother with Klinefelter's syndrome; they both suffered from congenital muscular dystrophy and infantile cataract. In the family there were five other children with muscular dystrophy and infantile cataract, one of whom was found on histological examination to have slight atrophy of the ovaries. Our patient appears to be the third case of muscular dystrophy occurring in a patient with gonadal dysgenesis.

The cause of the severe kyphoscoliosis is uncertain. There is no evidence that it was due to osteoporosis, and it seems doubtful whether poliomyelitis was the cause. It is unlikely that it was due to muscular dystrophy, since in this disease the muscular wasting is usually symmetrical.

SUMMARY

The case is recorded of a girl aged 17 who suffered from infantilism and had the following congenital abnormalities of Turner's syndrome: shortness of stature, webbing of the neck, a high-arched palate, a poorly developed mandible, elongation of the clavicles, and cubitus valgus. There was evidence of early closure of the epiphyses. The nuclear chromatin pattern was female. The urinary gonadotrophins were greatly raised, indicating primary ovarian failure. At laparotomy the ovaries were found to be macroscopically normal, and a section removed for biopsy showed no evidence of maturation of the follicles or corpora albicantia. It is considered that arrest of ovarian development occurred at the time that puberty should normally have taken place. In addition she had bilateral wasting of the deltoid muscles and winged scapulae, attributed to acquired muscular dystrophy. She also suffered from severe kyphoscoliosis, the cause of which is uncertain: there was no evidence of osteoporosis or definite history of poliomyelitis.

REFERENCES

Albright, F., Smith, P. H., and Fraser R. (1942) *Amer. J. med. Sci.* 204:625.

Bassöe, H. H. (1956) *J. clin. Endocr.* 16:1614.

Brown, J. B., Bulbrook, R. D., and Greenwood, F. C. (1957) *J. Endocr.* 16:49.

Castillo, E. B. del, Balze, F. A. de la, and Argonz, J. (1947) *J. clin. Endocr.* 7:385.

Ford, C. E., Jones, K. W., Polani, P. E., de Almeida, J. C., and Briggs, J. H. (1959) *Lancet* 1:711.

Greenblatt, R. B., Carmona, N., and Higdon, L. (1956) *J. clin. Endocr.* 16:235.

Grumbach, M. M., Van Wyk, J. J., and Wilkins, L. (1955) *Ibid.* 15:1161.

Hoffenberg, R., and Jackson, W. P. U. (1957a) *Brit. med. J.* 1:1281.

——— (1957b) *Ibid.* 2:1457.

——— and Muller, W. H. (1957) *J. clin. Endocr.* 17:902.

Meyer, R. (1931) *Arch. Gynak.* 145:2.

Natoli, A., and Pedrini, P. de (1957) *Rif. Med.* 71:917.

Pela, G. (1935) *Endocr. Pat. cost.* 10:558.

Pich, G. (1937) *Beitr. path. Anat.* 98:218.

Schneider, R. W., and McCullagh, E. P. (1943) *Cleveland Clin. Quart.* 10:112.

Sellheim, H. (1924) *Arch. Frauenk. Eugen. 10*:215.

Tronci, L. (1938) *Riv. ital. Ginec. 21*:627.

Turner, H. H. (1938) *Endocrinology 23*:566.

Varney, R. F., Kenyon, A. T., and Koch, F. C. (1942) *J. clin. Endocr. 2*:137.

Wilkins, L. (1957) *The Diagnosis and Treatment of Endocrine Disorders in Childhood and Adolescence*, 2nd ed., p. 232. Blackwell, Oxford.

—— and Fleischmann, W. (1944) *J. clin. Endocr. 4*:357.

26

THE FREQUENCY OF THE POSITIVE SEX-CHROMATIN PATTERN IN MALES WITH MENTAL DEFICIENCY

H. David Mosier, M.D., Lawrence W. Scott, and
Lloyd H. Cotter, M.D.

IN 1942 Klinefelter *et al.*[1] described a group of infertile males who had gynecomastia, elevated urinary gonadotropin and small testes that histologically showed tubular fibrosis and hyalinization but preservation of Leydig cells. This disorder subsequently came to be designated Klinefelter's syndrome.

In 1955, Nelson[2] reported the occurrence of positive sex-chromatin pattern* in cell nuclei in a 19-year-old youth with Klinefelter's syndrome. Examination of the sex-chromatin pattern thereafter came to be applied to infertile males on a widespread scale, resulting in the recognition of many more cases of Klinefelter's syndrome and a rapidly expanding literature on the subject. As new cases became recognized, associated abnormalities were noted. By now Klinefelter's syndrome with a positive sex-chromatin pattern has been found in the same individual or sibship with retinitis pigmentosa and sexual infantilism, athyreotic cretinism, schizophrenia,[3] myotonic dystrophy,[4] hypogonadism with a negative sex-chromatin pattern,[5] mental deficiency,[3, 6-10] and mongolism.[11]

The association of mental deficiency and Klinefelter's syndrome was first noted as an apparently random finding in one of the

Reprinted from *Pediatrics*, February 1960, pp. 291-297.

Supported by grant S-58-16 from the National Research Council.

The authors are grateful to Dr. George Tarjan, Director of the Pacific State Hospital, Pomona, California, for granting the opportunity to conduct the survey and to the many employees of the Pacific State Hospital who have given generously of their talents.

* Also referred to as "female" chromatin pattern, a term liable to aggravate psychologic complication surrounding patients with problems of this kind.

patients described in the original report by Klinefelter *et al.*[1] Pasqualini *et al.*[12] reported that 11 of 31 patients with Klinefelter's syndrome were feeble-minded. None of these patients had determinations of sex-chromatin pattern performed. It has been found that, of 13 cases of Klinefelter's syndrome with positive sex-chromatin pattern, 11 had a severe personality disorder or mental deficiency.[3]

These findings prompted the authors to begin a survey of the sex-chromatin patterns in the male patients at the Pacific State Hospital, Pomona, California. This is a hospital for the mentally deficient with a total patient population of 3,100 and a male population of 1,500. Since this study was begun, reports of results of similar surveys have appeared.[6-10]

METHODS

Determinations of sex-chromatin pattern were done by the oral smear technique in 1,252 male patients. There was no planned selection of this group from the total male population in the hospital. Most of the remaining patients either had smears obtained which were unsatisfactory, or were absent from the wards at the time the scrapings were made. In those patients found to have a positive sex-chromatin pattern, further clinical and laboratory studies were done including determinations of 24-hour excretion of 17-ketosteroids and gonadotropins in the urine** and testicular biopsies. Data relating to the patient group was processed under the supervision of Dr. Harvey Dingman.

RESULTS

Incidence of Positive Sex-chromatin Pattern

Ten of the 1,252 patients examined were found to have the positive sex-chromatin pattern, an overall incidence of 0.8%.

Clinical and Laboratory Findings

A summary of the salient clinical and laboratory findings is given in Table I. Figure 1, a and b, shows photographs of a pre-

---

** Determinations of 17-ketosteroids and gonadotropins were done by Bio-Science Laboratories, 12330 Santa Monica Blvd., Los Angeles, California.

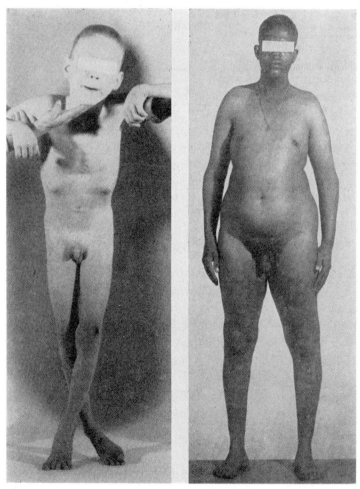

Fig. 1. Representative patients with positive sex-chromatin pattern. a) *(Left)* P. K., prepubertal; b) *(right)* J. W., postpubertal.

pubertal and postpubertal patient with positive sex-chromatin pattern. Nine of these patients are postpubertal with ages ranging from 15 to 38 years. One patient (P. K.), 7 years of age, is prepubertal (Fig. 1a). The intelligence quotient (IQ) ranged from 22 to 66. The physical proportions tended to be eunuchoid. There was minimal gynecomastia in six of the nine postpubertal patients. The testes were small in all; however, those of P. K. were in keeping as to size and consistency with his chronologic age. The concentration of 17-ketosteroids in urine were slightly reduced in five patients and normal in the remaining five; gonadotropins in the urine were elevated in four patients. The four oldest patients had sterilization by vasectomy 11 to 18 years ago in keeping with policies in practice in the state hospitals during that time; in two the finding of small testes prior to sterilization is recorded.

In one patient (L. P.) there are a few features suggesting mon-

TABLE 1

CLINICAL AND LABORATORY DATA IN PATIENTS WITH POSITIVE
SEX-CHROMATIN PATTERN

Patient	Age (Years)	IQ	Height (in.)	Span (in.)	Gyneco-mastia	Testis Length (mm)	17-KS* (mg/24 hr.)	FSH** (m.u./24 hr.)	
J. W.†	38	28	64.5	62	+	10	6.0	>16	<50
D. R.†	37	49	65.5	67	–	10	8.2	>16	<50
W. S.†	32	66	69.5	69	+	25	14.4	>50	<100
F. K.†	32	48	70	72	+	23	21.0	>16	<50
J. R.	23	53	70	67.5	–	10	8.1	>100	
H. H.	18	64	71	73	+	25	9.7	>50	<100
H. C.	15	55	67.5	69.5	+	25	7.7	>100	
C. R.	17	54	71	71.5	–	27‡	8.2	>16	<50
L. P.	15	49	67	67	+	20	15.5	>16	<50
P. K.	7	22	47	48	–	10	2.2		

* 17-ketosteroid excretion in urine.
** FSH = Follicle-stimulating hormone (mouse units/24 hr.).
† Vasectomy in the past.
‡ Right testis not palpable.

golism: slight epicanthic folds, high-arched palate and short, incurved fifth fingers. Two other patients had mongoloid siblings and in both cases twinning was associated. C. R. had twin siblings, one of whom was mongoloid. The youngest patient, P. K., is said to be one of identical twins. He was the first-born and was reported to be cyanotic at birth and to have several subconjunctival hemorrhages; the twin was born dead, apparently due to separation of the placenta during the birth of the patient. The mother had a boy with mongolism by a previous marriage when she was 17 years of age.

The ages of the mothers at the time of delivery are known in eight of the positive cases. These range from 17 to 30 years with an average of 25.5 years.

Testicular Pathology

Six of the patients have had testicular biopsies; in those post-puberty, the characteristic pathology of Klinefelter's syndrome is seen; in the prepubertal patient no tubular fibrosis is present.

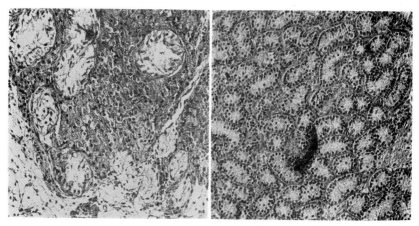

Fig. 2. Biopsies of testes. a) *(Left)* Patient L. P. Typical pathology of Kline-felter's syndrome with fibrosis and hyalinization of tubules and preservation of Leydig cells; b) *(Right)* Patient P. K. Prepubertal Klinefelter's syndrome. There is no fibrosis; the tubules are uniformily small in keeping with the level of maturity. There may be some reduction in germinal epithelium.

Some germinal epithelium is present, although it appears to be re-duced in amount (Fig. 2, a and b).

Correlations

The patients with positive sex-chromatin pattern (positive cases) were correlated with the population surveyed, in respect to the distribution according to race, age, IQ and diagnosis. The distribution of the positive cases according to race or age showed no remarkable difference from the distribution of the total group surveyed (Figs. 3 and 4). All the positive cases had IQs in the range of 20 to 69. Although there were 314 patients with IQs below 20, there were no positive cases in that group (Fig. 5).

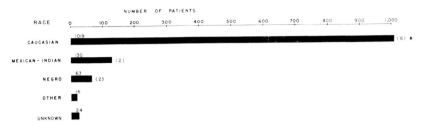

Fig. 3. Classification according to race. (°) Number in parenthesis indicates number of patients with positive sex-chromatin pattern.

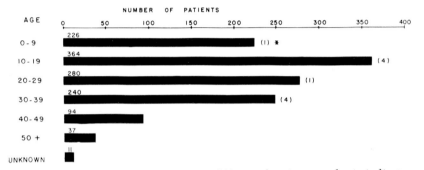

Fig. 4. Classification according to age. (°) Number in parenthesis indicates number of patients with positive sex-chromatin pattern.

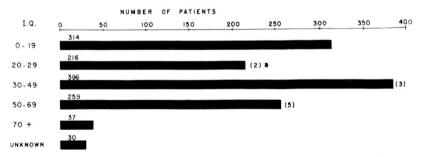

Fig. 5. Classification according to IQ. (°) Number in parenthesis indicates number of patients with positive sex-chromatin pattern.

In regard to diagnosis of mental deficiency, with the exception of P. K. who is listed in the category of trauma on the basis of somewhat sketchy historical data, all the patients with positive sex-chromatin pattern are in the *Undifferentiated, Familial* (on the basis of a retarded mother), or *Other* categories, on the basis of the diagnosis of schizophrenia or schizophrenic tendencies (Fig. 6). There was no significant difference in the distribution of diagnostic categories in the 0 to 19 range of IQ to account for the lack of cases in that group.

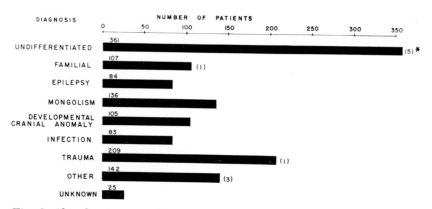

Fig. 6. Classification according to cause of mental deficiency. (*) Number in parenthesis indicates number of patients with positive sex-chromatin pattern.

DISCUSSION

Since this study began, similar surveys of males with mental deficiency have been reported. Ferguson-Smith[6] found four cases with positive sex-chromatin pattern among 325 surveyed; three were mildly and one severely retarded. Cornwell and Hermann[7] reported three patients, with IQs ranging from 33 to 58, from an unspecified number who had chromatin tests performed. Prader *et al.*[8] tested 336 mildly retarded boys and found eight positive cases whose IQs ranged from 62 to 94. In another study of 663 mildly deficient boys, Ferguson-Smith[9] found eight positive cases with IQs ranging from 50 to 77. Barr[10] has reported an incidence of 1% in a survey of 1,500 mentally deficient males. The present data suggests that one is more likely to find Klinefelter's syndrome among individuals with mild rather than severe degrees of mental deficiency.

The incidence of Klinefelter's syndrome with positive sex-chromatin pattern in males of the general population has been independently estimated to be 1 in 1,000[8] or 1 in 3,000.[9] A recent survey of newborn males in a general hospital indicated an incidence of 5 with a positive sex-chromatin pattern out of 1,911 tested.[13] If one takes into account the finding that a high proportion of noninstitutionalized males with this lesion have mental deficiency, the relationship between Klinefelter's syndrome with positive sex-chromatin pattern and mental deficiency appears to be significant.

The implication of the positive sex-chromatin pattern found in Klinefelter's syndrome to genetics has, until lately, been a confused issue. Since the report of the first case in 1955, there has been a tendency to regard the sex-chromatin pattern as indicative of the chromosomal sex of these patients. They were thus regarded as genetic "females" who had undergone sex reversal of the gonads during early fetal life.[4, 13, 15]

Improved techniques for the study of chromosomes have recently resulted in spectacular advances in problems concerned with the number of chromosomes in the human. One result has been the revision of the human chromosomal count to 46.[16, 17] Studies by Jacobs and Strong,[18] in a case of Klinefelter's syndrome with a positive sex-chromatin pattern, produced evidence that there was an XXY chromosomal constitution giving a total of 47 chromosomes. The normal nucleus of the male human has an XY chromosomal constitution. Independent studies by Jacobs *et al.*[19] and Lejeune *et al.*[20] have also shown the presence of 47 chromosomes in cases of mongolism. In these the extra chromosome appears to be autosomal.[19] Finally, Ford *et al.*[11] have shown that a patient exhibiting clinical features of mongolism and Klinefelter's syndrome had the XXY chromosomes of the Klinefelter's syndrome and in addition the extra chromosome of mongolism.

Direct studies of chromosomes will require further evaluation and confirmation; however, at this preliminary stage they dispel much of the confusion which has surrounded the relation of the sex-chromatin pattern to chromosomal sex. It is now clear that the individual with Klinefelter's syndrome cannot be regarded as a genetic or chromosomal female; the XXY chromosomal constitution is neither male nor female but represents a chromosomal intersex. Thus, theories that have been proposed to explain the pathogenesis of the gonadal changes in terms of sex reversal may, on re-examination, need to be revised or discarded in view of the new findings.

Relatively little is known about the psychic or behavioral abnormalities in Klinefelter's syndrome. Preliminary data indicate these patients commonly have a passive-aggressive personality with schizoid tendencies superimposed on the intellectual deficiency. Studies are in progress in the present patients to further characterize their personality traits in relation to IQ. It would be premature to speculate on the relation of the brain disorder to the abnormalities of chromosomes until such studies are completed.

SUMMARY

A survey of the sex-chromatin pattern in 1,252 males with mental deficiency revealed 10 apparent males with positive sex-chromatin patterns and with IQs ranging from 22 to 66. Nine of these are postpubertal and have findings characteristic of Klinefelter's syndrome. One patient is prepubertal and sexually immature. One of the patients has a few features suggesting mongolism. One patient is a twin; the other twin died at birth. He has an older half-brother who has mongolism. Another patient has twin siblings, one of whom has mongolism.

Recent reports of similar surveys confirm that about 1% of mentally deficient males have Klinefelter's syndrome. However, our data indicate the incidence is lower than that among the severely retarded and rises two- or threefold above that among the mildly retarded. The best control data indicate the incidence in the general population is about 0.2% or less. On the basis of these data, it appears that Klinefelter's syndrome with positive sex-chromatin pattern is likely to be associated with some degree of mental deficiency. The relation of the brain disorder to the anomalous sex-chromatin pattern is unknown.

REFERENCES

1. Klinefelter, H. F., Jr., Reifenstein, E. C., Jr., and Albright, F., Syndrome characterized by gynecomastia, aspermatogenesis, without aleydigism, and increased excretion of follicle-stimulating hormone. *J. Clin. Endocrinol.* 2:615, 1942.

2. Nelson, W. O., Evaluation of testicular function in reproduction and sterility, Michigan State University, Centennial Symposium Report. East Lansing, Michigan, 1955, pp. 79-85. Cited by Grumbach *et al.*[4]

3. Mosier, H. D., and Wilkins, L., Sex chromatin studies in human intersexuality. Proc. First Pan American Cancer Cytology Congress, Miami, Florida, April 25-29, 1957, to be published.

4. Grumbach, M. M., Blanc, W. A., and Engle, E. T., Sex-chromatin pattern in seminiferous tubule dysgenesis and other testicular disorders: relationship to true hermaphroditism and to Klinefelter's syndrome. *J. Clin. Endocrinol. 17*:703, 1957.

5. Bunge, R. G., and Bradbury, J. T., Newer concepts of the Klinefelter syndrome. *J. Urol. 76*:758, 1956.

6. Ferguson-Smith, M. A., Chromatin-positive Klinefelter's syndrome (primary microrchidism) in a mental deficiency hospital. *Lancet 1*:928, 1958.

7. Cornwell, J. G., and Hermann, W., Intersexuality in mentally deficient patients. *Acta endocrinol. 27*:369, 1958.

8. Prader, A., Schneider, J., Züblin, W., Francés, J. M., and Rüedi, K., Die Häusigkeit des echten, chromatin-positiven Klinefelter-Syndromes und seine Beziehungen zum Schwachsinn. *Schweiz. med. Wchnschr.* 88:917, 1958.

9. Ferguson-Smith, M. A., The prepubertal testicular lesion in chromatin-positive Klinefelter's syndrome (primary microrchidism) as seen in mentally handicapped children. *Lancet 1*:219, 1959.

10. Barr, M. L., Tests of chromosomal sex in Klinefelter's syndrome and in mental deficiency (abstract). Proc. IX International Congress of Pediatrics, Montreal, Canada, July 19-25, 1959, p. 16.

11. Ford, C. E., *et al.*, The chromosomes in a patient showing both mongolism and Klinefelter's syndrome. *Lancet 1*:709, 1959.

12. Pasqualini, R. Q., Vidal, G., and Bur, G. E., Psychopathology of Klinefelter's syndrome. *Lancet 2*:164, 1957.

13. Moore, K. L., Sex reversal in newborn babies. *Lancet 1*:219, 1959.

14. Segal, S. J., and Nelson, W. O., Developmental aspects of human hermaphroditism: the significance of sex chromatin patterns. *J. Clin. Endocrinol. 17*:676, 1957.

15. Witschi, E., Nelson, W. O., and Segal, S. J., Genetic, developmental and hormonal aspects of gonadal dysgenesis and sex inversion in man. *J. Clin. Endocrinol. 17*:737, 1957.

16. Tjio, J. H., and Levan, A., The chromosome number of man. *Hereditas 42*:1, 1956.

17. Ford, C. E., and Hamerton, J. L., The chromosomes of man. *Nature 189*:1020, 1956.

18. Jacobs, P. A., and Strong, J. A., A case of human intersexuality having a possible XXY sex-determining mechanism. *Nature 183*:302, 1959.

19. Jacobs, P. A., Baikie, A. G., Brown, E. M. C., and Strong, J. A., The somatic chromosomes in mongolism. *Lancet* 1:710, 1959.
20. Lejeune, L., Gautier, M., and Turpin, R., Le chromosomes humains en culture de tissus. *Compt. rend. Acad. sc.* 248:602, 1959.

27

THE HUMAN CHROMOSOMAL SATELLITES IN NORMAL PERSONS AND IN TWO PATIENTS WITH MARFAN'S SYNDROME*

J. H. Tjio, T. T. Puck, and A. Robinson

IN 1958, quantitative characterizations of all the human chromosomes were published in which measurements of total length and centromere position of each member were presented.[1] These measurements were shown to be sufficiently reproducible to permit unequivocal identification of each chromosome (including the sex chromosomes), provided that a sufficiently large number of clearly defined and well separated mitotic figures is available for analysis, a feature characteristic of the methodology employed by us, since it permits indefinite cell multiplication *in vitro* without change in chromosome constitution.[2, 3] Two pairs of satellited chromosomes were described and characterized, listed as number 18 and 21 in Figure 1. Subsequently two other laboratories also published quantitative morphologic analyses of the entire human karyotype which agreed with ours virtually completely, within the limits of the experimental uncertainty (which need be no more than a few per cent), and confirmed the group identity of the satellited chromosomes.[4, 5] However, question was raised whether the satellited chromosome pair of group VII is indeed the largest pair (i.e. number 18 in the Tjio and Puck classification system) or one of the smaller pairs.

In a preceding work, we had described characteristic variations in the satellite structures of two human subjects.[3] These ex-

Reprinted from the *Proceedings of the National Academy of Sciences*, Vol. 46, No. 4, pp. 532-539, April, 1960.

* Contribution No. 103 from the Department of Biophysics, Florence R. Sabin Laboratories, University of Colorado Medical Center, Denver, and from the Institute of Arthritis and Metabolic Disease, National Institutes of Health, U. S. Public Health Service, Bethesda. Aided by a grant from the National Foundation.

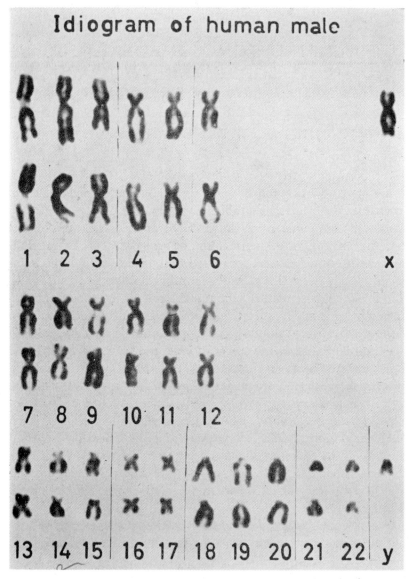

Fig. 1. Idiogram of chromosomes from the normal human male.[1] The female is identical but with two X chromosomes and no Y. Chromosome pairs number 18 and 21 are satellited as previously described[1] although the structures are so lightly delineated in normal cells that they photograph only faintly and often fail to be reproduced in printing.

hibited heterozygously enlarged satellites, in the one case on both numbers 18 and 21, and in the other only for the latter chromosome. While both of these subjects had been hospital patients, no feature of their records revealed any genetic defect that could be related to their unusual satellite conditions, nor were the patients' families available for study of the inheritance of this

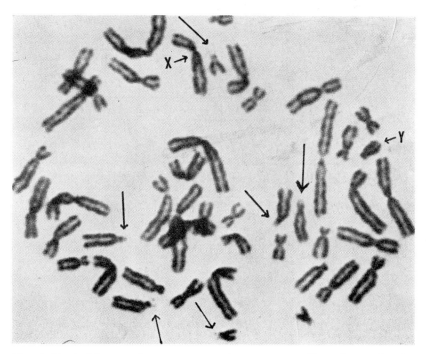

Fig. 2. Typical human chromosome set showing six satellites (arrows). The satellites often are too faint to be well delineated, but this number has now been found in several human subjects, with unrelated genetic conditions.

cytogenetic marker. While the poor response of the satellites to the conventional chromosome stains and the need to obtain chromosomes in early metaphase for clearest delineation of satellite morphology make such studies difficult, the problem is of an importance warranting careful study. This communication deals with two further findings concerning the human satellites.

In analysis of the chromosomes of a variety of human subjects, several instances have been found in which additional satellites are observed. In every case these have been present on another chromosome pair of group VII, probably number 20, in addition to the ones previously described on pairs 18 and 21. The uncertainties of visualization of these structures makes it impossible yet to ascertain whether 6 satellited chromosomes always appear in human cells, but the fact that these are visualized at times in cells

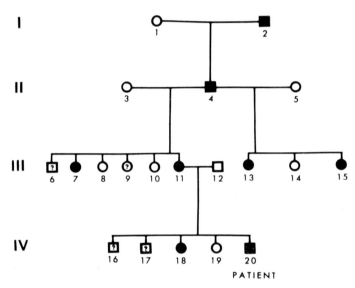

Fig. 3*a*. Inheritance of Marfan's Syndrome (Patient of Fig. 4). The genealogy was established from the patient's hospital record. Circles indicate females and squares males. Presumptive evidence of the presence of the condition as indicated by heart disease, with or without arachnodactyly and eye defects, has been indicated by a solid figure. Possible presence of the syndrome as indicated by reported death in infancy or other suggestive symptoms is shown by a question mark.

from a variety of different human subjects makes it probable that these will turn out to be a frequent, if not universal, characteristic of Man's karyotype. This finding also resolves the apparent discrepancy about the identity of the satellited pair of group VII, since two pairs can carry these structures. A photograph of a chromosome set with six clear satellites is presented in Figure 2. It is obvious that means must be found to delineate the satellites with greater reliability.

Further interesting features of the human satellited chromosomes have appeared in an analysis of the cells of patients in whom the disease, Marfan's syndrome, had been diagnosed. This condition is a relatively poorly characterized clinical situation, usually inherited as a simple, Mendelian, autosomal, dominant character.[6] However, the first patient available to us had occurred in a family with no history of this disease, or, indeed, any

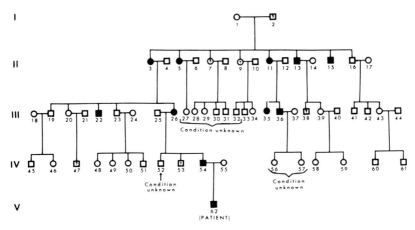

Fig. 3*b*. Inheritance of Marfan Syndrome in patient corresponding to Figure 5. The genealogy was established from questioning of members of the patient's family, who have been very cooperative. The system followed is the same as in 3*a*. The pattern indicates the typical autosomal, dominant transmission.

indication of previous metabolic abnormality. The patient was not available for examination by us, and while the diagnosis of Marfan's syndrome was made on the basis of arachnodactyly, congenital heart disease, with probable ventricular septal defect, dislocated lens, a high, arched palate, and arthrogryposis, the absence of any other familial history of this disease renders it uncertain whether this case is identical to those in which a clear, hereditary pattern exists. The chromosomes of this patient were found to be normal, as indicated in a previous publication.[7]

In a second patient in whom the diagnosis of Marfan's syndrome was made, a clear familial history was evident. The pertinent clinical findings were: hypotonia, arachnodactyly, inguinal

hernia, pigeon breast, high, arched palate, and cyanotic, congenital heart disease (tricuspid atresia, atrial and ventricular septal defects). The genealogy, indicating transmission by a single,
dominant, genetic determinant is shown in Figure 3a. Chromo-

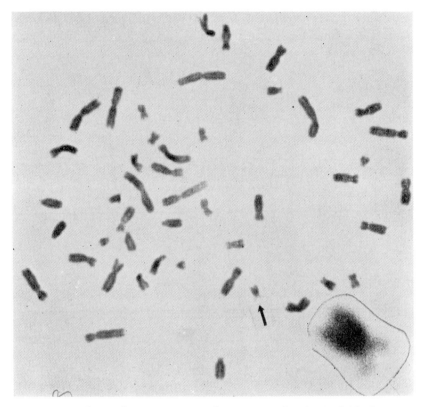

Fig. 4. Metaphase chromosome set of patient with inherited Marfan syndrome. The arrow indicates the enlarged satellite on one member of chromosome pair 21, which is also shown enlarged in the lower right-hand corner
of the picture.

somal analysis carried out on cells originating from a tiny biopsy
of the skin and cultivated *in vitro* in accordance with the method-
ologies previously described[2, 3, 8] revealed a normal 46/XY complement, with the individual members all essentially normal in
total size and arm length. However, an outstanding characteristic
of this patient's karyotype is the possession of a tremendously en-

larged satellite on one member of pair number 21. This structure, as shown in Figure 4, was consistent in all the cells examined, and was clearly greater than that of any other satellite previously seen, not excluding those which we had already described as enlarged.[3] Unfortunately, no other members of this patient's family are available for study.

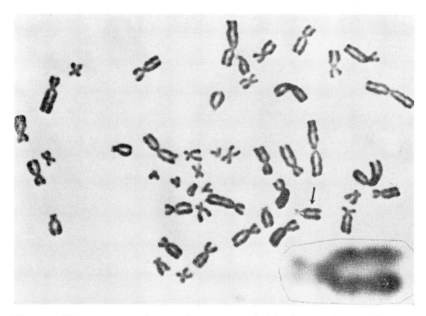

Fig. 5*a*. Chromosomes of second patient with Marfan syndrome, showing the enlarged satellite on one member of pair 18 (arrow and enlargement in corner).

A third patient with the same diagnosis of Marfan syndrome has also been analyzed chromosomally. The diagnosis was established on the basis of a typical habitus including arachnodactyly, dolichomorphism, marked pectus excavatum and brachycephaly in an 18-month-old boy, and a genealogy indicating a simple, dominant mode of inheritance of Marfan syndrome (Fig. 3*b*). This patient again exhibited a set of chromosomes completely normal except for the satellites (Fig. 5). In this case, however, the abnormality was on a chromosome of pair number 18, instead of 21. Again, it was consistent in all cells, and involved an enlarge-

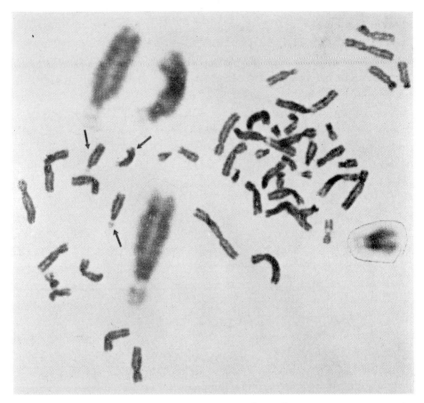

Fig. 5*b*. An early metaphase chromosome set from the same patient as in 5*a*, demonstrating the enlarged satellite on one member of pair number 18 (lower arrow). Two of the other satellited chromosomes of Group VII are also clearly shown in this picture. Enlargements of each of these chromosomes have been attached close to the corresponding arrows. At the right side an enlargement of one of the satellited chromosomes of pair number 21 has been included for comparison.

ment clearly beyond the range of those seen in any other human subjects.

Discussion.—The satellite enlargements here described conceivably may arise through any of several mechanisms, such as duplication of the material of which the satellite is composed; interchange or reciprocal translocation between the satellite and part of some other chromosome; or an intrachange within the satellited chromosome itself, such as an inversion containing the satellited region, or a reciprocal interchange between the 2 arms of the chromosome. Hence it is possible that satellite enlargement of itself might be accompanied by a variety of different kinds of phenotypic behavior.

While the present data do not prove the given abnormalities to be the underlying cause of Marfan's syndrome, a relationship is definitely suggested, since in the analysis of chromosomes from more than 30 human subjects, satellites enlarged to the degree here described have been found only in those two patients who exhibit this particular disease, and in the form which displays a dominant genetic pattern. The heterozygosity of the defect in each case is in accord with the mode of inheritance. It is unexpected, however, that the structural defect obtained in these two cases should involve different chromosomes, and a causal connection between this aberration and the given clinical condition can only be maintained on the assumption that damage to either satellite can cause similar cellular derangement. While the role of satellites in the economy of the cell is still far from clear, evidence shows that the satellited chromosomes involve function of the nucleolus.[9] Therefore, the suggestion is tenable that at least some forms of Marfan's syndrome are due to a dominant genetic defect involving satellite formation which affects a cell function requiring normal interaction of satellites from more than one chromosome. Work is continuing on this problem, investigating satellite cytology and nucleolar behavior in families with this disease. In a forthcoming report, additional pictures will be presented of normal and abnormal human satellited chromosomes, demonstrating their characteristic changes from prophase through late metaphase.

Summary.—Human chromosomal complements have been found with six instead of four satellites. These observations reconcile one of the contradictions in the literature dealing with the human karyotype, and raise the possibility that the higher figure may be a common or possibly universal satellite number in man.

Chromosomes of three patients with a diagnosis of Marfan syndrome have been described. One patient with no familial history of the disease, revealed a normal chromosomal constitution. The other two patients' genealogies exhibited the typical pattern of a simple dominant, autosomal defect. Both patients' chromosomes demonstrated a single, abnormally enlarged satellite, in the one case on a chromosome of pair number 18, and in the other on number 21.

REFERENCES

1. Tjio, J. H., and Puck, T. T., these *Proceedings 44*:1229 (1958).
2. Puck, T. T., Cieciura, S. J., and Robinson, A., *J. Exptl. Med. 108*:945 (1958).
3. Tjio, J. H., and Puck, T. T., *J. Exptl. Med. 108*:259 (1958).
4. Chu, E. H., and Giles, N. H., *Am. J. Human Genetics 11*:63 (1959).
5. Levan, A., and Hsu, T. C., *Hereditas 45*:665 (1959).
6. McKuisik, V. A., in *Hereditable Disorders of Connective Tissue* (St. Louis: C. V. Mosby Co., 1960), p. 42.
7. Tjio, J. H., Puck, T. T., and Robinson, A., these *Proceedings 45*:1008 (1959).
8. Puck, T. T., Robinson, A., and Tjio, J. H., *Proc. Soc. Exp. Biol. and Med. 103*:192 (1960).
9. Swanson, C. P., *Cytology and Cytogenetics* (Englewood Cliffs, N. J.: Prentice Hall Inc., 1957), p. 131-134.

28

A MONGOL GIRL WITH 46 CHROMOSOMES

P. E. Polani, M.D. Pisa, M.R.C.P., J. H. Briggs, M.B. Lond., M.R.C.P.,
C. E. Ford, Ph.D. Lond., C. M. Clarke, Ph.D. Durh., and
J. M. Berg, M.B. W'srand, M.Sc. Cape Town

THAT mongols have 47 chromosomes and are trisomic for one of the two short pairs of acrocentric chromosomes has been invariably demonstrated in the 30 cases reported so far (Lejeune et al. 1959a and b, Jacobs et al. 1959, Ford et al. 1959, Böök et al. 1959). These two chromosome pairs are numbers 22 and 23 of Ford et al. (1958), and, although they were not distinguished, it is now recognised that one is a little longer than the other and may exhibit a small "satellite" to the short arm. Since there is now evidence that it is the longer satellited chromosome that is implicated in mongolism (Tjio and Puck 1958, Chu and Giles 1959), we shall refer to this chromosome as no. 22.*

"Non-disjunction" at one of two meiotic divisions during gametogenesis, leading to the production of a gamete with 24 instead of 23 chromosomes, is the most probable origin of trisomy. Because of the well-known maternal age effect in mongolism (Shuttleworth 1909, Jenkins 1933, Penrose 1933, 1934) it is generally assumed that the error is more likely to be one of oögenesis than of spermatogenesis. Possibly other factors than those associated with advancing maternal age may cause mongolism, and it is conceivable that mongolism might arise through other chromosomal mechanisms, in which case chromosome studies might reveal the postulated differences.

It is difficult to select mongols in whom such special ætiological factors and/or chromosomal mechanisms might have operated.

Reprinted from *The Lancet*, April 2, 1960, pp. 721-724.

* The need for standard numbering of human chromosomes is accepted, and it is hoped that agreement on classification will soon be reached. Meanwhile, it is best for each group to adhere to its own system.

One approach might be dictated by the following considerations:

It is likely that most mongols whose chromosomes have been studied and reported on were the offspring of older mothers. The distribution of maternal ages at the birth of mongol children is known to be skew to the left and often frankly bimodal, as Penrose (1951, 1954a) has pointed out, with a peak at the average maternal age for normal controls and the major peak at a considerably higher age. This skewness and bimodality can be interpreted as an expression of ætiological heterogeneity in respect of factors that relate mongolism to maternal age. Furthermore, when mongolism is found in maternal (but not paternal) ascendants and collaterals, the *mean* maternal age at the birth of mongol children is significantly lowered (Penrose 1951). This also happens in the group of mothers who have more than one mongol child, though it is difficult to discern how much the lowering of the mean maternal age is independent of that which will automatically result from "having to fit" more than one affected child into a sibship (Penrose 1951). The lowering of maternal age in familial mongolism may indicate that genetic factors (in the mother) may increase the frequency with which "non-disjunction" occurs and render it less dependent upon advancing maternal age.

It appeared that a study of the chromosomes of mongols born to young mothers might be rewarding. It can be thought that this group may be compounded of at least three subgroups: (1) where the condition is related to the same causes which produce mongols from older mothers; (2) where mongolism is familial (through the mother) or shows sibship concentration or both; and (3) a residual and probably miscellaneous subgroup where yet other factors than the above *may* operate.

MATERIAL

We selected three mongol children because they were born from *young* mothers and there was no sibship or family concentration of mongolism. Bone-marrow suspensions from these three mongols were sent to Harwell. The observers there knew that the marrows were from mongols but did *not* know the special reason for the investigation or the criteria of selection of these patients. Of these three marrow cultures, one failed and another yielded a chromosome count of 47, with trisomy of one of the two short acrocentric chromosomes presumably chromosome 22. The result in the third is the object of this communication.

CASE RECORD

A, a female born on Dec. 29, 1949, weighing 6 lb. 14 oz. was diagnosed neonatally as a mongol. Her mother, who was 21, had an uneventful pregnancy. She was X-rayed repeatedly for inactive

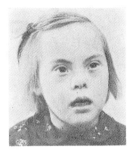

Fig. 1. Mongol child, aged 10 years.

pulmonary tuberculosis (Dec. 13, 1948, and March 21, July 4, Aug. 29, and Oct. 31, 1949). A's father was 23 years of age. There is no family history of mongolism, mental defect, or any other abnormalities. The mother had one other pregnancy resulting in the birth of a normal male in 1952. A is a typical mongol and shows no associated abnormalities (fig. 1). She was admitted to the Fountain Hospital at the age of 3¼ years. Her intelligence-quotient has varied between 38 and 40 on repeated testing on the Merrill-Palmer scale or the Stanford-Binet (T.M. revision) form L. Each palmar A T D angle (Penrose 1954b) measures 91°.

CYTOLOGICAL OBSERVATIONS

The marrow was processed according to the technique of Ford et al. (1958). Preparations were made and examined independently by two observers (C. E. F., C. M. C.). Their findings, compared after completion of the observations, agreed. The counts, summarised in the accompanying table, show that the chromosome number was 46. On detailed analysis of 15 cells, only 4 short acrocentric chromosomes were found, as in normal females (fig.

2). Of the group of 6 chromosomes of pairs 14, 15, and 16 normally present, 5 were found; but there were 17 medium-length chromosomes instead of 16 as in a normal female. Careful matching of these chromosomes in photographs of five cells revealed that the "extra" was not certainly distinguishable from the two members of pair no. 12. The great similarity of pairs 14, 15, and 16

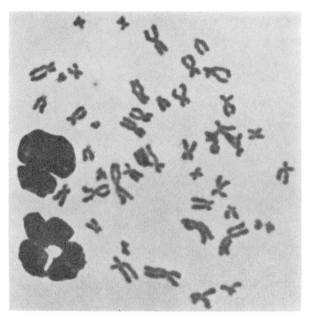

Fig. 2. Chromosomes in a bone-marrow cell.

made it difficult to determine which of them was represented singly. It is considered most likely to be no. 15, and accordingly what is believed to be the extra chromosome is placed beside a single "chromosome 15" in fig. 3.

CHROMOSOME COUNTS IN CELLS FROM BONE-MARROW OF A MONGOL GIRL

Observer	Chromosome Count					Total Cells	
	43	44	45	46	47	COUNTED	ANALYSED
C. M. C.	. .	. .	. .	21	. .	21	7
C. E. F.	2	2	2	39	. .	45	8
Totals	2	2	2	60	. .	66	15

INTERPRETATION

On present knowledge it is difficult to believe that there might be a genetic mechanism causing mongolism that did not involve the presence in triplicate of at least the greater part of chromosome 22. The clinical diagnosis of mongolism in the present case is undoubted, and it is therefore reasonable to suppose that the "extra" chromosome is compounded of the greater parts of the

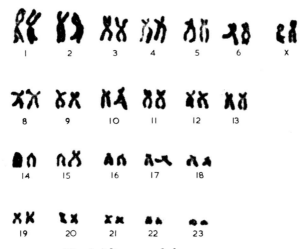

Fig. 3. Idiogram of chromosomes.

missing chromosome ?15 and of the expected additional chromosome 22. The literature of cytogenetics does not support the possibility of a permanent end-to-end fusion of two chromosomes, such as these, by their short arms (v.i). Therefore, the most likely interpretation of the findings is an unequal reciprocal translocation between chromosomes ?15 and 22 with both points of exchange close to the centromere (fig. 4). The morphology of the "extra" chromosome is entirely in accord with this interpretation. The long arm corresponds in length to the long arm of a chromosome 15, and the short arm to the long arm of a chromosome 22.

Since the distinction between the pair of chromosomes 12 and the extra chromosome is uncertain, the cytological evidence alone does not exclude trisomy of chromosome 12 combined with mono-

somy of chromosome ?15 as the explanation. However, the hypo-
thetical combination in one individual of viability of a monosomic
condition and of mongolism originating through a chromosomal
mechanism entirely different from the one demonstrated hitherto
is considered to be so highly unlikely as to justify rejection.

An alternative mechanism by which mongolism might come to
be expressed in an individual with 46 chromosomes is through the
origin of an *iso*chromosome from the long arm of chromosome 22.
These abnormal chromosomes arise very rarely by *misdivision*
(Darlington 1939, 1940) at mitosis or meiosis: that is, the centromere divides transversely instead of equationally, yielding two
symmetrical, but genetically unequal, products, each being a
duplication of one arm of the original chromosome. Since isochro-
mosomes are, by definition, symmetrical about their centromeres,
this explanation is excluded in the present case.

ORIGIN OF THE DEFECT

There are five formal possibilities of the origin of such a translocation, two somatic, two germinal, and one which is both germinal and somatic. It may have taken place: (1) during embryogenesis from a zygote with a normal complement of 46 chromosomes, or even locally in the bone-marrow after embryogeny was
complete; (2) during embryogenesis from a zygote with the 47
chromosomes usual in mongolism, or again at a later stage locally
in the bone-marrow; (3) during gametogenesis in one of the parents; (4) during embryogenesis in one of the parents with consequent involvement of all or part of one or both gonads; (5) during
embryogenesis or gametogenesis of one of the four grandparents.

The first possibility could only come about as a consequence
of a rearrangement (a symmetrical chromatid interchange) occurring after the chromosomes had reproduced in preparation for the
next anaphase separation.

This restriction does not apply to the second possibility: the
observed abnormality could be derived from a 47-chromosome
mongol complement by rearrangement either *before or after* chromosome reduplication. In either case, however, the loss of the
smaller of the two products of the rearrangement would be necessary to yield the observed set of 46 chromosomes.

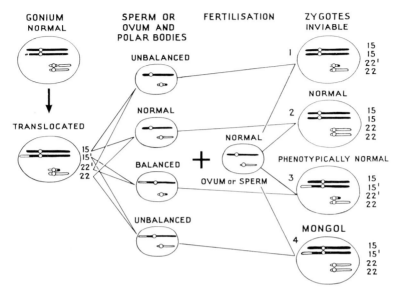

Fig. 4. Diagram showing suggested origin of the translocation and its genetic consequences. For illustration, the translocation is shown as having occurred in a spermatogonium or oogonium. In the latter case, only one of the meiotic products becomes a functional gamete; the others become polar bodies. If the translocation originated earlier in development, the change would be propagated at each mitosis and more gonia would be affected in the same way. The exact positions of breakage cannot be defined and the points indicated have been chosen arbitrarily. *Offspring:* 1 is a chromosomally unbalanced (presumably) inviable zygote. 2 is normal, phenotypically and chromosomally. 3 is chromosomally balanced, phenotypically normal. He is chromosomally distinct and will produce the same types of gametes and offspring as the affected parent. 4 is a mongol like A.

If the first cleavage division is excluded, both possibilities, whether occurring early or late in development history and whether locally in bone-marrow or elsewhere, would lead to chromosomal mosaicism (i.e., the presence in the body of two types of cell differing in chromosome constitution). In view of its wide regional distribution, the looseness of its structure, and the ready migration of stem cells from one region to another, bone-marrow is the tissue par excellence in which chromosomal mosaicism (if present) might be detected. The observations give no hint of it.

There are also the morphological consequences of postulates

1 and 2 to consider. A mosaic of the first type would be genetically normal in part of the body. Some hint of regional difference might therefore have been detected at clinical examination—such as the absence of the usual stigmata of mongolism on one hand or foot. The second case is different. Both components of the mosaic would, by hypothesis, contain the chromosome material necessary for the expression of mongolism, and morphological indications of mosaicism would not be expected. Although neither of the two mosaic possibilities can be rigorously excluded on the present evidence, neither is likely.

The third and fourth possibilities differ principally in their genetic implications and both could apply to *either parent*. If the translocation had occurred in a single primary spermatocyte or oöcyte, then at most two gametes would have carried the rearranged chromosome and both would have been shed together. But it is equally possible that the translocation took place during embryonic development of one parent, or even later, and that several, many, or even all gonia are affected. The parent would then be a gonosomic mosaic, a "name . . . used for cases where mosaicism is due to a difference in genetical *(or chromosomal)* constitution between all or part of the soma and all or part of the gonads" (Sidky 1939-40).

The fifth possibility is that, in origin and chromosomal make-up, one of the parents of A may be similar to the "phenotypically normal" zygote mentioned above (see fig. 4, zygote 3). The distinct chromosomal make-up would exist both in the gonia and in the somatic tissues, and the hypothesis can be tested by studying the somatic chromosomes of the parents.

The cytogenetic behaviour of reciprocal translocations at gametogenesis is well known in other species. In man gametes of four principal types would be formed in nearly equal numbers. In the present case, assuming that both gonads are wholly affected (and neglecting some rarer types of abnormal gamete), one-quarter of the offspring will be mongols, one-quarter normal, one-quarter phenotypically normal (but chromosomally distinct and reproductively like the parent), and one-quarter of the zygotes produced will be inviable (fig. 4). From a genetic standpoint, the last class (fig. 4, zygote 1) would be practically monosomic for chromosome

22. The most obvious outward manifestation of the last three possibilities would be a sibship and/or family concentration of mongols.

In the present instance, we have no reason for preferring either hypothesis 3, 4, or 5, nor for assigning the origin of the defect to either parent.

The present finding of a different chromosome constitution and hence a different mechanism for mongolism may be a sporadic chance happening, and if so is of limited interest. However, the manner in which the patient was selected suggests that this is not so—in which event the conclusion would be not only that different chromosome mechanisms may underlie mongolism but also that the condition may be brought about as a consequence of different causal factors operating (on either parent) before conception.

This is the second instance of a presumptive translocation to be reported in man. Turpin (1959) and Lejeune (1959) found only 45 chromosomes in dividing cells of three independent tissue-cultures established from fascia lata of a boy with multiple abnormalities of the spine—a condition described as *polydysspondylie*. A single apparently rearranged chromosome was present that was similar to the one identified here, but there were only three instead of four short acrocentric chromosomes. Turpin et al. ascribed their rearrangement to a translocation of the greater part of chromosome V_s (23) on to the long arm of T_2 (15). It is remarkable that, in both these presumptive translocations in man, the exchange appears to have taken place between a long and a short acrocentric chromosome. Furthermore, all the four breaks that must be postulated evidently occurred close to the centromere—two in chromosome no. 15 and one each in no. 22 and no. 23. This suggests that certain chromosome regions may be specially favoured for participation in chromosome rearrangement, but a departure from randomness could also arise secondarily as a consequence of differential survival at the cellular or zygotic level. The chromosomes of pair no. 22 bear satellites on their short arms close to their centromeres; so also do two of the long acrocentric chromosomes—either the longest pair (Tjio and Puck 1958) (no. 14) or the second longest pair (Chu and Giles 1959) (no. 15). It follows that three of the four breaks may have occurred in the neighbourhood of a satellite. The fact that Levan and Hsu (1959) have found nucleolar remnants attached to one of the satellited chromosomes supports the assumption that in man, as in other organisms, the "stalk" which attaches satellite to main chromosome body is the site of a nucleolar organiser. Nucleoli are formed independently in telophase but are frequently reduced by fusion to a single one by interphase. Hence the satellited chromosomes, and particularly the regions adjoining the nucleolar organisers, would tend to lie near one another. Close association between points of breakage favours the occurrence of chromosome rearrangements (such as reciprocal translocations), and a nucleolar organiser therefore might well influence the probability that structural changes will take place in its vicinity (Darlington 1939), while there exists the possibility of increased tendency to breakage (or reduced restitution) in this neighbourhood (Darlington 1937, Swanson 1958).

The presence of a nucleolar organiser on pair no. 22 may be important in a different way and relevant to the origin of "regular" mongolism. Persistence of nucleolar remnants in meiotic prophase may interfere with the approach and pairing of these two short chromosomes (Darlington 1937) to such a degree that no chiasma is formed (Darlington 1935, Upcott 1936). They would then enter the first meiotic spindle as unpaired bodies (univalents) and assort at random to the poles, so yielding gametes in the proportions 2 normal; 1 nullo-22; 1 duplex-22. The other satellited chromosome (no. ?15) is at least twice as long as chromosome no. 22; and interference of pairing through the same mechanism of nucleolar interference would not be expected to be so severe, if, indeed, it occurred at all.

If this analysis is correct, two conclusions follow: (1) the primary event (failure of chromosome no. 22 to pair) would be four times as frequent as mongolism itself: and (2) two chromosomes no. 22 would be inherited from the one parent without crossing-over having occurred between them—an eventuality that perhaps will be testable in the far future of human cytogenetics.

One further and final point can be made that they may have a bearing on the relationship of mongolism to advancing maternal age. It is generally accepted that all primary oöcytes are differentiated before birth, or at latest very shortly afterwards. The nucleoli in the oöcytes of a 45-year-old woman would therefore have been in existence for 45 years, and it is conceivable that, in consequence of some progressive biochemical change, they would be more resistant to the normal nucleolar breakdown processes that take place in meiotic prophase. Spermatogenesis presents a sharp contrast: there is no reason to suppose that any primary spermatocyte has a life longer than a week or two, so that nucleolar breakdown would be expected to proceed at normal rate and not interfere with meiotic pairing.

SUMMARY

A mongol girl, selected because she was born from a young mother, in contrast with reported chromosome findings in mongols, had only 46 chromosomes in her bone-marrow cells and had four small acrocentric chromosomes like normal females. There were only 5, instead of 6, of the longer acrocentric chromosomes (pairs 14, 15, or 16) but an extra chromosome was present that was not certainly distinguishable from chromosome 12; and this may have carried the major part of the genetic material of chromosome 22.

A reciprocal translocation between chromosomes ?15 and 22 is suggested as the origin of the anomaly. The possibility that it originated during the development of the patient herself is unlikely but not excluded. It is more likely to have occurred in one of the parents, or even a grandparent, possibly during development. If one parent were affected, he or she would be a gonosomic mosaic, and there would be an increased probability of further mongol births, as well as other familial and genetic implications. Were one of the grandparents affected, the genetic implications would be the same, but one of the parents would be distinct in his or her somatic (and germinal chromosomal makeup).

REFERENCES

Böök, J. A., Fraccaro, M., Lindsten, J. (1959) *Acta pædiat., Stockh.* 48:453.
Chu, E. H. Y., Giles, N. H. (1959) *Amer. J. hum. Genet.* 11:63.
Darlington, C. D. (1935) *Proc. roy. Soc. B,* 118:59.
———— (1937) *Recent Advances in Cytology;* p. 39. London.

—— (1939) *J. Genet.* 37:341.

—— (1940) *ibid.* 39:351.

Ford, C. E., Jacobs, P. A., Lajtha, L. G. (1958) *Nature, Lond.* 181:1565.

—— Jones, K. W., Miller, G. J., Mittwoch, U., Penrose, L. S., Ridler, M., Shapiro, A. (1959) *Lancet, i*:709.

Jacobs, P. A., Baikie, A. G., Court-Brown, W. M., Strong, J. A. (1959) *ibid.* p. 710.

Jenkins, R. L. (1933) *Amer. J. Dist. Child.* 45:506.

Lejeune, J. (1959) Conference on Human Chromosome Abnormalities, King's College Hospital, London.

—— Gautier, M., Turpin, R. (1959a) *C.R. Acad. Sci., Paris* 248:1721.

—— Turpin, R., Gautier, M. (1959b) *Ann. Génétiques, 1*:41.

Levan, A., Hsu, T. C. (1959) *Hereditas, Lund,* 45:665.

Penrose, L. S. (1933) *J. Genet.* 27:219.

—— (1934) *Ann. Eugen.* 6:108.

—— (1951) *J. ment. Sci.* 97:738.

—— (1954a) The Biology of Mental Defect; p. 186. London.

—— (1954b) *Ann. hum. Genet.* 19:10.

Shuttleworth, G. E. (1909) *Brit. med. J.* ii:661.

Sidky, A. R. (1939-40) *J. Genet.* 39:265.

Swanson, C. P. (1958) Cytology and Cytogenetics; pp. 133, 359. London.

Tjio, J. H., Puck, T. T. (1958) *Proc. nat. Acad. Sci. Wash.* 44:1229.

Turpin, R. (1959) *Int. pædiat. Congr.*

Upcott, M. B. (1936) *Cytologia,* 7:118.

29

A NEW TRISOMIC SYNDROME

J. H. Edwards, M.R.C.P., D. G. Harnden, Ph.D. Edin.,*
A. H. Cameron, M.D. Durh., V. Mary Crosse, O.B.E.,
M.D. Lond., D.P.H., and O. H. Wolff, M.D.
Cantab., M.R.C.P., D.C.H.

IN this paper we present the case report of a female child with multiple congenital abnormalities in whom postmortem cytological studies revealed an extra chromosome. Lejeune et al. (1959) have recently reported the presence of an extra chromosome in mongols. In the mongols so far examined there are 47 chromosomes, the extra chromosome being a small autosome (that is, other than a sex chromosome) which is indistinguishable from one of the smallest pairs of autosomes of the normal chromosome complement. Mongols are, therefore, said to be trisomic for this chromosome. Trisomy is most likely to occur as a result of nondisjunction (that is, failure of a pair of chromosomes to separate) during gametogenesis in one of the parents. We believe the case reported in this paper to be trisomic for an autosome other than that involved in mongolism.

CLINICAL RECORD

The infant, a girl, was delivered at term by cæsarean section (Mr. G. S. Lester) at Marston Green Maternity Hospital on May 22, 1959.

Reprinted, with additions, from *The Lancet*, April 9, 1960, pp. 787-790.

* Present address: M.R.C. Group for Research on the General Effects of Radiation, Department of Radiotherapy, Western General Hospital, Crewe Road, Edinburgh, 4.

We are grateful to Dr. C. E. Ford and Prof. D. V. Hubble for much help with the preparation of this report; to Dr. Elizabeth Robson for defining the haptoglobin and transferrin types; to Dr. Sylvia Lawler for attempting to determine the blood-groups from an old specimen of blood taken before extensive transfusion; to Miss C. M. Scammell for technical assistance; to Mr. D. B. Peakman for the photographs.

Her mother and father, aged 31 and 32 respectively, and her brother, aged 6, are healthy. Between the births of her two children the mother had two miscarriages. During this pregnancy hydramnios was suspected, and she had mild toxæmia. Cæsarean section was carried out because of disproportion.

The birth weight was 5 lb. 1 oz., length 17 in., head circumference 13½ in. Some unusual features were immediately obvious: an odd-shaped head with wide occipitoparietal and narrow frontal diame-

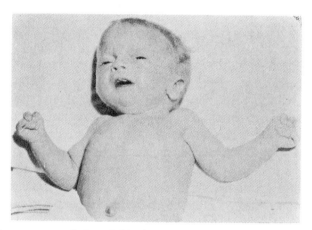

Fig. 1. Appearance of the child showing triangular mouth, low-set ears, and position of hands.

ters; a broad and flat bridge of the nose; low-set ears; a small mouth, inadequate for breast-feeding; webbed neck; hypermobility of the shoulders, so that they could almost be made to meet; and very short big toes with webbing between the 2nd and 3rd.

On the second day a loud systolic murmur was noted, with its maximum intensity in the 4th left intercostal space near the sternum; the femoral pulses were normal. During the first week of life she had several cyanotic attacks and transient jaundice; then her condition improved and after four weeks she was discharged. At six weeks she again became jaundiced. She was admitted to Little Bromwich Hospital and, after investigation had shown the jaundice to be obstructive, was transferred to the Children's Hospital, Birmingham.

She was then 9 weeks old and weighed only 6 lb. 3 oz.; length 19½ in.; head circumference 14½ in. Some other features had now become obvious (figs. 1 and 2)—a triangular mouth, a receding chin, and a wide-open metopic suture. The ears were long and oblique, the main axis lying downwards, forwards, and inwards. All the components of the ear were present, but their relative proportions were abnormal. In particular there was an abnormally great distance between the crus antihelicis and the helix margin, giving the ear a pixie-look. The chest was shield-like with nipples almost in the anterior axillary line; the fingers and toes were short

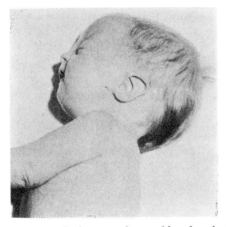

Fig. 2. Photograph showing shape of head and of ears.

and stubby with short irregular and flat nails; the fingers were tightly clenched though they could be straightened. The carrying-angle of the elbow was normal and the external genitalia were normal. The liver was enlarged. The systolic blood-pressure was 130 mm. Hg. Mental development was retarded: she did not smile, focus, or listen to voices.

Investigations allowed us to rule out the following conditions as causes of the jaundice: galactosæmia, syphilis, toxoplasmosis, Weil's disease, glandular fever, and hæmolytic disease of the new-born.

Summary of Other Investigations

Urine—No inclusion bodies seen.

Blood.—White cells: drumsticks present. Group A Rh+. Hapto-globins type 2 : 2; transferrins type C.

Buccal smear.—Chromatin-positive.

X-rays (R. Astley.)—On screening of the *chest*, the heart was seen to be moderately enlarged with a rather globular shape; some pulmonary plethora. The descending aorta had an uneven contour in its upper part. The appearances suggested left-to-right shunt. *Skeleton:* bone age normal; skull, clavicles, and cervical spine normal; thorax dome-shaped. *Pelvis:* iliac index normal according to the data of Caffey and Ross (1956).

Progress

The jaundice persisted, uninfluenced by a ten-day course of prednisolone. After a needle biopsy of the liver (see below) an exploratory operation was performed by Mr. Arnold Gourevitch, on Sept. 21: the liver was greatly enlarged, the gallbladder was small and contained bile; the right, left, and common hepatic ducts and the common bile duct were present but very small. The ovaries, fallopian tubes, and uterus were normal. Cholecyst-jejunostomy was carried out and biopsy specimens obtained from the liver and right ovary. After operation the jaundice deepened and bleeding occurred from the wound and in the bowel. Despite repeated blood-transfusions the infant died on Oct. 2.

PATHOLOGICAL FINDINGS

Liver Biopsy

The needle biopsy and that taken at laparotomy showed the appearances of giant-cell hepatitis (fig. 3). The portal tracts and peripheral parts of the lobules were normal. The central parts contained numerous bile thrombi and showed disorganisation with multinucleated giant cells and interstital fibrosis.

Biopsy of Right Ovary

Normal ovarian tissue with a normal complement of immature and maturing follicles.

Necropsy

The external features have already been described.

Hæmorrhage from the cholecystojejunal anastomosis filled the small and large intestine. The mesentery was unfixed. The *liver* was firm, was considerably enlarged, and had a smooth external surface. The cut surface was green and the lobular pattern accentuated. The intrahepatic bileducts were not dilated. The common bileduct was small in calibre but patent, and its mucosa was bilestained. The hepatic and cystic ducts were not dissected out, because of adhesions. The *heart* weighed 41.5 g. Both ventricles were hypertrophied and dilated and there was a high ventricular septal defect, 0.6 cm. in diameter. The *ductus arteriosus* admitted the passage of a probe 2 mm. in diameter. The *left ovary* and the remaining part of the *right ovary* were normal. The *spleen*

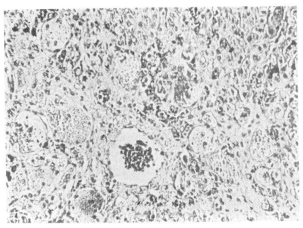

Fig. 3. Low-power view of centrilobular zones of liver showing many multinucleated giant liver cells. (Hæmatoxylin and eosin.)

was moderately enlarged, firm, and showed congestion of the pulp and slightly increased trabecular markings. The *thymus* was markedly involuted and lay behind the innominate vein. The *skull* showed a patent metopic suture continuous with a wide anterior fontanelle. The anterior third of the *falx cerebri* was narrow and did not extend for the normal distance into the longitudinal cerebral fissure. The brain was slightly underweight (456 g.). In both frontal lobes and the left parietal lobe the gyri were unusually prominent but not irregular; the sulci were wide and there was a moderate excess of subarachnoid fluid. The arachnoid, like the falx, did not penetrate deeply between the two frontal lobes but there was no abnormal continuity of cerebral tissue crossing the midline. Slicing after fixation showed no further abnormality.

There was slight but definite *thoracic scoliosis.* The *sternum* was thinner than normal and wide, and contained two long thin centres of ossification.

Histological examination of a portion of liver from near the hilum showed normal portal ducts and bileducts. There was fibrosis in the centrilobular zones with considerable loss and disorganisation of liver cells. Many were arranged in acinar groups.

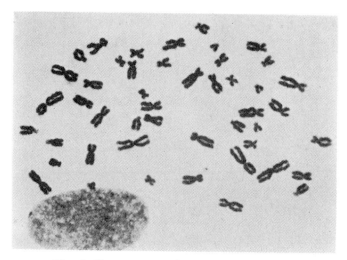

Fig. 4. Chromosomes of cell (× approx. 800).

Cells with three or four nuclei were common but there were few giant cells. Three small extrahepatic bile ducts were seen in the hilar tissue. One contained granular bile pigment.

CYTOLOGICAL EXAMINATIONS

Tissue specimens were removed during postmortem examination three hours after death. These were collected in sterile Glaxo medium 199 and set up in tissue cultures twenty hours later using the method described by Harnden (1960). Samples of ovary and kidney proved to be infected and these were discarded but successful cultures were established from skin and muscle taken from the scapular region. Cytological studies on the muscle culture were carried out ten days after the tissue was established in culture and on the skin culture after twenty-one days. These showed that the great majority of cells from both cultures contained 47 chromosomes:

Tissue		Chromosome Counts					Sex Chromosomes
	<45	45	46	47	48	>48	
Skin	..	1	..	22	3	..	XX
Muscle	1	..	2	35	..	..	XX

Counts other than 47 can probably all be attributed to technical errors such as breakage of cells during preparation. Six

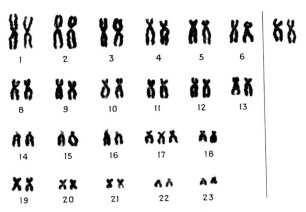

Fig. 5. Chromosomes arranged in pairs.

cells from the muscle culture and five cells from the skin culture were carefully analysed and all showed that there were 5 chromosomes resembling pairs 17 and 18 (Ford et al. 1958) of the normal complement in size and position of the centromere (fig. 4). On the basis of examination of the analysed cells and of other cells not completely analysed, it was decided that there were 3 chromosomes indistinguishable from the no. 17 chromosomes of the normal complement. The most likely explanation for the defect is that the extra chromosome has arisen as a result of non-disjunction during gametogenesis in one of the parents, and that the patient was therefore trisomic for the no. 17 chromosome.

DISCUSSION

There are 22 pairs of autosomes in man, and it is possible that 22 syndromes of autosomal trisomy exist; some, however, may be incompatible with intra-uterine life. Mongolism is due to trisomy of one of the smallest chromosomes (Lejeune et al. 1959) and, as it seems reasonable to suppose that the larger the extra autosome the worse the disturbance, most other trisomic syndromes might be expected to be at least as severe. In man such aberrations would probably lead to generalised disorders of shape and size and to multiple structural abnormalities rather than to a single localised deformity.

The main abnormalities were an odd-shaped skull, low-set and malformed ears, a triangular mouth with receding chin, webbing of the neck, a shield-like chest, short stubby fingers and toes with short nails, webbing of toes, ventricular septal defect, mental retardation, and neonatal hepatitis. The presence of the hepatitis was probably fortuitous but the constellation of other abnormalities is consistent with the type of disorder to be expected from autosomal trisomy, and it seems likely that it may denote a clinical syndrome as specific as mongolism.

The nomenclature and classification of syndromes in which multiple defects occur in association with webbing of the neck are confused, but it now seems possible that chromosomal studies of such cases will lead to clarification. However, until agreement has been reached on a system of numbering or lettering the human chromosomes it would be premature to advance a new name for the syndrome described in this paper.

In the meantime, we suggest that, of the several eponymous syndromes described, only the term "Turner's syndrome" (Turner 1938) should be retained, and that it should refer to females with varying degrees of gonadal dysgenesis and some of several associated abnormalities. Of these, short stature, neck webbing, and cubitus valgus occur most commonly; lymphœdema of the extremities, congenital heart-disease, peculiar ears, renal anomalies, a shield-like chest, osteoporosis, and osteochondrosis of the spine, and many others, have also been described. Most cases are chromatin-negative. The majority so far examined have been shown to have an XO sex chromosomal constitution (Ford et al. 1959, Fraccaro et al. 1959) or are XO/XX mosaics (Ford 1959). Our patient with normal ovaries, normal sex chromatin, normal sex chromosomes, and an abnormal set of autosomes cannot be regarded as an example of this syndrome.

Some features of Turner's syndrome were included by Ullrich (1936) in his definition of the Bonnevie-Ullrich syndrome, and our case might be regarded as an example of the latter condition. However, in later writings Ullrich (1938, 1949) has unfortunately so widened the scope of this syndrome, in which he now includes such diverse abnormalities as congenital amputations, hygroma, popliteal webbing, and agenesis of the cranial nerve nuclei, that the term lacks precision. Another disadvantage inherent in its use is the eponymic implication that these conditions are analogous in their genesis to the familial anencephaly in the mouse which has been extensively studied by Bonnevie (1934). Further in the English-speaking countries the term Bonnevie-Ullrich syndrome is widely used as a synonym for Turner's syndrome (e.g., Nelson 1959).

A few cases similar to the present one have been reported.

Bizarro (1938) described a mentally defective boy with widespread abnormalities including webbing of the neck and low ears. James (1952) described a mentally defective boy of 2 years, with low ears, webbing of the neck, slight webbing of the middle and ring fingers, inward curving of the little finger, and a loud systolic murmur. The photograph shows short big toes. Rossi and Caflisch (1951), classifying the various types of webbing, described, as an example of "status Ullrich bilateralis," a 12-year-old girl of short stature with webbing of neck, low-set malformed ears, a shield-like chest, and widely set eyes. Pubertal development was normal.

These three cases and ours do not differ more from each other than would four arbitrarily selected mongols, and the possibility of chromosomal identity seems reasonable. For further clarification it seems essential that other similar syndromes should, when possible, be described in association with chromosomal studies.

It remains to be explained how some of the multiple abnormalities associated with an additional autosome in our case may also occur in association with a missing sex chromosome in Turner's syndrome.

SUMMARY

A female infant presenting with a peculiar facies, webbing of the neck, congenital heart-disease, neonatal hepatitis, and many minor abnormalities was found on postmortem chromosomal study to have an extra chromosome apparently identical to the 17th pair (Ford's nomenclature). This is the second condition of autosomal trisomy to be reported in man.

REFERENCES

Bizarro, A. H. (1938) *Lancet, ii*:828.

Bonnevie, K. (1934) *J. exp. Zool. 67*:443.

Caffey, J., Ross, S. (1956) *Pediatrics, 17*:642.

Ford, C. E. (1959) King's College Hospital Symposium, London.

——— Jacobs, P. A., Lajtha, L. G. (1958) *Nature, Lond. 181*:1565.

——— Jones, K. W., Polani, P. E., de Almeida, J. C., Briggs, J. H. (1959), *Lancet, i*:711.

Fraccaro, M., Kaijser, K., Lindsten, J. (1959) *ibid.* p.886.

Harnden, D. G. (1960) *Brit. J. exp. Path. 41*:31.

James, T. (1952) *Edinb. med. J. 59*:344.

Lejeune, J., Gautier, M., Turpin, R. (1959) *C. R. Acad. Sci., Paris, 248*:602.

Nelson, W. E. (1959) Text Book of Pædiatrics; p. 1198. Philadelphia and London.

Rossi, E., Caflisch, A. (1951) *Helv. pædiat. Acta. 6*:119.

Turner, H. H. (1938) *Endocrinology, 23*:566.

Ullrich, O. (1936) *Handb. Neurol. 16*:139.

——— (1938) *Klin. Wschr. 17*:185.

——— (1949) *Amer. J. hum. Genet. 1*:179.

30

CHROMOSOMAL ABNORMALITIES IN FATHER AND MONGOL CHILD

M. Fraccaro, M.D. Pavia, K. Kaijser, M.D. Stockholm, and
J. Lindsten, Med. kand., fil. kand., Uppsala

SOME mongol patients of each sex have a somatic cell complement of 47, instead of the common 46 chromosomes; and
morphological evidence indicates that it is one of the small acrocentric autosomes which is triplicated in the diploid complement
(Böök et al. 1959, Ford et al. 1959, Jacobs et al. 1959, Lejeune
et al. 1959).

If non-disjunction at parental gametogenesis is responsible for
the trisomy in mongol patients it must occur with a relatively high
frequency. The incidence of mongolism at birth is difficult to
assess, but has been generally estimated as more than 1 in 1,000
births (Böök and Fraccaro 1956). The screening of a large number of patients with detailed study of their chromosomes should
indicate whether it is likely that all the cases actually have
trisomy.

In this paper we describe a mongol boy whose cultured mitotic
somatic cells displayed a complement of 46 chromosomes. This
chromosome number was at first interpreted as the product of a
translocation between 2 of the acrocentric chromosomes usually
present in triplicate in mongolism. At subsequent examination of
the parent's karyotypes it was, however, found that the mongol's
father had 47 chromosomes and was probably trisomic for pair
no. 19. (Pending agreement on classification we adhere to our
provisional system. The chromosome present in triplicate in mongolism is in this system no. 21.)

Reprinted from *The Lancet*, April 2, 1960, pp. 724-727.

This research has been aided in part by a grant from the Swedish Cancer Society to one of us (M. F.).

CASE RECORD

S is a boy born on June 29, 1959, weighing at birth 4560 g. The mother, who was 37, had an uneventful pregnancy and no history of irradiation of the pelvic region. She had had four other pregnancies resulting in the birth of three normal females (1941, 1945, 1950) and one normal male (1952), all weighing over 4000 g.

S was diagnosed neonatally as a mongol and admitted to an institution for defective children. At examination at the age of 5 months (fig. 1) the following were noted: flat face with squat nose and oblique palpebral fissures, protruding lower lip, and slightly fissured tongue with enlarged papillæ; evident palmar transverse fold on hands; iliac index 43°, a value which is considered below the normal range and typical of mongolism (Caffey and Ross 1956); distinct systolic murmur. It was not possible to determine his mental status. The father, a minister of religion, was 58 at the birth of S. He has no noteworthy history of illness and appears to be in good health.

CYTOLOGICAL OBSERVATIONS

Chromosome Number

Bone-marrow and skin biopsies were obtained from S, a skin biopsy from his father, and a bone-marrow punctate from his mother. The cells were cultured in vitro and handled according to the technique of Fraccaro et al. (1960a). Chromosome counts were performed on both primary and transferred cultures. The results are summarised in the accompanying table. The chromosome

RESULT OF CHROMOSOME COUNTS

Individual	Type of Culture	≤43	44	45	46	47	Total
	Bone-marrow:						
	Primary	8	3	3	21	. .	35
S	1st transfer	. .	. .	. .	5	. .	5
	Skin:						
	Primary	2	3	. .	25	. .	30
	Skin:						
	Primary	.	. .	. .	. .	2	2
Father	1st transfer	2	2	1	3	19	27
	2nd transfer	1	1	. .	.	8	10
	3rd transfer	. .	1	1	1	14	17
	4th transfer	. .	. .	. .	1	1	2
	Bone-marrow:						
Mother	Primary	1	. .	. .	22	. .	23

number was 46 both in S and in his mother and was 47 in his father.

Karyotype of S

Microscopic examination of more than 60 mitotic cells and detailed analysis of 6 cells (3 from bone-marrow and 3 from skin) by the study of enlarged photomicrographs showed only 4 short acrocentric chromosomes, 1 of them being easily identified

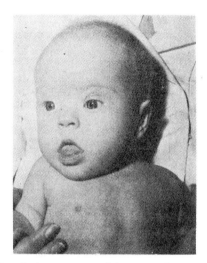

Fig. 1. Appearance of the mongol patient.

(by appearance and arm measurements) as the Y chromosome. Five chromosomes in the small-size range with submedian centromere were found instead of the 4 normally present.

The chromosomes of pairs nos. 19 and 20 are normally difficult to identify. By arranging them with respect to total arm length *and* centromere position (arm ratio) it is possible, however, to pair off 2 chromosomes with slightly higher arm ratio and total length. In the same way we first "classified" the "5th" chromosome by labelling as such the longest one. The mean length (in arbitrary units) was 1.12 and 1.04 for nos. 19 and 20 and 1.24 for the "5th" chromosome. The mean arm ratios (the long arm divided by the short) were 1.28, 1.21, and 1.18 respectively. At this stage of the analysis (before knowing the father's karyotype) we thought that the "5th" chromosome was the product of a reciprocal translocation between two of the triplicated no. 21 chromosomes. Fig. 2, composed at this stage, shows the "5th" chromosome (indicated by an arrow) placed according to this interpretation.

We had little doubt that the odd short chromosome actually belonged to the pair no. 21. It was thus identified because both its mean length (0.85) and arm ratio (3.17) were greater than those of pair no. 22 (0.77 and 2.44 respectively). Moreover, in good preparations, we found only 1 short acrocentric chromosome dis-

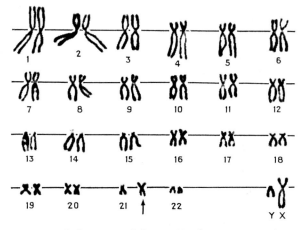

Fig. 2. Karyotype of the mongol boy: 46 chromosomes (arranged from a mitotic skin cell).

playing satellites, while we usually observe 2 such chromosomes in normal karyotypes and 3 in mongols with 47 chromosomes (Böök *et al.* 1959).

Karyotype of S's Father

Detailed analysis of 8 mitotic cells showed that the 47th chromosome was small with a submedian centromere. In nearly all the cells counted it was possible to recognise 5 such chromosomes. The 47th chromosome was classified on morphological grounds as homologous to those of pair no. 19 and it was tentatively concluded that the father was trisomic for this chromosome. The chromosomes of fig. 3 are arranged according to this interpretation.

Karyotype of S's Mother

All evidence indicated an apparently normal female karyotype.

Reliability of the Observations

There was no evidence for mosaics of two-cell types. In the case of S's father in 2 of the 4 cells with a count of 46 chromosomes it was possible to identify five short submedian chromosomes; in the other 2 the chromosomes were very spread, as in the 3 cells with a count of 45 chromosomes in the case of S.

Our observations are based on cells isolated from the donor's

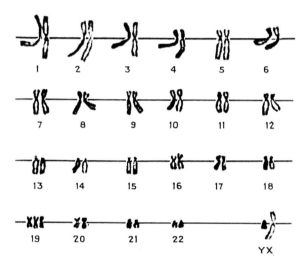

Fig. 3. Karyotype of the father: 47 chromosomes (arranged from a mitotic skin cell).

body and allowed to divide mitotically in vitro. Whether the abnormalities are produced by some factor(s) inherent in the cell culture methods can be determined on indirect evidence. Cell populations in vitro undergo changes in metabolic patterns, nutritional requirements, and chromosome number. Open system-fluid medium cultures, however, have been recently found to favour karyotype constancy for remarkably long periods (Tjio and Puck 1958, Fraccaro *et al.* 1960a). When cells of different origin are cultured—e.g., bone-marrow and skin—and both present constancy and equality of karyotype in primary and transferred cultures, it is reasonable to assume that the abnormalities observed have not primarily arisen in vitro. S's cells fulfilled these requirements. From S's father only skin cells were cultured and they showed karyotype uniformity and constancy through 4 transfers.

If mitotic non-disjunction takes place in vitro the resulting abnormal cells may have selective advantages over the others. In our experience, however, based on the examination of cultured cells from some 60 individuals we found no evidence of abnormalities arising in vitro, and karyotype constancy has been the rule for normal and abnormal karyotypes. The only exception was found in a presumptive mosaic of bone-marrow cells with both 45 and 46 chromosomes. In this case evidence indicated that the "normal" cells with 46 chromosomes had a selective advantage during successive transfers (Fraccaro *et al.* 1960b).

Our results fulfill the requirements of concordance between cells of different origin and uniformity and constancy of karyotype from primary cultures through transfers, and we are therefore inclined to believe that the chromosome abnormalities are characteristic of the individuals.

INTERPRETATION AND DISCUSSION

Trisomy in man has so far been found only in individuals with pathological phenotypes. The possibility exists that S's father is a mosaic of normal and trisomic cells and that the skin cells cultured have been sampled from the trisomic sector. But if S's father is trisomic for chromosome no. 19 it follows that trisomy does not necessarily involve pathological manifestations. This might be explained by the assumption that one of the 2 chromosomes is genetically inert as are generally the supernumerary (accessory) chromosomes found in some plant and invertebrate species which are, however, by definition non-homologous to those of the normal complement. These chromosomes are in some animals present in the gonads but inconstant or absent in the somatic cells of adult individuals, and they are generally heterochromatic (Melander 1950).

The report by Kodani (1958) of supernumerary chromosomes in meiotic metaphases in human testes indicates that a similar situation may exist in man. The 47th chromosome in S's father is apparently homologous and constant and is therefore unlikely to be a supernumerary chromosome. No heterochromatic chromosome of this size was found in preparations stained by Feulgen's method nor were characteristic heterochromatic bodies observed in resting nuclei, which were uniformly sex-chromatin negative.

We may interpret the situation in S in two alternative ways:

1. The "5th" submedian short chromosome is homologous to pair no. 19.—i.e., S is trisomic for chromosome no. 19, having received 2 such chromosomes from the father and 1 from the mother. In this case he must be monosomic for pair no. 21.

2. He has received from the father only 1 chromosome no. 19, and the "5th" chromosome has been produced by a reciprocal translocation between two chromosomes no. 21 with subsequent loss of the other complementary chromosome.

In both cases an error in the division of chromosomes no. 21 must have taken place in either parent's gametogenesis or during his embryonic development.

The total length of the "5th" chromosome is nearly twice that of the long arms of no. 21. By this criterion the hypothesis of a reciprocal translocation between the 2 acrocentric chromosomes (a situation sometimes called a "centric fusion" [White 1954]) seems likely. On the other hand, arm measurements cannot exclude trisomy of chromosome no. 19. Because of its mean arm ratio above unity the 5th chromosome is unlikely to be an "isochromosome." These are chromosomes with median centromeres, produced by the duplication of one chromosome arm following a transverse division of the centromere.

It was therefore concluded that it was not possible on morphological evidence to decide between hypotheses (1) and (2). If hypothesis (1) is correct S is trisomic *and* monosomic for two different autosomes. (The monosomic may have originated from failure of chromosome no. 21 to pair at paternal meiosis.) Trisomy and monosomy in the same individual has been considered very unlikely but it has been reported in two cases of mongolism with 46 chromosomes (Böök 1960). It can also be postulated that certain individuals, because of their genetical background and/or because of particular environmental conditions, have a tendency to a "lability" at mitosis or meiosis during their embryonic development or gametogenesis. S's father could be such an individual. If hypothesis (2) is correct, reciprocal translocation may occur also between homologous chromosomes. The two known instances of translocation in human material were between non-homologous chromosomes (Turpin *et al.* 1959, Polani *et al.* 1960). Chromosomes no. 21 are satellited and the nucleolar organisers may lie in vicinity during interphase—a condition which may favour the occurrence of structural changes between them (Polani *et al.* 1960).

The phenotype of S can be explained in the case of hypothesis (1) by the assumption that genes located on the single chromosome no. 21 manifest themselves since they are in a hemizygous state. Under hypothesis (2) S has the greatest part of 3 chromosomes no. 21—a sufficient condition for the phenotypical presence of mongolism, in keeping with the observation by Polani *et al.*

We have at present no evidence for preferring either of these two hypotheses. We can only reasonably assume that the defect in S is related to the chromosomal anomaly found in the father. The examination of the four apparently normal sibs of S may reveal whether some of them are also trisomic for chromosome no. 19, and we hope to obtain biopsy material in the near future.

Different causal factors may have produced the trisomy in the father. These are those commonly said to account for chromosomal anomalies in man (Polani *et al.* 1960).

SUMMARY

In the case of a mongol boy the somatic cells had 46 chromosomes, in contrast to the 47 commonly found in mongolism.

The mongol's father, an apparently healthy man, was found to have 47 chromosomes in skin cultures. In the mongol there were only 4 short acrocentric chromosomes, instead of 5; but an extra chromosome was present that was similar to those of pairs nos. 19 and 20. In the father the 47th chromosome was similar to those of pair no. 19.

The father is probably trisomic for chromosome no. 19. The mongol may be trisomic for chromosome no. 19 *and* monosomic for no. 21, or else the extra chromosome may be the product of a reciprocal translocation between 2 chromosomes no. 21. It is not possible, on the evidence available, to decide which hypothesis is correct.

The findings show that fertile, clinically healthy individuals may have a chromosome anomaly and that mongolism may arise from chromosome situations other than the trisomy of chromosome no. 21.

REFERENCES

Böök, J. A. (1960) *Acta Soc. Med. Uppsala* (in the press).
—— Fraccaro, M. (1956) *Neo-natal Stud.* 5:39.
—— Lindsten, J. (1959) *Acta pædiat., Stockh.* 48:453.
Caffey, J., Ross, S. (1956) *Pediatrics* 17:642.
Ford, C. E., Jones, K. W., Miller, O. J., Mittwoch, U., Penrose, L. S., Ridler, M., Shapiro, A. (1959) *Lancet* i:709.
Fraccaro, M., Kaijser, K., Lindsten, J. (1960a) *Ann. hum. Genet.* 24:45.
—— Gemzell, C. A., Lindsten, J. (1960b) *Acta endocr., Copenhagen* (in the press).
Jacobs, P. A., Baikie, A. G., Court-Brown, W. M., Strong, J. A. (1959) *Lancet* i:710.
Kodani, M. (1958) *Amer. J. hum. Genet.* 10:125.
Lejeune, J., Gautier, M., Turpin, R. (1959) *C. R. Acad. Sci., Paris* 248:1721.
Melander, Y. (1950) *Hereditas* 36:19.
Polani, P. E., Briggs, J. H., Ford, C. E., Clarke, C. M., Berg, J. M. (1960) *Lancet* i:721.
Tjio, J. H., Puck, Th. T. (1958) *J. exp. Med.* 108:259.
Turpin, R., Lejeune, J., Lafourcade, J., Gautier, M. (1959) *C. R. Acad. Sci., Paris* 248:3636.
White, M. J. D. (1954) *Animal Cytology and Evolution.* London.

31

SOMATIC CHROMOSOME COMPLEMENT IN CONTINUOUSLY CULTURED CELLS OF TWO INDIVIDUALS WITH GONADAL DYSGENESIS*

M. Fraccaro, K. Kaijser and J. Lindsten

INTRODUCTION

THE methods recently developed for growing cells *in vitro* directly on glass surfaces in the presence of a fluid medium have permitted a considerable improvement of the cytological methods for the study of human chromosomes. It was by determining the chromosome complement of human foetal cells growing *in vitro* that Tjio & Levan (1956) showed for the first time that the common number of human somatic chromosomes is forty-six. A further advance has been the method devised by Ford, Jacobs & Lajtha (1958) based on the short-time incubation of sternal marrow cells. This method has implications of great practical importance because, being rapid and inexpensive, it is particularly suited for large-scale screening purposes. In addition, it is not complicated by the structural and numerical chromosome changes which are alleged to be present in long-term cell cultures. Continuous cultivation of somatic cells *in vitro*, on the other hand, gives access to a wealth of information on important phenomena and appears essential for the study of cells derived from somatic tissues other than bone marrow.

Reprinted from *Annals of Human Genetics* (London), Vol. 24, 1960, pp. 45-61.

* Aided by a grant from the Swedish Medical Research Council to Prof. J. A. Böök and by a grant from the Nilsson-Ehle Foundation for Genetical Research to M. Fraccaro.

Thanks are due to Dr. E. Diczfalusy of the Hormone Laboratory, Gynaecological Clinic, Caroline Hospital, Stockholm, for the hormone titrations, Dr. G. Sundelin, Eskilstuna, for the gynaecological investigations of the patients and Dr. L. Santesson, Radiopathology Institute, Caroline Hospital, Stockholm, for the histological examination of the surgical specimen in one of the patients. The technical assistance of Miss E. B. Larsson with the cell culture and the photographic work is gratefully acknowledged.

The present paper is an account of our experiments in the cultivation of human somatic cells *in vitro* and the use of this method in the study of the chromosome complement of cells derived from two patients with gonadal dysgenesis.

Common features in gonadal dysgenesis are short stature, under-development of secondary sex characteristics at puberty, primary amenorrhoea, elevated urinary gonadotrophin levels. Individual patients may display a variety of other congenital abnormalities (Haddad & Wilkins, 1959).

The status of the gonads is often inferred indirectly from the results of hormone titrations, but when explorative laparotomy is performed in such cases the gonads are generally found to be absent or rudimentary and hypoplasia of the uterus and Fallopian tubes are also common features. Histological examinations of the gonadal tissue reveals contradictory pictures from complete absence of follicles, as in one of the cases described in this paper, to the presence of active ovarian tissue with multiple primordial follicles (Hutchings, 1959).

A peculiar condition characterized by infantilism, webbing of the neck, *cubitus valgus* and sexual under-development was described by Turner (1938) and gonadal dysgenesis in females is often broadly referred to as Turner's syndrome.

Results of the so-called "nuclear sexing," following the discovery by Barr & Bertram (1949) of a dimorphism of the chromatin patterns between female and male cells, showed that a proportion of patients with gonadal dysgenesis are chromatin-negative, i.e. the structure of the nuclei of their somatic cells is similar to that observed in normal males (Polani, Hunter & Lennox, 1954).

The proportion of chromatin-negative individuals in samples of patients with the clinical diagnosis of gonadal dysgenesis is about 80% (Lamy, Frézal & Thiriez, 1957; Wiedemann, 1958).

By indirect evidence from data on the incidence, in these patients, of recessive sex-linked colour blindness it was inferred by Polani, Lessof & Bishop (1956) that the chromatin-negative patients had probably only one *X* chromosome. It was, however, not then possible to decide whether their sex chromosome constitution was of the *XY* or *XO* type.

The theoretical possibility of haploidy of the whole chromosome set has been excluded by Platt & Stratton (1956) because of the evidence from blood-group data.

The *XO* sex-chromosome constitution was postulated by Danon & Sachs (1957) who also suggested that some of these patients might have a somatic mosaicism of two cell types.

Direct observation of the mitotic chromosomes was the next step. Ford, Jones, Polani, de Almeida & Briggs (1959) determined the chromosome complement of incubated bone marrow cells derived from a chromatin-negative case of Turner's syndrome. The cells proved to contain forty-five chromosomes instead of the normal forty-six and very probably it was an *X* chromosome that was missing.

This finding was confirmed by Fraccaro, Kaijser & Lindsten (1959) who determined the chromosome complement of skin and bone marrow cells continuously cultivated *in vitro*.

Recently, Ford, Harnden, Jones & Polani (1959) obtained evidence, as yet confined to bone-marrow preparations, that some of these patients are *XO/XX* mosaics.

2. METHODS

(i) Culture of Bone Marrow Cells

Marrow cells obtained by sternal puncture are transferred directly into a silicone-treated (New Desicote, Beckman Inc.) test-tube containing 3 ml. of heparinized (2 drops of 1% heparin[®1] vitrum) culture medium.

The medium consists of 40% pooled human serum, 30% medium 199 (Parker, 1950) (Difco Lab., Detroit), 30% Hank's balanced salt solution containing phenol red as indicator (Hanks, 1955). To each 100 ml. of this mixture are added 5 ml. of bovine embryo extract (Difco desiccated EE 100 diluted to EE 20 with Hank's balanced salt solution). Penicillin (100 i.u./ml. medium) and streptomycin (1 mg./ml. medium) are routinely added to the medium. This medium is designed to support the active and rapid multiplication of cells. If a maintenance medium is required the amount of serum, medium 199 and embryo extract can be greatly reduced. The cell density is usually determined microscopically in a Bürker chamber before culturing.

There is great variation depending on the puncture technique and the physical state and age of the individuals. With a high density of cells, inocula of 0.5 ml. from the original test-tube are generally sufficient to give rise to actively multiplying cultures in a few days.

Routinely the original cell suspension is plated, in discrete amounts of 1 ml. each, into three Petri dishes (59 mm.) containing a glass cover-slip (21 × 26 mm.) and 2 ml. of medium are then added. The cultures are incubated at 37° C. in plastic boxes which are kept fairly air tight and permanently gassed with a humidified mixture of 5% CO_2 in air. After 2 or 3 days the cover-slip is lifted with a pair of sterile tweezers and moved to a Petri dish containing fresh medium. This passage is not essential but it is useful in freeing the layer of cells to be used for cytological examination from debris, droplets of fat and blood cells which are abundant in the original suspension. The cells attached to the cover-slip serve as the material for chromosome preparations while those attached to the bottom of the Petri dish may be used for subculture. For this purpose the cells are loosened from the glass surface with trypsin, centrifuged at 400 rev./min. and 4° C. for 10 min. washed in Hanks's balanced salt solution (this stage can be omitted), resuspended in culture medium and plated in the desired amounts into new Petri dishes.

A solution of trypsin (Difco 1:250) 0.08% in Hank's balanced salt solution frees the cells from the glass in about 10 min. at 37° C. The action of the trypsin can be stopped by adding an equal amount of culture medium. Refreshment of the medium is done every fourth day unless it is required more often as indicated by the change in colour of the phenol red.

(ii) Cultures of Skin Cells

Skin biopsies, obtained by surgical removal of small pieces of epidermis, are collected in a test-tube containing the culture medium. This consists of 20% pooled human serum, 35% medium 199, 5% bovine embryo extract EE 20 and 40% Hank's balanced salt solution. The specimens are divided into small fragments by mincing with a pair of sharp ophthalmological scissors. The fragments are then transferred into a Petri dish, covered with a solution of trypsin 0.08% in Hanks's balanced salt solution and allowed to stand at 37° C. for about 1 hr. The resulting cell suspension and the undigested fragments are centrifuged at 400 rev./min. for 10 min., washed with Hanks's balanced salt solution and re-suspended in the desired amount of medium. The cultures are prepared and treated as described above for the bone marrow cultures.

(iii) Screening and Staining Procedures

The living cultures are routinely inspected by the use of a phase-contrast inverted microscope. For the study of the mor-phology of the cell aggregates the cells on the cover-slip, or at-tached to the bottom of the Petri dishes, are fixed with absolute alcohol (1 min.) stained *in situ* with Giemsa stain 1:20 (*ca.* 1 min.) dehydrated with acetone (few seconds), cleared in xylol and mounted in Depex (T. G. Gurr). For the routine study of the fine structure of the intermitotic nucleus and of "sex chro-matin" (cf. Fraccaro & Lindsten, 1959) the cells are fixed in Kahle's modified fixative, stained with basic fuchsin after hy-drolysis with 1 N-HCl for 15 min. at 60° C., and counter-stained with light green. This method gives good differential staining of the chromosomal and nucleolar structures. Other stain combina-tions occasionally used are modifications of the azur A-acid fuch-sin and safranin-anilin blue methods described by Reitalu (1957).

Chromosome preparations are obtained as follows. The cover-slip on which the cells are attached is transferred to a 0.7% sodium citrate solution which has been prewarmed to 37° C. Ten minutes at room temperature generally suffices to produce a good spread-ing of the chromosomes even if variations in the reaction to hypo-tonic treatments have been observed with different types of cells and crowding conditions. The cells are then simultaneously fixed and stained by about 2 min. immersion in a solution of 2% natural orcein (T. G. Gurr) in 50% acetic acid (Tjio & Levan, 1954). The cover-slip is inverted on to a microscope slide and superfluous fluid removed with filter-paper. At this stage the effect of the hy-potonic treatment can be checked in the microscope. Squashing is made by manual pressure and repeated until a satisfactory re-sult is observed in the microscope. The preparation is then sealed with Krönig cement or made permanent by the dry-ice method.

(iv) Counting Procedures

The chromosomes are counted in cells in metaphase or late prophase and sometimes in anaphase. All counts are made with a phase-contrast microscope. The chromosomes are matched after cutting photographic enlargements of photomicrographs.

In addition to the errors inherent in the squashing techniques (excessive spreading of chromosomes, mixing of adjacent metaphase plates, etc.), subjective errors are easily introduced by the individual observer. Whenever possible, therefore, an individual plate was first counted separately by two observers and then, if necessary, joint observations were made until agreement was reached. The choice of "countable" and "uncountable" cells has, of course, an important effect on the distributions of chromosome number.

3. NATURAL HISTORY OF CULTURES

(i) Bone Marrow

The cells of the original inoculum attach themselves to the glass within a short time. After 24 hr. all the cells are firmly attached and often active multiplication has begun.

The smallest number of cells required for a successful inoculum has not been determined, but a high cell density is more likely to provide actively multiplying cultures after 2-3 days. At this stage many cells have assumed the characteristic fibroblast-like (in cell culture semantic) morphology, but a wide variety of other cellular types is present, mostly clearly belonging to the haemic series. In time, the cell population becomes morphologically more uniform, the fibroblast-like cells being prevalent. Smaller, round cells can, however, be seen and they are often still present after transplantation. We are not in a position to decide whether the tendency toward uniformity of cellular types is due more to differential mortality of different cell types or to the convergence into the same morphology of originally different cells; both processes are probably involved. After trypsinization and subculture, the cells rapidly re-attach themselves to the glass, and multiplication is resumed after a few hours. Twenty-four hours after subculture is an optimal time for making chromosome preparations; there is then generally intense mitotic activity in the culture. In the phase of active growth the cells form quasi-continuous monolayers.

Occasionally in the primary cultures and often in the transplanted cultures the cells dispose themselves in round compact aggregates, ranging in size from 1 to 5 mm. The presence of

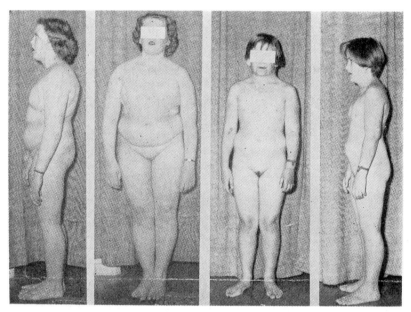

Fig. 1. Patient K. S. at the age of   Fig. 2. Patient B. H. at the age of
           19 years.   14 years.

foreign bodies seems to stimulate the formation of these aggregates in which mitotic activity remains normal.

(ii) Skin

The lag period between inoculation and commencement of the active phase is much longer in skin cultures, being in extreme cases up to 1 month in duration. Cells derived from skin biopsies do not attach themselves readily to the glass surface. Growth may begin both from isolated cells and from the undigested tissue fragments which remain in the original suspension. The morphology is constantly of the fibroblast-like type, the cells being long, spindle-shaped, and often growing in characteristic whirl-like formations. When active growth has started, the cells can be handled easily and any number of successful subcultures can be obtained.

Both bone marrow and skin cells provide very good material for observations on the fine structure of the interphase nucleus and on the "sex chromatin" body. The appearance of "sex chro-

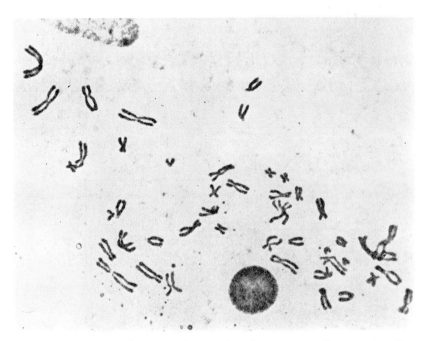

Fig. 3. Mitotic metaphase in a human female marrow cell grown *in vitro*. Photomicrograph 3000×.

matin" in human somatic cells cultivated *in vitro* has been described in detail by Fraccaro & Lindsten (1959).

(iii) Heteroploidy

Heteroploid and polyploid cells are observed in cultures of all ages, even if the basic number of chromosomes has been maintained all the time in the largest proportion of cells in all the cultures. No attempt has yet been made to quantitate the phenomenon precisely, and our statements are based on preliminary observations. When exact counts are possible, a large proportion of the cells demonstrating an increased number of chromosomes are polyploid. The highest degree of polyploidy so far counted and matched in cells from our cultures was an eightfold increase of the haploid number.

Endomitotic phenomena are probably the most common mechanism producing polyploidy in this material. It should, however,

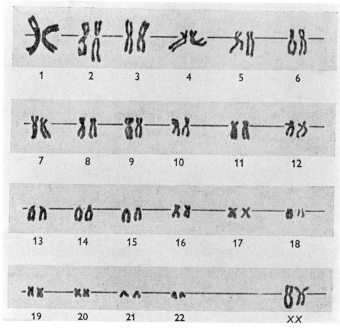

Fig. 4. The chromosomes of Fig. 3 arranged according to size and centromere position. The sex chromosomes have been marked XX.

be recalled that our observations are based on metaphases and that the orcein squash technique does not permit the observation of other phenomena, such as C-mitotic duplication and nuclear reconstruction. The most common form of endomitosis in our cultures seems to be endoreduplication, in the sense defined by Levan (1939). This is a process in which internal doubling occurs by an extra division of chromosomes during the resting phase, without any mitosis-like manifestations. This event is followed by a regular mitotic division, the final products of which are two daughter nuclei with doubled chromosome numbers (Levan & Hauschka, 1953).

At the prophase and metaphase of this division each chromosome is observed in duplicate. This is seen particularly clearly at prophase, as shown in Fig. 10.

The proportion of cells which undergo endoreduplication tends

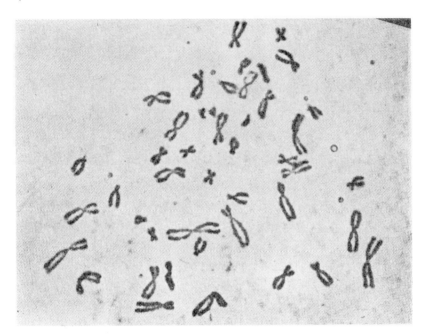

Fig. 5. Mitotic metaphase in a bone marrow cell grown *in vitro*. Forty-five chromosomes (patient B. H.). Photomicrograph 3700×.

to increase with transfers, and the variation of the phenomenon is large both within and between individual sets of cultures. After the second or third transfer skin cultures display on the average a higher proportion of such cells.

4. CLINICAL DESCRIPTION OF THE PATIENTS

Relevant personal and family data pertaining to these patients may be found in Appendices 1 and 2. The patients were encountered during a survey intended to cover all the known cases of gonadal dysgenesis in Sweden (Kaijser, Enell & Söderhjelm, 1959).

(i) Patient K. S. (Fig. 1)

Her parents are healthy. She is the only child from her mother's first marriage. In a second marriage the mother had two boys

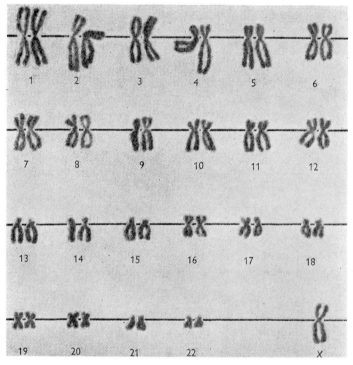

Fig. 6. The chromosomes of Fig. 5 arranged to size and centromere position. The sex chromosome has been marked X.

and one girl (all normal). Maternal health was good during pregnancy and the delivery was normal. The patient was admitted to the Pediatric Department in 1958, at the age of 18 years, for primary amenorrhoea. She was of short stature, obese, had a short neck with a slight tendency towards webbing. The breasts were moderately developed but consisted of adipose tissue without palpable glands. The nipples and areolae were of small size. There was no axillary or pubic hair and numerous pigmented naevi were present on the upper part of the body. No abnormalities were noted in the cardiovascular system, mental status or colour vision. Radiological investigation showed a sella turcica 5 × 7 mm., and a bone age within the normal range. Examination per rectum revealed undersized internal genitalia. The clinical diagnosis was gonadal dysgenesis. No drum-sticks were found in 600 neutro-

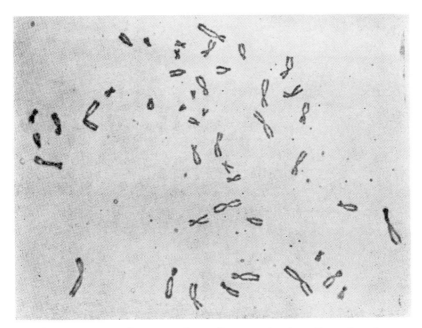

Fig. 7. Mitotic metaphase in a skin cell grown *in vitro*. Forty-five chromosomes (patient B. H.). Photomicrograph 2500×.

phils counted in blood smears. In 1959 sternal marrow punctate and skin biopsy were obtained.

(ii) Patient B. H. (Fig. 2)

Her parents are healthy. Maternal health was good during pregnancy with a normal delivery. The patient was admitted to the Paediatric Department in 1954, at the age of 12 years, for stunted growth. She was of short stature, had a short webbed neck and low implantation of hair. Some scanty pubic hair was present and the breasts were undeveloped. Pigmented naevia were scattered all over the body. Menstruation had not begun at the time of admission. No abnormalities were noted in the cardio-vascular system or the mental status. Radiological investigation showed a sella turcica of 9 × 6 mm. and bone age within normal range.

An explorative laparotomy performed in 1955 revealed an infantile uterus of small size. Thin, white fibrous strings were ob-

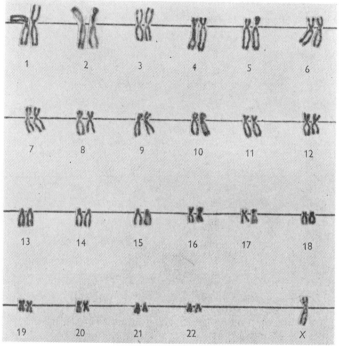

Fig. 8. The chromosomes of Fig. 7 arranged to size and centromere position. The sex chromosome has been marked X.

served at the site of the gonads. The string on the right side was removed, together with a portion of the contiguous tube. A histological examination showed a normal appearance of the tube, while the string consisted of vascularized fibrous tissue but no epithelial structures were present. In 1955 oestrogen therapy was started. This produced at first a modest swelling of the mammary glands but no other detectable changes and no bleeding. The clinical diagnosis was gonadal dysgenesis of Turner's type. At the age of 14 the patient was still amenorrhoeic. In 1957 the status of the patient was unchanged. No drumsticks were found in 600

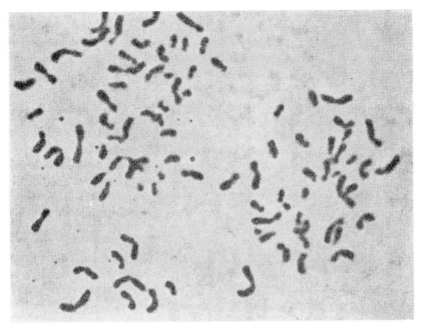

Fig. 9. Mitotic anaphase in a bone marrow cell grown *in vitro*. Ninety chromosomes (patient K. S.). Photomicrograph 5000×.

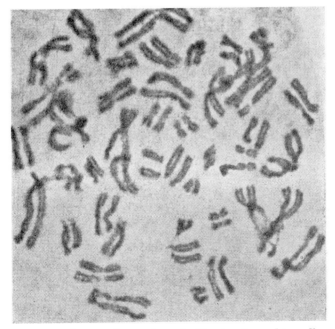

Fig. 10. Late prophase endomitotic reduplication in a skin cell grown *in vitro* (patient K. S.). Photomicrograph 2500×.

357

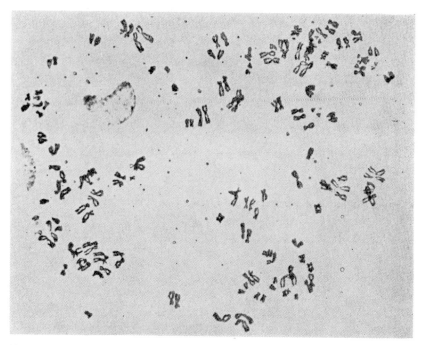

Fig. 11. Metaphase endomitotic reduplication of an octaploid marrow cell grown *in vitro*. 180 chromosomes (patient K. S.). Photomicrograph 1500×.

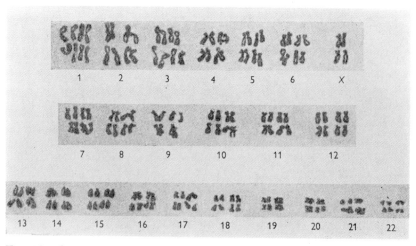

Fig. 12. The chromosomes of Fig. 11 arranged to size. Twenty-two quadruple pairs and one double pair, marked X.

neutrophils counted in blood smears. In 1959 bone marrow punctate and skin biopsis were obtained.

5. RESULTS OF THE STUDY OF THE CELLS OF THE PATIENTS CULTIVATED IN VITRO

(i) Cultures

Sternal marrow and skin cells derived from both patients were cultivated by the methods described above. Number, type and age of these cultures are set out in Table 1.

TABLE 1

TYPE, AGE AND NUMBER OF CULTURES OF CELLS DERIVED FROM THE TWO PATIENTS

	Bone Marrow		*Skin*	
Patient	NO. OF SUBCULTURES	AGE OF THE LAST SUBCULTURE (DAYS)	NO. OF SUBCULTURES	AGE OF THE LAST SUBCULTURE (DAYS)
K. S.	16	106	7	71
B. H.	5	40	3	47

The diagnosis of "nuclear sex" made in blood smears was confirmed in the cells growing *in vitro*. In both cases the cells were sex chromatin negative as in normal males.

(ii) Chromosome Counts

Chromosome counts have been made in primary and transplanted cultures. The results of the counts, both primary and revised (as defined in §2 (iv)) are given in full in Appendix 3.

Cells from both patients showed constantly a modal number of forty-five chromosomes in both marrow and skin cells.

Counts were made at metaphase but occasionally also at anaphase. One such anaphase displaying ninety chromosomes is illustrated in Fig. 9.

Furthermore, in most cells with an increased number of chromosomes the count was an exact multiple of forty-five and paired chromosomes could still be matched. An endoreduplicated metaphase with 180 chromosomes is illustrated in Fig. 11. The paired chromosomes matched from this plate are shown in Fig. 12.

(iii) The Normal Female Cell Karyotype and the Karyotypes in the Two Cases

The karyotype of a number of cells has been studied in detail. For purposes of comparison the karyotype of cells divided from normal females has been also studied. One such cell in metaphase is illustrated in Fig. 3 and paired chromosomes matched from the same cell and arranged according to size and centromere position in Fig. 4. For a description of the normal male karyotype, see Böök, Fraccaro & Lindsten (1959). The normal female chromosome complement is as follows. The numbers refer to Fig. 4.

Pairs nos. 1 and 3 are large chromosomes with median, no. 2 with submedian and nos. 4 and 5 with subterminal centromeres. This group of chromosomes is well characterized and easily matched. A group of medium-sized chromosomes follow (nos. 6-12). Their identification and location in the sequence are not easy because of the similarities in size and centromere position. The X chromosomes lie within this size category and they can be tentatively identified through comparison with the male complement in which one of these chromosomes occurs unpaired. The supposed X chromosomes are set apart in Fig. 9 and are not numbered. They have submedian centromeres and by the criterion of size can be tentatively placed either between pairs nos. 5 and 6 or between 6 and 7.

Pairs nos. 13, 14 and 15 are well-characterized acrocentric chromosomes of approximately the same size. Occasionally two chromosomes in this group have two satellite-like chromatic bodies connected to the short arms by thin chromatin threads.

Pairs 16, 17 and 18 have median, submedian and subterminal centromeres, respectively. Pairs 19 and 20 are chromosomes of approximately the same size and have median centromeres. Chromosomes of pairs 16-20 are easily identified and matched. The last two autosomal pairs, nos. 21 and 22, are small acrocentric chromosomes and in most cases it is possible to place them in order of magnitude, one pair being slightly larger. This pair occasionally displays satellite-like formations. The chromosome pattern of cells displaying forty-five chromosomes was the same in the two cases. When the pairs are matched one chromosome with a submedian centromere in the medium size range is left unpaired. By comparison with the normal complement it is inferred that an X chromosome is missing. Marrow and skin cells displaying forty-five chromosomes at metaphase and the matched chromosome complement are illustrated in Figs. 5-8. A number of the cells from both patients which had forty-six chromosomes were photographed and the chromosomes matched. In no case were we able to match the chromosomes in a similar way. In one cell a large portion of the sister chromatids of one chromosome have been clearly lost in a fashion resembling the typical picture of artificially induced iso-chromatid breaks.

In other cells the situation was even more complicated with several chromosomes which were not possible to pair. No cell was similar to the others in this respect. We were not, however, able to demonstrate any real mosaic of cells with forty-six and forty-five chromosomes.

6. DISCUSSION

The results of the present investigation provide strong confirmation of the hypothesis that certain patients with a gonadal dysgenesis of Turner's type have in their somatic cells a complement of forty-five chromosomes. The same configurations of chromosomes were observed in skin and bone-marrow cultures from both patients, the modal number of chromosomes and the karyotype were unchanged after several transplants and, furthermore, in the polyploid cells, the chromosomes could still be matched.

We have not yet been able to determine whether a mosaic of different cell types is present in cultures. The possible occurrence of somatic non-disjunction with the formation of cells some with forty-six chromosomes and others with forty-four chromosomes demands careful studies on the behaviour of cells in cultures.

We incline to the view that the sex-chromosome constitution of these patients is of the XO type. Our description of the normal female chromosome complement is in general agreement with the descriptions of Ford *et al.* (1958), Tjio & Puck (1958) and Chu & Giles (1959). We agree at the same time with Ford and his colleagues that the precise identification of the X chromosomes is not easy. It should, however, be stressed that these concordant results have been obtained by techniques similar in principle but different in many important details. Our chromosome preparations were made without pretreatment with colchicine which has been used by all the workers cited above. This shows that the use of an agent like colchicine, which is necessary in the method of Ford *et al.*, does not change the general morphology of the chromosomes.

The most reasonable explanation of the *XO* constitution of these patients is non-disjunction occurring either in the maternal oogenesis (as in the classical example of *Drosophila melanogaster* (Morgan, Bridges & Sturtevant, 1925)) or in the paternal spermatogenesis. By non-disjunction in either sex, a gamete lacking a sex chromosome can be formed and on fertilization an *XO* zygote produced. Somatic non-disjunction at an early stage of the embryological development must also be considered. The possibility should also be considered that some of these individuals have parents, one of whom is *XO*. Of the possible combinations arising from non-disjunction during gametogenesis, two have already been found, namely, *XO* and *XXY* (Jacobs & Strong, 1959), and possibly also *XXX* has been observed.* The theoretical expectancy for the occurrence of both *XO* individuals (Turner's syndrome) and *XXY* individuals (Klinefelter's syndrome) in the same sibship has been confirmed, at least on clinical evidence (Bassöe, 1956).

There is indirect evidence, from the data on colour vision defects, that in the case of *XO* individuals non-disjunction may occur during paternal spermatogenesis (see discussion in Ford, Jones, Polani, de Almeida & Briggs, 1959). The case reported by Walton (1956) of a chromatin-negative girl affected with the sex-linked recessive type of muscular dystrophy supports this concept. Recently Welshons & Russell (1959) discovered that in the mouse *XO* females inherit their *X* chromosome from the mother and that the *XO* constitution is probably due to loss or non-disjunction of the sex chromosomes during spermatogenesis in the male, even if the possibility that patroclinous *XO* individuals occur has not yet been completely excluded. On the other hand, there is evidence (Stern, 1959) to suggest that most *XXY* individuals (males with Klinefelter syndrome) originate from non-disjunction in their

---

* Refers to the case which has now been described by Jacobs *et al.* (1959).

mothers. The apparent discrepancies in the occurrence of colour vision defects in these individuals can be explained by the occurrence of equational non-disjunction, a phenomenon described in *Drosophila* (Bridges, 1916).

Instances of presumptive mosaic pattern of the *XO/XX* and *XXY/XX* types both occurring in sternal marrow cells have been reported by Ford, Harnden, Jones & Polani (1959) and by Ford, Polani, Briggs & Bishop (1959).

The evidence is, however, based only on a regenerating tissue as bone marrow, where there are signs of competitive replacement of one cell genotype by another (Ford, Micklem & Gray, 1959). It should also be noted that Danons & Sachs (1957) found in two patients with Turner's syndrome patches of chromatin-positive and chromatin-negative cells in the skin epithelium of the same individual. Mitotic non-disjunction at an early stage of morphogenesis could be the origin of these mosaics.

The findings discussed here have implications of both theoretical and practical importance. We are beginning to get a clearer insight into the human pattern of sex determination, which seems to be significantly different from the patterns encountered in the classical examples from lower organisms (see Goldschmidt, 1955, for review). All the evidence so far collected strongly suggests that the Y chromosome in man is a bearer of male-determining factors. A similar situation appears to exist in the mouse (Welshons & Russell, 1959).

It is significant that whereas individuals with Turner's syndrome are sterile, *XO* mice are fertile females. This may mean that either the sex-determination mechanism is not exactly the same in the two species or that some additional factor not immediately obvious accounts for the sterility in humans.

A first practical consequence is that patients such as those described in this paper should simply be designated as females with an abnormal genotype. A number of new problems, however, arise. If non-disjunction is the basic phenomenon of all these processes, more evidence is required about factors which may possibly cause it and affect its frequency.

Special attention should be paid to the biological status and reproductive performances of parents of affected individuals. Families showing accumulation of the conditions (Kaijser, 1949) should be carefully studied and chromosome complement determinations done whenever possible. The detailed study of clinical cases will help the understanding of the complex pathways between an abnormal chromosome complement and its external manifestation in the individual.

SUMMARY

1. Previous evidence in favour of the concept that certain patients with gonadal dysgenesis have a sex-chromosome constitution of the type *XO* and that this originates through non-disjunction during gameto-genesis of the parents is discussed.

2. The methods for *in vitro* cultivation of cells derived from sternal marrow and skin of adult individuals and the screening, staining and chromosome-counting procedures are described in detail.

3. Some aspects of the natural history of these cultures are discussed.

4. The clinical findings in two girls affected with gonadal dysgenesis of the Turner's type are briefly reported.

5. Marrow and skin cells derived from these patients have been continuously cultivated *in vitro* and their chromosome numbers and complements determined. In both cases the cells displayed a modal number of forty-five chromosomes. Analysis of the karyotype of these cells and comparison with the normal female cell karyotype showed that an *X* chromosome is probably missing. After several transfers *in vitro* the chromosome number and the karyotype were unchanged.

6. The theoretical and practical implications of these findings are discussed. In man the *Y* chromosome is a bearer of male-determining factors. Patients with this type of gonadal dysgenesis are to be considered females with an unusual genotype.

ADDENDUM

Since this paper was submitted for publication (June 1959) we have further investigated the family pedigrees of both patients: no parental consanguinity was found.

Colour vision of patient B. H. has been tested and found normal. In September 1959, after four years of oestrogen treatment B. H. had for the first time a slight vaginal bleeding.

APPENDIX 1

PERSONAL AND FAMILY DATA

Patient	Date of Birth	Weight at Birth (g.)	Length at Birth (cm.)	Age of Parents at Time of Childbirth		No. and Sex of Sibs		Position in Sibship	No. and Sex of Mother's Sibs		No. and Sex of Father's Sibs	
				FATHER	MOTHER	MALE	FEMALE		MALE	FEMALE	MALE	FEMALE
K. S.	1- 9-40	3050	46	19	20	0	0	1	4	6	1	1
B. H.	1-12-41	3750	52	35	34	2	0	2	5	5	6	3

APPENDIX 2

HEIGHT, WEIGHT AND LABORATORY TESTS AT THE DIFFERENT EXAMINATIONS

Patient	Age at Examination		Height (cm.)	Weight (kg.)	Hormone Titrations in Urine			Basal Metabolic Rate (%)	Serum Protein Bound Iodine (γ%)
	Years	Months			TOTAL GONADOTROPHINS (MU./24 HR.)	OESTROGENS (MU./L.)	17-KETO-STEROIDS (MG./24 HR.)		
K. S.	18	2	150	68.2	> 13 < 53	...	4.4	− 8	5.7
	18	5	...	66.3	> 192	...	...	...	...
	18	7				20		...	...
B. H.	12	7	134	40	>96	< 20	5.4	...	...
	12	9	...	...	>96	...	...	...	...
	13	11	139	42.3	>96	< 20	...	+11	...

APPENDIX 3

CHROMOSOME NUMBER COUNTS IN DIFFERENT CULTURES

Patient	Type of Culture	Chromosome Number							Cells Counted
		≤42	43	44	45	46	47	48	
		Bone Marrow							
K. S.	Primary	3	2	4	26	4	1	..	40
	2nd transfer	13	8	13	37	11	1	1	84
	6th transfer°	2	3	3	22	5	..	1	36
	9th transfer	..	2	2	6	..	..	..	10
	11th transfer	..	..	2	3	..	..	..	5
	12th transfer°	..	..	2	13	4	..	..	19
	15th transfer°	..	..	..	9	..	..	..	9
		Skin							
	1st transfer	4	1	6	8	4	..	..	23
	3rd transfer	..	..	1	1	..	1	..	3
	5th transfer°	1	2	5	21	2	2	..	33
	6th transfer	1	1	2	2	..	..	..	6
	8th transfer	1	1	1	4	..	..	..	7
		Bone Marrow							
B. H.	Primary°	4	6	9	31	2	..	1	53
	1st transfer°	1	1	5	48	2	..	..	57
		Skin							
	1st transfer	1	1	5	35	1	..	..	43
	3rd transfer	1	1	4	5	..	..	..	11

° Indicates revised count as defined in text.

REFERENCES

Barr, M. L., and Bertram, E. G. (1949) A morphological distinction between neurones of the male and female, and the behaviour of the nucleolar satellite during accelerated nucleoprotein synthesis. *Nature, Lond. 163:676.*

Bassöe, H. H. (1956) Familial congenital muscular dystrophy with gonadal dysgenesis. *J. Clin. Endocrin. Metab. 16:1614.*

Böök, J. A., Fraccaro, M., and Lindsten, J. (1959) Cytogenetical observations in mongolism. *Acta paediat. Uppsala 48:453.*

Bridges, C. B. (1916) Non-disjunction as proof of the chromosome theory of heredity. *Genetics 1:107.*

Chu, E. H. Y., and Giles, N. H. (1959) Human chromosome complements in normal somatic cells in culture. *Amer. J. Hum. Genet. 11:63.*

Danon, Mathilde, and Sachs, L. (1957) Sex chromosomes and human sexual development. *Lancet ii:20.*

Ford, C. E., Harnden, D. G., Jones, K. W., and Polani, P. E. (1959) Non-disjunction and anomalies of human sexual development. (Manuscript.)

Ford, C. E., Jacobs, P. A., and Lajtha, L. C. (1958) Human somatic chromosomes. *Nature, Lond. 181*:1565.

Ford, C. E., Jones, K. W., Polani, P. E., de Almeida, J. C., and Briggs, J. H. (1959) A sex-chromosome anomaly in a case of gonadal dysgenesis (Turner's syndrome). *Lancet i*:711.

Ford, C. E., Micklem, H. S., and Gray, S. M. (1959) Evidence of selective proliferation of reticular cell-clones in heavily irradiated mice. *Brit. J. Radiol. 32*:280.

Ford, C. E., Polani, P. E., Briggs, J. H., and Bishop, P. M. F. (1959) A presumptive human *XXY/XX* mosaic. *Nature, Lond. 183*:1030.

Fraccaro, M., Kaijser, K., and Lindsten, J. (1959) Chromosome complement in gonadal dysgenesis (Turner's syndrome). *Lancet i*:886.

Fraccaro, M., and Lindsten, J. (1959) Observations on the so-called "sex chromatin" in human somatic cells cultivated *in vitro*. *Exp. Cell Res. 17*:536.

Goldschmidt, R. B. (1955) *Theoretical Genetics*. University of California Press: Berkeley and Los Angeles.

Haddad, H. M., and Wilkins, L. (1959) Congenital anomalies associated with gonadal aplasia. *Pediatrics 23*:885.

Hanks, J. H. (1955) In *Outline of the Cooperstown Tissue Culture Course*. (Mimeographed.)

Hutchings, J. J. (1959) Complete sex reversal: a case report. *J. Clin. Endocrin. Metab. 19*:375.

Kaijser, K. (1949) Sexual infantilism with rudimentary ovaries. *Acta Endocrin. 3*:351.

Kaijser, K., Enell, H., and Söderhjelm, L. (1959) Förekomsten av gonadal dysgenesis i Sverige. *Nord. med. 61*:98.

Jacobs, P. A., Baikie, A. G., Court Brown, W. M., MacGregor, T. N., Mac-Lean, H., and Harnden, D. G. (1959) Evidence for the existence of the human "super female." *Lancet ii*:423.

Jacobs, P. A., and Strong, J. A. (1959) A case of human intersexuality having a possible *XXY* sex-determining mechanism. *Nature, Lond. 183*:302.

Lamy, M., Frézal, J., and Thiriez, H. (1957) Détermination du sexe chromatinien dans dix cas de syndrome de Turner. *Bull. Mém. Soc. Hôp., Paris 4-5-6*:146.

Levan, A. (1939) Cytological phenomena connected with the root swelling caused by growth substances. *Hereditas 25*:87.

Levan, A., and Hauschka, T. S. (1953) Endomitotic reduplication mechanisms in ascites tumors of the mouse. *J. Nat. Cancer Inst. 14*:1.

Morgan, T. H., Bridges, C. B., and Sturtevant, A. H. (1925) The genetics of *Drosophila*. *Bibliogr. genet. 2*:1.

Parker, R. C. (1950) *Methods of Tissue Culture*. New York: P. B. Hoeber, Inc.

Platt, R. and Stratton, F. (1956) Ovarian agenesis with male skin sex. Evidence against parthenogenesis. *Lancet ii:*120.

Polani, P. E., Hunter, W. F., and Lennox, B. (1954) Chromosomal sex in Turner's syndrome with coarctation of the aorta. *Lancet ii:*120.

Polani, P. E., Lessof, M. F., and Bishop, P. M. F. (1956) Colour-blindness in "ovarian agenesis" (gonadal dysplasia). *Lancet ii:*118.

Reitalu, J. (1957) The appearance of nucleoli and heterochromatin in mesothelial cells and cancer cells of ascites tumours of the mouse. *Acta path. microbiol. scand. 41:*257.

Stern, C. (1959) Colour-blindness in Klinefelter's syndrome. *Nature, Lond. 183:*1452.

Tjio, J. H., and Levan, A. (1954) Some experiences with acetic orcein in animal chromosomes. *Anal. Estac. exp. Aula Dei 3:*225.

Tjio, J. H., and Levan, A. (1956) The chromosome number of man. *Hereditas 42:*1.

Tjio, J. H., and Puck, T. T. (1958) The somatic chromosomes in man. *Proc. Nat. Acad. Sci., Wash. 44:*1229.

Turner, H. H. (1938) A syndrome of infantilism, congenital webbed neck and *cubitus valgus. Endocrinology 23:*566.

Walton, J. N. (1956). The inheritance of muscular dystrophy: further observations. *Ann. Hum. Genet., Lond. 21:*40.

Welshons, W. J., and Russell, L. B. (1959) The Y-chromosome as the bearer of male determining factors in the mouse. *Proc. Nat. Acad. Sci., Wash. 45:*560.

Wiedemann, H.-R. (1958) The result of haematological determination of the genetic sex in disturbances of sexual development. In *Symposium on Nuclear Sex*, p. 102. London: W. Heinemann.

32

THE PREPUBERTAL TESTICULAR LESION IN CHROMATIN-POSITIVE KLINEFELTER'S SYNDROME (PRIMARY MICRO-ORCHIDISM) AS SEEN IN MENTALLY HANDICAPPED CHILDREN

M. A. Ferguson-Smith, M.B. Glasg.

THE finding of chromatin-positive Klinefelter's syndrome (primary micro-orchidism) in just over 1% of male patients in a mental-deficiency hospital (Ferguson-Smith 1958) has led me to try to ascertain the frequency of the condition among the much larger number of mental defectives who remain out of hospital. At the same time, opportunity has been taken to learn more about the nature and time of onset of the testicular lesion. I hoped that, as it is now possible to diagnose the condition before puberty by nuclear sexing techniques, means might be found to prevent or modify the invariable sterility (at least in those with normal intelligence) and the often distressing stigmata of gynæcomastia, eunuchoidism, and androgen deficiency observed in adult patients.

The relatively high incidence among mental defectives has been confirmed in a similar survey by Prader et al. (1958) who found 8 cases among 336 feebleminded boys (2.4%), and independently by Cornwell and Herrmann (1958) who describe 3 cases detected clinically in a training school for the mentally re-

Reprinted from *The Lancet,* January 31, 1959, pp. 219-222.

This survey would have been impossible without the most willing cooperation of Dr. James Ewan, principal medical officer, Glasgow School Health Service, Mr. James A. Stewart, his assistant administrative officer, and the head teachers and staffs of the special schools visited. I am also most grateful to Mr. W. S. Mack for testicular biopsies, to Dr. A. D. T. Govan for hormone assays, Mr. Andrew McGhie for intelligence testing, and Dr. A. M. MacDonald and Dr. James A. Imrie for necropsy material.

Finally I wish to record my sincere thanks for the personal interest and encouragement of Dr. Bernard Lennox, whose work on nuclear sexing initiated the study of which this is a part.

tarded. The frequency of the condition among persons with normal intelligence is harder to assess. It is clearly high enough to be important, however, for investigation of a male infertility clinic showed that approximately 3% of all subfertile patients had female nuclear sex (Ferguson-Smith et al. 1957). Certainly no more than a quarter of these patients showed signs of subnormal intelligence and some appeared to have more than average intelligence.

There has been much speculation about the nature, or even the

SPECIAL INVESTIGATIONS

Case	Age at Biopsy (Yrs. Mos.)		Mental Age (Yrs. Mos.)		I.Q.*	Testis Size† (mm.)		Urinary F.S.H. (Mouse Units Per 24 Hours)	Urinary 17-keto-steroids (mg. Per 24 Hours)
						RIGHT	LEFT		
1	7	0	4	8	65	13	15	<10	1-2
2	8	6	5	6	66	14	13	<10	2
3	8	10	6	6	74	14	14	. .	2-3
4	9	8	5	0	51	14	14	<10	2
5	10	8	6	3	58	18	18	<10	2
6	11	4	8	9	77	. .	14	<10	3-4
7	11	8	7	0	62	17	17	<10	2
8	12	0	6	6	50	25	24	10-20	6

F.S.H. = follicle-stimulating hormone.
  * Intelligence quotient assessed by Terman Merrill revision of the Stanford-Binet scale.
  † Length measured at exposure during biopsy.

existence, of a testicular lesion before puberty (see particularly de la Balze et al. 1952, Crumbach et al. 1957, Witschi et al. 1957). As the micro-orchidism and other clinical features are not usually apparent until adolescence, the only means of detecting pre-pubertal cases is by demonstrating female nuclear sex. In the general population opportunities for this are few, and in fact only 1 early case had been reported (Bunge and Bradbury 1957) before systematic survey of mental defectives uncovered another (Ferguson-Smith 1958). Testicular biopsies in 2 more cases (aged 11 and 13) have now been described by the Zurich group; they interpret the histological appearances as indicating that the testes in chromatin-positive cases (with female nuclear sex) are normal until puberty, when development of the characteristic tubular hyalinisation is preceded by regression of the germinal epithelium (Siebenmann and Prader 1958). Close study of the evidence presented by these workers, and examination of testicular biopsies in 8 cases found in the present survey, suggests that this conclusion is unjustified. In the cases so far investigated a testicular abnormality could be demonstrated long before puberty.

INCIDENCE

The nuclear sex was determined, by the oral-mucosal-smear technique (Moore and Barr 1955), in 85% of all male children between the ages of 5 and 12 attending special schools for the mentally handicapped in Glasgow. The intelligence quotient of these children ranged from 45 to 85. Of the 663 children examined, 8 were found to have female nuclear sex, giving an incidence of 1 in 83 or 1.2%. In this age-group there were at this time, according to the records of the school medical department, 63,070 male children in Glasgow, and thus the frequency in this sample of the general population must be at least 1 in 6,640. Other cases no doubt exist among defective children showing a greater degree of mental defect, who, being ineducable, do not attend the special schools and so are not included in the survey. In addition, judging by the proportion of adult cases with normal intelligence, there must be at the very least an equal number in this population attending schools for normal children. On the basis of an earlier investigation (Lennox et al. 1958) we concluded that the incidence in Glasgow could not be less than 1 in 10,000. Our present figures raise our estimate of *minimum* incidence to 1 in 3,000. It may well be considerably higher.

CLINICAL FEATURES

Seven of the 8 chromatin-positive cases showed no obvious related physical abnormality. Case 6 was overweight and only one testis could be found in the scrotum; the right testis was impalpable and presumably undescended, although the possibility of true hermaphroditism with unilateral testis cannot be excluded without further investigation. All cases, including the oldest (case 8), are prepubertal and show no evidence of development of secondary sex characteristics.

I have not been able to obtain measurements in a complete range of normal testes, but the testicular lengths in these chromatin-positive cases, as measured at exposure for testicular biopsy (see table 1), seem to be much smaller than controls of comparable age at present available. Unfortunately this difference in size is not sufficiently obvious clinically to be as helpful in diagnosis as it is in postpubertal chromatin-positive cases. It provides some justification, however, for continuing to group these cases

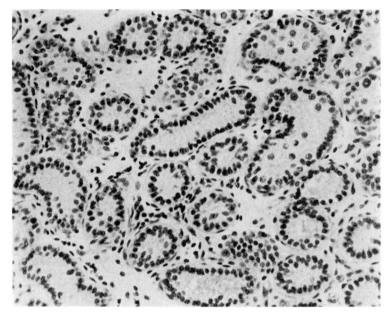

Fig. 1. Case 5. Numerous small tubules without spermatogonia and several larger "fertile" tubules (upper right) with a normal complement of spermatogania. Hæmatoxylin and eosin. ×245.

under the term chromatin-positive micro-orchidism in preference to Klinefelter's syndrome, which, as originally described (Klinefelter et al. 1942), does not exist as a clinical syndrome before puberty, and exists in only a proportion of chromatin-positive cases after puberty. Further details, including hormone assays, are recorded in table 1.

TESTICULAR HISTOLOGY

Testicular biopsies were obtained in all cases, and the histological appearances were compared with those of testes from 20 necropsies on male children dying from conditions in which there was no particular involvement of the gonads. None of the chromatin-positive cases show normal testicular histology. The most obvious and significant abnormality is a reduction in germinal cells, amounting to absence in case 3. In 6 cases, two clearly defined types of seminiferous tubule can be identified (fig. 1); the majority are smaller than normal controls of the corresponding age, contain no spermatogonia, and are lined exclusively by un-

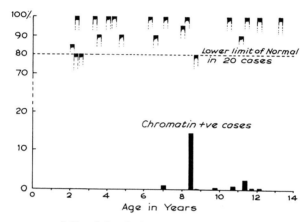

Fig. 2. Percentage of "fertile" tubules in normal controls and in cases 1-8.

differentiated Sertoli cells; standing out among these "sterile" tubules is a very occasional "fertile" tubule which is about the same size as the normal control and contains a normal complement of spermatogonia, the spherical nuclei and usually clear cytoplasm of the latter contrasting with the closely packed oval nuclei of the supporting Sertoli cells. It is possible to estimate the proportion of seminiferous tubules which show spermatogonia on cross-section. All the controls assessed in this way contain at least 80% of "fertile" tubules and most contain over 90% (fig. 2). The highest proportion of "fertile" tubules in the chromatin-positive group is found in case 2, but this does not exceed 20%. All tubules are "sterile" in the biopsy material from case 3, and in the remaining 6 cases "fertile" tubules do not exceed 5%.

The testicular appearances in the oldest patient (case 8), aged 12 at the time of biopsy, are of additional interest and show a more advanced lesion. At this age, and before the appearance of secondary sex characteristics, the normal testis usually shows evidence of maturation with enlargement of tubules, differentiation of the Sertoli and Leydig cells, and active division of germinal cells. These maturation changes are present also in case 8, except that there is a virtually complete absence of germinal cells; in some areas there is commencing tubular hyalinisation and several newly formed small "ghost" tubules without elastic tissue are seen. These histological changes are associated in this case with abnormally high urinary gonadotrophins. I hope to present later a more detailed study of the changes which lead to the characteristic testicular appearance in the adult: they are clearly of some complexity.

In 5 of the 8 cases, biopsy specimens contain structures resembling corpora amylacea. These appear to be within the seminiferous tubules and probably represent products of the tubular epithelium retained in the more severely dysgenetic tubules. They stain strongly by the periodic-acid-Schniff method, and the apparent "nuclei" are consistently Feulgen-negative. Similar structures are occasionally seen in normal prepubertal testes and in cryptorchids, and without more positive evidence the suggestion that these are "ova" (Bunge and Bradbury 1957) does not seem to be acceptable.

DISCUSSION

The main purpose here is to demonstrate that a defect already exists in the prepubertal testis of chromatin-positive cases. Although it is unwise to prophesy sterility in a patient known to have germ-cells, however few, the reduction in the normal complement of spermatogonia in these children is probably sufficient for a forecast of gross infertility, if not sterility, and treatment is unlikely to influence this. As they grow older and approach puberty, the judicious use of androgens may be of benefit in producing normal development of secondary sex characteristics and preventing disproportionate growth in adolescence.

No relation is found between the age of the child and the proportion of tubules containing spermatogonia; and, although the youngest case observed was 7 years old, it is probable that in each the complement of germ-cells does not vary significantly from birth or even earlier. At first this deficiency of germ-cells seems to support the suggestion of Witschi et al. (1957), from experiments on amphibia, that sex differentiation (depending on the relative supremacy of the cortex or medulla of the developing fœtal gonad and the resultant induction of the genital ducts and external genitalia along male or female lines) depends on the number of primordial germ-cells; this in turn is said to be adversely affected by degradation of the ovum either initially or at an early stage of embryogenesis. Against this point of view is the observation that such a deficiency in germ-cells before puberty is not confined to chromatin-positive cases, but is common to several other types of testicular dysgenesis; for I have seen almost exactly the same histological features in cases of true cryptorchidism and in 3 prepubertal cases of testicular feminisation (Morris 1953). It is also very probable that cases of true lateral hermaphroditism and of chromatin-negative micro-orchidism (Ferguson-Smith et al. 1958) show the same defect at this stage. In view of the wide variation in sex differentiation, ranging from the most extreme cases of male pseudohermaphroditism (e.g., testicular feminisation) to near-normal men complaining of infertility, these almost identical prepubertal testicular findings seem to indicate that the number of primordial germ-cells is not the fundamental controlling factor in sex differentiation. These also indicate that although a deficiency in germinal cells is an important associated defect, it cannot be considered the cause of chromatin-positive micro-orchidism and the apparent sex reversal: the primary disorder in this condition has still to be discovered. They indicate, again, that, in some if not all cases of true cryptorchidism (as opposed to ectopic testes and retractile testes), deficiency of germcells is an inherent defect rather than the result of a progressive degenerative process due to the abnormal position of the testis as is generally supposed (see, for example, Brunet, de Mowbray, and Bishop, 1958).

The changes which occur at puberty in chromatin-positive micro-orchidism are complex, and their proper consideration must await additional cases. In the patients so far investigated tubular hyalinisation has by this time usually become quite conspicuous. In this respect there is a clear difference from the chromatin-negative group in which tubular hyalinisation occurs less often, and much later, as is readily shown by studies on the tubular elastic tissue (Ferguson-Smith et al. 1958).

SUMMARY

The frequency of chromatin-positive micro-orchidism (Klinefelter's syndrome) among 663 male prepubertal children attending special schools for the mentally handicapped was determined by the oral-mucosal-smear technique of nuclear sexing and found to be 1.2%.

In the 8 cases discovered, testicular biopsy was performed. Comparing the histological appearances with those of 20 normal testes obtained at necropsy, the most significant difference was a big reduction in the complement of spermatogonia. Such a deficiency of germinal cells is seen in other varieties of testicular dysgenesis before puberty, and so cannot be considered the primary cause of chromatin-positive micro-orchidism.

In children with chromatin-positive micro-orchidism maturation of the testis, at about the age of 12, appears to be followed by tubular hyalinisation.

The significance of these findings is discussed in relation to treatment, to the ætiology of cryptorchidism, and to sex differentiation.

REFERENCES

Brunet, J., de Mowbray, R. R., Bishop, P. M. F. (1959) *Brit. med. J. i*:1367.
Bunge, R. G., Bradbury, J. T. (1957) *J. Urol.* 78:775.
Cornwell, J. G., Herrmann, W. (1958) *Acta. endocr., Copenhagen* 27:369.
de la Balze, F. A., Arrillaga, F. C., Irazu, J., Mancini, R. E. (1952) *J. clin. Endocrin.* 12:1426.
Ferguson-Smith, M. A. (1958) *Lancet i*:928.
——— Lennox, B., Mack, W. S., Stewart, J. S. S. (1957) *ibid. ii*:167.
——— Stewart, J. S. S., Mack, W. S. (1958) *Mem. Soc. Endocrin.* (in the press).
Grumbach, M. M., Blanc, W. A., Engle, E. T. (1957) *J. clin. Endocrin.* 17:703.
Klinefelter, H. F., Jr., Reifenstein, E. C., Jr., Albright, F. (1942) *ibid.* 2:615.
Lennox, B., Ferguson-Smith, M. A., Mack, W. S., Stewart, J. S. S. (1958) Symposium on Nuclear Sex. London.

Moore, K. L., Barr, M. L. (1955) *Lancet ii*:57.

Mooris, J. McL. (1953) *Amer. J. Obst. Gynec.* 65:1192.

Prader, A., Schneider, J., Züblin, W., Francés, J. M., Rüedi, K. (1958) *Schweiz. med. Wschr.* 88:917.

Siebenmann, R., Prader, A. (1958) *ibid.* p. 607.

Witschi, E. Nelson, W. O., Segal, S. J. (1957) *J. clin. Endocrin.* 17:737.

33

THE CHROMOSOME COMPLEMENT IN
TRUE HERMAPHRODITISM

M. A. Ferguson-Smith, M.B. Glasg., A. W. Johnston, M.B.
Cantab., M.R.C.P., and Arnold N. Weinberg, M.D.

ABNORMALITIES of the chromosome sex-determining
mechanism in man have long been considered a possible
cause of human intersexuality (Painter 1923). It is, however, only
with the recent advances in cytological technique that this hypothesis could be tested satisfactorily.

In an effort to learn more about the specific role of the sex
chromosomes in sex determination, we have examined the chromosome complements in several disorders of human sexual differentiation. One of the most interesting, though possibly the
rarest, is true hermaphroditism, in which both male and female
gonads differentiate in the same individual. During the past year
we have studied two true hermaphrodites, one with testis and
ovary, the other with ovotestis and ovary.

CASE HISTORIES

Case 1 (previously reported by Goodwin et al. 1954).–The
patient, a healthy Negro, was brought up as a boy. He was born
in 1933 at which time his mother was 17 years old and his father
16. He was noted to have perineal hypospadias, a bifid scrotum,
and an undescended left testis. At puberty the breasts began to
enlarge, and it was observed that the right descended testis was
small. Laparotomy revealed an immature uterus, a fallopian tube,
and a normal left ovary; these were removed. A vas deferens
emerged from the right internal inguinal ring and joined a rudimentary prostate. Histological examination of the ovary showed
germinal follicles and normal ovarian stroma. A testicular biopsy

Reprinted from *The Lancet*, July 16, 1960, pp. 126-128.

Our thanks are due to Dr. John Money for referring case 1 and to Dr. W. J.
Young for reading the manuscript.

specimen showed Leydig-cell hyperplasia, tubular hyalinisation, and germinal aplasia suggestive of chromatin-positive Klinefelter's syndrome (Ferguson-Smith et al. 1957). The patient is now married, and although childless gives a normal marital history. Axillary, pubic, and facial hair is within normal masculine limits and the gynæcomastia remains unchanged. Both buccal smear and review of previous histological material demonstrated a chromatin-positive pattern with single sex chromatin bodies. [J. H. H. no. 448002.]

Case 2.—The patient was born in 1945 when his mother was 24 and his father 25. He was brought up as a boy, although the diagnosis of sex was uncertain at birth owing to ambiguity of the external genitalia. There was a bifid scrotum containing a testis on the right side only, and a hypospadic phallus with perineal urethra and separate rudimentary vaginal orifice. Internal genitalia comprised a normal left ovary and fallopian tube, no true uterus, and a right vas deferens. The tube and ovary were removed in infancy. At puberty he developed striking enlargement of the breasts, together with deepening voice, facial acne, penile erections, and nocturnal emissions. Exploration of the right scrotal sac revealed a small ovotestis. Histological examination of this gonad reveals Leydig-cell hyperplasia and poorly developed seminiferous tubules, some containing a few spermatogonia. An area at the superior pole is composed of typical ovarian stroma, though no ova are seen. Nuclear sex is chromatin-positive.

METHOD OF CHROMOSOME ANALYSIS

Cells for chromosome analysis are obtained by using a short-term culture technique for bone-marrow based on the method of Ford et al. (1958).

Bone-marrow is removed by sternal puncture under local anæsthetic, and approximately 0.5-1.0 ml. of the specimen is dispersed into each of several sterile tubes containing 10 ml. of heparinised Ringer's solution (50 units heparin per ml.). After removal of Ringer's solution by gentle centrifugation, the cell deposit is resuspended in 3 ml. of the patient's own serum. This is transferred to sterile 2-ounce prescription bottles containing 5 ml. of cell-culture fluid (Difco N.C.T.C. 109) and these are incubated on their sides at 37°C. It is usually possible to obtain enough marrow for several preparations. The first bottle is incubated for 5-7 hours only. During the last 2 hours of this period, deacetylmethyl-colchicine ("Colcemide" Ciba) is added to a final strength of 2 μg. per ml. (This drug is thought to interfere with the formation of the mitotic spindle and so serves to arrest and accumulate cells in mitosis.) After incubation the cell culture is centrifuged and the cells resuspended in 10 ml. of 1.12% (hypotonic) aqueous sodium citrate

TABLE 1

SYSTEM OF CHROMOSOME ANALYSIS

Group	Size and Centromere Position	Idiogram Number	Normal Total Number
I	Largest, median/sub-median	1-3	6
II	Large, sub-median	4-6	6
III	Medium, sub-median	7-12 and X	13 (male) or 14 (female)
IV	Medium, sub-terminal	13-15	6
V	Small, sub-median	16 and 17	4
VI	Small, median	18-20	6
VII	Small, sub-terminal	21, 22 and Y	5 (male) or 4 (female)
		Total	46

TABLE 2

RESULTS OF CHROMOSOME COUNTS IN BONE-MARROW CELLS

			Number of Cells with a Chromosome Count of				Total Cells
	Case	44	45	46	47	48	Counted
1	....	8	15	74	22	0	119
2	....	1	7	75	2	1	86

for 20-30 minutes at 37°C. The hypotonic treatment distends the cells and disperses the chromosomes throughout each mitotic cell. The suspension is once again centrifuged and the supernatant replaced by two changes of 50% glacial acetic acid. The cells are fixed for 15 minutes and then resuspended in 2-3 drops of 2% lacto-aceto-orcein stain (Welshons and Russell 1959). Squash preparations are made from this cell-stain mixture. The remaining bottles are treated similarly on successive days.

We have found it useful to divide the marrow specimen in this way because each cell culture may show a different degree of mitotic activity and the peak of activity varies. Usually the 24-hour specimen is the most satisfactory with regard to frequency of mitotic cells.

The squash preparations are scanned microscopically and the cells selected for counting and analysis. Those in which the chromosomes are either poorly dispersed or widely scattered are rejected. Once a cell is considered suitable, its chromosome complement is counted and recorded. With the help of camera-lucida drawings and photographic prints at ×3000 magnification, the chromosomes of each cell are graded according to total length and centromere position into one of seven groups (table 1). This method of analysis enables the maximum amount of information to be obtained from the largest possible number of cells without

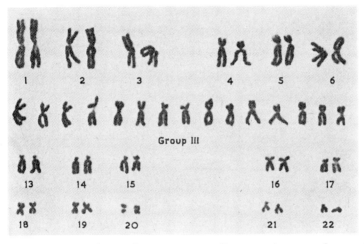

Fig. 1. Chromosomes from a bone-marrow cell in case 1 arranged according to table 1. An extra chromosome is present in group III. (×1500 approx.)

requiring pairing of each chromosome. The sex-chromosome constitution is obtained by determining the number of chromosomes of groups III and VII (see table 1). The Y is unique, and readily identified as the largest chromosome in group VII. The X chromosome cannot always be identified with certainty as the largest chromosome in group III, because the chromosomes in this group are all very similar.

RESULTS

The results of the chromosome counts are recorded in table 2. In both cases most of the cells have the normal basic diploid number of 46. Of these cells, nine in case 1 and sixteen in case 2 are especially suitable for critical analysis. They all contain 14 group-

III chromosomes and 4 group-VII chromosomes, a finding consistent with an XX sex-chromosome constitution.

A remarkable feature of case 1 is the high proportion of cells containing 47 chromosomes. Eleven mitotic plates are suitable for analysis. The extra chromosome in each clearly belongs to group III although it is impossible to identify it with a specific chromosome pair (fig. 1). Only one of the fourteen cells in this case with a diploid number of 45 is suitable for critical analysis. The missing chromosome again belongs to group III but it is not possible to

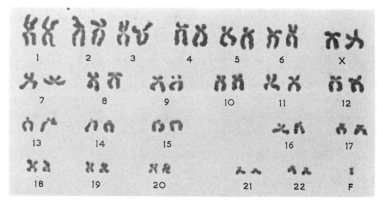

Fig. 2. Chromosomes from a bone-marrow cell in case 2 with an additional chromosomal fragment. (×1500 approx.)

identify it more exactly. Fragmentation of the chromosomes can be excluded as a cause of the observed aneuploidy because no structural abnormalities of the chromosomes can be seen.

In case 2, three cells with 46 chromosomes show in addition a small chromosome fragment, similar in each cell and reminiscent of an isochromatid deletion (see fig. 2, "F"). The few cells in which a count lower than 46 is observed do not show consistently loss of the same chromosomes and must be regarded as abnormal or damaged cells.

In most of the cells in both cases where a complete analysis of all the groups is not possible, the chromosomes in groups I, IV, VI, and VII can be identified. In no cell from either case are there more than 4 chromosomes in group VII. No characteristic Y chromosome can be found in any of the preparations.

DISCUSSION

The possibility that true hermaphroditism in man is associated with an abnormal complement of sex chromosomes, such as an XXY constitution, had been suggested (see for example Painter 1923) ever since the classical work of Bridges (1916) on non-disjunction of the sex chromosomes in Drosophila. The demonstration of a normal basic diploid number of 46 and an XX chromosome constitution in the two cases described here, together with the results from two similar cases recently reported (Hungerford et al. 1959, Harnden and Armstrong 1959), excludes this possibility at least in the cases studied to date. It does not, however, exclude the possibility that the condition arises from some other type of abnormality of the sex chromosomes which causes a disturbance in the normal balance between the genes determining sex. Present techniques of chromosome analysis are not yet sufficiently refined to detect such chromosome aberrations, which might arise as small deletions or translocations.

It is possible that the high proportion of cells in case 1 which have one chromosome too many may be explained by the presence of three X chromosomes. This is suggested by the fact that in every cell of this type suitable for complete analysis the extra chromosome is in group III. This trisomic condition could be due to a high frequency of mitotic non-disjunction of the X chromosomes influenced by a chromosomal defect which may be associated with that producing hermaphroditism. This is the only indication of an abnormality in the X chromosomes. If mitotic non-disjunction of the X chromosomes were the explanation of the high frequency of cells with a count of 47, it would seem reasonable that an equal proportion of cells should contain only one X chromosome and have a total count of 45. The evidence for this is inconclusive. The only complete analysis available shows that the missing chromosome is in group III and might be an X.

The amount of aneuploidy found in case 1, on the other hand, may be of no significance with regard to the cause of the hermaphroditism. It may represent a phenomenon confined to the bone-marrow, a site where the normal rate of cell-division is high and where abnormal mitoses in the maturing erythroblast might be expected. It is note-worthy that in the case of Hungerford et al. (1959) two cells from the leucocyte culture are interpreted as having 47 chromosomes.

There remains another explanation for the high incidence of cells with counts of 47 in case 1. It is possible that the patient is an XXX/XX mosaic of a type similar in ætiology to the case reported by Ford et al. (1959b) as an XXY/XX mosaic. They interpreted the findings as due to mitotic non-disjunction in an individual whose XXY constitution was derived from meiotic non-disjunction. However, the XXX individual reported by Jacobs, Baikie, et al. (1959) has no features in common with case 1 and has in addition a double complement of sex chromatin in a high proportion of intermitotic nuclei.

The recent discoveries that the sex-chromosome constitution is XXY in chromatin-positive Klinefelter's syndrome (Jacobs and Strong 1959), and is XO in chromatin-negative Turner's syndrome (Ford et al. 1959a), seemed to indicate that the Y chromosome is strongly male-determining in man (Ford et al. 1959b). In the house mouse exceptional female mice may have an XO pattern (Welshons et al. 1959), indicating that in these mammals the Y chromosome is necessary for male differentiation. This concept is contrary to previous theories of sex determination in mammals which have been based largely on studies in Drosophila, where sex is determined by a balance between male-determining genes carried on the autosomes and female-determining genes carried on the X chromosomes, the Y playing no significant part in this system. The absence of a normal Y chromosome in the four cases of true hermaphroditism studied to date is so far the only evidence against the hypothesis that the Y chromosome is essential to male determination in man. Support for alternative hypotheses is derived from the fact that the histological differentiation of the male gonad in the true hermaphrodite lacking a Y chromosome is as complete as that occurring in the XXY individual with chromatin-positive Klinefelter's syndrome.

An alternative explanation is that male-determining genes carried by the Y chromosome have been transferred in the true hermaphrodites to another chromosome by translocation. As the basic diploid number in these cases is 46, the presumed translocation must have taken place during meiosis resulting in an X gamete with the addition of masculinising genes from the Y chromosome. With the present cytological methods one cannot be certain that a small translocation has not taken place in the two cases reported here. There is at least no evidence of a large translocation involving most of the Y chromosome. The finding of an additional small chromosome fragment in three cells in case 2 is of interest in this respect, because this could be interpreted as the centromere-bearing remains of the Y chromosome which has taken part in a translocation and has persisted in a small proportion of cells.

In discussing the ætiology of true hermaphroditism, those cases reported by Grumbach and Barr (1958) to have male (chromatin-negative) nuclear sex must also be considered. Unfortunately there are no reports of chromosome analysis in these patients, but present views on the origin of the sex-chromatin suggest that they have only one X chromosome. In Grumbach and Barr's series 6 out of 25 were found to be chromatin-negative. No correlation was observed between the type of sex differentiation and the nuclear sex. This observation in itself suggests that there are several causative factors and that more than one karyotype may be associated with true hermaphroditism.

In the absence of an obvious chromosome anomaly as the cause of true hermaphroditism, other factors must be considered. We shall not discuss the embryological aspects except to emphasise that an abnormal stimulus, in order to produce unilateral male sex differentiation in a female fœtus, must exert its effect principally on one gonad and must operate on the undifferentiated gonadal anlage at a very early stage of gestation, almost certainly before seven weeks. It is difficult to see how the abnormal stimulus could be hormonal or be derived from the maternal environment, and there is in fact no evidence to support this in man. Another theory (Witschi et al. 1957) involves degradation of the fertilised egg and embryo, with specific damage to the developing and migrating germinal cells which are considered important in the initiation of differentiation of the appropriate gonad and thereafter the appropriate genital ducts.

SUMMARY

Chromosome analyses are described in two cases of true hermaphroditism. The basic diploid number in each is 46 and the sex-chromosome constitution is interpreted as XX. In one patient 18.5% of cells had a chromosome count of 47. Despite the presence of a testis in one case and an ovotestis in the other, no Y chromosome was present. This finding is discussed in the light of modern views on the function of the Y chromosome in human sex determination.

ADDENDUM

Since the submission of this paper, a standard system of nomenclature for human chromosomes has been proposed (*Lancet*, 1960, *i*:1063). This Denver system, which for the sake of uniformity should be generally adopted, differs from the one used above, in the numbering of chromosomes 16, 17, and 18. The corresponding numbers in our system are 18, 16, and 17.

REFERENCES

Bridges, C. B. (1916) *Genetics 1:*1, 107.

Ferguson-Smith, M. A., Lennox, B., Mack, W. S., Stewart, J. S. S. (1957) *Lancet ii:*167.

Ford, C. E., Jacobs, P. A., Lajtha, L. G. (1958) *Nature, Lond. 181:*1565.

———— Jones, K. W., Polani, P. E., Almeida, J. D. de, Briggs, J. H. (1959a) *Lancet i:*711.

———— Polani, P. E., Briggs, J. H., Bishop, P. M. F. (1959b) *Nature, Lond. 183:*1030.

Goodwin, W. E., Scardino, P. L., Scott, W. W. (1954) *J. Urol. 71:*748.

Grumbach, M. M., Barr, M. L. (1958) *Recent Prog. Hormone Res. 14:*255.

Harnden, D. G., Armstrong, C. N. (1959) *Brit. med. J. ii:*1287.

Hungerford, D. A., Donnelly, A. J., Nowell, P. C., Beck, S. (1959) *Amer. J. hum. Genet. 11:*215.

Jacobs, P. A., Baikie, A. G., Court Brown, W. M., MacGregor, T. N., MacLean, N., Harnden, D. G. (1959) *Lancet ii:*423.

———— Strong, J. A. (1959) *Nature, Lond. 183:*302.

Painter, T. S. (1923) *J. exp. Zool. 37:*291.

Welshons, W. J., Russell, L. B. (1959) *Proc. Nat. Acad. Sci. 45:*560.

Witschi, E., Nelson, W. O., Segal, S. J. (1957) *J. clin. Endocrin. 17:*737.

34

CHROMOSOMAL CONSTITUTION AND NUCLEAR SEX OF A TRUE HERMAPHRODITE

Licio Marques de Assis, M.D., Dorina Reichhardt Epps, M.D., and Cassio Bottura, M.D.

THE findings of nuclear dimorphism in human tissues of both sexes and the introduction of new techniques for the ascertainment of the chromosomal constitution have added new interest to the study of intersex patients (Moore and Barr 1953, Décourt et al. 1954, Nelson 1956, Tjio and Levan 1956, Jacobs and Strong 1959, Ford et al. 1959).

We report here the results of chromosomal counts and the determination of nuclear sex in a case of true hermaphroditism. Chromosomal study was performed according to the new technique developed by one of us (C. B.). Nuclear sex was studied in oral smears. (After acid hydrolysis, buffered toluidine-blue was used.)

CASE REPORT

A "boy," 14 years old, was admitted to the metabolic department complaining of excessive development of the mammary region. Micturition had never been of the male type, the external genitals being abnormal. He had always had good health. Physical development had been normal.

At the age of 13, a quick growth spurt, coinciding with the appearance of pubic and axillary hair, was noted. (Facial hair has not appeared hitherto.) At the same time, after an initial painful period, quick and excessive growth of the mammary glands was noted (fig. 1). The patient has three normal brothers and a normal sister. The mother is healthy. The father died when the patient was 3 years of age.

Reprinted from *The Lancet*, July 16, 1960, pp. 129-130.
With the technical assistance of Iris Ferrari, M.D.

The patient's general condition was fair. Psychological study revealed a masculine personality with a few feminine traits. Height: 5 ft. 3 in. Weight: 88 lb. Span: 5 ft. 5 in. Pubis-heel measurement: 2 ft. 11 in. Pubis-head measurement: 2 ft. 4. in. Relation of superior segment to inferior segment 1:1.2. Biacromial diameter 1 ft. 2 in. Bitrochanteric diameter 10 in.

Clinical examination revealed no abnormality except for the external genitals; pubic hair in fair quantity, long and thick, in female distribution; axillary hair scarce and long. Penis 6 cm. long, without the urethral meatus, bending ventrally through a ligament connecting the ventral surface to the perineum (fig. 2). Thus the scrotum appeared to be bifid; a depression with a small meatus was visible in the midline. No testes could be felt in the labio-scrotal folds. A small mass, about 1 in. in diameter, was felt in the right groin, giving the impression of being elastic. In the left groin no evidence of a testicle was found.

The connection between the perineal meatus and the urogenital sinus was shown by urethroscopic examination. Urethrocystography indicated a connection between the urogenital sinus and the vagina, uterus, and a left oviduct. There was also a connection with the urethra and the bladder.

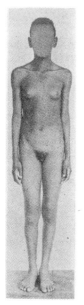

Fig. 1. The patient.

A small uterus (2-3 cm. long), a left ovary, a round ligament, and a left fallopian tube were revealed by laparoscopy, and these findings were confirmed by subsequent laparotomy. On the right side a round ligament was present, but no ovary or adnexa were seen. At the right inguinal canal an elongated mass, similar to an almond, was noted: ovarian tissue was present in two-thirds of it (subepithelial follicles were visible); the elasticity of the remaining third suggested testicular tissue. Over the ovarian pole an oviduct with a pavilion at its free end was noted. Connected by loose connective tissue to the fallopian tube, and parallel to it, was an apparently normal vas deferens. No epididymis was felt.

Biopsy of the inguinal mass showed both ovarian and testicular tissue. In the ovary, follicles in different maturation stages were found, with a single large mature one; atresic follicles were also present. There was no corpus luteum. In the testicle, the tubules had the appearance found in the ectopic gonad. Urinary œstrogens (Allen-Doisy method): more than 8 rat units per 24 hours; 17-ketosteroids (Dreckter method): 3.8 mg. per 24 hours; 17-hydroxycorticosteroids (Porter-Silber method): 3.3 mg. per 24 hours. The bone age and texture were normal. The sex chromatin was found to be female in material obtained from the mucosa of both

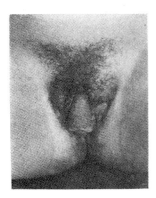

Fig. 2. External genitalia.

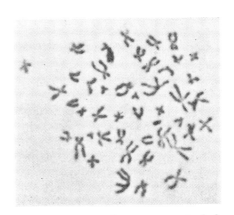

Fig. 3. Forty-six chromosomes, including 4 small acrocentric chromosomes.

the left and the right cheek. Basal temperature charts showed lack of ovulation. Vaginal cytology: no evidence of œstrogenic activity. Pregnanediol estimations: inconclusive. The bone-marrow specimens, for studying the chromosomal constitution, were obtained by sternal puncture, after intravenous administration of colchicine, according to Bottura's method. In the 25 cells examined, a constant number of 46 chromosomes was found. In 16 cells, in which the chromosomes were particularly well spread, four small acrocentric chromosomes could be perfectly identified (fig. 3). After pairing, the chromosomal constitution was found to be XX, indicating female sex (fig. 4).

DISCUSSION

Harnden and Armstrong (1959) have published a case of true hermaphroditism showing the same chromosomal constitution but with a more definite masculine appearance (male hair distribution, no breast development). Hungerford et al. (1959) published a case with male phenotype with testis and ovotestis, and the sex chromosomes were interpreted as XX.

Considering the attempts which are being made at a pathogenic interpretation of intersex, all reports of such cases are of interest.

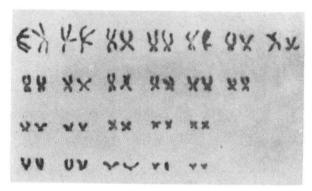

Fig. 4. Forty-six chromosomes, paired according to size, showing XX constitution.

In view of the special features of the present case, we hope that this report will prove a useful contribution.

REFERENCES

Bottura, C., Ferrari, I. (1960) *Acta physiol. lat. Amer.* (in the press).

Décourt, L. V., Sasso, W. S., Chiorboli, E., Fernanfez, I. M. (1954) *Rev. Ass. med. Brazil* 1:203.

Ford, C. E., Jones, K. W., Polani, P. E., de Almeida, J. C., Briggs, J. H. (1959) *Lancet i*:711.

Harnden, D. G., Armstrong, C. N. (1959) *Brit. med. J. ii*:1287.

Hungerford, D. A., Donnelly, A. J., Nowell, P. C., Beck, S. (1959) *Amer. J. hum. Genet.* 11:215.

Jacobs, P. A., Strong, J. A. (1959) *Nature, Lond.* 183:302.

Moore, K. L., Barr, M. L. (1953) *J. comp. Neurol.* 98:213.

Nelson, W. O. (1956) *Acta Endocr., Copenhagen* 123:227.

Tjio, J. H., Levan, A. (1956) *Hereditas, Lund* 42:1.

35

CHROMOSOME COUNT IN A HERMAPHRODITE WITH SOME FEATURES OF KLINEFELTER'S SYNDROME

R. R. Gordon, M.C., M.D. Glasg., M.R.C.P., F. J. P. O'Gorman, M. B. Glasg., F.R.C.S.E., M.R.C.O.G., C. J. Dewhurst, M.B. Manc., F.R.C.S.E., M.R.C.O.G., and C. E. Blank, M.B. Wales, Ph.D. Lond.

IN 1956 Tijo and Levan, analysing the chromosome complement of normal lung fibroblasts derived from a series of aborted human fœtuses, demonstrated that these cells each had 46 chromosomes. Shortly afterwards Ford and Hamerton (1956), working with testicular tissue, confirmed this figure. It is now accepted that man has a diploid chromosome number of 46—22 pairs of autosomes and a single pair of sex chromosomes, XX in the female and XY in the male. The revolutionary techniques used by these workers were soon applied to the study of human congenital malformations, and at least twenty different chromosomal anomalies have been shown to be associated with clinical abnormalities. Undoubtedly other similar associations remain to be discovered.

Among the first human disorders to be analysed for chromosome number and morphology was Klinefelter's syndrome (Jacobs and Strong 1959, Ford et al. 1959a and b, Stewart 1959, Crooke and Hayward 1960, Bergman et al. 1960). The chromatin-positive cases of Klinefelter's syndrome so far described have 47 chromosomes—presumably 22 pairs of homologous autosomes and an XXY sex-chromosome-complement.

We report here a case which presented some of the clinical

Reprinted from *The Lancet*, October 1, 1960, pp. 736-739.

Our thanks are due to Dr. C. C. Bowley and Dr. F. I. N. Dunsford, of the Sheffield Regional Blood Transfusion Centre, for the detailed report of the patient's blood-groups; to Dr. S. Varadi, consultant hæmatologist, City General Hospital, Sheffield, for performing the marrow biopsy for the chromosome analysis; and to Dr. C. G. Paine, consultant pathologist, Jessop Hospital for Women, Sheffield, for help with the histology and for supplying the photomicrograph.

features of Klinefelter's syndrome—a diagnosis which was strengthened by the finding of chromatin-positive nuclei in the buccal smear. Chromosome analysis, however, did not confirm this diagnosis and stimulated a search for ovarian tissue. The patient, is, in fact, a lateral hermaphrodite with an ovary and a testis.

Cases of hermaphroditism are exceedingly rarely reported, and until 1959 only about 88 had been recorded (Lewis 1959). Of these, 8 have had their "chromatin-state" recorded. Only in 2 cases have the chromosome number and morphology been reported (Harnden and Armstrong 1959, Hungerford et al. 1959). We report a 3rd case.

CASE RECORD

In 1956, at the age of 11 years, the patient presented because of pronounced penile hypospadias, the opening of the urethra being

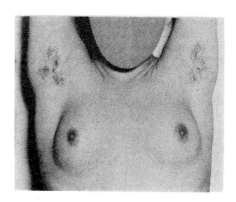

Fig. 1. Gynæcomastia with distinct development of nipple and areola, and axillary hair.

some 4.5 cm. from the tip of the glans. At that time there were no secondary sex characteristics; the left testis could not be palpated, and the right testis was in the scrotum and felt normal. In other respects he seemed a normal boy. The hypospadias was repaired by the Denis Browne operation, and the functional result was sufficiently satisfactory to justify discharge from the follow-up clinic a year later.

In 1960, aged 14 years, he was referred again because, as he had advanced in puberty, it was noticed that his breasts were enlarging much more than was thought to be normal for a boy of his build (fig. 1). He was finding this a very great embarrassment at school and was anxious to have something done about it. He was quite tall (5 ft. 4½ in.) and thin (body-weight 7 st. 10 lb.) and of eunuchoid proportions (span 5 ft. 7 in.; U/L 0.87; head to pubis 30 in., pubis to feet 34½ in. (fig. 2). His intelligence appeared to be of low average, and he was of a quiet but pleasant disposition. His voice was partially broken, but he had no facial hair. He did, however, have plenty of pubic and axillary hair, but the former was of feminine distribution (fig. 2). The right testis was in the scrotum and was of normal consistency, but felt slightly smaller than would be expected for his degree of maturity (fig. 3). The left testis could not be palpated in the scrotum, nor in the inguinal canal. He had pronounced gynæcomastia with well-developed nipples each surrounded by a distinct areola. On clinical examination the other systems were entirely normal.

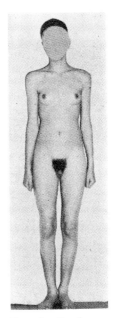

Fig. 2. Configuration of the patient, showing feminine distribution of pubic hair.

Initial investigations revealed that he had a normal output of 17-ketosteroids and ketogenic steroids (3.9 and 7.4 mg. per day respectively). His white-blood-cell count was 8300 per c. mm. with a normal differential count. Female "drumsticks" were present in the neutrophils, and the buccal smear confirmed that he was "chromatin-positive." It was at this stage that we felt he represented chromatin-positive Klinefelter's syndrome, and accordingly it was decided that bilateral mastectomy should be undertaken. This was done, and at the same time testicular biopsy and marrow puncture were performed.

Testicular biopsy (fig. 4) showed that varying degrees of tubular atrophy had occurred as a result of intratubular fibrosis and collagen deposition: some tubules had atrophied completely. Surviving tubules were lined solely by Sertoli cells, and no evidence of spermatogenesis was present. The interstitial cells, which were somewhat reduced in quantity, were in small clumps lying in a loose stroma. The appearances were similar to those described by Ferguson-Smith (1959) and Plunkett and Barr (1956) in some cases of chromatin-positive Klinefelter's syndrome.

Chromosome analysis.—Bone marrow specimens, obtained by

sternal puncture, were treated by a modification of the method described by Ford et al. (1958). Squash preparations were made from the final, Feulgen- and aceto-orcein-stained, cell suspension. These were searched systematically for cells in metaphase of mitosis. Forty-two cells, in which the chromosomes could be counted accurately, were recorded. Thirty-nine cells each contained 46

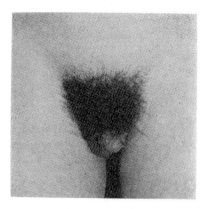

Fig. 3. Pubic hair and genitalia: the penis is of reasonable size but only right testis can be seen in scrotum.

chromosomes; and in no cell were 47 chromosomes counted. The results were as follows:

No. of chromosomes

<45	45	46	47	>47
2	1	39	0	0

Sex chromosomes XX. No chromosomal abnormality apparent.

Chromosome morphology was examined in six cells. Each cell appeared to contain a set of 23 pairs of chromosomes as in a normal female.

Hormone assays showed that the excretion of urinary gonadotrophins was 24 mouse units per day (normal 8-48 mouse units). There was a normal output of 17-ketosteroids (as has already been mentioned), but the urinary excretion of oestrogens (60 I.U. per day) was in excess for a boy of this age (normal 8-26 I.U. per day).

Diagnosis.—The normal output of gonadotrophins, the high output of oestrogens, and the absence of the left testis were somewhat against the diagnosis of Klinefelter's syndrome. Above all, however, the chromosome analysis, although confirming the presence of two X chromosomes, excluded the diagnosis since the Y chromosome was absent. The most likely alternative diagnosis was hermaphroditism, with the probability that the left gonad was intra-abdominal and contained ovarian tissue.

Laparotomy.—It was, therefore, with some degree of confidence that laparotomy was carried out. On the right side of the pelvis there was no gonad and no internal genitalia. On the left side there was a normal-sized ovary and fallopian tube and a

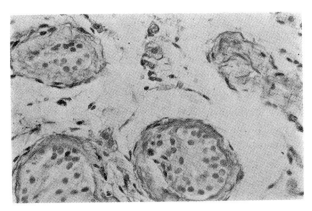

Fig. 4. Microscopic appearance of testis, showing severe atrophy and fibrosis of tubules and complete absence of spermatogenesis.

unicornuate uterus. The uterine body seemed to represent normal development of the left mullerian system, but, where the junction of the "body" and the cervix should have been, the uterus tapered away into a thickened cord which continued downwards to disappear beneath the bladder base. The uterus, tube, ovary, and as much of the thickened cord as could easily be dealt with, were removed.

Histological examination of these structures showed that the uterus had a normal muscle wall and was lined by a small amount of regenerative-type endometrium; the thickened cord had a fibromuscular wall and was lined by tall columnar mucus-secreting epithelium resembling normal endocervical tissue. The architecture of the fallopian tube was normal. The ovary contained one follicular cyst 2.5 cm. in diameter and a second smaller one; microscopically, numerous primary follicles were seen and there was one corpus albicans.

Postoperatively the boy did well, and over the next few weeks there was an increase in the urinary output of gonadotrophins to 36 mouse units per day and a decrease in the output of œstrogens (to 20 I.U. daily). These findings presumably were related to the removal of the ovary, the rise in gonadotrophins being secondary to the fall in œstrogens.

The patient was put on methyl testosterone 20 mg. daily, and it is proposed continuing with this for some time. Before his discharge from hospital, the father was told exactly what had been found and what had been done. It was our opinion, and the father agreed, that the boy was completely oriented as a male, and he certainly fitted in well with the other members of the male adolescent ward on which he was nursed during his hospital stay. The boy himself took all the surgical procedures with great calmness, and his main emotional reaction to it all was of delight at having got rid "of these things" from his chest wall.

Blood-groups.—Unfortunately, we could not make any attempt to establish mosaicism in this child, but the blood-groups were all established in detail and were as follows:

A_1 MNS, P_1+ve, CDe/CDe, Lu(a–), K(a–), Le(a+b–), Fy(a+), Jk(a–), Wr(a–), C^w–ve. Non-secretor.

Family history.—There was nothing of any great interest in the family history. He was the eldest child of healthy parents who said no such thing had ever occurred before on either side of the family. Next to him in birth order were twin boys aged 12 years, a boy aged 9 years, a girl aged 5 years, and a 2-year-old girl. All the other children were said to be normal.

DISCUSSION

Clinical Features

When this boy first presented, the sound advice of Lewis (1959) had not been published. This advice is that hermaphroditism should always be suspected in a boy with hypospadias and an undescended testis. In the light of the present case this seems to be sound advice. Whenever such a combination is encountered the sex chromatin should be determined.

When our patient presented for the second time, it seemed probable, on clinical grounds, that he had Klinefelter's syndrome. The hypospadias and the undescended testis, although not characteristically associated with this syndrome, could presumably occur with it. Once the buccal smear showed that the patient was chromatin-positive, it seemed almost certain that the diagnosis was correct, although the results of the testicular biopsy were not available at that stage. We had, however, established that the patient was a eunuchoid male with female distribution of pubic hair, absence of facial hair, primary micro-orchidism (Ferguson-Smith 1959), and considerable gynæcomastia: on these features the preliminary diagnosis was made.

Gonadal and Hormone Changes

Testicular biopsy certainly showed very considerable atrophy of the testis (Nelson 1956). Surviving tubules were lined solely by Sertoli cells and showed no spermatogenesis; other tubules showed varying degrees of intratubular fibrosis and collagen deposition. The Leydig cells were reduced in quantity—a finding previously described in some cases of chromatin-positive Klinefelter's syndrome, although an increase in their number is more common.

This absence of hypertrophy in the interstital cells in the testis was compatible with the normal level of gonadotrophins in the urine since it is thought (Klinefelter et al. 1942) that the hypertrophy is secondary to overstimulation of the Leydig cells by pituitary gonadotrophins as a response to the underproduction of the internal secretion of the Sertoli cells. As was expected, the 17-ketosteroid excretion in the urine was perfectly normal for the patient's age, but the excretion of œstrogens was excessive for either a normal male or a patient with chromatin-positive Klinefelter's syndrome.

The ovary on the other hand was well developed and of normal size. Microscopically it showed primitive follicles and a corpus albicans, which indicated that ovulation had occurred. It was structurally a much more active gonad than the testis.

Operative Intervention

The initial operations on the hypospadias have been exceedingly successful and will enable the patient to lead a much more normal male life in the future, as will, of course, the complete bilateral mastectomy which he underwent. At the time of the mastectomy, the testicular biopsy and marrow puncture were performed so as to reduce the number of separate anæsthetics administered. We were glad that it had been done that way, when eventually, as a result of the further studies, it became clear that laparotomy would have to be undertaken. The condition found inside the pelvis was really quite striking, since on the right side there were no genitalia but on the left the ovary, tube, and left horn of the uterus were all present and of reasonable size. The findings in this case bear out the suggestion of Jost (1953) that the development of the internal genitalia on each side may depend on the nature of the gonad on that side.

The reasoning which lay behind the removal of all the female genitalia is more fully discussed later under treatment. We all agreed that if female internal genitalia and an ovary were found, as we expected, then they should be removed in their entirety.

Chromosome Analysis

This was perhaps the most important single finding in leading us away from the diagnosis of Klinefelter's syndrome, since it seems fairly certain that at least in all true cases of the chromatin-positive variety there will be an extra sex chromosome (either an X or a Y) so that the individual is genetically XXY. Hitherto chromosomes have been counted mainly in known congenital malformations to find out if there is any abnormality of number or of gross morphology. In the present case, however, it was used as a straight clinical investigation with most useful and revealing results.

Treatment

It could be safely argued that this child was more female than male in that his sex-chromosome pattern was XX, his ovary was a much more adequately functioning organ than his testis, he had some uterine tissue, and he had pronounced breast development. On the other hand, he was physically a male in general appearance and his external genitalia were masculine. He had not even a vestigial vagina. Most important of all, he was psychologically oriented as a male, and it has been strongly recommended (Marshall

1954, Hampson 1955, Money et al. 1955, Wilkins 1957) that in these cases of intersex where the individual is not completely of either sex the patients should be brought up in the sex to which they have been accustomed and to which, superficially, they appear to belong. In order to achieve this, it is necessary to remove the evidence of the other sex, so as to avoid embarrassment later on and, as far as possible, to leave the evidence of the obvious sex intact. Since the whole future of the child is at stake, it is exceedingly important to make a firm decision at the time the child is under investigation and treatment (Lewis 1959), to carry out the treatment radically at the time and then to send the patient out into the world with the greatest possible security and confidence. As with so many other things, it is doubts that may lead to trouble, and in the patient's mind these should be reduced as far as possible.

ADDENDUM

Since this article was submitted Ferguson-Smith et al. (Ferguson-Smith, M. A., Johnston, A. W., Weinberg, A. N. *Lancet,* 1960, ii, 126) have reported 2 cases of hermaphroditism and de Assis et al. (de Assis, L. M., Epps, D., Bottura, C., Ferrari, I. *Lancet,* 1960, ii, 129) have reported 1 case: in all 3 cases the normal basic diploid number of 46 chromosomes was thought to be present with an XX constitution. Hirschhorn et al. (Hirschhorn, K., Decker, W. H., Cooper, H. L. *Lancet,* 1960, ii, 319), however, have described the case of an infant who is a hermaphrodite and who appears to be an XO/XY mosaic.

REFERENCES

Bergman, S., Reitalu, J., Nowakowski, H., Lenz, W. (1960) *Ann. hum. Genet.* 24:81.

Crooke, A. C., Hayward, M. D. (1960) *Lancet* i:1198.

Ferguson-Smith, M. A. (1959) *ibid.* p. 219.

Ford, C. E., Hammerton, J. L. (1956) *Nature, Lond.* 178:1020.

——— Jacobs, P. A., Lajtha, L. G. (1958) *ibid.* 181:1565.

——— Jones, K. W., Miller, O. J., Mittwoch, U., Penrose, L. S., Ridler, M., Shapiro, A. (1959a) *Lancet* i:709.

——— Polani, P., Briggs, J. H., Bishop, P. M. F. (1959b) *Nature, Lond.* 183:302.

Hampson, J. G. (1955) *Bull. Johns Hopk. Hosp.* 96:265.

Harnden, D. G., Armstrong, C. N. (1959) *Brit. med. J. ii:*1287.

Hungerford, D. A., Donnelly, A. J., Nowell, P. C., Beck, S. (1959) *Amer. J. hum. Genet. 11:*215.

Jacobs, P. A., Strong, J. A. (1959) *Nature, Lond. 183:*302.

Jost, A. (1953) *Rec. Progr. Horm. Res.* 8:379.

Klinefelter, H. F., Reifenstein, E. C., Allbright, F. (1942) *J. clin. Endocrin.* 2:615.

Lewis, E. L. (1959) *J. Urol. 81:*309.

Marshall, V. F. (1945) *ibid. 72:*77.

Money, J., Hampson, J. G., Hampson, J. L. (1955) *Bull. Johns Hopk. Hosp.* 97:301.

Nelson, W. O. (1956) *Acta endocr., Copenhagen* 23:227.

Plunkett, E. R., Barr, M. L. (1956) *Lancet ii:*853.

Stewart, J. S. S. (1959) *ibid. i:*1176.

Tijo, J. H., Levan, A. (1956) *Hereditas 43:*1.

Wilkins, L. (1957) The Diagnosis and Treatment of Endocrine Disorders in Childhood and Adolescence; p. 285. Oxford.

36

TRISOMIC CONDITION OF A LARGE CHROMOSOME IN A WOMAN WITH MONGOLOID TRAITS

L. De Carli, D.Sc. Pavia, F. Nuzzo, D.Sc. Rome, B. Chiarelli, D.Sc. Florence, and E. Poli, M.D.

HAVING noted in a young woman atypical mongoloid traits, one of us (E. P.) thought it would be interesting to ascertain her chromosome pattern and compare it with that of a typical mongol.

The patient, aged 19, is 167 cm. in height and weighs 49.5 kg. Habitus longilineus-asthenicus. Palpebral fissures slightly slant upwards at the outer corner of the eyes. Thyroid: moderately enlarged and firm (basal metabolic rate –12, –6); ^{131}I intake increased (71% in 24 hours) with delayed excretion (30% in 24 hours) and conversion index increased (73%). Menstruation rather frequent and abundant. External genitals and breast slightly underdeveloped with hypoplastic uterus. Pubic hair normal. Vaginal smear (Papanicolaou): good œstral modification. Urinary excretion of 17-ketosteroids 9.04 mg. in 24 hours. Urinary excretion of gonadotrophin <29 mouse units. No mongoloid palmar patterns; no cataract. Psychological examination (psychological institute, Catholic University of Milan): low global intellectual efficiency; intelligence quotient 70 (Wechsler-Bellevue test). Electroencephalogram normal. Colour-vision normal. Barr chromatin body (Prof. M. Preto and Dr. G. Roncoroni, histological institute, University of Milan): as for female. The proportion of cells containing chromatin bodies (57%) is greater than that found in buccal smears of normal women and some of the nuclei (8% certainly, 8% doubtfully) contain two chromatin bodies.

Fragments of fascia lata, one from this "paramongol" and one

Reprinted from *The Lancet*, July 16, 1960, pp. 130-131.

from a typical mongol, were sent for investigation at the institute of genetics, University of Pavia.

These fragments were cultured in plasma clot on coverslips placed in petri dishes. For growing the cells Puck's medium for fibroblasts was used and the cultures were incubated in a CO_2 atmosphere. Ten days later explantation preparations were made by a method which combines the technique of Tjio and Puck (1958) and Lejeune, Gauthier, and Turpin (1959). To avoid dis-

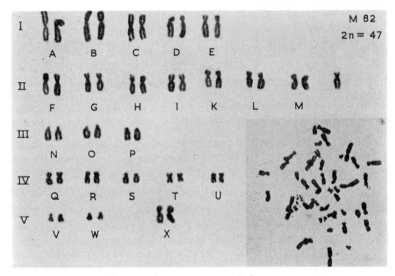

Mitotic metaphase and arrangement of chromosomes in pairs.

tortion of the normal appearance of the chromosomes, colchicine was not used.

In the tissues of the typical mongol we found the additional small chromosome characteristic of mongolism (Lejeune, Gauthier, and Turpin 1959). In the "paramongol," too, the chromosome counts showed a modal diploid number of 47:

Number of chromosomes	42	43	44	45	46	47	48	94
Number of cells	1	..	2	2	2	24	..	2

But in this patient the extra chromosome was of medium size. Arrangement of chromosomes in pairs (see figure), which we performed in ten metaphase plates, clearly demonstrates that this

chromosome can be assigned to group II of our classification (Chiarelli et al. 1959) or to group III of the classification proposed by Levan and Hsu (1959).

Since the X chromosomes are similar in length and arm ratio to some members of the group involved, the possibility was also considered that the 47th chromosome might be an extra X. Data so far collected, however, make it likely that the additional chromosome is an autosome, possibly homologous to the pair K or L of our classification. Careful morphometric analysis of the chromosomes which belong to our group II will permit more precise identification. Detailed data will be published later. They will include analysis of the karyotype of other tissues from the same patient and of the chromosomal constitution of the parents and sibs. At the moment we wish to draw attention to the fact that this represents a clear demonstration of a trisomic condition for a large chromosome in man, and that such abnormal karyotype is evidently compatible with normal development.

REFERENCES

Chiarelli, B., Nuzzo, F., De Carli, L., Aulisa, B. (1959) (in the press).

De Carli, L., Nuzzo, F., Chiarelli, B. (1960) *Atti Accad. med. lombard* 15:1.

Lejeune, J., Gauthier, M., Turpin, R. (1959) *C. R. Acad. Sci* 248:602.

——— Turpin, R., Gauthier, M. (1959) *Ann. Génét.* 2:41.

Levan, A., Hsu, T. C. (1959) *Hereditas, Lund* 45:665.

Poli, E. (1960) *Atti Accad. med. lombard* 15:1.

Tjio, J. H., Puck, T. T. (1958) *Proc. nat. Acad. Sci., Wash.* 44:1229.

37

COMMENT: TRISOMIC CONDITION OF A LARGE CHROMOSOME

P. A. Jacobs, D. G. Harnden, W. M. Court Brown, and A. G. Baikie

W E have read with interest the paper by Dr. De Carli and his colleagues (July 16) in which they report the finding of an additional chromosome in a woman said to be a "para-mongol." It is apparent that the chromosome is not that associated with mongolism, and in interpreting their findings the authors claim to have found a trisomic condition involving a large autosome, but one only showing minimal developmental defects. The authors considered but discarded the possibility that the additional chromosome was an X chromosome. A leading article in *The Lancet* (July 23) suggested that the authors' interpretation should be viewed with caution. We wish to endorse this view, and we believe there to be grounds for the belief that the additional chromosome is in fact an X chromosome.

The patient appears to be essentially a high-grade mental defective, and to our minds the outstanding abnormality she exhibits is the presence of two sex-chromatin bodies in some of her buccal mucosal cells. The only recognised sign of mongolism was some upward obliquity of the outer palpebral fissures. In respect of this, Penrose[1] points out that "the individual signs of mongolism are not specific to the condition but may occur, though less frequently, in other types of cases and even in normal subjects. . . ." The only other finding was some hypoplasia of the genitalia and the breasts.

We should like to raise, in regard to this case, three points which are of general importance in the diagnosis of abnormalities involving the X chromosome. Firstly, in all cases where two sex-chromatin bodies have been found in the nuclei of buccal mucosal cells, an extra chromosome interpreted as an X chromosome has been found. Conversely, no case to our knowledge has been pub-

Reprinted from *The Lancet*, August 13, 1960, p. 368.

lished in which an extra chromosome has been interpreted as an autosome and in which the nuclear sex has been modified from the normal finding of a single chromatin body in females and none in males. One case has been published of a chromatin-positive male mongol by Ford et al.;[2] this patient, however, was known to have the clinical features of both mongolism and Klinefelter's syndrome, and the double pathology was substantiated by chromosome analysis.

The second point is that, as regards size, the extra chromosome found by De Carli and his colleagues falls within the range of chromosomes in which all authorities agree the X chromosome is found (6-12 Denver classification). The authors contend that measurement of the chromosome reveals the additional one to be at the smaller end of this range, whereas most authorities feel that the X chromosome conforms more closely to the larger chromosomes in the range—i.e., nos. 6, 7, and possibly 8. There is no doubt that the X chromosome is difficult to identify, and in this circumstance we feel it unwise to disregard the positive evidence from sex-chromatin studies and the helpful negative evidence from the clinical examination. To rely simply on measurements in the present state of knowledge seems unjustifiable. It could, moreover, lead to an erroneous conclusion if the additional chromosome is an X chromosome that has suffered a partial deletion. Jacobs et al.[3] have shown that such deletions occur. In fact if a small deletion is postulated as the explanation for the discrepancy in length (as suggested in your leader of July 23), such a hypothesis may also explain the rather low percentage of cells showing two sex-chromatin bodies.

The final point to make is that the clinical state of the patient is more consistent with a sex-chromosome abnormality than one involving an autosome. The presence of an additional autosome has always, with one exception, been associated with widespread developmental defects. The single exception is the apparently normal father of a mongol as reported by Fraccaro, Kaijser, and Lindsten,[4] who had an additional small autosome. It is a reasonable supposition that trisomy involving an autosome as large as that in the case of De Carli and his colleagues would produce widespread and severe defects, and it might even be incompatible with life. In contrast the clinical state of this patient is compatible with that associated with a chromosomal sex of XXX. Individuals with this abnormality, on present knowledge, range from those with external genital and breast hypoplasia, accompanied by secondary amenorrhœa, to females of normal physical development and with normal reproductive cycles.[3, 5, 6]

We believe, therefore, that the most reasonable interpretation of the findings of De Carli and his colleagues is that the additional chromosome is an X chromosome, and that the patient has a sex-chromosome complement of XXX. Also, it is possible that one of the X chromosomes has suffered a small deletion. On the basis of this interpretation the findings on chromosome analysis, sex-chromatin analysis, and clinical examination are mutually compatible.

REFERENCES

1. Penrose, L. S., *The Biology of Mental Defect*. London, 1954.
2. Ford, C. E., Jones, K. W., Miller, O. J., Mittwoch, U., Penrose, L. S., Ridler, M., Shapiro, A., *Lancet*, 1959, *i*:709.
3. Jacobs, P. A., Harnden, D. G., Court Brown, W. M., Goldstein, J., Close, H. G., MacGregor, T. N., Maclean, N., Strong, J. A. *ibid*. 1960, *i*:1213.
4. Fraccaro, M., Kaijser, K., Lindsten, J. *ibid*. p. 724.
5. Jacobs, P. A., Baikie, A. G., Court Brown, W. M., MacGregor, T. N., Maclean, N., Harnden, D. G. *ibid*. 1959, *ii*:423.
6. Stewart, J. S. S., Sanderson, A. *ibid*. July 2, 1960, p. 21.

38

TRISOMY OF A LARGE CHROMOSOME
Association with Mental Retardation

AVERY A. SANDBERG, M.D., LOIS H. CROSSWHITE, B.A., and
EDWIN GORDY, M.D.

IT has been well established that the normal diploid number of chromosomes in human somatic cells is 46, consisting of 22 pairs of autosomes and two sex chromosomes (XX in the female, XY in the male).[1-3] Deviations from the normal number of 46 chromosomes, involving either the autosomes or the sex chromosomes, have been described in the recent past. One of the first chromosomal abnormalities to be described was the presence of an extra autosome (trisomy) in subjects with mongolism, resulting in a total of 47 chromosomes.[3-6] This trisomy involves one of the smallest chromosomes. More recently, the presence of 46 chromosomes with a presumed translocation in two persons with mongolism and the finding of 47 chromosomes in the father of one of these patients was described.[7, 8] In addition, three syndromes have been described in children with congenital abnormalities, accompanied in four cases by trisomy of one of the medium-sized chromosomes (total number 47) and in one case by translocation onto one of these chromosomes (total number 45).[7, 9, 10] In this contribution we are reporting the finding of a hitherto undescribed trisomy of one of the six largest chromosomes in an adult female with mental retardation and some other minor congenital abnormalities.

Reprinted from the *Journal of the American Medical Association*, Vol. 174, pp. 221-225, September 17, 1960.

From the Roswell Park Memorial Institute and the Medical Foundation of Buffalo.

We wish to thank Dr. Robert Warner of Children's Hospital of Buffalo for his help in the study of the patient, Mr. Paul Edwards of the Association for the Help of Retarded Children who supplied background information about the patient, and Dr. Theodore S. Hauschka for his advice during this study.

REPORT OF A CASE

The individual to be described is one of a group of patients with various abnormalities who are being studied in our laboratory. This patient is a female, now 21 years of age, weighing 220 lb. 99.8 kg.), and standing 67.75 in. (172.1 cm.) in height. She was born when her mother was 41 years of age. She was the fourth of her mother's pregnancies, which included one miscarriage at five months (in 1930), one daughter born in 1923 who died after one week because of respiratory difficulty, and one surviving son born in 1920 and allegedly normal. The patient weighed 9 lb. 10 oz. (4 kg. 385 Gm.) at birth. The father, who died of "high blood pressure" four years prior to the time of writing, was 49 years old when the patient was born. The pregnancy and delivery were uneventful, and the mother gave no history of undue x-ray exposure of the pelvic region. There is no family history of mongolism or mental retardation. The patient was breast fed and was weaned at the age of 10 months. She held her head up at 3 months of age, sat up alone at 11 months, and did not walk until the age of 18 months. While she did speak some words at the age of 2 years, she could not utter sentences until the age of 7. She was toilet trained without difficulty at the age of 2 years. The patient had measles in 1944 and chicken pox in 1950. She started menstruating at the age of 11 and has had regular periods since then.

The general physical appearance of the patient can be seen in Figure 1. There is a definite webbing of the neck and flat occiput. Her head circumference is 20⅛ in. (51.1 cm.). Her ears are of normal shape and location. Her eyes, which are blue and do not contain Brushfield's spots (often found in patients with mongolism), are somewhat widely separated and have no epicanthal folds. Her facial skin is scaly, especially over the forehead and malar areas. She has no simian folds, and her hands and feet show normal relationships among the various digits. Her palate and tongue appear normal, although poor dentition is evident. The external genitalia are normal, as are the remainder of her physical findings.

The patient's blood pressure was 140/80 mm. Hg. She belonged to blood group O (C-negative, D-positive, E-positive, c-positive, M-positive, N-positive, K-positive, and Fya-positive). The mother belonged to blood group B (C-negative, D-positive, E-positive, c-positive, M-positive, N-negative, K-positive, and Fya-positive). The patient was enrolled in kindergarten at the normal age but

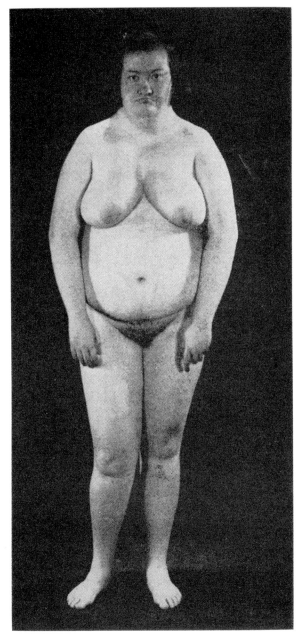

Fig. 1. General appearance of patient with trisomy of large chromosome in association with mental retardation.

was withdrawn after approximately two weeks and never again admitted to public school classes because of mental retardation. Psychometric tests revealed an I. Q. in the neighborhood of 40. The patient has an unusually good memory for certain events and for numbers, such as for telephone numbers and addresses. She is able to do most simple household tasks but requires constant supervision and is apt to wander around.

The patient was originally referred to us as a case of mongolism because of mental retardation associated with superficially mongoloid facies. More critical examination of the patient by several observers with a large clinical experience in mongolism did not substantiate the referring diagnosis. Admittedly, the patient has a suggestion of mongoloid facies; the latter, however, is shared by her normal mother.

METHODS AND FINDINGS

Methods.—A marrow specimen (2 ml.) was obtained by needle aspiration of the sternum and put into Earle's solution (20 ml.) containing heparin (1:20,000). The cells were suspended in the Earle's solution by gentle shaking, and 4 volumes of hypotonic citrate solution (0.36%) were added. The mixture was incubated at 37.0° C. (98.6° F.) for 10 to 15 minutes. The cells were spun down by centrifugation, and acetic-alcohol was added. After one hour the acetic-alcohol was decanted and 45% acetic-acid added. The cells were left in the acid for at least 45 minutes; the acid was then decanted and acetic-orcein stain added. Metaphase preparations were made by previously described methods.[3] Buccal mucosa smears were performed according to the method of Moore and Barr.[11] In this method, cresylecht violet is used as the stain. This dye has an optical absorption maximum in the 590 mμ region, which suggested the use of a sodium lamp as a light source to enhance the contrast of the sex chromatin bodies in microscopy and photography.

CHROMOSOME COUNTS IN CELLS FROM BONE MARROW OF PATIENT AND HER MOTHER

					Count	
	CHROMOSOMES				TOTAL CELLS	
Subjects	45	46	47	48	Counted	Analyzed
Patient		5	52	1	58	10
Patient's mother	6	32	1		39	3

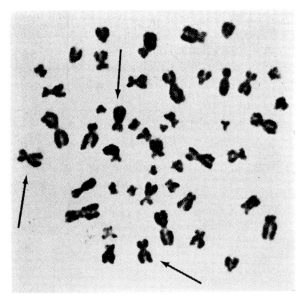

Fig. 2. Metaphase spread, of a bone-marrow cell from patient reported on, containing 47 chromosomes. *Arrows* indicate autosome for which patient is trisomic.

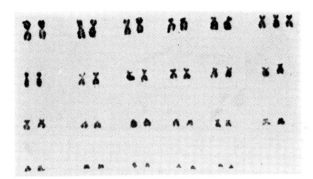

Fig. 3. Karyogram of cell shown in Fig. 2. Each chromosome was cut out and paired with its mate. Cell is trisomic for sixth largest chromosome. The two X-chromosomes (first pair in 2nd row) are allocyclic and show positive heteropyknosis.[3]

Cytological Findings.—In 90% of the 58 metaphases counted, the number of chromosomes was 47 (see the table). Ten cells were analyzed for chromosome-structural detail and revealed the presence of an extra chromosome. The patient was clearly trisomic for the sixth-largest chromosome. A typical metaphase and also a corresponding karyogram from the patient's bone marrow cells may be seen in Figures 2 and 3.

Examination of her mother's bone marrow revealed a normal constitution with 46 chromosomes. The patient's buccal mucosa

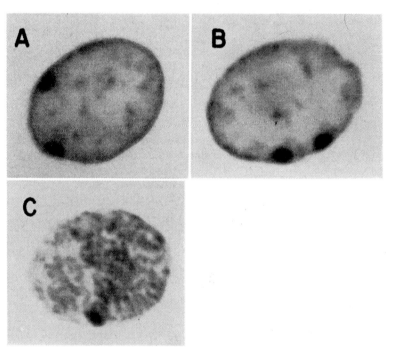

Fig. 4. Two "sex-chromatin" bodies (nuclei *A* and *B*) in buccal mucosa cells of patient. The two bodies assumed no fixed circumferential relationship with respect to each other. Nucleus *C* shows single sex-chromatin body in buccal mucosa cells of patient's mother. These cells were stained with cresylecht violet and photographed by means of the monochromatic radiation from a sodium lamp.

was unusual in that 70% of the nuclei revealed the presence of two satellites instead of one (Fig. 4). Her mother's buccal mucosa smear showed the usual female sex-chromatin picture, i.e., a single satellite in about 20% of the cells. Blood smears revealed the presence of only one "drum stick" in 5% of both the patient's and her mother's neutrophilic cells.

COMMENT

From the reports that have appeared so far and from the present findings it follows that trisomy is associated with various congenital defects, the exact syndrome depending on the chromosomes involved and the resulting impact on over-all genic balance. Trisomy *per se* may not always result in obvious congenital defects, as is evident from the report of Fraccaro and co-authors.[8] These authors found trisomy (total number of chromosomes, 47) in the reportedly normal father of a child with mongolism. The latter had 46 chromosomes with possible translocation of one of the small acrocentric chromosomes to a larger autosome. It appears that mongolism is accompanied by trisomy of one of the smallest autosomes, or by reciprocal translocation involving this same small autosome. Other chromosomal abnormalities, which may be the cause of, or related to, the many variations seen in mongolism, will probably come to light.

In the other trisomic syndromes described (exclusive of the case reported here), the number of congenital defects has been multiple and appeared shortly after birth. [9, 10] The chromosomes involved were in the medium-sized class. In contrast to these cases, our patient demonstrates primarily mental retardation and webbing of the neck. It has been reasoned on the basis of gene content that the larger the chromosome involved in trisomy, the more lethal and complicated the abnormalities in the resulting phenotype.[1, 9] The findings in our case would seem to indicate that there may not be any significant correlation between the size of the chromosome involved in trisomy and the extent and number of congenital abnormalities.

The presence of two "sex-chromatin" bodies in the nuclei of the buccal mucosa cells (but not in the blood) of our patient is of interest. Most observers have indicated that the sex-chromatin is related to the presence of two X-chromosomes in the female, with a possibility that either one or both of the chromosomes show positive heteropyknosis.[12] The absence of sex-chromatin in male nuclei is attributed to the isopyknosis of the single X-chromosome. The two "sex-chromatin" bodies in the cells of our patient need not be derived from two X-chromosomes, but may indicate that such bodies may also be related to certain autosomal trisomic conditions. Up to the time of writing, only one sex-chromatin body has been found in the other cases of autosomal trisomy that have been published. It should be pointed out, however, that double sex-chromatin bodies were seen in a patient with three X-chromosomes. [13-16]

The rather advanced age (41 years) of the mother at the time of the birth of our patient poses the question of the relation of the age of the mother to the occurrence of chromosomal and congenital anomalies in the children. Most authors seem to favor the view that the chromosomal trisomy is due to nondisjunction of certain chromosomes during gametogenesis in either parent.

The question might be raised whether the trisomy in the case reported here does not involve the X-chromosomes. Several findings point against this. Our case does not resemble in any fashion the case reported by Jacobs and co-authors,[13] which is characterized by the presence of 47 chromosomes (three X-chromosomes. The trisomy in our case involves a chromosome in which the ratio of the arm lengths was not characteristic of the X-chromosomes. Furthermore, the two X-chromosomes could be identified with certainty in some of the metaphases, because of the allocycly and heteropyknosis of the sex chromosomes.[3]

The extension of chromosomal studies in patients with mental retardation and other congenital anomalies should be of considerable aid in establishing genetic distinction within groups of superficially similar syndromes.

SUMMARY

A 21-year-old woman with mental retardation was shown to have 47 chromosomes in her bone-marrow cells and to be trisomic for the sixth largest autosome. The nuclei of the patient's buccal mucosa contained two "sex-chromatin" bodies. Her mother was found to have a normal diploid number of chromosomes (46) and a single sex-chromatin body in the buccal mucosa nuclei. This unusual case of trisomy differed in various aspects (discussed in detail) from other published cases of trisomic syndromes.

ADDENDUM

The method described is presently in use in our laboratory for the determination of human chromosomes. 1. One to 2 ml. of bone marrow aspirate are added to 20 ml. of 0.6% glucose (dextrose) in 0.7% NaCl. Mix by gentle inversion. 2. Seven milliliters of this mixture are added to 28 ml. of 0.44% sodium citrate ($C_6H_5Na_3O_7 2H_2O$) and gently mixed by inversion. 3. This mixture is incubated at $37°$ C. for 10 to 15 minutes. The hypotonic sodium citrate causes the cells to swell. 4. This mixture is then centrifuged for 3 to 5 minutes. Decant supernatant and discard. 5. To the packed cells add 5 ml. of acetic-alcohol fixative (1 part glacial acetic acid and 3 parts absolute ethyl alcohol). Do not disturb the sediment. Let stand for 30 minutes. Decant fixative and discard. 6. Add 5 ml. of 45% acetic acid and let stand at least one hour in a refrigerator, although better results are obtained by lengthening this period to overnight. If necessary, the cells can be kept in 45% acetic acid for days before proceeding with next step. Decant acetic acid and discard. 7. To the packed cells add approximately 1 ml. of freshly filtered aceto-orcein stain with Pasteur pipette. Mix by aspirating several times. Let stand at least 10 minutes. 8. Place two drops of stained cellular suspension on a microscope slide, cover slip, and remove excess fluid by gently blotting in bibulous paper book. 9. Cover slide with several dry pages in bibulous paper book and spread cells by applying firm thumb pressure (through the paper) to the cover slip for 30 seconds. Seal edges with beeswax. The slides can be kept in good condition for at least two weeks when stored under refrigeration. 10. The slides are examined under the microscope with a Wratten 58 green filter. In our laboratory, satisfactory photographs are routinely taken with an AO Microstar microscope equipped with a 35 mm. camera. Best results are obtained with High Contrast Copy film (Microfile) developed in D-76 for nine minutes at $20°$ C., under continuous agitation.

REFERENCES

1. Ford, C. E., Human Cytogenetics: Its Present Place and Future Possibilities. *Am. J. Human Genet.* 12:104-117 (March) 1960.

2. Chu, E. H. Y., Chromosome Complements of Human Somatic Cells. *Am. J. Human Genet.* *12*:97-103 (March) 1960.

3. Sandberg, A. A., Koepf, G. F., Crosswhite, L. H., and Hauschka, T. S., Chromosome Constitution of Human Marrow in Various Developmental and Blood Disorders. *Am. J. Human Genet.*, to be published.

4. LeJeune, J., Gautier, M., and Turpin, R., Étude des Chromosomes somatique de neuf enfante Mongolien. *C. R. Acad. Sci., Paris* *248*:1721-1722, 1959.

5. Jacobs, P. A., Baikie, A. G., Court-Brown, W. M., and Strong, J. A., Somatic Chromosomes in Mongolism. *Lancet* *1*:710-713 (April 4) 1959.

6. Böök, J. A., Fraccaro, M., and Lindsten, J., Cytogenetical Observations in Mongolism. *Acta paediat.* *48*:453-468 (April 2) 1960.

7. Polani, P. E., and others, Mongol Girl with 46 Chromosomes. *Lancet* *1*:721-724 (April 2) 1960.

8. Fraccaro, M., Kaijser, K., and Lindsten, J., Chromosomal Abnormalities in Father and Mongol Child. *Lancet* *1*:724-727 (April 2) 1960.

9. Edwards, J. H., and others, New Trisomic Syndrome. *Lancet* *1*:787-790 (April 9) 1960.

10. Patau, K., and others, Multiple Congenital Anomaly Caused by Extra Autosome. *Lancet* *1*:790-793 (April 9) 1960.

11. Moore, K. L., and Barr, M. L., Nuclear Morphology, According to Sex, in Human Tissues. *Acta anat.* *21*:197-208, 1954.

12. Barr, M. L., Sex Chromatin. *Science* *130*:1302, 1959.

13. Jacobs, P. A., and others, Evidence for Existence of Human "Super Female." *Lancet* *2*:423-425 (Sept. 26) 1959.

14. Stewart, J. S. S., and Sanderson, A. R., Fertility and Oligophrenia in Apparent Triple-X Female. *Lancet* *2*:21-23 (July 2) 1960.

15. Ferguson-Smith, M. A., Johnston, A. W., and Handmaker, S. D., Primary Amentia and Micro-Orchidism Associated with XXXY Sex-Chromosome Constitution. *Lancet* *2*:184-187 (July 23) 1960.

16. More Chromosome Anomalies, editorial. *Lancet* *2*:191-192 (July 23) 1960.

Editor's (M.F.A.M.) Comment: The presence of two chromatin bodies in the buccal cells, the fact that the trisomic chromosome was within the X chromosome size range, and the fewness of somatic abnormalities, all make a triplo-X interpretation of this case rather more likely than trisomy for any other chromosome.

39

FERTILITY AND OLIGOPHRENIA IN AN APPARENT TRIPLO-X FEMALE

JOHN S. S. STEWART, M.B. Glasg., and ANN R. SANDERSON, B.Sc., Ph.D. St. And.

IT is known that medullary dygenesis and cortical dysgenesis are associated with oligophrenia. Since the sex-chromosomal constitution in these conditions is heteroploid it seemed likely that the recently discovered triplo-X condition might also be associated with oligophrenia, although in the only reported case (Jacobs et al. 1959) the patient was of average intelligence. The present report concerns an apparently triplo-X female discovered during a survey of the population of an institution for mental defectives. It is of special interest that she is of established fertility.

CASE HISTORY

Date of birth, Nov. 18, 1925. Intelligence quotient, 70. This patient (fig. 1), apart from her oligophrenia, is an apparently normal female. The fourth of five children, she was born when both her parents were aged 42. Although unmarried, she has four chil-

SEX-CHROMATIN COUNTS IN ORAL MUCOSAL SMEARS FROM THE PATIENT

Specimen Number	Number of Sex-Chromatin Bodies		
	0	1	2
1	49	40	11
2	54	29	17
3	53	40	7
4	55	33	12
5	38	47	15
6	35	41	24
Total	284	230	86
Percentage	47.3	38.3	14.3

Reprinted from *The Lancet*, July 2, 1960, pp. 21-23.

We are indebted to Dr. M. M. Macrae, physician-superintendent, Strathmartine Hospital, Angus, for permission to report this case.

417

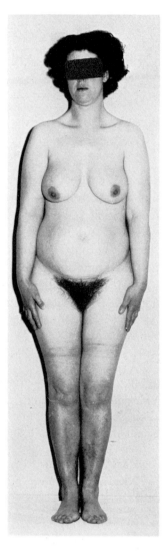

Fig. 1. The patient is an apparent normal female.

dren: a boy of 12, dizygotic twin boys of 10, and a boy of 8. Having left hospital some months previously, she was lately readmitted
because she was three months pregnant.

Facial, trunk, and abdominal hair is absent; pubic and axillary
hair is normal; breasts are well developed with mature nipples;
external genitalia are normal. Height 66 in., span 64½ in., pubes to
sole 33 in. Colour-vision normal by the Ishihara test.

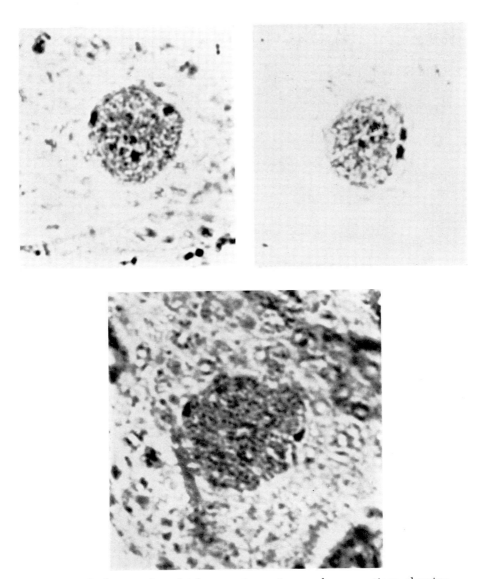

Fig. 2. Oral mucosal nuclei from aceto-orcein squash preparations, showing two sex-chromatin bodies. The diameter of the nuclei varies from 10 to 15 μ in the nuclei illustrated.

Nuclear sex.—Sex-chromatin counts were obtained from oral mucosal smears prepared by the aceto-orcein squash technique. In several specimens (see table) an average of 38% of nuclei showed one sex-chromatin body in its characteristic position at the nuclear membrane and 14% of nuclei showed two sex-chromatin bodies at the nuclear membrane (fig. 2).

Chromosomal sex.—The chromosomal sex was established on

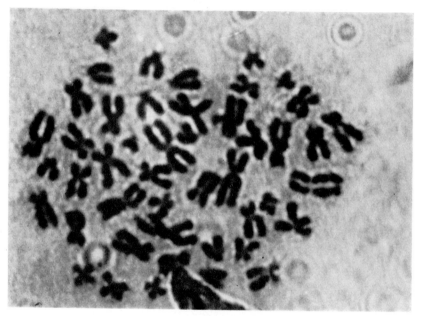

Fig. 3. The chromosomes in an aceto-orcein squash preparation from a culture of peripheral blood.

leucocytes obtained by the culture of cells from peripheral blood (Hungerford et al. 1959). After exposure to colchicine and hypotonic citrate the cells were squashed in aceto-orcein. In nine well-spread mitotic plates a chromosomal count of 47 was obtained, and analysis of these showed an extra chromosome in the medium range consistent with the interpretation that three X chromosomes are present (figs. 3 and 4).

Investigation of family.—Oral mucosal smears were obtained from several relatives of the patient: both parents, an elder sister, and all four sons. In every case nuclear sex was in accord with phenotypic sex.

DISCUSSION

Evidence is presented that this patient is a fertile triplo-X female of low intelligence. Several points of interest therefore arise. The association of the triplo-X condition with oligophrenia

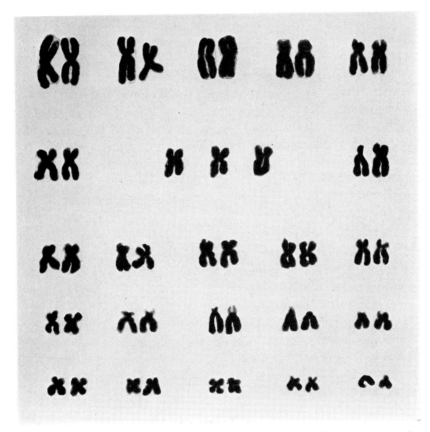

Fig. 4. Analysis of the chromosomes showing an extra chromosome in the medium-size range.

suggests a causal relationship; its association with fertility suggests the possibility of secondary non-disjunction; and this in turn suggests a possible basis for familial gonadal dysgenesis.

It is also noteworthy that this patient had dizygotic twins. Raised gonadotrophin levels, if present before conception, might explain twinning in this patient.

Oligophrenia and Heteroploidy

There is only one recorded example (Jacobs et al. 1959) of a human triplo-X female (the term seems preferable to the ambiguous "super female"). Jacobs et al. suggested that the phenotypic effect of the triplo-X condition may be restricted to the genital tract, but in the case we describe the genital tract is normal and oligophrenia is present. The discovery of such a case in a small group of institutional patients suggests that the association between the triplo-X condition and oligophrenia is not due to chance. Oligophrenia is also associated with cortical dysgenesis in which the sex-chromosomal constitution is XO (Stewart 1960). Hence it seems likely that in some chromosomal intersexes the abnormal karyotype causes oligophrenia in consequence of disturbed genic balance. Since an individual with a sex-chromosome constitution which is hypodiploid (XO) or hyperdiploid (XXX) may be oligophrenic, a direct genic effect is less probable.

Non-disjunction

During oogenesis in a subject with a normal karyotype primary non-disjunction may produce ova with a hypohaploid or hyperhaploid number of chromosomes. It is theoretically possible that a defect of the first or second or both meiotic divisions may produce XX-, XXX-, or even XXXX-eggs. Since primary non-disjunction is uncommon, the occurrence of two such events in a sibship should be rare. In the present case there is already an abnormal karyotype in which secondary non-disjunction would give X- and XX-eggs in equal numbers.

It is of great clinical importance that the eggs of a heteroploid mother may have a normal number of X chromosomes. The patients has four sons. All are chromatin-negative and have therefore apparently inherited only one X from their mother. It may be simply due to chance that all the children are normal and were born when the mother was young.

Familial Gonadal Dysgenesis

Defects of oogenesis have been mentioned. Similarly during spermatogenesis, primary non-disjunction at one or both meiotic divisions can give XY-, XX-, YY-, XXY-, XYY-, or XXYY-sperm. These possibilities are relevant to a discussion of familial gonadal dysgenesis because parental transmission could be due to secondary non-disjunction. In medullary dysgenesis transmission could be maternal if XXX, XXXX, or XXXXX karyotypes occur in fertile females, and paternal if XYY, XXYY or XXXYY karyotypes occur in fertile males. Stewart et al. (1958) found an excess of paternal uncles of cases of medullary dysgenesis. Further data (Stewart, unpublished) show that there are other families with a similar excess of childless maternal uncles. As previously emphasised by Stewart et al. (1958) these exceptional families may include "exceptional" individuals.

SUMMARY

A fertile triplo-X female of low intelligence is reported. Oligophrenia in heteroploid subjects is probably due to disturbed genic balance. Fertility in a triplo-X individual suggests the possibility of secondary non-disjunction and familial gonadal dysgenesis.

REFERENCES

Hungerford, D. A., Donnelly, A. J., Nowell, P. C., Beck, S. (1959) *Amer. J. hum. Genet. 11*:215.

Jacobs, P. A., Baikie, A. G., Court-Brown, W. M., MacGregor, T. N., Maclean, N., Harnden, D. G. (1959) *Lancet ii*:423.

Stewart, J. S. S. (1960) *Acta endocrin. (Copenhagen)* 33:89.

——— Ferguson-Smith, M. A., Lennox, B., Mack, W. S. (1958) *Lancet ii*:117.

40

PRIMARY AMENTIA AND MICRO-ORCHIDISM ASSOCIATED WITH AN XXXY SEX-CHROMOSOME CONSTITUTION

M. A. Ferguson-Smith, M.B. Glasg., A. W. Johnston, M.B. Cantab., M.R.C.P., and S. D. Handmaker, A.B. Johns Hopkins

A NUCLEAR-SEXING survey among mentally defective patients in a State training school (Ferguson-Smith, Handmaker, and Hill) has revealed 2 male patients (out of 916) with a double complement of sex chromatin in somatic nuclei. This finding suggests that these patients have a more complex sex-chromosome constitution than, for example, the chromatin-positive cases of Klinefelter's syndrome which have a single sex-chromatin mass and an XXY sex-chromosome constitution (Jacobs and Strong 1959). A similar observation has been made recently in a *female* patient with ovarian dysgenesis, and apparently average intelligence, who was shown to have an XXX sex chromosome constitution (Jacobs et al. 1959). It appears that this particular nuclear sex anomaly may not be very rare among mentally retarded individuals, for both male and female patients have been found in at least two mental-deficiency hospitals (Barr et al. 1959, Ferguson-Smith, Handmaker, and Hill).

We report here the clinical findings and chromosome analyses of these two patients with primary amentia, micro-orchidism, and two sex-chromatin bodies in intermitotic nuclei.

Reprinted from *The Lancet,* July 23, 1960, pp. 184-187.

We gratefully acknowledge the cooperation of Dr. Harry G. Butler, clinical director, and the members of the medical and nursing staff of Rosewood State Training School, Maryland, U. S. A. We are grateful to Dr. Claude J. Migeon for the hormone assays (work supported by research grant A.180 from the National Institutes of Arthritis and Metabolic Diseases, U. S. Public Health Service), to Dr. W. N. Toole for performing the testicular biopsies, and to Ciba Pharmaceutical Products, Inc. for a generous supply of "Colcemide."

CASE HISTORIES

The First Case

The patient [J. H. H. no. 877961] is 22 years of age and of Polish-Austrian ancestry. Two brothers and seven sisters are healthy and all have children except the eldest brother, who is single. One sister has a male child (chromatin-negative) with hydrocephalus and multiple skeletal anomalies. At birth the patient was normal, but thereafter his rate of physical and mental development was retarded. Therefore at the age of 9 he was admitted to Rosewood State Training School. He is a placid, easily managed boy, who does simple work in the laundry. He does not shave, has had no acne, and is stated to lack libido.

He is a thin, asthenic male with a small head (51.5 cm. diameter) and disproportionately long legs (fig. 1). The chest is thin. He

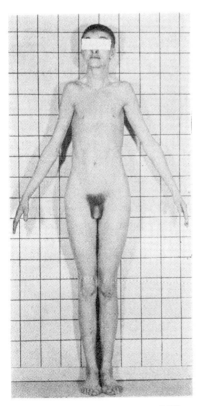
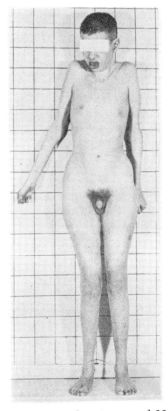

Fig. 1. First patient, aged 22.   Fig. 2. Second patient, aged 22.

has round shoulders, lumbar lordosis, and webbing of the neck. There is bilateral radio-ulnar synostosis. The teeth are small, irregular, and partially erupted. The eyes are markedly myopic (−20D.) and the voice is in the high range for the normal male. The penis and scrotum show normal adolescent development. Very small firm testes are palpable bilaterally. The prostate is small. Pubic hair is profuse, but facial, axillary, and abdominal hair is scant, and there is no recession of the hair at the temples. Gynæcomastia is not present.

The Second Case

This patient [J. H. H. no. 178523] is also 22; his ancestry is Polish-Russian-Austrian. He has one sister, who is healthy and unmarried. The family history on the maternal side is non-contributory, but on the paternal side there is strong history of schizophrenia, involving the father, uncle, grandmother, and cousin. At an early age he was noted to be very retarded and was admitted to Rosewood at the age of 9 with an estimated intelligence quotient below 20. He is unable to dress, feed, or care for himself, and his vocabulary is limited to a few simple words. Though of an anxious and nervous nature, he responds to simple directions and is generally cheerful and affectionate to those who look after him. He appears much younger than his stated age (fig. 2) and, like the first patient shows a low upper segment/lower-segment ratio. The pelvis is broad with android proportions, and there is no webbing of the neck. There is bilateral gynæcomastia, and the breasts have large areolæ with well-formed nipples. The larynx is normally developed. Facial hair is scant and there is slight temporal recession. Axillary and pubic hair are present, but chest and abdominal hair are absent. There is no acne. The penis and scrotum are adolescent. The testes are very small and are felt with difficulty high up in the scrotum. The prostate is palpable but small.

Tables 1 and 2 give further clinical data as well as the results of special investigations.

THE INVESTIGATIONS

The Testicular Lesion

At exposure for biopsy, the testes in both patients measured about 18 mm. in greatest length and appeared identical. The vas

TABLE 1
CLINICAL DATA

Case	Age	Maternal Age at Birth	Paternal Age at Birth	Sibship Position	I.Q. Wechsler Full-Scale	Skeletal Age	Height (cm.)	Span (cm.)	Lower Segment (cm.)	Ratio-of Upper Segment to Lower Segment
1	22	38	52	10/10	49	17	170.5	164	93	0.83*
2	22	27	31	1/2	<20	22	175.0	177	94	0.86*

* Average for normal white males aged 22 is about 0.92 (McKusick et al.).

deferens and epididymis were normally developed on both sides without evidence of abnormal development of mullerian derivatives.

The histological appearance of the testis is very similar in the two cases. Apart from the presence of two sex-chromatin bodies in a large proportion of nuclei, it is that already reported in chromatin-positive Klinefelter's syndrome (Ferguson-Smith et al. 1957). Almost all the seminiferous tubules are completely atrophic and

TABLE 2
SPECIAL INVESTIGATIONS

| | Nuclear Sex | | | Urinary Excretion in 24 Hours | | Testis Length at Biopsy (mm.) |
Case	DOUBLE SEX CHROMATIN	SINGLE SEX CHROMATIN	DRUMSTICK POLY-MORPHS	F.S.H. MOUSE UNITS	17-KETO-STEROID (MG.)	
1	42%	38%	6/433	>52 <96	4.2	18
2	36%	35%	6/725	<96	14.83	18

F.S.H. = follicle-stimulating hormone.

TABLE 3
CHROMOSOME COUNTS IN BONE-MARROW CELLS

| | No. of Cells with Chromosome Count of | | | | | Total Cells Counted |
Case	45	46	47	48	49	
1	10	11	13	116	2	153
2	8	13	9	87	1	118

are represented by small hyalinised basement membranes which contain no elastic fibres. These "ghost" tubules blend into an amorphous connective-tissue stroma in which large islands of abnormal and pigmented Leydig cells are present. A few small seminiferous tubules, some partially hyalinised, are lined by Sertoli cells but contain no germinal cells. Hyalinisation is also apparent in some of the smaller arterioles in case 2.

Chromosome Analysis*

Squash preparations were made from short-term bone-marrow cultures, and suitable mitotic cells were analysed as described

---

* An addendum to the paper by Ferguson-Smith, Johnston, and Weinberg, published last week, explains the method of numbering the chromosomes.

previously (Ferguson-Smith, Johnston, and Weinberg 1960). In both cases the basic somatic number is 48 (see table 3). Analysis of fifteen especially suitable cells in case 1 and five cells in case 2 clearly demonstrates the presence of a Y chromosome, and 15 chromosomes in group III. Measurements of these group III chromosomes reveal that the largest chromosome, with a submedian to median placed centromere, is trisomic (fig. 3). These results indicate that the sex-chromosome constitution in both cases is

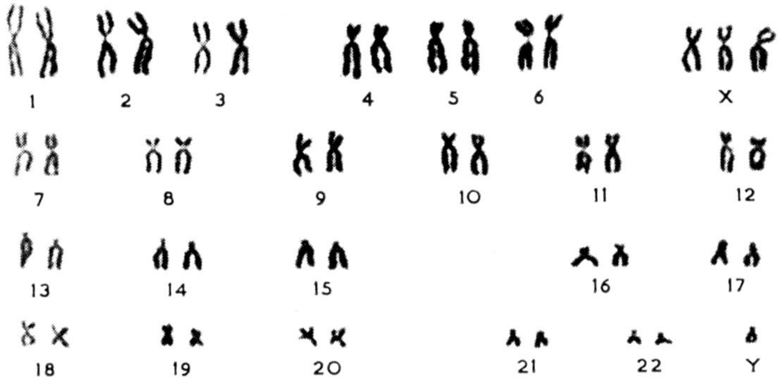

Fig. 3. Chromosomes from a bone-marrow cell in first patient, arranged in pairs. 2n = 48 (XXXY).

XXXY, for in our experience the largest chromosome in group III is the X chromosome.

Nuclear-sex Findings

As indicated in table 2, the percentage of chromatin-positive nuclei in the oral smears (fig. 4) is high. This was not reflected in the frequency of the "drumsticks" in the polymorphonuclear leucocytes, and no double drumsticks were found.

In the relatives available for buccal smear—who included both parents of case 2 and the mother of case 1—the nuclear sex was normal.

DISCUSSION

The severity of the mental defect in these two patients, and the additional congenital malformations in case 1, suggest that the XXXY sex-chromosome constitution is associated with a greater disability than the XXY constitution in chromatin-positive Klinefelter's syndrome. However, sex differentiation is the same in these two sex-chromosome anomalies, indicating that the additional X has no influence in this regard. The testicular lesion is almost indistinguishable in the two conditions, and by this criterion the XXXY syndrome must be considered a fourth variant of the Klinefelter syndrome (Ferguson-Smith et al. 1960).

The type of sex-chromosome anomaly reported here is more complex, and accordingly more difficult to explain on present theories, than those previously described. The XO constitution in chromatin-negative gonadal aplasia (Ford et al. 1959), the

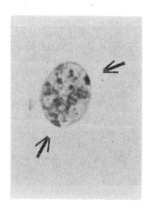

Fig. 4. Nucleus of an oral mucosal cell of first patient, showing two typical sex-chromatin masses. (Cresyl echt violet. ×1500.)

XXY constitution in chromatin-positive Klinefelter's syndrome, and the XXX constitution in the double chromatin-positive patient with ovarian dysgenesis, may be satisfactorily explained by *non-disjunction* of the sex chromosomes at one cell division, either during meiosis in the parental germ-cells, or during the early divisions of the fertilised ovum. The various types of non-disjunction and the possible factors affecting the frequency of non-disjunction in these conditions are considered in detail in a recent review (Ferguson-Smith 1960). It is sufficient to say here that non-disjunction at *one* cell division cannot lead to a zygote with an XXXY complement. For this to occur by the mechanism of non-disjunction, there are several theoretical possibilities:

1. Primary meiotic non-disjunction of the sex chromosomes in both parents: fertilisation of an XX-bearing ovum by an XY-bearing sperm.

2. Primary meiotic non-disjunction at both the reductional and equational divisions in either parent: fertilisation of an XXX-bearing ovum by a Y sperm, or an X-bearing ovum by an XXY-bearing sperm.

3. Secondary meiotic non-disjunction in an XXX mother with or without primary meiotic non-disjunction in the father: fertilisation of an XXX- or an XX-bearing ovum by a Y- or an XY-bearing sperm.

4. Mitotic non-disjunction in an XXY zygote at the first cleavage division: development from the XXXY daughter cell and elimination of the XY daughter cell.

We have excluded secondary non-disjunction as a possible mechanism only in so far as the mothers have only a single complement of sex chromatin (and presumably have only two X chromosomes), and the father of case 2 is chromatin-negative. Secondary non-disjunction in the deceased father of case 1 is considered very unlikely, since none of the numerous reported cases of chromatin-positive Klinefelter's syndrome have shown enough spermatogenesis to be fertile. Conclusive evidence on secondary non-disjunction must await chromosome analyses of the parents.

The alternative mechanisms cannot be tested until we can mark the human X-chromosome with several sex linked genes (such as colour-blindness) and so trace the fate of the individual X chromosomes in a given pedigree. Recently this method has been used successfully to demonstrate the origin of the XO exception in the house mouse (Russell et al. 1959).

The Origin of the Sex Chromatin

The finding of two sex-chromatin bodies in the nuclei of these patients, and the very convincing evidence that they have three X chromosomes raises a problem concerning the origin of the sex chromatin.

An early suggestion was that the sex chromatin is formed of heterochromatic parts of the two X chromosomes which remained paired in the intermitotic nucleus (see Bar 1959). On this hypothesis one might expect to find *four* and not three X chromosomes in cells which have two sex-chromatin bodies. An alternative explanation would be that the sex chromatin is derived from heterochromatic parts of one X chromosome. Observations on nuclear-sex dimorphism in some lower species—e.g., the domestic fowl (Kosin and Ishizahi 1959)—support this because the sex chromatin is found in the heterogametic and not the homogametic sex. In addition, Ohno et al. (1959) have found that at mitotic prophase in the female rat, one of the X chromosomes shows positive heteropyknosis compared with the other chromosomes, and this chromosome can be related morphologically to the sex chromatin in the intermitotic nucleus. The male rat lacks this specific chromocentre and does not show differential heteropyknosis of any of the prophase chromosomes.

This hypothesis for the origin of the human sex chromatin is attractive because it does not invoke somatic pairing of the chromosomes and could explain the findings in the sex-chromosome anomalies. If these studies on prophase cells could be confirmed in man, the number of sex-chromatin bodies could be related directly to the number of heterochromatic X chromosomes, and there would be very strong evidence for differential behaviour of the two X chromosomes. It is possible that the differentiation is induced by paternal transmission and lost during oogenesis.

The theoretical implications of this are far-reaching. As an example, in the present context, it suggests that, in the genesis of the XXXY individual, non-disjunction occurs during spermatogenesis at both meiotic divisions leading to formation of an XXY-bearing sperm which fertilises a normal X-bearing ovum; for, in order to have two sex-chromatin bodies the two heterochromatic X chromosomes must have been derived from the father.

SUMMARY

Survey of a mental-deficiency hospital has revealed two male patients with a double complement of sex chromatin in intermitotic nuclei. Chromosome analysis indicates that they have a chromosome number of 48 and an XXXY sex-chromosome constitution.

The findings are discussed in regard to the origin of the sex-chromosome anomaly and the significance of nuclear sexing.

REFERENCES

Barr, M. L. (1959) *Science 130*:679.

———— Shaver, E. L., Carr, D. H., Plunkett, E. R. (1959) *J. ment. defic. Res. 3*:78.

Ferguson-Smith, M. A. (1960) *Arch. intern. Med. 105*:627.

———— Handmaker, S. D., Hill, R. N. (in preparation).

———— Johnston, A. W., Weinberg, A. (1960) *Lancet ii*:167.

———— Lennox, B., Mack, W. S., Stewart, J. S. S. (1957) *ibid. ii*:167.

———— Stewart, J. S. S., Mack, W. S. (1960) Klinefelter's Syndrome. Memoirs of The Society for Endocrinology no. 7 (edited by C. R. Austin).

Ford, C. E., Jones, K. W., Polani, P. E., Almeida, J. C. de, Briggs, J. H. (1959) *Lancet i*:711.

Jacobs, P. A., Baikie, A. G., Court Brown, W. M., MacGregor, T. N., Maclean, N., Harnden, D. G. (1959) *ibid. ii*:423.

———— Strong, J. A. (1959) *Nature, Lond. 183*:302.

Kosin, I. L., Ishizahi, H. (1959) *Science 130*:43.

McKusick, V. A. et al. (to be published).

Ohno, S., Kaplan, W. D., Kinosita, R. (1959) *Exp. Cell Res. 18*:415.

Russell, W. L., Russell, L. B., Gower, Y. S. (1959) *Proc. nat. Acad. Sci. 45*:559.

41

MULTIPLE CONGENITAL ANOMALY
CAUSED BY AN EXTRA AUTOSOME

Klaus Patau, Ph.D. Berlin, David W. Smith, M.D. Baltimore,
Eeva Therman, Ph.D. Helsinki, Stanley L. Inhorn, M.D.
New York, and Hans P. Wagner, M.D. Berne

SINCE the introduction of new methods which made possible the reliable determination of the chromosome number in man and the identification of individual chromosomes or at least groups of chromosomes, it has become evident that the presence of the normal complement of exactly 22 pairs of autosomes and 2 sex chromosomes is essential for normal development.

Abnormal chromosome numbers are most likely to arise by non-disjunction in the first meiotic division. Should this happen to the sex chromosomes in either parent, fertilisation will result in one of four abnormal sex-chromosome constitutions. Of these possibilities one, YO, would unquestionably be lethal. All of the remaining combinations have been observed. XO, with a total of 45 chromosomes, causes gonadal dysgenesis (Ford, Jones, Polani, de Almeida, and Briggs 1959), and XXY chromatin-positive Klinefelter's syndrome (Jacobs and Strong 1959, Ford, Jones, Miller, Mittwoch, Penrose, Ridler, and Shapiro 1959). XXX results in disturbances (Jacobs, Baikie, Court Brown, MacGregor, Maclean, and Harnden 1959) that seem to indicate merely an œstrogen deficiency. On genetical grounds it was not to be expected that the addition of an autosome to the normal complement would have a similarly restricted effect. Only one type of autosomal trisomic has been reported to date, and although the extra chro-

Reprinted from *The Lancet,* April 9, 1960, pp. 790-793.

We wish to thank Mr. H. Montague and Mr. J. Tiedt from the photographic laboratory for technical assistance.

The work has been supported in part by a grant from the U. S. Public Health Service (C-3313) and by an institutional grant from the American Cancer Society, Inc.

434

mosome is one of the two smallest autosomes of the haploid set, its presence in triplicate results in mongolism (Jacobs, Baikie, Court Brown, and Strong 1959, Lejeune, Turpin, and Gautier 1959).

It was to be expected that other autosomal trisomics, if they should be at all viable, would also display multiple congenital disturbances. During a search among infants afflicted with such anomalies we have recently found two clinically similar cases, a boy and an unrelated girl, each with 47 chromosomes. The syndrome is quite distinct from mongolism and includes anomalies of ears, hands, and feet, a small mandible, apparent mental retardation, spasticity, and a congenital heart defect. The heart defect proved fatal at 2 and 2½ months of age. The cytological analysis is still in progress; it seems that the extra chromosome belongs to the E group (in our classification as proposed in fig. 2). The present communication concerns a third type of autosomal trisomic which is distinct from mongolism as well as from the above-mentioned syndrome.

CLINICAL DATA

The patient, a full-term female infant, was born in January, 1959, and is still alive (February, 1960).

This was her mother's first pregnancy. Both parents are Caucasian; they were 25 years of age and in good health at the time of conception. A survey of the parental family trees disclosed 3 first cousins, 7 aunts and uncles, and 31 great-aunts and great-uncles with no reported anomalies. The parents had 89 first cousins, of whom 1 had a lumbar meningocele. One of the patient's 88 second cousins has a clubfoot deformity, another a congenital shortness of one leg. The grandparents are said to be normal. Thus among 224 relatives of three generations only three anomalies were found, none similar to those observed in the patient.

At 6 months' gestation the mother had an influenza-like illness. She received no X-ray exposure during the pregnancy and experienced no bleeding. At birth, the patient weighed 6 lb. 5 oz. and was 19 in. in length. Intermittent cyanosis was noted in the first 3 postnatal hours and oxygen was administered in an incubator during the first 3 days. No cyanosis has been observed since.

The infant was first seen at the age of 1 month by one of us

(D. W. S.). She appeared to be a well-nourished infant with the following anomalies: apparent anophthalmia, hare lip, cleft palate, and polydactyly of the left foot (fig. 1). She weighed 7 lb. 13 oz., was 21.0 in. long, and had a head circumference of 14.25 in., and a chest circumference of 14.0 in., all of which are within the normal range. The appearance of the external genitalia was that of a normal female infant.

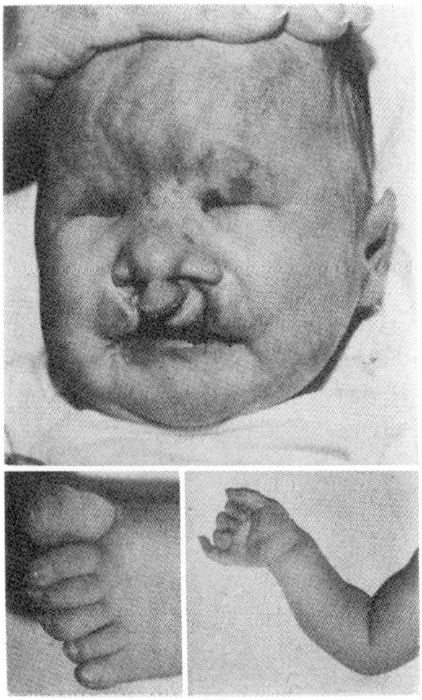

Fig. 1. The patient.

The cranium was normal in size and contour and could not be transilluminated. Poor ossification of the cranial bones with wide membranous gaps between them was revealed by X-rays. When the eyelids, which seemed to be normal, were pried open no organised ocular tissue could be seen or palpated. The condition of the posterior orbit remains unknown as no biopsy was taken. The bilateral hare-lip deformity was worse on the right side. The cleft in the palate was complete. The left ear was smaller than the right. In the 6th toe of the left foot X-rays disclosed normal phalanges based on a fully developed 6th metatarsal. Both thumbs were maintained in a flexed position. Upon their passive extension two small "clicks" were palpable at the metacarpal-phalangeal joint, an anomaly sometimes called "trigger thumb."

A grade-iii rough systolic murmur was audible to the left of the sternum with maximal intensity over the 2nd to 3rd intercostal spaces. The blood-pressure in the right arm was 90 mm. Hg. by flush technique and the pulse-rate was 120. Chest X-rays and fluoroscopy revealed a globular heart of normal size with the main mass of the heart projecting in a convex manner to the right. The aorta was seen to descend on the left. Pulmonary vascularity was increased. The electrocardiogram was interpreted as showing a vertical position with marked right axis deviation. The clinical impression was a rotational anomaly with intraventricular septal defect.

Non-elevated simple capillary hæmangiomata were present on the nasal bridge, both upper eyelids, the posterior neck, and scattered small areas on the forehead and lower back. A neurological study showed that the infant moved all extremities with fair muscular tone. The deep tendon reflexes were normal. A fair Moro reflex was elicited by sudden movement, but no such reaction was

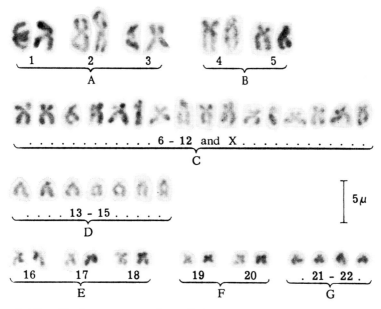

Fig. 2. The 47 chromosomes of a cell from the bone-marrow of the right tibia. The D group contains 7 instead of, as normal, 6 autosomes.

provoked by a loud sound. As the infant showed no response to sound she was considered to be deaf. In a subsequent evaluation at 5 months of age it was estimated that she performed at the developmental level of a 1-month-old. Since the age of 3 months she has had frequent brief seizures of myoclonic type.

Laboratory studies of urine and blood yielded normal values, as did measurements of the concentrations in the serum of CO_2, chloride, sodium, potassium, calcium, phosphorus, serum alkaline phosphatase, total protein, and fasting blood-sugar.

Particular attention was paid to the question whether the patient might be an atypical mongoloid. She does have simian creases in the palms of both hands, but in every other aspect of the physical evaluation she did not appear mongoloid. X-ray photographs of the pelvis were normal for her age. She lacked the hypotonia usually evident in an infant mongoloid. In addition, the skin patterns of the hands and feet render mongolism very unlikely. We are obliged to Dr. Irene A. Uchida for a detailed

CHROMOSOME COUNTS IN BONE-MARROW MITOSES

Specimen from	Chromosome Number						Number of Mitoses
	44	45	46	47	48	49	
Right tibia				4		1	5
Left tibia			1	6			7
Right tibia			2	37			39
Total			3	47		1	51

analysis of these patterns. Their overall logarithmic index is −1.81, a value which is smaller than that found by Walker (1957) in all but 2 of 150 investigated mongoloids and which is well within the range of non-mongoloids. This index, in conjunction with the clinical picture, justifies the conclusion that the patient is not a mongoloid. It will be seen that the cytological analysis leads to the same conclusion.

CYTOLOGICAL OBSERVATIONS

The chromosomes were studied in cells from bone-marrow cultures. The culture technique followed was essentially that recommended by Ford, Jacobs, and Lajtha (1958).

Marrow specimens were obtained by aspiration first from the right tibia, later from the left tibia, and still later again from the right tibia. In the case of the first two specimens only the buffy layer of the centrifuged marrow was cultured in saline with AB serum from a blood-bank. The third specimen, without centrifugation, was put into a culture medium (about 0.25 ml. marrow per 4.0 ml. medium) consisting of equal parts of Hanks' balanced saline (with antibiotics, adjusted to pH 7.4) and fat-free serum collected from an AB donor after fasting. The first two specimens yielded only a few countable mitoses; the third produced an abundance. Observations on bone-marrow from other

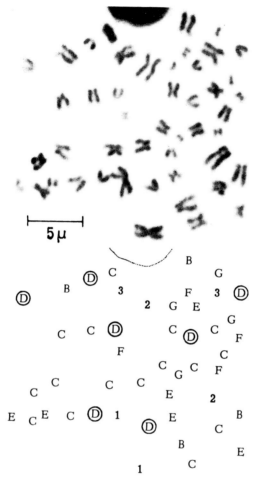

Fig. 3. A cell with 47 chromosomes, including 7 of the D group, from the bone-marrow of the left tibia. The letters designate chromosome groups as in fig. 2.

individuals also suggest the last-described technique to be superior; but it, too, often fails to provide more than a few usable mitoses.

The cultures, 4 ml. aliquots in 25 ml. screw-cap tubes, were kept for approximately 24 hours at room temperature, then for 5 hours in an incubator at 37°C, and after the addition of colchicine for 2 more hours in the incubator. The colchicine concentration in the culture medium was 0.0001%. Sodium citrate was used as by the above authors. After fixation in 1:3 acetic alcohol, the material was either left in 75% alcohol in a refrigerator for future use or stained immediately by the usual Feulgen procedure. The squashing was done in 45% acetic acid. Thereafter the slides were either made semi-permanent by surrounding the coverslips with Kroenig cement or mounted in "Euparal." To that end the preparations were frozen on dry ice, the coverslips pried off, and the slides passed through 95% into absolute alcohol.

Semipermanent slides have the advantage that microscopically controlled additional squashing can be applied. This often renders the chromosomes countable in a cell that was not suitable before. Even more important, sufficiently severe squashing tends to spread the chromatids of the smaller chromosomes in a horizontal plane, an almost necessary condition if the latter are to be reliably classified. It matters little that squashing, when carried that far, may distort some of the larger chromosomes (see fig. 2).

Chromosomes were counted for the record only when their arrangement suggested that none had been lost by over-squashing. Absolute assurance on this point is impossible; indeed, in one instance of repeated squashing we observed a chromosome being expelled from a cell that continued to have an unbroken appearance. However, such cases are evidently rare. The outlay of the chromosomes of each cell judged to be acceptable in the above sense was first sketched. The decision to count them for the record was made by two of us (K. P. and E. T.) who had both to be satisfied that the sketch contained no errors. We refrained from any attempt to ascertain the chromosome number before this decision. Thereafter the count obtained from the drawing was not open to further revision. It is obviously impossible to estimate, without a deliberate count, the number of some 46 scattered chromosomes with any precision. Therefore, the above procedure will ensure that, within the narrow range of chromosome numbers which are of any interest in the present context, subconscious bias can affect neither the selection of cells to be counted nor the counts themselves. A very few cells with less, mostly much less, than 44 chromosomes were discarded, as were polyploid mitoses which seem to occur in every bone-marrow.

It is evident from the table that the basic chromosome number of the patient is 47. As this number predominates in the marrow of both tibias the possibility of mosaicism can be dismissed. The few cases with numbers other than 47 may have come about in part by loss of chromosomes during preparation, in part by counting errors; but we would not rule out the possibility of having encountered an occasional cell with an atypical chromosome complement.

There was no lack of cells in which all chromosomes or major groups of them could be analysed. In all suitable cells with 47 chromosomes an apparently entirely normal female complement was found, including 4 small chromosomes (group G in fig. 2) and 16 of the group to which the X chromosomes belong (group C in fig. 2). The presence of two X chromosomes was further borne out by buccal smears, fixed and stained with acetic orcein, in which 25 out of 100 nuclei were chromatin-positive. The extra chromosome belongs to the group of medium-sized acrocentric autosomes (D in fig. 2). In at least five cells all 7 D chromosomes were about as clear as in fig. 2, each showing the very small short arm characteristic for this group. There were, of course, still other cells—e.g., that of fig. 3, in which all 7 D chromosomes could be identified.

We cannot say to which of the three pairs of the D group the extra chromosome belongs, the reason being that we cannot identify the individual pairs. It will be pointed out elsewhere that the "pairing-off" of chromosomes by size in the case of this, as of certain other groups, is almost meaningless because it neglects the not at all negligible random variation of the apparent chromosome length. One of the D pairs has a minute satellite (Tjio and Puck 1958, Chu and Giles 1959). We have seen it, but too infrequently —even in orcein slides made for this purpose—to have much hope that the presence or absence of a satellite at the extra chromosome could be established with the present technique.

DISCUSSION

It will, we presume, not be doubted that the observed abnormality of the chromosome complement is the cause of the clinical anomalies; but the question could be raised whether the extra chromosome might not be a translocation chromosome which merely happens to have the size and shape of a D chromosome.

If so, the chromosome piece actually duplicated could be considerably shorter than a whole D chromosome. Suffice it to say that for various reasons we consider this unlikely in the present case and that we are confident future findings will confirm the extra chromosome to be a genuine D chromosome. If it is, the present combination of a specific cytological situation with a certain pattern of anomalies is bound to be encountered again. In independent cases of translocation a similar clinical pattern might reoccur but would not consistently coincide with the presence of an extra chromosome of the D type.

Trisomy no doubt always has its origin in non-disjunction. The latter represents, if the original chromosome complement is structurally homozygous, a meiotic or (more rarely) a mitotic malfunction. Such an accident can involve any chromosome, even though some chromosomes may be much more prone to it than others, depending on their length and centromere position. We suspect that non-disjunction occurs occasionally in the healthiest of tissues. The frequency of this as of any malfunction is, however, apt to be influenced by genetical and environmental factors. One need not be surprised that there is a correlation between the incidence of mongolism, now understood to result from non-disjunction, and the age of the mother, which, after all, is to the oocyte an environmental factor. This strong positive correlation is not likely to be restricted to one particular chromosome. In consequence, we should expect that the frequency of trisomics other than mongoloids will also be found to increase with the age of the mother. This appears to be the case. Out of four such trisomics observed so far only the present patient has a young mother. The mothers of the two autosomal trisomics of another type that had been mentioned in the introduction were both about 46 years of age at the time of conception. The mother of the XXX female reported by Jacobs, Baikie, Court Brown, MacGregor, Maclean, and Harnden (1959) was 41 years of age at conception. These are not likely to be mere coincidences.

Of the 22 conceivably viable types of autosomal trisomics three have been found so far. How many more are viable is not known, but it seems certain that not all of them are. As each of the viable ones will probably show a clinically distinguishable syndrome, we may expect that an ætiologically unique group of a limited number of "autosomal trisomy syndromes" will become established. To the human geneticist these will be of continuing interest; he will in particular look forward to cases in which the presence of known genes in the parents can be related to peculiarities in the trisomic child. It seems likely that every component anomaly of a trisomy syndrome reflects, by way of a dose effect of gene action, the presence in the respective chromosomes of at least one gene locus that plays a prominent role in the normal development of the afflicted organ; indeed, we suspect that many of the trisomy anomalies can also be produced individually in euploid persons by the heterozygous or homozygous presence of a suitable mutated allele of the responsible gene. Polydactyly and hare lip with cleft palate in the present patient may be cases in point. These also suggest that trisomy may become instrumental in establishing for the first time autosomal linkage groups in man.

SUMMARY

The patient, a girl infant, has 47 chromosomes, the extra chromosome being one of the medium-sized acrocentric autosomes.

The presence of this extra chromosome is regarded as the cause of the following observed combination of congenital anomalies: Cerebral defect, apparent anophthalmia, cleft palate, hare lip, simian creases, "trigger thumbs," polydactyly, capillary hæmangiomata, heart defect.

ADDENDUM

Since this report was written, another patient, an unrelated female infant, has been found to combine a similar set of congenital anomalies with possession of an extra D chromosome which no doubt is the same as the one in the present case.

REFERENCES

Chu, H. Y., Giles, N. H. (1959) *Amer. J. hum. Gen.* 11:63.

Ford, C. E., Jacobs, P. A., Lajtha, L. G. (1958) *Nature, Lond.* 181:1565.

———— Jones, K. W., Miller, O. J., Mittwoch, U., Penrose, L. S., Ridler, M., Shapiro, A. (1959) *Lancet* i:709.

———— Polani, P. E., de Almeida, J. C., Briggs, J. H. (1959) *ibid.* p. 711.

Jacobs, P. A., Baikie, A. G., Court Brown, W. M., MacGregor, T. N., Maclean, N., Harnden, D. G. (1959) *ibid.* *ii*:423.
—— Strong, J. A. (1959) *ibid.* *i*:710.
—— Strong, J. A. (1959) *Nature, Lond.* *183*:302.
Lejeune, J., Turpin, R., Gautier, M. (1959) *Ann Génétique,* *1*:41.
Tjio, J. H., Puck, T. T. (1958 *Proc. nat. Acad. Sci., Wash.* *44*:1229.
Walker, N. F. (1959) *J. Pediat.* *50*:19.

42

A NEW AUTOSOMAL TRISOMY SYNDROME: MULTIPLE CONGENITAL ANOMALIES CAUSED BY AN EXTRA CHROMOSOME

David W. Smith, M.D., Klaus Patau, Ph.D., Eeva Therman, Ph.D., and Stanley L. Inhorn, M.D.

THE normal human complement of chromosomes consists of 22 pairs of autosomes and 2 sex chromosomes. On the basis of their size and structure they can be classified into identifiable groups. The members of the 23 pairs are segregated during meiosis when the number of somatic chromosomes is reduced from 46 to 23, the number found in gametes. An accidental failure of this disjunction of pairs of chromosomes has been found to occur occasionally in many organisms and no doubt can happen also in man. In the latter, nondisjunction of one pair will result in a gametic chromosome number of 22 or 24. The combination of a gamete with 24 chromosomes with a normal one would produce a "trisomic" zygote in which one chromosome exists in triplicate rather than as a normal pair, the total number of chromosomes being 47. The presence of an extra chromosomes amounts to an altered genetic balance which is almost bound to interfere with development in a variety of ways. This might result in death of the fetus or at least in a complex of congenital anomalies.

Until very recently it was unknown whether any human trisomics would be at all viable. If so, it was to be expected that individuals having the same extra chromosome, which means the same extra set of gene loci, would show sufficient similarity in their anomalies to be recognized as representatives of a specific

Reprinted from *The Journal of Pediatrics*, September, 1960, pp. 338-345.

From the Departments of Pediatrics and Pathology, Medical School, University of Wisconsin, Madison, Wis.

This investigation was supported in part by Grant No. C-3313 and Grant No. A-3645 from the National Institutes of Health, Public Health Service, and an Institutional Grant from the American Cancer Society, Inc.

445

syndrome. To date 3 such "trisomy syndromes," as Patau, Smith, Therman, Inhorn, and Wagner[1] called them, have been recognized. In one of them the extra chromosome is the X chromosome, in the other two an autosome.

Jacobs, Baikie, Court Brown, MacGregor, Maclean, and Harnden[2] found 3 instead of the normal 2 X chromosomes in a woman who had signs suggestive of an estrogen deficiency. Jacobs, Baikie, Court Brown, and Strong,[3] and Lejeune, Turpin, and Gautier[4] showed that the syndrome of Mongolism is due to an extra chromosome which belongs to one of the 2 pairs of smallest autosomes. Patau and associates[1] described a complex of congenital anomalies in an infant who was found to be trisomic for one of the medium-sized autosomes. It can be expected that more individuals trisomic for this particular chromosome will become known and that they will display a similar clinical pattern. For this reason, this complex of anomalies will henceforth be referred to as a trisomy "syndrome." However, since the characterization is based on only 1 case, it is necessarily tentative. Patau and associates have also mentioned briefly 2 cases of another trisomy syndrome. These cases are the subject of the present communication.

CASE REPORTS

Case 8. *History.* The patient, a Caucasian girl, was born July, 1959, and was admitted at 2 months of age to the University Children's Hospital because of failure to gain weight. At the time of conception the mother was 46, the father was 49, and both were in good health. There are 14 living siblings ranging from 2 to 29 years of age, none of whom are known to have anomalies. The mother had 2 spontaneous abortions at the age of 41 years and 2 normal children since then.

A survey of the parental family trees disclosed a total of 12 aunts and uncles and 28 first cousins, none of whom is known to have a congenital anomaly.

The pregnancy was uncomplicated and lasted 7½ months. At birth the patient weighed 5 pounds 4 ounces. She was 17.5 inches long and was cyanotic.

Physical examination. At 2 months of age the patient was slim, dyspneic, sucked poorly, and had a weak cry. Her color was ashen, and she became cyanotic with crying. She was 19.5 inches long and weighed 5 pounds. There was a marked lack of subcutaneous fat. The circumference of the cranium was 14.0 inches and the anterior fontanelle was 3.0 by 4.0 cm. The skull could not be trans-illuminated. The ears were low set and the upper ears inclined in a posterior direction. The auricles were thin, and the right one looked elfinlike with a poorly formed scapha helix; the left was more ovaloid. Neither tragus was well developed, and anterior

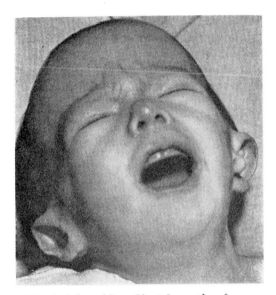

Fig. 1. Infant (Case 8) at 2 months of age.

to the left ear were 2 pedunculated skin tags 0.5 and 0.7 cm. in length. The mandible was small. The hands appeared abnormal. The fingers were partially flexed and could be fully extended only with difficulty. The thumbs appeared small and were relatively narrow at the base. The fifth fingers were also small with no in-turning of the distal phalanx. The wrists were partially flexed with a 15-degree ulnar deviation. The elbows, knees, and hips were partially flexed and it was difficult to extend them fully. There were symmetric deformities of the feet with convex soles and a 1 cm. posterior extension of the heels. This has been called "rocker bottom" feet.

The thoracic cage was wide in the anterior posterior diameter with a short sternum.

The heart was not enlarged as estimated by percussion. There was a palpable thrill at the left sternal border, and a Grade IV coarse systolic murmur was audible with maximal intensity in the third to fourth interspace to the left of the sternum. The second pulmonic sound was loud and split. The systolic blood pressure by flush technique was 90 mm. Hg in the arms and 80 in the legs. The infant was dyspneic and occasional râles were audible at the posterior lung bases. The liver edge was palpable 2 cm. below the right costal margin.

The muscle tone in the extremities was increased to a degree suggesting spasticity. The Moro reflex was feebly present. A 1 cm. umbilical defect was present. No further anomalies were found. The external genitalia were normal.

Laboratory data. The urine was acid with a specific gravity of 1.007; no albumin, reducing substances, or cells were demonstrated. The hemoglobin was 8.4 Gm. per 100 ml. The serum urea nitrogen was 20 mg. and the fasting blood glucose was 50 mg. per 100 ml.

Roentgenographic examination of the skull showed poor ossification. Roentgenograms of the hand demonstrated a relatively small fifth metacarpal and small phalanges; those of the chest revealed increased pulmonary vascularity. The heart appeared slightly enlarged with an essentially normal contour.

Hospital course. The infant failed to thrive, took only 1 ounce of formula at a time, had cyanotic episodes with crying, and suddenly died on the ninth hospital day. She was then 2½ months of age. The patient did not vomit during the hospital stay.

Findings at necropsy. The heart was markedly enlarged, with moderate thickening of the wall of the right ventricle. A 1.0 cm. interventricular defect and a patent ductus arteriosus were found. The lungs revealed no gross anomaly but on microscopic examination showed moderate congestion and hypercellularity of the alveolar septa.

The pylorus was hard with a markedly thickened muscular wall. The pancreas appeared normal on gross evaluation. A section through the tail of the gland showed acinar and islet tissue within a dense fibrous network. The ducts were dilated. The appearance was considerably different from that ordinarily found in cystic fibrosis. Just proximal to the ligament of Treitz were 2 small nodules in the wall of the duodenum which were composed of well-formed acinar and islet tissue without fibrosis.

A rather large diverticulum of the ileum was located 76 cm.

from the ileocecal valve. A horseshoe kidney was present with fusion of the lower poles over which the ureters passed from the normal-appearing pelvis. Microscopic examination revealed poly-morphonuclear leukocyte infiltration within and around the renal tubules. The brain, bones, and joints were not investigated.

Case 19. The patient, a Caucasian boy, was born Oct. 5, 1959, and was seen at the Madison General Hospital where he had been

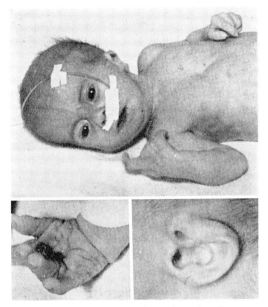

Fig. 2. Infant (Case 19) at 7 weeks of age.

admitted at 6 weeks of age because of multiple anomalies and failure to thrive.*

History. Each parent was 46 years of age at the time of con-ception of the patient. The mother was then suffering from ap-parent osteoarthritis of the spine. She became deaf following mastoiditis at 7½ years of age. The father has been deaf since he had spinal meningitis at the age of 14. There are 4 normal siblings, 2 boys and 2 girls, who range in age from 7 to 20 years. A survey of the parental family trees disclosed no known anomalies in 7 aunts and uncles, 17 first cousins, 20 great aunts and uncles, and

---

* This patient was seen through the courtesy of Dr. Curtis R. Weatherhogg of Madison, Wis.

44 first cousins once removed. The pregnancy was said to be full term. On Jan. 9, 1959, close to the likely time of conception, the mother received diagnostic x-ray exposures during studies of the upper and lower gastrointestinal tract and of the dorsal spine. Fetal movement was less than had been experienced in previous pregnancies. The delivery was uncomplicated, and the baby weighed 5 pounds 1 ounce at birth. From birth the patient failed to thrive and had a poor dietary intake. Congenital heart disease with cardiac failure had been recognized.

Physical examination. At 2 months of age the infant showed constant dyspnea with dusky coloration which increased to cyanosis on crying; his sucking was poor, he was lethargic and had a weak cry. He was 20.0 inches long and weighed 5 pounds 13 ounces. Subcutaneous fat was noticeable only in the buttocks and cheeks. The cranium was symmetrically small; the circumference was 13.0 inches. The ears were low set, and the scapha helix was incompletely developed and folded over with an acute angulation at the posterior border. The tragus was poorly developed. The mandible was symmetrically small. There were small inner epicanthic folds of the upper lid. The lens of the right eye contained a partial hazy white opacity. The optic discs appeared white. There was no retinal pigmentation.

The hands were abnormal. The fingers were held in a flexed position, and it was difficult to extend them fully. The third, fourth, and fifth fingers deviated in an ulnar direction in contrast to the position of the index finger. This gave rise to a V-shaped gap between the second and third fingers. The middle phalangeal joint of the index finger was partially fixed in extension. The palmar creases were anomalous, coming to a peak between the second and third fingers. In the feet there was partial syndactyly of the second and third toes.

The infant did not appear alert and did not follow objects with his eyes. A weak Moro reflex could be elicited. He was unable to support his head when held in the prone position. The extremities were maintained in a partially flexed position with increased resistance to passive flexion and extension. The deep-tendon reflexes were hyperactive.

The heart was enlarged to the left arterior axillary line as determined by percussion. There was a palpable thrill, and a Grade IV systolic murmur was audible over the entire precordium; it was loudest at the base in the third interspace to the left of the sternum. The pulmonary second sound was accentuated. The liver was palpable 3 cm. below the right costal margin.

A 1.5 cm. diastasis recti was palpable in addition to a 0.5 cm. umbilical defect. Bilateral inguinal hernias were present. The external genitalia were those of a normal male with testes in the scrotum.

Laboratory data. The hemoglobin was 13.1 Gm. per 100 ml. and the white blood count was 17,900 per cubic millimeter with 46 per cent segmented neutrophils, 2 per cent basophils, 1 per cent eosinophils, 36 per cent lymphocytes, and 15 per cent monocytes. The urinalysis showed an acid reaction; albumin, reducing substances, and cells were absent.

Roentgenographic examination of the chest showed enlargement of the heart both to the left and right and fullness of the pulmonary conus area. The pulmonary vascularity was increased. No abnormality was noted in the skull. An intravenous pyelogram appeared normal. The roentgenographic findings in the hands demonstrated no abnormality other than the anomalous position of the fingers as previously mentioned. There was a spina bifida of the ninth, tenth, and eleventh thoracic vertebrae.

Skin patterns. In an effort to exclude the possibility of Mongolism, skin patterns were studied.* A logarithmic index of –6.65 was obtained. According to Walker[5] this is well within the normal range and entirely outside that of Mongoloids.

Hospital course. The evidences of cardiac failure continued until the infant died suddenly at 2 months of age.

Findings at necropsy. The heart was enlarged with a large right auricle and right ventricle; the wall of the latter was 8 mm. in thickness. There was a 0.5 cm. patency of the foramen ovale and a 1.0 cm. high interventricular septal defect. The ductus arteriosus was anatomically patent and small in caliber.

A 2 cm. diverticulum lined by intestinal mucosa was present 20 cm. above the ileocecal valve.

Microscopic sections of the lungs revealed a moderate amount of acute inflammatory cells in the walls of the bronchi, which also showed edema of the mucosa.

---

* The study of the skin patterns was conducted by Dr. Irene Uchida of The Children's Hospital, Winnipeg.

Gross and microscopic examinations of the brain, kidneys, adrenals, pancreas, liver, lymph nodes, and thymus demonstrated no abnormality.

CHROMOSOME ANALYSIS

Chromosomes were studied in Feulgen slides made from cultures of bone marrow. The marrow was obtained by aspiration from a tibia of each patient. (For details of the culture technique, a modification of the procedure used by Ford, Jacobs, and Lajtha,[6] and for a description of the precautions taken to prevent

TABLE 1

CHROMOSOME COUNTS IN BONE MARROW CELLS

Patient	Chromosome Number					Number of Mitoses
	45	46	47	48	49	
Female (Case 8)	..	..	9	..	..	9
Male (Case 19)	..	1	6*	..	..	7
Total	..	1	15	..	..	16

* This includes two oversquashed mitoses which had been counted only to obtain a lower limit of the chromosome number.

subconscious bias from influencing the chromosome counts see Patau and others.[1]

The basic number of chromosomes of each patient was found to be 47 (Table 1). The cell listed as having 46 chromosomes was a borderline case of acceptability for counting purposes and a miscount appears possible. In most cells there was no doubt about the number. There was at least one cell in the material from either patient which was clear enough to determine with confidence the number of chromosomes in each of the Groups A through G in the classification of Patau and associates. Apart from the presence of an extra chromosome, the complements of both patients appeared to be normal for their sex, which means in particular that the girl (Case 8) had 16 C chromosomes and 4 G chromosomes while the corresponding numbers in the boy (Case 19) were 15 and 5, C and G being the groups to which the X and the Y chromosomes belong, respectively. This, in conjunction with the results obtained in buccal smears (Case 8, chromatin-positive; Case

19, chromatin-negative), leaves no doubt that one (Case 8) had the sex chromosome constitution XX while the other had XY.

The extra chromosome in each patient belonged to the autosomal E group as this contained 7 chromosomes in contrast to the 3 pairs, No. 16, 17, and 18 (17 to 19 in the enumeration by Ford, Jacobs, and Lajtha[6]), which are characteristic for the normal complement. The chromosomes of these 3 pairs are appreciably larger than the autosomes of the 2 F and the 2 G pairs and not much smaller than the 3 pairs of acrocentric D chromosomes to which the extra chromosome belongs that is presumably responsible for the syndrome described by Patau and others. The 3 pairs of E chromosomes can be distinguished from each other, but none of the relatively few mitoses found in the present material showed all 7 E chromosomes with that optimal clarity which is required for a definite identification of the extra chromosome within the E group. As both patients died before more bone marrow could be collected, the question must be left open which of the E chromosomes, when present in triplicate, causes the syndrome described in this report.

DISCUSSION

The similarity in the clinical pattern of the anomalies in the present 2 cases leaves little doubt that the extra chromosome is the same in each, even though the chromosome analysis revealed only that it belongs to the E group in the classification of Patau and associates. The clinical findings, in conjunction with the type of the extra chromosome, distinguishes these cases from both Mongolism and the case of trisomy described by Patau (Table 2).

The most striking anomalies in the present patients are the small mandible and the low-set malformed ears, indicating incomplete development of the hypomandibular arch. Potter[8] reported the very same type of anomalous development in 20 patients with bilateral renal agenesis, 4 of whom were afflicted with contractures of hips and elbows and 7 of whom had clubfeet. The girl (Case 8) in this report had an anomaly of the kidney in addition to flexion deformities and clubfeet. This invites the speculation that some instances of renal agenesis with low-set ears might

TABLE 2
Autosomal Trisomy Syndromes[*]

| | | Description of Syndrome | | |
| | | PRESENT REPORT | | |
Area of Involvement and Anomaly	Case 8	Case 19	PATAU AND OTHERS[1]	Mongolism[†] (%)
Extra chromosome belonging to group[‡]	E	E	D	G
Neural system — Mental defect	P	P	+	100
Deafness (neural ?)	–	–	+	..
Spasticity	+	+	–	.
Minor motor seizures	–	–	+	2
Neural or muscular system — Hypotonia	–	–	–	66
Hands — Flexion of fingers	+	+	–	..
Ulnar deviation of third, fourth, fifth fingers	–	+	–	..
Trigger thumbs	–	–	+	?
Inturned fifth fingers	–	–	–	68
Horizontal palmar crease	–	–	+	48
Feet — Rocker bottom	+	–	–	..
Syndactyly	–	+	–	..
Polydactyly	–	–	+	..
Wide gap first to second toe	–	–	–	44
Thoracic cage — Pigeon breast	+	–	–	14
Vertebrae — Spina bifida occulta	?	+	?	?
Cranium — Flat occiput	–	–	–	82
Mandible — Micrognathia	+	+	–	..
Auricle — Malformed	+	+	–	48
Low set	+	+	–	Unusual
Eye — Inner epicanthic fold	–	+	–	50
Cataract	–	+	–	..
Apparent anophthalmia	–	–	+	..
Speckled iris	–	–	–	30
Mouth — Cleft palate	–	–	+	..
Harelip	–	–	+	..
Skin — Multiple hemangiomata	–	–	+	..
Abdominal wall — Umbilical hernia	+	+	–	?
Inguinal herniae	–	+	–	?
Diastasis recti	–	+	–	76
Heart — Unspecified anomaly				28
Interventricular defect	+	+	+	Common
Patent ductus	+	+	–	?
Rotational anomaly	–	–	+	?
Kidney — Horseshoe	+	–	?	?
Intestine — Diverticulum (Meckel's ?)	+	+	?	?
Pyloric tumor	+	–	?	?
Ectopic pancreatic tissue	+	–	?	?
Maternal age at conception (years)	46	45	25	Over 40 24%

† Frequencies as found in random sample of 50 Mongoloids analyzed by Levinson, Friedman, and Stamps.[7]

‡ This classification was proposed by Patau and associates.[1]

* +, anomaly present; P, probably present; –, absent; ?, uncertain.

possibly be examples of the present trisomy syndrome, but with a more severe manifestation of the renal defect.

In the girl (Case 8) and to a lesser extent in the boy (Case 19) the anomalies of joint mobility, while not conforming with the classical picture, were suggestive of arthrogryposis multiplex congenita. This abnormality was claimed by Middleton[9] to result

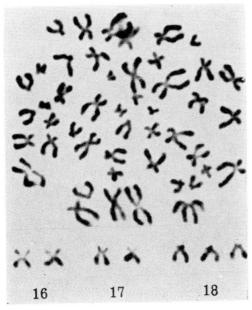

Fig. 3. Top: 47 chromosomes in bone marrow cell of an infant (Case 41) trisomic for chromosome No. 18; magnification ×2,840. Bottom: the E chromosomes from the same cell; magnification ×4,030.

from a failure of normal development of certain muscles with subsequent degenerative changes in these muscles leading to secondary joint fixation. However, the basic cause of this disease remains unknown. A 5-month-old white boy, recently admitted to the University Children's Hospital, exhibited a classical picture of arthrogryposis multiplex congenita as described by Stern.[10] The number of chromosomes in the marrow cells of this patient was 46, suggesting that this disease is not generally caused by an extra chromosome.

The two patients appeared to be mentally defective, but this cannot be stated with certainty, as they had cardiac failure at the time of examination and died at 2 and 2½ months of age, respectively. Both infants were developmentally retarded with signs of spasticity. If, in the future, cases surviving the period of early infancy should be found, the question of mental defect could be solved. In view of the complexity of cerebral structure and function the presence of mental deficiency in the two known autosomal trisomy syndromes is not surprising (Table 2). Quite likely a mental defect will also be a frequent or even ubiquitous feature in the present syndrome.

The occurrence of an extra chromosome is presumably always the result of mondisjunction, which is essentially a sporadic accident. There is no history of similarly affected infants or of other major congenital anomalies in the families of either of the present patients. The recurrence of Mongolism in the same family is rare; Benda,[11] for instance, found it twice in 255 families. The increase in frequency of Mongolism with maternal age indicates that nondisjunction is more frequent in older women. It is, therefore, not surprising that the mothers of both patients were of advanced age at the time of conception (Table 2). The mother of one (Case 19) also received diagnostic x-ray exposure close to the presumed time of conception. Whether this had any etiologic significance in the present case is a question which must remain open.

In Mongolism a multiplicity of anomalies are seen but, with the exception of mental retardation, there is not one which is found in all Mongoloid patients. However, the pattern of anomalies is usually sufficiently characteristic to permit a clinical diagnosis. In the instance of the present syndrome the situation is likely to be similar. As more cases are identified, the range of anomalies can be established. The most regularly-occurring ones will then form a pattern upon which the diagnosis can be based. The individual anomalies, which characterize Mongolism when they occur together, are occasionally found as isolated features in non-Mongoloids. Similarly, all the component anomalies of the present syndrome probably also occur as single or even multiple defects in individuals having the normal complement of chromosomes. Such occurrences can come about by mutation or, perhaps, by a nongenetic prenatal accident.

The true incidence of the present syndrome is unknown. Nondisjunction of the responsible chromosome may not be as frequent as in the case of Mongolism. Furthermore, the severe nature of the anomalies displayed by the 2 patients suggests that fetal death, stillbirth, or death in early infancy may lower the observed frequency of the syndrome.

SUMMARY

Two patients are described who died in early infancy. Each displayed similar complexes of congenital anomalies of which the following ones were found in both: low-set and malformed ears, small mandible, flexion deformities of the fingers, anomalous feet, interventricular septal defect, spasticity with probable mental defect, and diverticulum of the intestine.

The chromosome number was 47, the extra chromosome appearing to be the same one in each instance; it belongs to the E group in the classification of Patau and associates.[1]

The mothers of both patients were of advanced age at the time of conception.

ADDENDUM

Since the submission of the present report, 4 more infants, all unrelated, with the same syndrome have been discovered by the authors. All have 47 chromosomes as illustrated, for one of them, in Fig. 3. The extra chromosome is No. 18, which is also its number in the classification by Ford and colleagues.[6] Recently Edwards and colleagues[12] have described a trisomy syndrome that seems to be the same as the one presented above. However, these authors identify the extra chromosome as No. 17.

REFERENCES

1. Patau, K., Smith D. W., Therman, E., Inhorn, S. L., and Wagner, H. P., Multiple Congenital Anomaly Caused by an Extra Autosome, *Lancet* 1:790, 1960.
2. Jacobs, P. A., Baikie, A. G., Court Brown, W. M., MacGregor, T. N., Maclean, N., and Harnden, D. G., Evidence for the Existence of the Human "Super Female," *Lancet* 2:423, 1959.
3. Jacobs, P. A., Baikie, A. G., Court Brown, W. M., and Strong, J. A., The Somatic Chromosomes in Mongolism, *Lancet* 1:710, 1959.

4. Lejeune, J., Turpin, R., and Gautier, M., Le Mongolisme: premier exemple d'aberration autosomique humaine, *Ann génét. 1:*41, 1959.
5. Walker, N. F., The Use of Dermal Configurations in the Diagnosis of Mongolism, *J. Pediat. 50:*19, 1957.
6. Ford, C. E., Jacobs, P. A., and Lajtha, L. G., Human Somatic Chromosomes, *Nature 181:*1565, 1958.
7. Levinson, A., Friedman, A., and Stamps, F., Variability in Mongolism, *Pediatrics 16:*43, 1955.
8. Potter, E. L., Bilateral Renal Agenesis, *J. Pediat. 29:*68, 1946.
9. Middleton, D. S., Studies on Prenatal Lesions of Striated Muscle as a Cause of Congenital Deformity, *Edinburgh M. J. 41:*401, 1934.
10. Stern, W., Arthrogryposis Multiplex Congenita, *J.A.M.A. 81:*1507, 1923.
11. Benda, C. E.: Mongolism and Cretinism, ed. 2, New York, 1949, Grune & Stratton, Inc.
12. Edwards, J. H., Harnden, D. G., Cameron, A. H., Crosse, V. M., and Wolff, O. H.: A New Trisomic Syndrome, *Lancet 1:*787, 1960.

43

CHROMOSOMAL TRANSLOCATIONS IN MONGOLISM AND IN NORMAL RELATIVES

L. S. Penrose, M.D. Cantab., F.R.S., J. R. Ellis, Ph.D. Manc., and Joy D. A. Delhanty, B.Sc. Lond.

THE suggestion that mongolism is associated with a chromosomal aberration was made by Waardenburg in 1932[1] and non-disjunction was specifically mentioned. Last year, in reporting their finding of trisomy, Lejeune et al.[2] said that this could be caused by non-disjunction facilitated by advancing maternal age. Investigation of familial examples, however, shows the presence of a group in which maternal age is not an appreciable ætiological factor and in which transmission is usually through the mother (Penrose[3]). In view of the work of Snell, Bodemann, and Hollander[4] on hereditary malformations in mice, it seemed likely that translocation of chromosomes would best explain this familial pattern (Penrose[5]). A translocation in mongolism was recently reported by Polani et al.;[6] cells from bone-marrow of a female aged 10 showed fusion of two chromosomes—nos. 14 and 21 in the Denver nomenclature. Fraccaro et al.[7] found unusual chromosomes in bone-marrow and skin cultures from a male mongol age 5 months; an extra chromosome was seen in most cells of a skin culture from the father. The present communication describes translocations occurring in three patients, two of whom are sibs.

Patient A is a male, aged 48, who is a healthy, characteristic mongol imbecile. The father, now dead, was 41 at the patient's birth and the mother was 33. There is one healthy female sib aged 50; her karyotype was examined but no abnormality was detected.

A culture from a skin biopsy, taken from the patient in 1959, revealed that only 46 chromosomes were present. The karyotype appeared similar to that reported by Fraccaro et al.:[7] it was

Reprinted from *The Lancet*, August 20, 1960, pp. 409-410.

deficient in two small acrocentric chromosomes and had an extra small metacentric chromosome. Biopsy from the right testis indicated that spermatogenesis was fairly active in the early stages; at diakinesis fewer than the normal number of 23 masses were identified and it was thought that a quadrivalent could be seen in some cells.[8] In the culture from a second skin biopsy, taken in 1960, the cytological peculiarity previously found was again present, but this time it was noticed that some cells contained an ad-

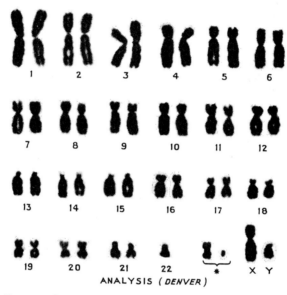

Fig. 1. Somatic chromosomes in a dermal-cell culture from patient A.

ditional minute, Feulgen-positive, centric particle (see fig. 1). In some cells three small acrocentric chromosomes were clearly satellited. Although this suggests that the extra metacentric had arisen through union between two no. 22 chromosomes, this was not regarded as conclusive since recent findings of many workers suggest that both chromosomes 21 and 22 may be satellited. Moreover the report of a quadrivalent during meiosis suggests that the extra metacentric had arisen by a reciprocal translocation between chromosomes 21 and 22, the other product being an unstable minute centric fragment. Since this had not been eliminated from all cells, the translocation is thought to have been of relatively recent origin.

Patient B, a female aged 8, is a healthy, typical mongol with intelligence above the average level for such children. At the time of her birth the father was 21 and the mother 23 years old.

There were two surviving sibs, a normal girl aged 6 and patient C; also there were two miscarriages.

Cells cultured from a skin biopsy showed a complement of 46 chromosomes. Among these were only five large acrocentrics (group 13-15), four small acrocentrics (group 21-22), and an extra chromosome in the group 7-12. The extra chromosome was thought to have arisen by fusion of major portions of a no. 15 and a no. 21.

Patient C, a male aged 2 years and 8 months, is affected typically with mongolism; though much retarded, he is healthy and alert. Cells in culture, derived from skin biopsy, show a complement of 46 chromosomes. As in cells from patient B, there were only five large acrocentrics and one extra chromosome in the group 7-12. There were five small acrocentrics present, one of which was assumed to be the Y-chromosome.

Five normal and healthy members of the family of patients B and C have been tested by culture from skin biopsy. The cells from the father showed no abnormality of karyotype, nor did those derived from the patients' mother's father. However, skin-biopsy cultures from the mother herself, her own mother, and her own normal daughter all showed the same peculiarity. In every cell studied the number of chromosomes was 45. There were only five large acrocentrics in group 13-15, three small acrocentrics in group 21-22, and one extra chromosome in group 7-12 (see fig. 2).

The simplest interpretation of the cytology in this pedigree is that a reciprocal translocation, involving a no. 15 and a no. 21 chromosome, occurred in an ancestor on the female side. A centric fragment has since been lost and the large fused chromosome has been transmitted through several generations of normal individuals. These normals with the translocation can produce unbalanced gametes which contain excess or deficit of chromatin belonging to the pair of chromosomes concerned. Mongolism in

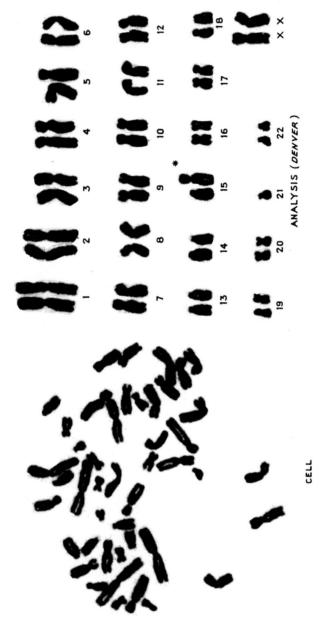

Fig. 2. Somatic chromosomes in a dermal-cell culture from the mother of patients B and C.

these patients B and C has thus been caused by fertilisation by normal sperm of unbalanced ova containing nearly double quantities of chromosome no. 21. The result is a condition in the zygote which is almost equivalent to the trisomy of no. 21 found in most cases of mongolism.

REFERENCES

1. Waardenburg, P. J. Das menschliche Auge und seine Erbanlagen. The Hague, 1932.
2. Lejeune, J., Gautier, M., Turpin, R. *C. R. Acad. Sci., Paris*, 1959, *248*:1721.
3. Penrose, L. S. *J. ment. Sci.* 1951, 97:738.
4. Snell, G. D., Bodemann, E., Hollander, W. *J. exp. Zool.* 1934, 67:93.
5. Penrose, L. S. *J. ment. Sci.* 1939, 85:1141.
6. Polani, P. E., Briggs, J. H., Ford, C. E., Clarke, C. M., Berg, J. M. *Lancet*, 1960, *i*:721.
7. Fraccaro, M., Kaijser, K., Lindsten, J. *ibid*. p. 724.
8. Miller, O. J., Mittwoch, U., Penrose, L. S. *Heredity*, 1960, *14*:456. (Abstract of paper read before the Genetical Society.)

44

THE XXX SYNDROME FREQUENCY AMONG MENTAL DEFECTIVES AND FERTILITY

Jean H. Fraser, M.B. Glasg., J. Campbell, M.B. Glasg.,
R. C. MacGillivray, M.B. Edin., F.R.F.P.S., D.P.M.,
Elizabeth Boyd, B.Sc. Glasg., and B. Lennox,
M.D. Durh., Ph.D. Lond., M.R.C.P., F.R.F.P.S.

A S part of a wide investigation of chromatin-positive (XXY) Klinefelter's syndrome in Glasgow (Ferguson-Smith et al. 1957, Stewart et al. 1959) Ferguson-Smith (1958) surveyed most of the male population of Lennox Castle Mental Deficiency Hospital, and established that the frequency of XXY cases was rather over 1%. When the description by Jacobs et al. (1959, 1960) of their so-called superfemale with an XXX chromosome complement provided what seemed a feminine counterpart on the genetic side to the XXY Klinefelter's syndrome, it seemed logical to institute a similar search for cases of this type on the female side of the same mental deficiency hospital.

Investigation of the cases found has not yet been completed, but some points which have been already established deserve report.

METHODS

Buccal mucosal smears were taken from as many as possible of the 637 female patients in the hospital, and 595 satisfactory preparations have so far been examined. These cases seem to be a representative sample of the varieties of mental defect seen in the majority of similar institutions in this country, although, owing to the policy of finding outside employment for as many patients as possible, we have seen relatively few of the highest grade of mental defectives.

Reprinted from *The Lancet*, September 17, 1960, pp. 626-627.

Our thanks to Mr. N. Russell for technical assistance, to Mr. G. Kerr for photography, and to Ciba Laboratories Ltd. for a gift of "Colcemid" alkaloid.

Buccal smears were stained by the original cresyl-echt-violet method of Moore and Barr (1955), a hundred suitable nuclei being examined in every case. Mitotic chromosome counts were performed in 3 cases on cultures of peripheral blood by the method of Hungerford et al. (1959) with some modifications mostly suggested by Miss Patricia Jacobs, and in 1 case on sternal marrow by the method of Ford et al. (1958).

RESULTS

Of the 595 cases examined, 4 appear to be examples of the XXX syndrome (see accompanying table). Buccal smears from all 4

FINDINGS IN 4 CASES OF XXX SYNDROME

Case No.	Age (Yr.)	Intelligence Quotient	% Nuclei with Sex Chromatin		Chromosome No.	Maternal Age (Yr.)
			SINGLE	DOUBLE		
1	30	50	43	30	47	28
2	39	58	50	25	47	35
3	61	38	35	33	47	40+
4	73	50	33	30	47	. .

show the characteristic high count of chromatin-positive nuclei, many containing two sex-chromatin bodies.

In all 4 cases, chromosome counts showed a well-defined modal number of 47. In 3 cases preparations of sufficient quality to permit detailed analysis were obtained; and in these it was readily established that the extra chromosome is either an X, or at least something very near it (see figure).

These 4 cases present no very striking clinical features, and they stand out in no characteristic fashion from the general run of "non-specific" mental defect. All 4 patients are blood-group A, and all are epileptics; but these features may be coincidental. Family studies have so far disclosed nothing of note except high maternal age in 2 cases.

Fertility

Disregarding the oldest patient, whose previous menstrual history cannot be obtained, all appear to have a normal or nearly normal menstrual history. One of these patients, three years ago, gave birth to a single male child; and there is no doubt as to the maternity, as the child was born in the mother's present hospital. The child appears to be physically normal and of average intelligence. His mucosal smear is chromatin-negative, and blood-culture examinations show 46 normal chromosomes.

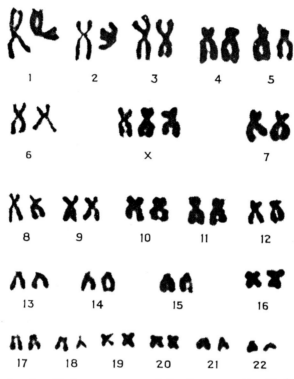

Ideogram showing 47 chromosomes and the 3 presumptive X chromosomes, identified as nearly as possible and numbered according to the "Denver" international system (1960).

DISCUSSION

Our figures suggest that the frequency of the XXX syndrome among mental defectives is 0.7%. It is improbable that the frequency of XXX in the general population will approach this figure. The relatively high maternal age supports the view that non-disjunction is responsible for the chromosomal anomaly. The figure is rather lower than that for Klinefelter's syndrome. This may be a matter of chance; but it may be noted that, at least as far as non-disjunction at first meiosis is concerned, only maternal non-disjunction can give rise to an XXX zygote, so that one would expect the condition to be less common than XXY Klinefelter's syndrome.

It is disappointing to find so far so little evidence of a characteristic syndrome. In view of the normal menstrual histories, and the fertility of one of our cases, it is tempting to suggest that the extra X chromosome is producing no clinical effect at all, but it must at least be responsible for the mental deficiency.

REFERENCES

"Denver" international system (1960) *Lancet, i:*1063.

Ferguson-Smith, M. A. (1958) *ibid. i:*928.

——— Lennox, B., Mack, W. S., Stewart, J. S. S. (1957) *ibid. ii:*167.

Ford, C. E., Jacobs, P. A., Lajtha, L. G. (1958) *Nature, Lond. 181:*1565.

Hungerford, D. A., Donnelly, A. J., Nowell, P. C., Beck, S. (1959) *Amer. J. hum. Genet. 11:*215.

Jacobs, P. A., Baikie, A. G., Court Brown, W. M., MacGregor, T. N., MacLean, N., Harnden, D. G. (1959) *Lancet, ii:*423.

——— Harnden, D. G., Court Brown, W. M., Goldstein, J., Close, H. G., MacGregor, T. N., MacLean, N., Strong, J. A. (1960) *ibid. i:*1213.

Moore, K. L., Barr, M. L. (1955) *ibid. ii:*57.

Stewart, J. S. S., Mack, W. S., Govan, A. D. T., Ferguson-Smith, M. A., Lennox, B. (1959) *Quart. J. Med. 28:*561.

45

MALFORMATION SYNDROME IN MAN
ASSOCIATED WITH TRIPLOIDY
(69 CHROMOSOMES)

J. A. Böök, M.D., and Berta Santesson, Fil. Lic.

THE importance of chromosomal variations in human pathology has been firmly established in the past two years. Fifteen different types are known to us at present. Eight have been discovered here.[1-4] The aberrations include trisomy, monosomy, and translocations. The highest chromosome number was 49, interpreted[4] as a double trisomy with XXY. All these numerical variations represent unbalanced karyotypes, probably caused by non-disjunction during oogenesis or spermiogenesis.

Polyploidy has been known in plants and lower animals for a long time. In natural population of vertebrates it is probably quite rare, but conclusive cases are known—e.g., among amphibia.[5] In mammals no conclusive post-term individuals have been found, but polyploid early embryos are known in rabbits and mice.[6]

The discovery of the first individual of the human species with triploid cells is of considerable interest from many viewpoints. It should, however, be remembered that this individual was found among a series of patients selected for chromosome studies. The condition with which the triploidy is associated may be accidental or peculiar to this particular individual. At this juncture and in this short note it can only be said that the findings have many important medical and genetical implications which we intend to consider fully in a later publication.

The patient is a boy born on Feb. 26, 1959, when his mother was 30 and his father 29 years old. Neither his parents (who were

Reprinted from *The Lancet*, April 16, 1960, pp. 858-859.

For the preliminary clinical information we are obliged to Dr. Olof Brandberg, head of the division of Pædiatrics, Örebro Central Hospital.

unrelated) nor his brother, born in 1957, showed clinical signs of disease or defect.

The pregnancy and delivery (breech presentation) were normal. Although born at full term, at birth he weighed only 2190 g. Malformations were observed at birth. His subsequent development was retarded and there were occasional feeding difficulties.

The boy was brought to the pædiatric clinic at Örebro on Feb. 2, 1960, because of recurrent attacks of fever combined with

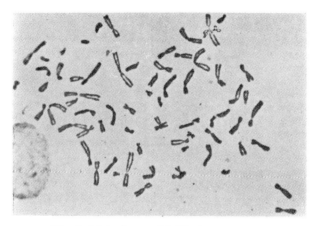

Fig. 1. Metaphase with 69 chromosomes.

disturbances of consciousness. On examination (Dr. Olof Brandberg) he was unable to raise his head when lying flat on his back. He showed some interest and played with toys but in general contact was deficient. He was small for his age (height 72 cm.). He had localised lipomatosis on the back of his hands, feet, and thighs. In contrast the lower legs were quite thin. His jaws were hypoplastic (micrognathia), and he had cutaneous as well as bony syndactyly of his hands and feet. The internal organs appeared normal. His genitalia were likewise normal with regard to his size and age. Both testes could be felt in the scrotum and had a normal consistence. The reflexes were normal; but a peculiar pattern of movements, including some ataxic features, was observed.

Radiographic examination.—In the skeleton 9 bone nuclei were found instead of the expected 16. No teeth had erupted, but germs were present. A pneumoencephalogram showed good filling of the ventricles with no displacement or deformity; but the basal cistern was much dilated, and large air spaces were observed bilaterally over the frontal convexity and parietally on the right side. The radiologist's diagnosis was porencephaly.

Laboratory data.—Meinicke-Kahn test, dye test (Sabin-Feld-

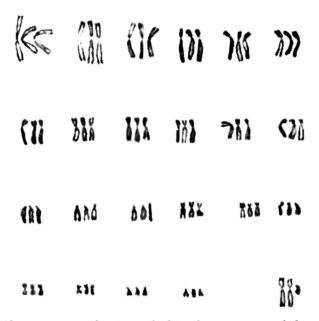

Fig. 2. Chromosomes in fig. 1 matched to show presence of three haploid sets: sex chromosomes interpreted as XXY.

man) test, and complement-fixation test for toxoplasma were all negative. Hæmoglobin 88%; red blood-cells 4,400,000 per c.mm.; white blood-cells 12,000 c.mm.; erythrocyte sedimentation rate 13 mm. in the first hour (Westergren).

Biopsy specimens were taken from skin. Chromosome studies were made according to our standard procedures[7] using the cell-culture technique. In the 11-day-old primary cultures which are the only ones analysed so far, practically all acceptable metaphases (>25) contained 69 chromosomes (fig. 1); occasional cells with lower or higher numbers were observed. The findings, exemplified in fig. 2, indicate the presence of three haploid sets—i.e., a chromosome complement of 3A+XXY.

REFERENCES

1. Böök, J. A. *Acta soc. med. Uppsala* (in the press).
2. Fraccaro, M., Kaijser, K., Lindsten, J. *Lancet,* April 2, 1960, p. 724.
3. Böök, J. A., *et al.* Unpublished.
4. Fraccaro, M., *et al.* Unpublished.
5. Böök, J. A. *Hereditas,* 1940, *26*:107.
6. Beatty, R. A. Cambridge Monographs on Experimental Biology, 1957, no. 7.
7. Böök, J. A., *et al. Acta pædiat., Stockh.* 1959,48:453.

46

FURTHER STUDIES IN CLINICAL CYTOGENETICS*

J. A. Böök and Berta Santesson

IN the several instances of associations between chromosomal variation and clinical syndromes discovered and studied at this institute,[1, 2, 3, 4, 5, 6, 7, 8, 9] the following progress was reported.

A pedigree with congenital auricular septal defect has been studied. In one family, the mother and her son displayed this defect but no other clinical signs of disease. The father and daughter were normal. The chromosome studies, according to our cell culture technique (bone marrow and skin),[2] revealed a mixture of cells some with a normal set of 46 chromosomes and others with 47 chromosomes in a proportion of approximately 1:3. The latter cells showed a consistent pattern of trisomy for group 19-20.[10] The skin and bone marrow material from the son showed cells with 46 chromosomes containing only 4 small acrocentric chromosomes. Furthermore, the cells were consistently trisomic for group 19-20 and monosomic for group 21-22. Both the father and daughter had a normal chromosome constitution. This appears to be the first recorded case of transmission in man of an extra chromosome associated with a specific pathology from one generation to the next.

The investigation on the association between a malformation syndrome and triploidy has been carried a step further.[4] This patient is a 14 month old boy. His mental and somatic development corresponded approximately to a child of 4-6 months. His clinical condition was dominated by a severe brain lesion while other malformations were less conspicuous. Chromosome studies have now been made on material from the skin of his right and left thigh, from *fascia lata* on his right side and from bone mar-

Reprinted from *Lunds Universitets Årsskrift* (in press).

* This investigation has been aided by a grant from the Foundations' Fund for Research in Psychiatry.

row. At least 5 primary cultures from each of 4 different biopsies have been examined. The cells derived from the skin and *fascia lata* were of two main categories. Most of them had 69 chromosomes and consistently displayed an apparently complete triploid set with an XXY combination. Reservations must of course be made for those individual chromosomes that are difficult or impossible to identify. All easily identifiable chromosomes occurred consistently in triplicates. A minority of cells had chromosome numbers at the diploid level. Cells containing 46 chromosomes were almost always clearly unbalanced; *i.e.*, not normal diploid cells.

The cells derived from the bone marrow were different. Firstly, the growth appeared subnormal. Secondly, no cells with 69 chromosomes have been found so far. All numbers were on the diploid level.

The present interpretation is that we are concerned with a case of mosaicism. For several reasons, it seems likely that this individual originates from the fertilization of an unreduced egg cell by a normal haploid sperm. The triploid cells are supposed to function less efficiently during mitosis—often giving rise to aneuploid cells. Competition and selection among these cells favoring the diploid level may explain the present situation. However, as yet nothing can be said about the function of such a mechanism *in vivo* as compared to that *in vitro*.

REFERENCES

1. Böök, J. A. *Acta Soc. med. Upsal. 64:*vii-viii, 1959.
2. Böök, J. A., Fraccaro, M. and Lindsten, J. *Acta paed.* 48:453-468, 1959.
3. Böök, J. A. *Acta Com. med. Upsal.* 65:i-ii, 1960.
4. Böök, J. A. and Santesson, Berta. *Lancet i:*858-859, 1960.
5. Fraccaro, M. *Acta Soc. med. Upsal* 64:viii, 1959.
6. Fraccaro, M., Kaijser, K. and Lindsten, J. *Lancet i:*886, 1959.
7. Fraccaro, M., Kaijser, A., and Lindsten, J. *Lancet ii:*1090, 1959.
8. Fraccaro, M., Kaijser, K. and Lindsten, J. *Ann. hum. Genetics, Lond.,* 24:45-61, 1960.
9. Fraccaro, M., Kaijser, K. and Lindsten, J. *Lancet i:*724-727, 1960.
10. *Lancet i:*1063-1065, 1960.

47

ABNORMALITIES INVOLVING THE
X CHROMOSOME IN WOMEN

Patricia A. Jacobs, B.Sc. St. And., D. G. Harnden, Ph.D. Edin.,
W. M. Court Brown, M.B., B.Sc. St. And., J. Goldstein, M.D.
Vienna, H. G. Close, M.D. Lond., T. N. MacGregor, M.D.
Edin., F.R.C.S.E., F.R.C.O.G., N. Maclean, M.B. Edin.,
M.R.C.P.E., and J. A. Strong, B.A., M.B. Dubl.,
F.R.C.P.E., M.R.C.P.

JACOBS and her colleagues (1959a) have published evidence for the existence of a human "super-female" with a sex-chromosome complement of XXX, the patient presenting as a case of secondary amenorrhœa. Ford et al. (1959a) have shown that chromatin-negative patients with Turner's syndrome have an XO sex-chromosome complement. We report here two new abnormalities which involve the X chromosome in women with amenorrhœa, and record data on a second "super-female."

The case-records are given in detail as the study of these patients raises important considerations, particularly in the clinical investigation of patients with persistent amenorrhœa. Each patient was identified as possibly having a sex-chromosome abnormality from a study of the sex chromatin in buccal mucosal cells.

CASE REPORTS

First Case

Clinical Data

The patient, a phenotypic female, was first seen by one of us (J. G.) because of anginal pain. It was found from her history that

Reprinted from *The Lancet*, June 4, 1960, pp. 1213-1216.

We are indebted to Miss K. Buckton for chromosome measurements, and to Miss I. Tough for some of the chromosome counts; to Dr. W. M. Harrowes and the nursing staff of St. Joseph's Institution, and also to Dr. E. J. Gilmore; to Dr. Eric Samuel, Dr. G. T. Loughborough, and Dr. F. Cosin, who kindly gave advice on X-ray interpretation; and to Miss M. Brunton, Miss S. Brunton, Mr. A. Ross, and Miss G. Woodcock for technical assistance.

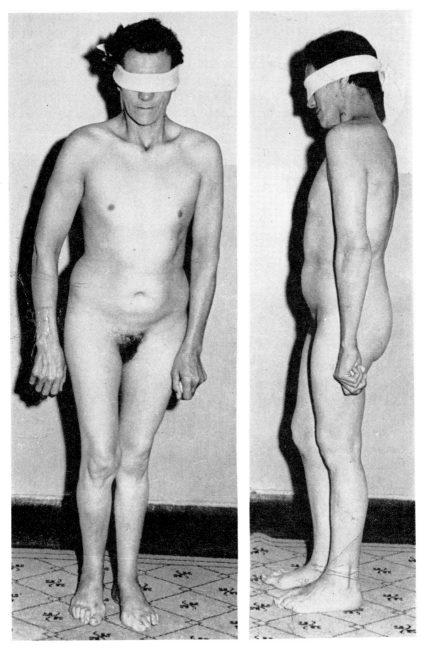

Fig. 1. Case 1: present appearance of patient.

she had never menstruated, and one of us (H. G. C.) noted that some of the buccal mucosal cells contained two sex-chromatin bodies. The patient was born in 1908, her father being 30 and her mother 32 years old at her conception. She is the fifth child in a sibship of six, her three elder brothers and her younger brother being married with families. Her sister, who died at the age of 24, had been married for fifteen months but had had no children.

The appearance of the patient is shown in fig. 1, and is note-worthy for the absence of breast development, the length of the arms, and the masculine character of the upper trunk and shoul-

TABLE 1

CASE 1: CHROMOSOME COUNTS

Tissue	Total No. of Cells	Chromosome Number					
		<44	44	45	46	47	>47
Sternal marrow	69	2	. .	67	. .	. .	. .
Blood	100	3	. .	71	5	11	1
Skin left shoulder	48	. .	. .	18	2	28	. .
Skin right leg	36	. .	1	15		20	
Totals	253	5	10	171	7	59	1

der-girdle. Her height is 5 ft. 1 in. and her arm span 5 ft. 7 in. Her crown-to-pubis and pubis-to-sole measurements are 2 ft. 6 in. and 2 ft. 7 in. respectively. X-ray examination reveals that not only are the dimensions of the bones of her shoulder-girdle those of a male, but her pelvis is android in shape, with its size and bone texture of male rather than female appearance.

The patient, whose aptitudes are feminine, is of low normal intelligence. Her head hair line is masculine; her pubic hair is of the normal female type, but her axillary hair is very scanty. The external genitalia are under-developed with the exception of the clitoris, the labia majora being small and the labia minora vestigial. She has several deeply pigmented nævi on her face and neck, but no other stigmata of Turner's syndrome. The vagina is absent and no uterus is palpable.

Blood-group studies have been made by Dr. Sylvia Lawler, of the Galton Laboratory, University College of London, and the findings are as follows:

$A_1(\beta)$. MN. Ss. R_1R_1.P–. Le(a+ B–). K–.
Lu(a–). Fy(a+ b+). Jk(a+ b+). Non-secretor ABH.

Colour-vision and hormone-excretion studies together with palm-print analysis are being made and will be reported later.

Nuclear Sex

Examination of smears from the buccal mucosa showed the proportion of cells with sex chromatin to be unusually large. Fifty two per cent of cells contained a single body and 37% two bodies. In our hands in normal women the mean percentage of cells with a single body is 41 (s.d. 3.4), and cells with two chromatin bodies have never been seen. In contrast the neutrophil polymorphs were of the male type and no "drumsticks" were seen in 1500 neutrophils (Davidson and Robertson Smith 1954).

Chromosome Analysis

Several different tissues were examined. Chromosome preparations were obtained from the sternal marrow by the method of Ford, Jacobs, and Lajtha (1958); from the peripheral blood by an adaptation of the method of Hungerford et al. (1959); and from two skin samples, one from the left shoulder and one from the right leg, by the method of Harnden (1960). The chromosome counts are shown in table 1.

Analysis of cells with 47 chromosomes from all cultures revealed a constant abnormality due to the addition of a chromosome in the medium-size range where the X chromosome is found. Analysis of cells with 45 chromosomes consistently showed a chromosome in the same range to be absent. In view of the finding of double chromatin bodies in the buccal mucosal cells and the absence of "drumsticks" on the polymorphs, the cells with 47 chromosomes are considered to have an XXX sex-chromosome complement and those with 45 an XO complement. In contrast analysis of the seven cells with 46 chromosomes failed to show a consistent pattern, and these are therefore presumed either to be cells with 47 chromosomes from which 1 has been lost during preparation, or cells with 45 chromosomes which have acquired an additional chromosome from a neighbouring broken cell. Similarly no consistent pattern was found in cells with counts of less than 45.

In both skin samples the majority of cells had 47 chromosomes. The high proportion of cells from the buccal mucosa with double chromatin bodies suggests that the cells in this site are mostly of the XXX type.

The leucocytes from the peripheral blood also show an admixture of two cell types, the majority containing 45 chromosomes with an XO complement. In contrast the bone-marrow appears to contain only cells with 45 chromosomes. The discrepancy between the blood and bone-marrow may be explained in at least three ways. Firstly the marrow may consist only of cells with 45 chromosomes, but the lymph-nodes and other sites in the reticulo-endothelial system may contain cells of the other type. Secondly the marrow sample may not have been representative of the marrow as a whole, which in other areas may contain cells of the alternative stem-line. Finally, it is possible that only the marrow cells with 45 chromosomes proliferated in culture. The first explanation seems to us the most likely as it is a reasonable supposition that some of the dividing cells found in blood-cultures are derived from the lymph-nodes and other sites in the reticulo-endothelial system.

Comment

Ford et al. (1959b) have described a presumptive XX/XXY mosaic in a phenotypic male with Klinefelter's syndrome, and Ford (1959) has reported several phenotypic females with Turner's syndrome whom he considers to be XO/XX mosaics.

The evidence now presented suggests that our patient is a mosaic whose body is composed of cells some with 47 and some with 45 chromosomes, and with sex-chromosome complements respectively of XXX and XO. Although we have no evidence for the presence of cells with 46 chromosomes and a sex-chromosome complement of XX, and while their existence seems unlikely, such cells may be present in tissues not examined.

Assuming that our patient is a 45/47 mosaic, the most likely explanation for this is that non-disjunction of the X chromosomes occurred during the first-cleavage division in a normally constituted zygote. Thus instead of producing two daughter cells each with 44 autosomes and two X chromosomes, cell division resulted in two unlike daughter cells, one with 44 autosomes and three X chromosomes and one with 44 autosomes and a single X chromosome.

It is theoretically possible for mosaicism to arise at any stage of development, but had this error occurred at a later stage than the first-cleavage division it would have given origin to a triple stem-line mosaic composed of cells with 45/46/47 chromosomes and with sex-chromosomes complements XO/XX/XXX. Probably not only will the composition of the mosaic be affected by the stage at which the divisional error occurs, but this may have important repercussions on the ultimate form of development of the individual.

Second Case

Clinical Data

This patient was first seen by one of us (T. M.) in 1947 with primary amenorrhœa. She was born in 1923, her father being 27

TABLE 2

CASE 2: CHROMOSOME COUNTS

Tissue	Total No. of Cells	Chromosome Number					
		<44	44	45	46	47	>47
Sternal marrow	25	2	1	1	21	. .	. .
Blood	103	3	2	7	87	4	. .
Skin left thigh	24	. .	2	4	18	. .	. .
Skin right thigh	34	. .	4	2	26	2	. .
Left gonad	15	. .	2	2	11	. .	. .
Right gonad	13	. .	. .	2	11	. .	. .
Totals	214	5	11	18	174	6	. .

and her mother 22 years old at her conception. The patient is the eldest in a sibship of four; her brother is married with one child, and both sisters menstruate regularly. Her height is 5 ft. 1 in. and her arm span 5 ft. 3½ in. Both her crown-to-pubis and pubis-to-sole measurements are 2 ft. 7 in. She weighed 8 st. 1 lb. in 1947 but since marriage in 1949 her weight has increased to 14 st. 4 lb.

The patient, whose aptitudes are feminine, is of low normal intelligence. When first seen she had scanty pubic and axillary hair, no breast development, and infantile external genitalia; no other external abnormalities were present. Oestrogen therapy produced some vaginal bleeding, along with breast development and increased growth of pubic and axillary hair.

At laparotomy the uterus was found to be under-developed and the gonads to be "streaks" of rudimentary tissue; ovaries were not seen in the normal sites nor were testes found. Histologically one gonad was composed of ovarian tissue in which only a few primitive follicles were found, but the tissue of the other was not recognisably ovarian.

Colour-vision and hormone-excretion studies together with palm-print analysis are being made and will be reported later.

Nuclear Sex

Examination of buccal smears on three occasions showed sex chromatin in only 7% of the cells. Altogether 500 cells were studied, and in only 36 was a chromatin body found. Not only was the proportion of chromatin-positive cells very low, but before the patient's chromosome constitution was known the chromatin bodies were noted by one of us (N. M.) as being smaller than usual. In blood films no "drumsticks" were found on 1,000 polymorphs. These findings were regarded as equivocal.

Chromosome Analysis

Sternal marrow, the leucocyte component of peripheral blood, two skin samples—one from the left and one from the right thigh—and material from both gonads were cultured. The chromosome counts are shown in table 2.

In all tissues the modal number was 46, and counts differing from this are considered mainly to be artefacts arising during the preparation of the cells (Court Brown, Jacobs, and Doll 1960). Thirty-four of the cells with 46 chromosomes, representing all of the tissues cultured, were analysed and all showed a constant morphological abnormality (fig. 2). There was an additional small submetacentric chromosome similar to autosome 16 of the normal complement, and 1 chromosome was absent from the range in which the X chromosome is found. These findings together with those of the nuclear sex as seen in the buccal smears, which was consistent neither with an XX constitution nor with an XO constitution, are interpreted as being due to an abnormality of one of the X chromosomes. We have found the length of the X chromosome in normal individuals to vary from 4.78% to 5.67% of the total haploid autosome length with a mean value of 5.34%. In this patient the apparently normal X chromosome, measured in four cells, varied from 4.82 to 5.66% (mean 5.35%) and the abnormal X only from 2.83 to 3.42% (mean 3.22%) of the total haploid autosome length. Measurement of the autosomes showed them to be within the normal range for length and arm ratio. The most reasonable explanation for the significant reduction in the length of the abnormal X chromosome is that part of it has been deleted.

Two other explanations, however, require consideration. First, the patient might have an XO sex-chromosome constitution together with an additional small submetacentric autosome or part

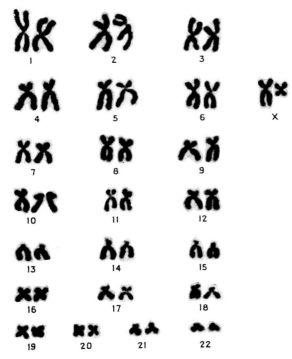

Fig. 2. Case 2: ideogram showing 44 autosomes and 1 normal and 1 abnormal X chromosome.

of an autosome. We feel, however, that this explanation can be dismissed for four reasons. Firstly, apart from deficient breast development, infantile genitalia, and the primitive appearance of the gonads, no other stigmata of Turner's syndrome were found; secondly, if she had an XO constitution the buccal smear should be chromatin-negative; thirdly, in the other two conditions known to be associated with an extra autosome multiple-system abnormalities are present (Lejeune et al. 1959, Jacobs et al. 1959b, Edwards et al. 1960); and fourthly this consideration requires two non-disjunctional errors to have occurred at the same time. The second possibility is that the small submetacentric chromosome is a Y chromosome with part of an X chromosome attached. This situation could arise if a segmental interchange occurred during spermatogenesis between the X and Y chromosomes. There are three reasons for dismissing this explanation. Firstly it would seem most unlikely that a tiny fragment of the X chromosome would nullify the masculinising effects of the Y, particularly as patients with an XXY constitution are phenotypic males. Secondly, those phenotypic females who are sex-reversed males with an XY constitution have been shown so far to be cases either of testicular feminisation or of pure gonadal dysgenesis (Jacobs et al. 1959c, Harnden and Stewart 1959), and the features of this case conform with neither of these conditions. Thirdly, some of the gonadal tissue was histologically recognisable as ovarian, but none as testicular tissue.

Comment

We presume that this patient is uniformly composed of cells containing one normal and one abnormal X chromosome, and that the latter is abnormal because a segment has been deleted; in consequence it is most likely that the causative error occurred during gametogenesis in one or other parent. It is reasonable to postulate the existence of a range of variation, depending on the size of the deletion, from the normal woman with two X chromosomes to the phenotypic female with an XO constitution. Consideration of the clinical and cytological findings in this patient suggest that she occupies an intermediate position in the range. Finally we must not overlook the possibility that a male may also carry a partially deleted X chromosome.

Third Case

Clinical Data

During a routine survey of the nuclear sex of the inmates of an institution for mental defectives, a phenotypic female was found to have double chromatin bodies in her buccal mucosal cells. This woman was born in 1939, but no details are known of her family history.

The patient is a high-grade mental defective. Her height is 5 ft. 0 in., her arm span 5 ft. 2 in., and her crown-to-pubis and pubis-to-sole measurements are 2 ft. 4 in. and 2 ft. 7 in. respectively. There is slight flexion deformity of the fingers of both hands. Her external sexual development is normal. Menstruation is said to have started at the age of 9, and at present she is menstruating regularly, although the possibility cannot be excluded that she may in the past have missed an occasional period.

Colour-vision and hormone-excretion studies together with palm-print analysis are being made and will be reported on later.

Nuclear Sex

Examination of buccal mucosal cells showed that the proportion of chromatin-positive cells was excessive, 41% having a single body

TABLE 3

CASE 3: CHROMOSOME COUNTS

Tissue	Total No. of Cells	Chromosome Number					
		<44	44	45	46	47	>47
Blood	32	..	..	1	2	29	..
Skin	29	..	..	2	2	25	..
Totals	61	..	..	3	4	54	..

and 48% double bodies. The blood polymorphs were those of a female, 11 "drumsticks" being found in 500 cells.

Chromosome Analysis

Peripheral blood and a sample of skin from the midline of the anterior chest wall were cultured. The chromosome counts are shown in table 3.

In both tissues the modal number was 47, and deviations from this are considered to be mainly due to artefacts arising during the preparation of the cells. Analysis of the cells with 47 chromosomes showed a consistent pattern with an additional chromosome present in the size range in which the X is found. In view of this and the buccal smear findings the patient is considered to be a "super-female" with an XXX sex-chromosome constitution.

Comment

As far as is known this patient has no physical abnormality related to her XXX constitution. It is uncertain whether her mental defect is incidental or is causally related to her chromosome constitution. She appears at present to menstruate regularly, and studies are being made to confirm that ovulation is occurring. She is, therefore, unlike the "super-female" previously reported who developed secondary amenorrhœa at the age of 17, and who also had had underdeveloped external genitalia prior to œstrogen therapy.

The findings in this patient raise the possibility that some women with an XXX constitution are fertile. If this is the case they will produce oocytes with X and XX sex chromosomes, and their progeny would therefore be expected to include individuals with an XXX and an XXY constitution. In consequence examination of the parents of persons found to carry an abnormality of the sex chromosomes is desirable. Some patients with other types of sex chromosome abnormality may also be fertile. If this is so the secondary non-disjunction which must occur may be an important additional cause of karyotype abnormalities involving the sex chromosomes.

DISCUSSION

The data in this report, together with previously published data, show that seven types of aberration of the sex chromosomes can be associated with amenorrhœa (table 4). Apparently such aberrations are not inevitably accompanied by amenorrhœa—in one case of Turner's syndrome with an XO constitution the patient menstruated regularly for six years (Stewart 1960); and in both patients with an XXX constitution menstruation began, ceasing in one after two to three years and continuing in the other at the age of 21. The information in table 4 is of necessity limited, but at this early stage of development of our knowledge it may be of some value to those investigating patients with persistent amenorrhœa.

There are good grounds for advocating routine examination for sex chromatin in buccal mucosal smears in all cases of amenorrhœa for which no satisfactory cause is found. If cells with double chromatin bodies are found, as well as cells with single bodies, it is likely that some or all of the patient's body cells contain more than two X chromosomes, and that she may be either a "super-

TABLE 4

KARYOTYPE ABNORMALITIES WHICH MAY BE ASSOCIATED WITH AMENORRHEA

Chromosome Count	Sex-Chromosome Complement	Sex Chromatin		Clinical Syndrome	References
		BUCCAL SMEAR	POLYMORPHS		
45	XO	Negative	Negative	Turner's syndrome	(a) Ford et al. 1959a (b) Jacobs and Keay 1959
45/46	XO/XX	Positive (? weakly) or negative	?	Turner's syndrome	Ford 1959
46	XY	Negative	Negative	(a) Testicular feminisation (b) Pure gonadal dysgenesis	(a) Jacobs et al. 1959c (b) Harnden and Stewart 1959
46	X+ partially deleted X	Weakly positive	Negative	Primary amenorrhea	This communication
47	XXX	Positive with double chromatin bodies	Positive	"Super-female"	(a) Jacobs et al. 1959a (b) This communication
47/45	XXX/XO	Positive with double chromatin bodies	Negative	"Super-female"/Turner syndrome mosaic	This communication

female" or a mosaic with one stem-line containing three X chromosomes, or she may have an even greater number of X chromosomes. More than three X chromosomes are theoretically possible, but, as the precise relationship between the number of X chromosomes and the number of chromatin bodies is not understood, the findings in the buccal smear cannot be predicted.

If examination of the buccal smear in a phenotypic female shows no chromatin bodies, then the patient may have either an XO or an XY constitution. Presumably an individual who is an XO/XX mosaic may show no chromatin bodies or, according to the degree of admixture of the two stem-lines, may show anything up to the normal number of such bodies. Similarly it is possible that individuals with a partial deletion of one X chromosome may show either a normal number of cells with chromatin bodies in the buccal smear or an equivocal number, or possibly none at all according to the extent of the deletion. Furthermore the data on case 2 suggest that if the deletion is between certain limiting sizes the chromatin bodies will appear unusually small.

Quite apart from their intrinsic clinical interest the data presented in this report raise more fundamental biological considerations—in particular the importance of mosaicism in human pathology and the possible genetical information to be obtained from the study of persons with partial deletions of one chromosome.

SUMMARY

Data are presented on a phenotypic female who is presumed to be an XXX/XO mosaic—i.e., she has two stem-lines of cells in her body containing 47 and 45 chromosomes with sex constitutions of XXX and XO respectively.

A phenotypic female who is presumed to have a partial deletion of one X chromosome is described.

A "super-female" who is menstruating regularly is described.

REFERENCES

Court-Brown, W. M., Jacobs, P. A., Doll, R. (1960) *Lancet, i:*160.
Davidson, W. M., Robertson Smith, D. (1954) *Brit. med. J. ii:*6.
Edwards, J. H., Harnden, D. G., Cameron, A. H., Crosse, V. M., Wolff, O. N. (1960) *Lancet, i:*787.

Ford, C. E. (1959) at conference on Human Chromosomes, King's College Hospital, London.

—— Jacobs, P. A., Lajtha, L. G. (1958) *Nature, Lond. 181*:1565.

—— Jones, K. W., Polani, P. E., Almeida, J. C., Briggs, J. H. (1959a) *Lancet, i*:711.

—— Polani, P. E., Briggs, J. H., Bishop, P. M. F. (1959b) *Nature, Lond. 183*:1030.

Harnden, D. G. (1960) *Brit. J. exp. Path. 41*:31.

—— Stewart, J. S. S. (1959) *Brit. med. J. ii*:1285.

Hungerford, D. A., Donnelly, A. J., Nowell, P. C., Beck, S. (1959) *Amer. J. hum. Genet. 11*:215.

Jacobs, P. A., Baikie, A. G., Court Brown, W. M., MacGregor, T. N., Maclean, N., Harnden, D. G. (1959a) *Lancet ii*:423.

—— Strong, J. A. (1959b) *ibid. i*:710.

—— Forrest, H., Roy, J. R., Stewart, J. S. S., Lennox, B. (1959c) *ibid. ii*:591.

—— Keay, A. W. (1959) *ibid. ii*:732.

Lejeune, J., Gautier, M., Turpin, R. (1959) *C. R. Acad. Sci., Paris, 248*:602.

Stewart, J. S. S. (1960) *Acta endocr., Copenhagen, 33*:89.

48

CHROMOSOME TRANSLOCATION AS A CAUSE OF FAMILIAL MONGOLISM

C. O. Carter, B.M. Oxon., M.R.C.P., J. L. Hamerton, B. Sc. Lond.,
P. E. Polani, M.D. Pisa, M.R.C.P., A. Gunalp, M.D. Ankara, and
S. D. V. Weller, M.D. Lond., M.R.C.P.

ARLIER this year Polani et al. (1960), examining the chromosomes of three mongols born to young mothers, found that
one of these mongols had 46, not 47 chromosomes. There were
two chromosomes of pair 21, but one member of pair 14 (Standard
System) was of unusual length and morphology. They postulated
that this abnormal chromosome had arisen by means of a translocation between a chromosome 14 and a chromosome 21, and
noted that this would provide a mechanism for familial mongolism. Subsequent examination of peripheral blood has shown
(J. L. H.) that, in fact, the parents had a normal chromosome
complement; therefore the translocation and non-disjunction in
this patient must have occurred during gametogenesis in one of
the parents or, less likely, in the embryogenesis of the child.

A large number of families of mongol patients attending The
Hospital for Sick Children have been followed for up to ten years,
and one of these families was felt to be the most suitable for
testing the hypothesis that translocation might provide a mechanism by which some apparently normal parents are predisposed
to have mongol children.

INVESTIGATION

The Family

A pedigree of this family is shown in fig. 1.

Reprinted from *The Lancet*, September 24, 1960, pp. 678-680.

We should like to thank the members of the staff of The Hospital for Sick
Children for access to their patients, Dr. J. A. Fraser Roberts for advice and encouragement, and Miss V. M. McGuire, Miss A. Horsley, and Mr. S. L. Yapp for
their skilled technical assistance.

The index patient M.A. (III.2 in the pedigree) attended The Hospital for Sick Children in 1952 at the age of one year and the diagnosis of mongolism was confirmed. In addition to the usual facial stigmata (see fig. 2), his palm prints were characteristic of mongolism [summed a t d angles at the age of 9 years are 166° the mean in normal children being 88° ± 16° (Penrose 1954)].

This boy is an imbecile who now attends an occupation centre.

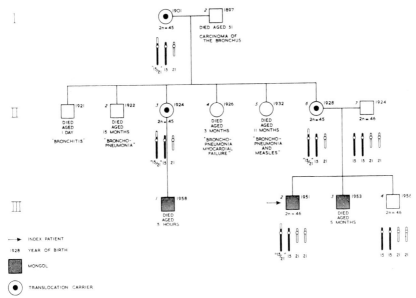

Fig. 1. Family tree showing mongol children and translocation "carriers."

He has no other congenital malformations. In November 1953, M.A.'s mother (II.6) had another boy (III.3) who died of congenital heart disease at the age of 5 months. He, too, was a mongol. The third boy (III.4), born in October, 1958, is normal. In September, 1958, M.A.'s maternal aunt (II.3) had her first and only child, a boy (III.1) who died at the age of 5 hours, probably of birth injury, and was also noted to be a mongol. Neither M.A.'s mother nor his aunt have had any miscarriages. Both these women and their mother (I.1) were of at least average intelligence and fitness.

M.A. had two maternal uncles (II.1 and 2) and two further maternal aunts (II.4 and 5), all of whom had died in infancy of bronchitis or bronchopneumonia. The death certificates of these children do not mention mongolism, but this does not exclude the possibility that one or more of them were mongols.

The Findings

The chromosome analyses were made from short-term cultures of peripheral blood by a modification of the technique of Hunger-

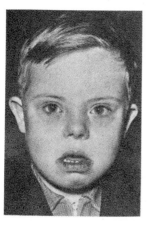

ford et al. (1959). The Standard System (Denver) of nomenclature (*Lancet* 1960) was used. The chromosomes of M.A., his surviving brother, his mother, father, maternal aunt, and maternal grandmother were examined. The counts are summarised in the table.

M.A.'s count was 46. Those of his mother, maternal aunt, and maternal grandmother were all 45. His father's (II.7) and brother's counts were 46, with normal chromosomes. M.A.'s karyotype is shown in fig. 3.

Fig. 2. The index patient.

This shows only 4 chromosomes in the 21-22 group plus one Y chromosome, as in a normal male, whilst in the 13-15 group 5 instead of 6 chromosomes were observed. In group 6-12, an additional submetacentric chromosome was seen.

CHROMOSOME-COUNTS IN THE INDEX PATIENT (M.A.) AND HIS RELATIVES

	Diploid Number	Chromosome-Counts				Total Cells	No. of Cells Analysed
		<45	45	46	47		
M.A. (III.2)	46†	3*	..	25	2*	30	(6)
Mother (II.6)	45†	9*	27	3*	..	39	(6)
Mother's mother (I.1) ..	45†	3*	8	..	..	11	(2)
Mother's sister (II.3) ...	45†	8*	7	..	..	15	(3)
Father	46	..	..	15	..	15	(3)
Brother	46	17*	6*	20	..	43	(6)

† Translocation present.　　* Cells broken.

The karyotype in M.A.'s mother (fig. 4) was identical with that of her sister and her mother.

This shows only 3 chromosomes instead of 4 in the 21-22 group,

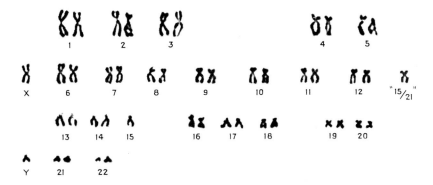

Fig. 3. Analysis of the karyotype of the index patient (iii.2)—Standard System.

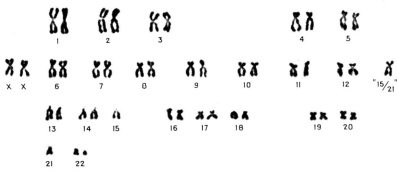

Fig. 4. Analysis of the karyotype of the mother (ii.6)—Standard System.

5 instead of 6 in the 13-15, and an additional chromosome in the group 6-12 similar to that seen in M.A.

The 6-12 groups of the four individuals are shown together in fig. 5, and the similarity of the additional chromosome in this group in each individual may be seen.

Interpretation

Because mongolism appears to require the presence in triplicate of the genetic material of chromosome 21, it is logical to assume that this is also the case in patient M.A. We therefore consider that the additional chromosome in the 6-12 group in all four individuals has arisen by means of a translocation, probably between chromosomes 21 and 15, at least as early as gametogenesis in the maternal grandmother's parents, or the embryogenesis of this grandmother. Examination of the additional chromosomes suggests that it is the same chromosome being inherited throughout the family.

The suggested mechanism for the translocation and its inheritance is shown in fig. 6.

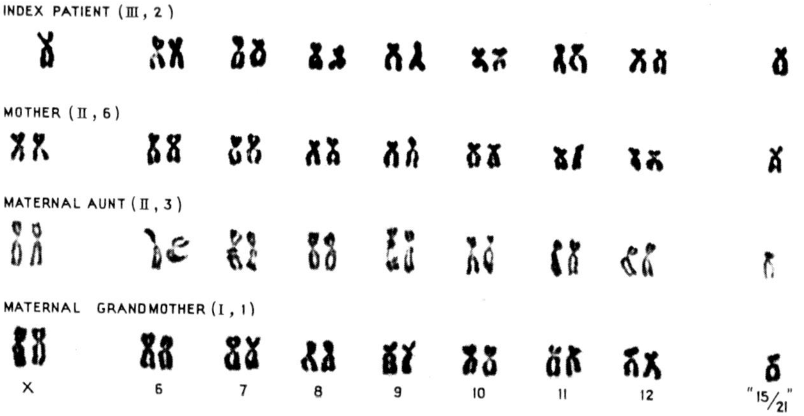

Fig. 5. Comparison of the 6-12 groups in the four members of the family carrying the translocation.

It is, however, by no means certain that the four possible types of gamete will occur with equal frequency. This will be greatly influenced by the pairing behaviour of the translocation at meiosis.

DISCUSSION

The clinical interest of the finding of "carriers" of a translocation, which may cause mongolism, is that it may make it possible both to be more precise in advising parents on the risks of their having a second mongol child, and to detect relatives of mongols who themselves have high risks of having mongol children. Experience at The Hospital for Sick Children has shown that the risk of parents having a second mongol child is almost certainly raised above the random risk, especially at the younger maternal ages. It has not, however, been possible to show whether this is in most part an overall increase, or whether there are two groups

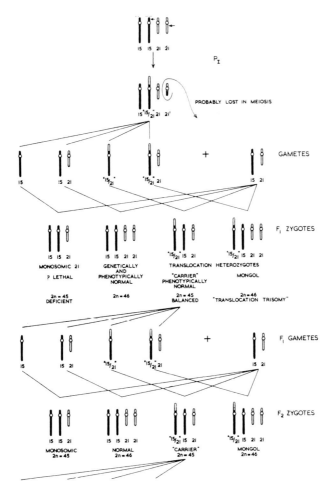

Fig. 6. Diagram to show the origin of the suggested translocation and its mode of inheritance.

of mongols, a majority with little, if any, increase in the risk of recurrence, and a minority with a relatively high risk. It is now important to discover, by systematic study, the extent to which the rare occasions in which one or other parent has an abnormal karyotype may account for the overall increased risk of recurrence of mongolism.

It is, perhaps, surprising that the "carriers" of the translocation are apparently normal. They have, however, presumably lost very little chromosome material, only part of the two short arms of chromosomes 15 and 21.

There are two other instances in which the parent of a mongol child has been found to have an abnormal karyotype. In the first family (Fraccaro et al. 1960) the father is reported to have had 47 chromosomes; it is difficult to interpret the situation in this family. In the other family the situation appears from the preliminary communication (Penrose et al. 1960) to be very similar to that in the present family.

It is noteworthy that all the examples of presumed chromosome translocation that have been reported in man involve the acrocentric chromosomes, which tend to lie close together at interphase in association with the nucleolus (Polani et al. 1960).

SUMMARY

A family is described in which a translocation, probably between chromosomes 15 and 21, occurring at least as early as the embryogenesis of the grandmother, was responsible for mongolism in three of her grandchildren and possibly one or more of her children. Further studies are needed to see what proportion of the overall increased risk of recurrence of mongolism in later siblings is due to such recognisably abnormal karyotypes in a small minority of the parents of mongol children.

REFERENCES

Fraccaro, M., Kaijser, K., Lindsten, J. (1960) *Lancet*, i:724.
Hungerford, D. A., Donnelly, A. J., Nowell, P. C., Beck, S. (1959) *Amer. J. hum. Genet.* 11:215.
Lancet (1960) i:1063.
Penrose, L. S. (1954) *Ann. hum. Genet.* 19:10.
———— Ellis, J. R., Delhanty, J. (1960). *Lancet*, ii:409.
Polani, P. E., Briggs, J. H., Ford, C. E., Clarke, C. M., Berg, J. M. (1960) *ibid.* i:721.

49

A NEW TYPE OF CHROMOSOMAL ABNORMALITY IN GONADAL DYSGENESIS

M. Fraccaro, D. Ikkos, J. Lindsten, R. Luft, and K. Kaijser

WE have studied the somatic chromosome complement of three female patients having primary amenorrhœa, infantilism, short neck, and undeveloped secondary sexual characteristics. They had elevated levels of urinary gonadotrophins and low levels of urinary œstrogens. Laparotomy in two of them revealed an undeveloped uterus and "streaks" of rudimentary tissue at the site of the gonads. The three patients were sex-chromatin positive and their bone-marrow and skin cells cultured in vitro yielded counts of 46 chromosomes.

Two of the patients were independently selected in two different clinics, as Turner's syndrome, one in March, 1959, and the other in January, 1960. The third one was selected under the influence of the findings of the other two because she was a sex-chromatin positive, "atypical" Turner.

Detailed study of the karyotypes revealed in all of them the presence of only one X chromosome and of a long metacentric, chromosome which, on morphological evidence, was similar to the chromosomes of pair no. 3.

The most likely interpretation of these karyotypes is that the abnormal chromosome is an "iso-chromosome" for the long arm of one X chromosome. The patients are therefore formally trisomic for the long arms and monosomic for the short arm of X, but two of the long arms must be, by the definition of iso-chromosomes,[1] genetically homologous. Other possible interpretations include duplication of part of one of the X chromosomes, translocation of other chromosomal material on to one X chromosome, and trisomy for chromosome no. 3 and monosomy for the X chromosome.

While we are preparing a detailed description of these cases, we wish to call attention to the fact that analysis of the karyotype may reveal peculiar cytological situations which are relevant to a

Reprinted from *The Lancet*, November 19, 1960, p. 1144.

better understanding of gonadal dysgenesis as shown by the case reported by Jacobs et al.,[2] and by those mentioned here.

REFERENCES

1. Darlington, C. D. *J. Genet.* 1940, 39:351.
2. Jacobs, P. A., Harnden, D. G., Court Brown, W. M., Goldstein, J., Close, H. G., MacGregor, T. N., Maclean, N., Strong, J. A. *Lancet,* 1960, i:1213.

50

CHROMOSOMAL TRISOMY ASSOCIATED WITH THE STURGE-WEBER SYNDROME

M. D. HAYWARD, B.Sc. Wales, and B. D. BOWER, M.D. Birm., M.R.C.P., D.C.H.

A SURPRISINGLY large number of aneuploid conditions have been reported in man in association with particular congenital defects. This applies to both the autosomes and the sex chromosomes. The known cases of sex-chromosome aneuploidy have been recently summarised by Jacobs et al. (1960) and Hayward (1960). These include monosomic and polysomic conditions. All known autosomal aneuploids are trisomics.

The first such occurrence was shown in conjunction with mongolism (Lejeune et al. 1959, Jacobs et al. 1959, Böök et al. 1959); more recently two additional cases have been described in children exhibiting multiple congenital defects (Edwards et al. 1960, Patau et al. 1960). Perhaps the most interesting report on autosomal trisomy is that of Fraccaro et al. (1960) who have found a trisomic condition in the apparently normal father of a mongol child. These four examples are all trisomic for different autosomes (see table). Our case provides a fifth distinct human male trisomic—in this instance associated with the Sturge-Weber syndrome.

CASE REPORT

The patient, a boy aged 3 years 10 months, has lived in a residential nursery since the age of 14 months. His mother died, aged 32, shortly after his birth. His father and two siblings are healthy

Reprinted from *The Lancet,* October 15, 1960, pp. 844-846.

Our thanks are due to Prof. K. Mather, Prof. D. V. Hubble, Dr. B. John, and Dr. O. H. Wolff, for helpful suggestions; to Dr. K. B. Rogers for performing the bone-marrow biopsies; to Dr. Roy Astley for the radiological investigation; to Prof. L. S. Penrose for his opinion on the palm-prints; and to Dr. C. C. H. Chavasse for cooperating in the investigation of the patient.

and there is no relevant family history. Before his admission to the
nursery he had frequent convulsions but since then phenobarbi-
tone has completely controlled them. Gross mental retardation was
present then and little progress has occurred since.

Present state.—His general physical development is average
(weight 35 lb. (16 kg.), height 38 in. (97 cm.) but his head circumference is only 18¾ in. (48 cm.)). He shows gross mental retardation with hyperkinesis: locomotor abilities are at 12-month
level on the Griffiths scale, while other abilities (personal-social,

A SUMMARY OF HUMAN AUTOSOMAL TRISOMIC CONDITIONS

Clinical Condition	Sex	Trisomic Chromosome No.	Reference
Mongolism	M & F	21	Lejeune et al. (1959), Böök et al. (1959), Jacobs et al. (1959)
Cerebral defect, simian creases, trigger thumbs, polydactyly, capillary hæmangiomata, hare-lip, cleft palate, apparent anophthalmia, heart defect	F	15	Patau et al. (1960)
Peculiar facies, webbed neck, heart defect, neonatal hepatitis	F	17	Edwards et al. (1960)
Normal	M	19	Fraccaro et al. (1960)
Sturge-Weber syndrome	M	22	Present paper

hearing and speech, eye and hand, and performance) are at 6-
month level. A "port-wine" nævus covers the distribution of the
ophthalmic and maxillary divisions of the right trigeminal nerve.
There is buphthalmos of the right eye (iridencleisis has been performed). His face is not suggestive of mongolism (fig. 1). Mild left
hemiparesis is present; the left calf is thinner than the right, the
left arm is used less well than the right, and the left-arm reflexes
are exaggerated.

Investigations

X-ray of skull.—The skull is smaller on the right. There is extensive calcification in the right parieto-occipital region, with the
gyral distribution typical of the Sturge-Weber syndrome (fig. 2).
Electroencephalogram (after quinalbarbitone).—There is
much less barbiturate fast activity over the right posterior region
than over the left, and the slow sleep-activity is also less marked

over the right parieto-occipital region than over the corresponding region on the left.

X-ray of pevis.—The iliac index is 76° (the normal range for male babies is 68°–97° [Caffey and Ross 1956]). It is not known whether this finding has any significance after the 1st year of life; but, if the method is applicable later in life, the result in this child is evidence against mongolism (Dr. Roy Astley).

X-ray of heart.—Within normal limits.

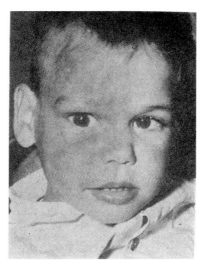

Fig. 1. The patient, showing the extent of the facial nævus and the right buphthalmos.

Analysis of prints of palms, soles, and fingers.—Not suggestive of mongolism (Prof. L. S. Penrose).

CYTOLOGICAL OBSERVATIONS

Iliac-marrow punctures were taken from both sides of the body and short-term cultures established. These were subsequently treated by a modification of the standard method described by Ford et al. (1958). Details of this may be found in Hayward (1960).

Chromosome counts on unbroken well-spread cells were:

	Number of Cells Counted	
Chromosome Number	RIGHT SIDE	LEFT SIDE
47	58	30
Polyploid	5	1
Total	63	31

Thirty-six cells were selected for detailed analysis and in these the sex-chromosome constitution was XY. In all these cells six small acrocentric chromosomes were found as compared with five in the normal male (fig. 3). Identification of the extra chromosome was difficult by size alone because of the similarity between pairs 21 and 22. It depended, therefore, on the presence or ab-

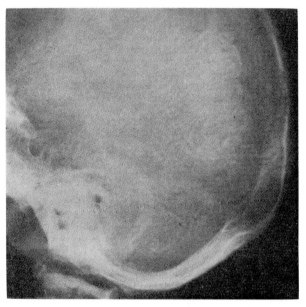

Fig. 2. Lateral radiograph of the skull, showing the "double-contoured" gyral calcification typical of the syndrome.

sence of satellites. In none of the cells were there more than two of the small acrocentric chromosomes with satellites. This means that the extra chromosome is probably no. 22 (fig. 4), and not no. 21, the trisomy of which is associated with mongolism (Lejeune et al. 1959). This is supported by the clinical data, for none of the signs are those of mongolism.

DISCUSSION

This is a typical case of the Sturge-Weber syndrome, with no other evident lesions. It is at first sight surprising that an apparently localised, although gross, disorder should be associated with an additional autosomal chromosome, for with one exception the other patients in whom autosomal trisomy has been found have had widespread abnormalities involving several systems (see table). There is, however, pathological evidence that the abnormalities in this syndrome are not as localised as they appear to be. Wohlwill and Yakovlev (1957) in a careful histological study of four cases, demonstrated angiomata in the lung, ovary, intestine, pituitary, choroid plexus, and the meninges, as well as

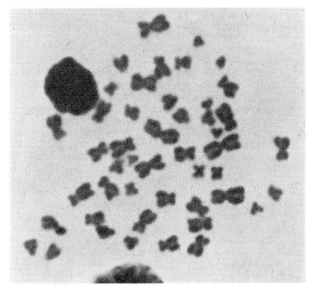

Fig. 3. Mitotic metaphase in a bone-marrow cell. 2n=47. (×2500.)

in the skin of the face. In addition there were heterotopic groups of nerve-cells, scattered throughout the nervous system, apparently the result of failure of migration, and these groups of cells were unrelated to the angiomatous malformations. The gasserian ganglion on the side of the facial nævus was abnormal in two cases. There is, therefore, evidence of widespread dysplasia, affecting both ectodermal and mesodermal structures. Nevertheless the syndrome does not exhibit the wide spectrum of abnormalities seen in mongolism, and in the cases of Edwards et al (1960) and Patau et al. (1960). It is of interest that the case described by Patau et al. had multiple hæmangiomata, and it was this which prompted chromosome-study of our patient. Angiomatous malformations are associated with artificially induced aneuploids in salamanders (Fankhauser and Humphrey 1950).

There are few recorded instances of autosomal polysomy in animals. Most of these occur in *Drosophila spp.*: thus in *D. Melanogaster,* individuals monosomic (haplo 4) and trisomic (triplo 4) for chromosome no. 4 are hardly distinguishable from normal individuals. Interestingly, however, flies tetrasomic for chromosome no. 4 are inviable. Viable autosomal trisomics also occur in *D. subobscura* (Philip et al. 1944). All of these conditions are known

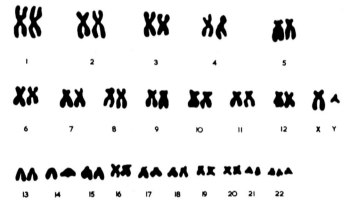

Fig. 4. Chromosomes arranged in pairs showing the trisomy for no. 22.

only from flies bred in culture. Callen (1941) has described a single individual, trisomic for the third largest autosome, in a wild population of *Mecostethus grossus.*

As polysomic types are apparently rare, the recent discoveries of at least five human autosomal trisomics may seem surprising. It would, however, be even more surprising if this reflected a genuine difference between man and other animals. The more probable reason for this discrepancy is that in man studies have been confined to phenotypically abnormal specimens selected from large populations. No comparable search has been made in other species. Indeed it is possible that in species other than man these polysomic individuals would not survive to a stage where such an examination could be carried out.

In any organism trisomy results from chromosome nondisjunction. This may occur at mitosis or meiosis.

As far as the results of mitotic non-disjunction are concerned one can distinguish that type which occurs during early cleavage divisions of a developing embryo from that arising during the premeiotic mitosis in an adult body. The first type should lead to somatic autosomal mosaicism: the second to the production of aneuploid meiotic cells whose behaviour parallels that of cells in which non-disjunction occurs during meiosis. In both cases the final result is the same—namely, the formation of unbalanced gametes. The possible causal mechanisms which determine mitotic non-disjunction have recently been dealt with in detail elsewhere (Hayward 1960).

Non-disjunction at meiosis may occur during first or second division. Since meiosis II is effectively a haploid mitosis the mechanism and consequences of non-disjunction during this division are essentially mitotic in character and, presumably, similar causal mechanisms operate.

Meiotic non-disjunction at the first division may depend upon three conditions the consequences of which are indistinguishable: (1) failure of bivalent formation; (2) failure of the homologues of a normal bivalent to disjoin at first anaphase; and (3) irregular segregation of the components of a multivalent in a numerical hybrid or of a multiple configuration in an interchange hybrid (cf. Darlington 1937).

(2) and (3) require no further consideration. But failure of bivalent formation may arise in one of three ways: (a) as a result of non-homology between the chromosome pair or pairs concerned; (b) as a result of asynapsis (i.e., failure of pachytene pairing between completely homologous chromosomes); or (c) as a result of desynapsis (i.e., failure of chiasma formation following successful pachytene pairing).

The first of these necessarily depends upon genic properties but the cause of both (b) and (c) may be either genotypic or environmental (cf. Rees 1960); this is also true of both bivalent non-disjunction and irregular segregation at first anaphase.

Which of these causal mechanisms determines the observed results of non-disjunction in our patient is not clear. Nor as yet can we postulate a direct causal relationship between the trisomic condition found and the distinctive phenotype of the Sturge-Weber syndrome. This uncertainty is by no means confined to our case; the same consideration may be applied without qualification to the trisomics described by Edwards et al. (1960) and Patau et al. (1960). In both of these cases it has still to be unambigously demonstrated that autosomal trisomy is the cause rather than an accompanying phenotypic effect expressed at the nuclear level, or a chance association of events. Indeed only in mongolism is it even possible to suggest a relationship between cause and effect; since no normal complement has yet been found in a mongol, it may be reasonably accepted that the abnormal chromosome condition is causal in the production of the defective phenotype. This whole problem of interpretation in such cases is made more difficult by the discovery of a clinically normal male, trisomic for the 19th autosome, by Fraccaro et al. (1960). Only further studies can clarify the situation in respect of autosomal polysomy in man.

SUMMARY

A case of autosomal trisomy associated with the Sturge-Weber syndrome is described. The extra chromosome is cytomorphologically comparable to the five smallest acrocentric chromosomes found in normal males. Reasons are given for its probably identification as no. 22.

The implications of the trisomy and its relation to the abnormal phenotype are discussed.

REFERENCES

Böök, J. A., Fraccaro, M., Lindsten, G. (1959) *Acta pædiat. Stockh.* 48:453.
Callan, H. G. (1941) *J. Hered.* 32:296.
Caffey, J., Ross, S. (1956) *Pediatrics, N.Y.* 17:642.
Darlington, C. D. (1937) Recent Advances in Cytology. London.
Edwards, J. H., Harnden, D. G., Cameron, A. H., Crosse, V. M., Wolff, O. H. (1960) *Lancet i*:787.
Fankhauser, G., Humphrey, R. R. (1950) *J. exp. Zool.* 115:207.
Ford, C. E., Jacobs, P. A., Lajtha, L. G. (1958) *Nature, Lond.* 181:1565.
Fraccaro, M., Kaijser, K., Lindsten, G. (1960) *Lancet i*:724.
Hayward, M. D. (1960) *Heredity* (in the press).
Jacobs, P. A., Baikie, A. G., Court-Brown, W. M., Strong, J. A. (1959) *Lancet i*:710.
——— Harnden, D. G., Court-Brown, W. M., Goldstein, G., Close, H. G., Macgregor, T. N., Maclean, N., Strong, J. A. (1960) *ibid. i*:1213.
Lejeune, J., Gautier, M., Turpin, R. (1959) *C. R. Acad. Sci.* 248:602.

Patau, K., Smith, D. W., Therman, E., Inhoorn, S. L., Wagner, H. P. (1960) *Lancet* i:790.

Philip, U., Rendel, J. M., Spurway, H., Haldane, J. B. S. (1944) *Nature, Lond.* 154:260.

Rees, H. (1960) *Bot. Rev.* (in the press).

Wohlwill, F. J., Yakovlev, P. I. (1957) *J. Neuropath.* 16:341.

51

A POSSIBLE SPECIFIC CHROMOSOME ABNORMALITY IN HUMAN CHRONIC MYELOID LEUKAEMIA

A. G. Baikie, W. M. Court-Brown, Karin E. Buckton, D. G. Harnden, Patricia A. Jacobs, and Ishbel M. Tough

THREE reports have been published which indicate that in some cases of acute leukaemia in man there are abnormalities of both number and morphology of the chromosomes in the leukaemic cells.[1, 2, 3] However, no consistent abnormality has yet been found which can be linked to a specific cytological type of acute leukaemia. Baikie and his colleagues[2] also reported that they were unable to detect any chromosome abnormality in bone marrow preparations from a number of cases of chronic myeloid and chronic lymphatic leukaemia. Nevertheless it was said at the time that the standard of the preparations was such that the possibility of a small chromosomal lesion could not be excluded. In recent months considerable developments have occurred as a result of the utilisation of the technique of Hungerford and his colleagues[4] for the culture of the leucocyte component of the peripheral blood. It is now recognised that chromosome preparations made from such cultures are of an appreciably better quality than those made from bone marrow. Using this blood culture technique Nowell and Hungerford[5] noted the presence of a minute chromosome in dividing cells from the peripheral blood of two male patients with chronic myeloid leukaemia, and they regarded this as an unusually small Y chromosome. At about the same time as these observations were published, we noted the presence, in blood culture preparations, of a similar small chromosome in two female patients with chronic myeloid leukaemia. It was apparent, therefore, that if the same abnormal chromosome was being viewed by both groups of work-

Reprinted from *Nature*, Vol. 188, p. 1165, 1960.

ers, then the abnormality must involve an autosome and not the Y chromosome. In the light of these findings we re-examined all our material from cases of chronic myeloid leukaemia, as well as studying two fresh cases of the disease. As a result of this we are satisfied that the presence of an unusually small autosome (Fig. 1) is a characteristic feature of many cases of chronic myeloid leukaemia.

Altogether we have studied the chromosomes in blood cultures from 12 patients (4 males and 8 females) suffering from chronic myeloid leukaemia. Among these were two patients who had had no previous treatment for their disease, either by x-irradiation or by chemotherapy. The remaining 10 patients had all been treated by radiotherapy sometime prior to our studies. The small chromosome was noted in preparations from eight patients inclusive of both the untreated patients. Included among the 12 patients were three in a terminal acute transformation of the disease, and the relevant chromosome was noted in cultures from one of these. Marrow preparations have been studied from 10 patients, of whom four were males, and the small chromosome has been clearly seen in three patients, all three being fresh untreated cases. These three latter patients include two of those in whom the chromosome was also seen in blood culture. The remaining 7 marrow preparations were of too poor a quality for us to be certain as to whether the abnormality was present or not. In no case has the abnormally small chromosome been seen in every cell. The frequency of its occurrence has varied from $1/7$ cells to $48/50$ cells studied, and in all patients some normal euploid cells have been seen.

In addition to re-examining our material from cases of chronic myeloid leukaemia, we have also re-examined our preparations from the peripheral blood of individuals with apparently normal karyotypes, and our marrow and blood preparations from patients with acute leukaemia in which we had thought no chromosome abnormality to be present. Blood preparations were available from 90 individuals with apparently normal karyotypes and 7 were selected at random, to which were added 5 preparations from cases of chronic myeloid leukaemia showing the small chromosome. These 12 preparations were then submitted to an independent observer who was ignorant of the patients involved. The 5 preparations with the small chromosome were readily identified, and in none of the 7 control preparations was the chromosome thought to be present. We have also reviewed marrow preparations from 11 patients and blood preparations from 6 patients with acute leukaemia having an apparently normal karyotype, and we have no evidence in these of the unusually small chromosome. Finally we have studied the blood cultures from 5 cases of mongolism associated with acute leukaemia and found no abnormality apart from the classical mongol karyotype which is presumed to be trisomy for autosome 21.

Before discussing the possible significance of these findings, the question of radiation exposure has to be considered as chronic myeloid leukaemia is increased in frequency in heavily irradiated populations.[6, 7] We have not been able to check with any certainty the histories of diagnostic x-ray exposure of our patients prior to the development of their leukaemic state. Two patients, however, have histories of radiotherapeutic exposure for conditions quite unrelated to leukaemia. One patient, a woman, was treated in December, 1953, for a simple papilloma of the bladder by means of a radium implant. An area 3 x 3 cms. on the base of the bladder was given a dose of 6,000 rads over a period of 146 hours. This patient was diagnosed as having chronic myeloid leukaemia in May 1958, and the unusually small chromosome has been identified in cultured blood cells. The second patient, a male, was treated for ankylosing spondylitis between February and April 1955, a total dose of 1,500 rads being given to the skin over the whole length of the spine and the sacro-iliac joints. A diagnosis of chronic myeloid leukaemia was made in March 1956. Only marrow cultures were available from this man and their quality was such that we could not be certain whether the small chromosome was present or not. On the basis of our knowledge of the distribution of the latent periods of radiation-induced leukaemias between radiation exposure and diagnosis, we cannot exclude the possibility that the first case was radiation-induced; it seems, however, unlikely that this was so in the second case, as the length of the latent period following a single heavy exposure usually lies between 4 and 8 years, and the increased frequency of leukaemia is not noted until the second post exposure year.

It now seems certain that the unusually small chromosome is one of the members of the two pairs of small acrocentric chromosomes numbered 21 and 22 in the Denver Classification. The most reasonable explanation for its small size is the occurrence of a deletion. The fact that we have in every preparation found some normal euploid cells suggest that the error does not occur in all the body cells and presumably is confined to cells from the bone marrow. We are at present undertaking the investigation of the chromosomes from skin culture preparations to help to clarify this point. We have not noted the unusually small chromosome in any other person that we have studied. Carter and his colleagues,[8] however, have published ideograms of the chromosomes from blood cultures made from a mother and her mongol son, and in both these ideograms an unusually small chromosome appears to be present. The mother has a diploid number of 45, and is considered to have a translocation involving autosomes nos. 15 and 21, while the son has the full complement of small acrocentrics in addition to the same translocation, and is presumed to be effectively trisomic for no. 21.

It has been established that mongols have a heightened probability of developing acute leukaemia,[9, 10, 11, 12, 13] but not apparently of developing chronic myeloid leukaemia. From unpublished observations on death certificate data (Court-Brown and Doll) it does not appear that this increased liability relates to any specific cytological type of acute leukaemia, although the unreliability of such data must be borne in mind. It is also known that in most mongols there is a morphological abnormality of the polymorphonuclear leucocytes which takes the form of a deficiency in nuclear lobulation.[14] It is not unreasonable, therefore, to suggest that the autosome involved in mongolism may possess a locus or loci concerned with some aspect of the control of leucopoiesis. Our present findings in relation to chronic myeloid leukaemia indicate that in many cases of this disease there appears to be a deletion involving either autosome 21 or 22. In the meantime it would seem not unreasonable to adopt the working hypothesis that the same autosome is involved in many cases of chronic myeloid leukaemia and in mongolism.

REFERENCES

1. Ford, C. E., Jacobs, P. A., and Lajtha, L. G., *Nature, 181*:1565 (1958).
2. Baikie, A. G., Court-Brown, W. M., Jacobs, P. A., and Milne, J. S., *Lancet, 2*:425 (1959).
3. Ford, C. E., *Proc. R. Soc. Med., 53*:491 (1960).
4. Hungerford, D. A., Donnelly, A. J., Nowell, P. C., and Bock, S., *Amer. J. hum. Genet., 11*:215 (1959).
5. Nowell, P. C., and Hungerford, D. A., *J. nat. Cancer Inst., 25*:85 (1960).
6. Court-Brown, W. M., and Doll, R., *Spec. Rep. Ser. med. Res. Coun., Lond.,* No. 295. (1959).
7. Heyssel, R., Brill, A. B., Woodbury, L. A., Nishimura, E. T., Ghose, T., Hoshino, T., and Yamasaki, M., *Blood, 15*:313 (1960).
8. Carter, C. O., Hamerton, J. L., Polani, P. E., Gunalp, A., and Weller, D. V., *Lancet, 2*:678 (1960).
9. Carter, C. O., *Brit. med. J., 2*:993 (1956).
10. Carter, C. O., *J. ment. Defic. Res., 2*:64 (1958).
11. Krivit, W., and Good, R. A., *A.M.A. J. Dis. Child., 91*:218 (1956).
12. Merrit, D. H., and Harris, J. S., *A.M.A. J. Dis. Child., 91*:218 (1956).
13. Stewart, A., Webb, J., and Hewitt, D., *Brit. med. J., 2*:1495 (1958).
14. Mittwoch, U., *J. ment. Defic. Res., 2*:75 (1958).

52

GENETIC AND POSTGENETIC
SEX DETERMINATION

E. Witschi

RECENT discoveries in the field of human sexuality are reviv-
ing the interest in the mechanisms which bring about male
and female differentiation. As in the discussions which at the beginning of the century followed the discoveries of sex chromosomes and of genetic mechanisms of sex differentiation, there
appears again a danger of misunderstanding the actual significance of the genetic factor. Even in organisms that have not been
available for analysis by conventional heterozygoty methods, it
must be assumed that sex morphology and physiology are based
in an essential way on genetic constitution. Thus, in the hermaphrodite freshwater snail *Valvata* (Fig. 1 a) the formation
of ovarian cortex and testicular medulla certainly is hereditarily
arranged for. However, when in the course of embryonic development cortical and medullary territories become established, the
differentiation is not brought about by any sort of genic segregation. Primary germ cells become eggs or sperms according to
their location in one or the other territory. Obviously, such a hermaphrodite may become a male by temporary or permanent in-
activation of the cortex, or a female by deficiency of the medulla.
Gonochorism of this type is widespread among invertebrates. For
instance, in *Crepidula* testicular maturation occurs during the
early phase of life; the small young snail is a male. Later testicles
and male secondary sex characters regress, following which ovarian development changes the growing individual into a female.
Predominance of testicular or ovarian induction seems to be determined mainly by internal milieu conditions correlated with

Reprinted from *Experientia*, Vol. XVI/6, 1960, pp. 274-278.
Supported by grants from the U. S. National Science Foundation and from the
U. S. Public Health Service.

511

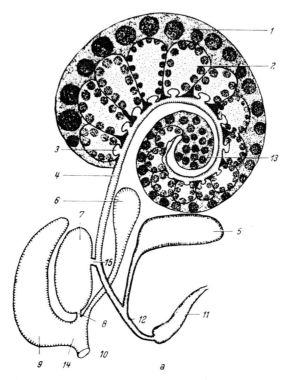

Fig. 1. Sexual differentiation induced by factors of internal milieu. C. L. Furrow, Z. *Zellf. mikr. Anat.* 22:282 (1935). *a* Hermaphrodite sex organs of the snail *Valvata tricarinata* (after Furrow); 1. cortex (female), 2. medulla (male), 3. atrium. 4. hermaphrodite duct, 5. prostate gland, 6. albumen gland, 7. bursa copulatrix, 8. oviduct, 9. shell gland, 10. female genital aperture, 11. penis, 12. sperm duct (vas deferens), 13. apical zone, 14. vestibule, 15. oviduct.

aging processes. In other invertebrates and even in some marine fishes external factors, such as ectoparasitism on an adult female as against unattached larval development, decide over realization of male or female differentiation.

While in these primitive hermaphrodites and gonochorists activation and suppression of inherent potentialities of sexual differentiation depend on a variety of milieu conditions, in other instances the same decisions are under genetic control. In the typically monoecious (hermaphrodite) maize plant two recessive gene

mutations were found which suppress, one the formation of female ears (ba ba), the other the differentiation of male flowers
(ts ts). By proper combination of stock, homozygous, and heterozygous for these two mutations, a self-perpetuating dioecious
(gonochoristic) maize can be synthesized. Evidently this case is
not a replica of the usual course of evolution of genetic sex de-

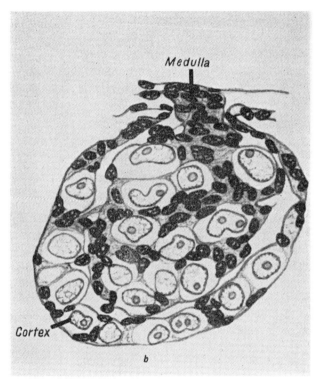

Fig. 1. *b* Cross section of amphibian gonad immediately before sexual
differentiation.

termination; however, it serves to demonstrate that gene mutations bearing on the development of reproductive organs may also
become factors of hereditary sex determination.

The comparative study of mechanisms of genetic sex determination in tetrapod vertebrates leads to the conclusion that their origin dates back to the Jurassic period, an estimated 150 million
years ago (Witschi[1]). It is safe to assume that evolution started

with a number of small gene mutations, leading to conditions similar to those now existent in fishes like Xiphophorus, Oryzias, and Lebistes. It is a fascinating problem how from such beginnings the heteromorphic sex chromosomes and the sex chromatin of mammals might have derived. The near future should provide possibilities for the experimental study of the phenomena.

Unfortunately most animal species favorable for genetic analysis do not equally lend themselves for embryologic and endocrine studies. This is particularly true for *Lymantria* and *Drosophila*, which served Goldschmidt and Bridges in the establishment of their concepts of *quantitative genic balance*. In Drosophila work on translocation of pieces of chromosomes has permitted to localize feminizing factors in the X chromosome (Dobzhansky and Schultz[2]; Patterson, Stone, Bedichek[3]) and masculinizing factors in the third chromosome (Pipkin[4]). Bridges' term of "genic balance" seems to imply a direct interaction between female and male determining genes; but considering their localization in separate chromosomes this seems hardly acceptable. Goldschmidt in many of his writings suggested some interaction between gene-substances, graphically expressed as a competitive race toward gaining control of developmental processes.

The study of the tetrapod vertebrates proves that the competition is not one between genes but between the cortical and medullary inductors of sexual differentiation. Germ cells—whether of female or male genic constitution—differentiate into eggs under the influence of the cortex and into sperms under the influence of the medulla. Gonia lost outside the gonadal territory always remain sexually undifferentiated (Witschi[5-7]). The quantitative rate of early development of cortex and medulla is genetically controlled. However, decisive for the outcome of the competition between the two inductors becomes the fact that they act as a pair of antagonists, each tending to suppress the other (Witschi[8]). In summary, genic control of sex differentiation in higher vertebrates assures the prevalence of one or the other member of a pair of antagonistic inductors. The cross section Figure 1 b, through the gonad of an amphibian larva just undergoing sexual differentiation, presents a condition which, temporarily, is identical with that of the hermaphrodite gland of *Valvata*.

It shows medulla and cortex, each with a number of yet undifferentiated gonia. The relative strength of the medulla reveals that the specimen is a genetic male. Hence, germ cell development in the cortex already seems doomed.

Since now we realize that the decision on male or female differentiation actually depends on a balance of inductors rather than genes, the question arises whether a strict and necessary harmony always exists between the two systems, or whether under special

Fig. 2. Mating pair of *Xenopus*, consisting of a male (ZZ) and a sex-reversed ZZ individual now functioning as a female. The deposited and fertilized eggs are all of male (ZZ) constitution (phot. by K. Mikamo).

circumstances, genetic and postgenetic determination may become contradictory. Simple evidence of "sex reversal," that is of differentiation contrary to the genetically predetermined pattern, gives no sufficient answer unless supplemented by definite proof that the genic constitution has remained unchanged.

The most complete and extensive proof of the possibility and actual occurrence of sex reversal without genic readjustment is furnished by the case of continuous breeding of purely homozygous, male (ZZ) stock of *Xenopus laevis*. In 1950[7] the writer reported that treatment of larvae with small doses of estradiol results in complete feminization of the genetic males (193 ♀ + 0 ♂, as against 43 ♀ + 52 ♂ in control group). Breeding of sex reversed males (♀ ZZ) with fraternal males (♂ ZZ) gives entirely male offsprings (Chang and Witschi[9, 10]). However, by treating any chosen number of eggs (genetically all ZZ) with estradiol, one obtains the homozygous females for the perpetual propagation of this stock (Fig. 2). So far this experiment has been carried on through four generations. The chromosome number remains constant (36 in the diploid cells). The question of what may be the possible effects on sex chromosomes that are repeatedly carried through individuals of contrary sex expression gains interest through attempts by the author[11] and possibly

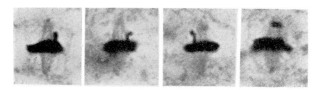

Fig. 3. Four spermatocytes from the testis of an ovariotomized hen showing precocious movement of single Z chromosome to one pole in anaphase of first meiotic division.

also Ohno[12] to explain the heterochromia of Barr's sex chromatin on the basis of genetic inactivity.

Only a few additional cases of sex reversal are adequately supplied with proof of unaltered genic and chromosomal constitution. Two adult hermaphrodite frogs, bred with normal males and females, brought evidence of female genic constitution (XX), both in the ovarian and the testicular parts of their gonads (Witschi[13]). On the other hand, well known experiments by Ponse[14] establish the genetic maleness (ZZ) of both testicular and cortical parts of the composite sex glands of male toads. Humphrey[15] by testicular implants transforms female salamanders (*Ambystoma*) into males, and progeny tests prove persistence of the female genotype (ZW). Gallien[16] in the newt caused genetic males to differentiate as females by the administration of estrogenic hormones; their constitution remained unchanged (ZZ) as revealed in breeding tests. Finally Miller[17] and Witschi[11] showed that in the hen, sex reversed by ovariotomy, spermato-genesis proceeds normally with unchanged female chromosomal arrangements (ZO, Fig. 3).

It will be noticed that five of the six presented examples refer to amphibian species; but the case of the sex reversed hen is particularly valuable because it serves as unequivocal proof that sex reversal without chromosomal compensation is possible even in the class with the most highly specialized chromosome type.

This short review leads to a number of conclusions of fundamental value. (1) The sexual differentiation of primordial germ cells is directly controlled by induction. (2) Induction may arise from external or internal milieu conditions. In gonochorists it assumes also antagonistic qualities. (3) In tetrapod vertebrates genetic mechanisms gain control of the development of the inductors and thereby, indirectly, of the sexual differentiation of the gonads. (4) However, there remain possibilities of postgenetic interference with the course of gene-initiated chain reactions. (5) In all sufficiently analyzed cases, deviations from the genetically indicated sex have been brought about by inhibition or elimination of the epistatic inductor. This may result in near or fully complete sterility. (6) In some instances the hypostatic inductor, having been relieved of its antagonist, responds with a compensatory development that may lead to partial or complete sex reversal.

It seemed desirable to review and reaffirm the evidence for postgenetic sex determination before entering on the discussion of recent discoveries bearing on abnormal sex development in man. During the last three years a number of French[19] and British[20-30] investigators have published a series of reports on unusual chromosome numbers which tend to be associated with abnormalities of various degenerative types. Attempts to interpret them in the light of the classical findings in polyploid and heteroploid *Drosophila* flies soon became complicated by the realization that the very type of genetic sex differentiation in mammals may not be the same as in Drosophila (Russell *et al.*[31]; Welshons and Russell[32]). More serious is the inconsistency of relationship between chromosomal and morphologic aberrations. In the Table the known viable chromosome combinations in man are summarized, and listed together with the physical types of their bearers.

Mongolism is the best established aberrant type. Chromosomally it consists of triplo-22 males and females (Fig. 4). Over 30 cases have been adequately studied, cytologically; however

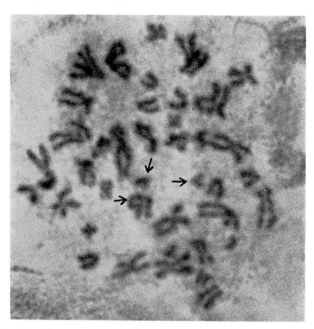

Fig. 4. Dividing bone-marrow cell of baby girl (possibly mongoloid) with 47 chromosomes; arrows point to the three chromosomes of next to smallest size; ×2600 (Zellweger, Mikamo, Witschi unpubl.).

little information is available about their sexual development and relative fertility. In other groups only 1 to 4 cases have been described (not taking into account the normal XX females and XY males). Manifestations of sexual abnormality are irregularly distributed and show no simple relationship to chromosomal pattern. An XX individual may be not only a normal female, but a Klinefelter (pseudomale), an agonadal Turner, or a true hermaphrodite. A similarly wide range is found in the XY group; it includes also the case of a woman who apparently is a completely sex reversed genetic male (Nilsson *et al.*[30]). Or, viewed from the other side, we note that the Klinefelter syndrome appears under five different chromosomal groups (XXY, XX, XXY– XX, XY, XXY + 22).

Some remarkable results were obtained from studies on the inheritance of color blindness. In three chromatin-positive Klinefelter cases (XX or XXY?) Nowakowski *et al.*[33] find evidence that both X chromosomes are derived from the mother. It is not

LIST OF VIABLE CHROMOSOMAL TYPES IN MAN WITH CORRELATED TYPES OF SEXUAL AND SOMATIC MANIFESTATIONS. BASED ON DATA BY BAIKIE,[20] FORD,[20-24] GRUMBACH,[25] HARNDEN,[26, 27] HUNGERFORD,[28] JACOBS,[29] NILSSON[30] ET AL., UNPUBLISHED MATERIAL OF ZELLWEGER, MIKAMO, AND WITSCHI, AND PERSONAL COMMUNICATIONS BY DR. C. E. FORD

| | *Chromosomes* | |
NUMBER	PATTERN M MOSAIC	*Manifestations*
47	XXX	+ Super female (1)**
47	XXY	+ Klinefelter (4)
46	XX	+ Klinefelter (1); + Turner (1)*; + True hermaphrodite (2); + *Normal female*
46-47	XXY–XX^m	+ Klinefelter (1)
46	XY	– Klinefelter (4); – Turner (1)*; Female; – *Normal male*
45	XO	– Turner (4)*; + Turner (1)*
45-46	XX – XO^m	+ Turner (3 or 4)*
47	XX + 22nd	+ Mongolism, female (5)
47	XY + 22nd	– Mongolism, male (6)
48	XXY + 22nd	+ Klinefelter and mongolism (1)
46-50	irregular	Leukemia patients

In parentheses: number of reported cases; * primary amenorrhea; ** secondary amenorrhea; + chromatin positive; – chromatin negative.

surprising that similar studies with 4 chromatin-negative Turner cases (XO or XY?) show that the single X is of maternal origin. Recently Grumbach *et al.*[25] reported on a chromatin-positive XO case. On the basis of Ohno's contention that it is particularly the paternal X that produces the sex-chromatin body, it would appear that in Grumbach's case the X was of paternal origin.

How is it possible to interpret the remarkable diversity of chromosomal arrangements and morphologic manifestations presented by this relatively still very small number of cases? In two previous publications that were written without knowledge of chromosomal aberrations (Witschi[18, 34]) it was shown that the peculiarities of the Turner and Klinefelter syndromes can be understood on common principles of developmental physiology. Experiments with amphibian eggs (Witschi[35, 36]) show that over-ripeness (by delayed fertilization) or exposure to CO_2 result in stepwise deterioration of the developmental capacities of the eggs. As a consequence one observes among others the following abnormalities: Irregularity and incompleteness of gastrulation, defective development of rostral parts of the embryo, twinning, polymelia, and other defects of limb development, cellular pathology, reduction in number and quality of the germ cells, dysgenesis of the sex glands, and masculinization of genetic females. It is evident that the abnormalities produced in these experiments duplicate not only the peculiar germinal and somatic traits of the Turner and Klinefelter syndromes and of true hermaphrodites but also the characteristic features of human mongolism.

In the author's earlier work not much attention had been given to chromosomal conditions in embryos from overripe cells. Only the occurrence of gross abnormalities in highly damaged eggs had been noted. In the meanwhile Beetschen[37] has reported on extensive irregularities in chromosome distribution in blastulae derived from overripe salamander eggs. A study of overripe rat eggs is now in progress in our laboratory. Overripeness is obtained by delayed ovulation induced in constant estrus females. One of the first eggs examined showed non-disjunction of one diad in the second meiotic division (Fig. 5). If permitted to develop further, this egg should have retained either two elements or none of this chromosome type. This observation in itself is sufficient to explain the origin of the triplo-22 condition in mongoloids, the presence of two maternal X chromosomes in colorblind, chromatin-positive Klinefelter cases and of the chromatin-positive XO Turner case that apparently received no maternal sex chromosome. Moreover, the observations by Beetschen parallel the reports by Ford *et al.* on XXY–XX and of XX–XO mosaics. Both indicate irregularities of chromosome distribution during cleavage. That pathology of cell development may lead to chromosomal abnormalities is well known to students of cancer cells, and is reaffirmed again by chromosome studies on human leukemia (Baikie *et al.*[20]), which re-

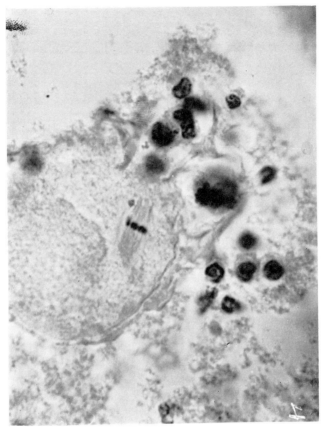

Fig. 5. Second polar spindle of a damaged unfertilized Rat egg. One diad (slightly out of focus) moves undivided to the upper pole; ×2000.

veal increases in chromosome numbers up to 50, particularly in cells of bone marrow.

Summing up old and new evidence and thought about the etiology of human sex deviations that are characterized by primary germinal dysgenesis and by frequent association with degenerative somatic malformations, the following generalizations may now be arrived at:

(1) The primary cause is a degenerative modification of the egg or the early germ which in itself is sufficient to explain gonad dysgenesis and teratologic development in general.

(2) The same original damage may also become the cause of chromosomal aberrations most of which seem to be lethal. The non-lethal ones probably exert some modifying influences on the course of sexual and somatic development in accordance with their genic value.

This interpretation which applies also to several other types of abnormal development, including monozygotic twinning, is compatible with the established fact that the frequency of most non-hereditary types of malformations shows a small increase among children of very young mothers and a more definite one in those from mothers older than 40. This may well be a consequence of difficulties in the ovulation process, resulting in delayed release of the egg from its follicle. At any rate, age dependency points to physiologic rather than pure chance determination of these abnormalities.

While it is concluded that degenerative types of sex deviation and somatic malformation have a postgenetic origin, evidently all cases which suffer chromosomal aberrations of any kind thereby acquire changes in their genetic constitution. Hereditary transfer of extra chromosomes may possibly become available for study in offspring from mongoloid parents. However, sterility of the involved types of sexual abnormality precludes the further genetic analysis of this class.

REFERENCES

1. E. Witschi, *Science 130*:372 (1959).
2. T. Dobzhansky and J. Schultz, *J. Genet. 28*:349 (1934).
3. J. T. Patterson, W. Stone, and S. Bedichek, *Genetics 22*:407 (1937).
4. S. Bedichek-Pipkin, *Univ. Texas Publ. 5914*:69 (1959).
5. E. Witschi, *Arch. mikr. Anat. 86*:1 (1914).
6. E. Witschi, *Arch. Entw. Mech. 49*:316 (1921).
7. E. Witschi, *Arch. Anat. micr. Morph. exp. 39*:215 (1950).
8. E. Witschi, *Anat. Rec. 66*:483 (1936).
9. C. Y. Chang and E. Witschi, *Proc. Soc. exp. Biol. Med., N. Y. 89*:150 (1955).
10. C. Y. Chang and E. Witschi, *Proc. Soc. exp. Biol. Med., N. Y. 93*:140 (1956).
11. E. Witschi, *Proc. int. Genetic Symposia, Tokyo, Cytologia Suppl.* 133 (1957).
12. S. Ohno, W. D. Kaplan, and R. Kinosita, *Exp. Cell Res. 18*:415 (1959).

13. E. Witschi, *Arch. Klaus-Stift. Vererb.-Forsch. 1:*127 (1925).

14. K. Ponse, *Rev. suisse Zool. 31:*177 (1924).

15. R. R. Humphrey, *Amer. J. Anat. 76:*33 (1945).

16. L. Gallien, *Bull. Biol. France et Belgique 88:*1 (1954).

17. R. A. Miller, *Anat. Rec. 70:*155 (1938).

18. E. Witschi, *Trans. Third Conf. Gest. Josiah Macy Found.*, Ed. C. A. Villee 119 (1956).

19. J. Lejeune, R. Turpin, and M. Gautier, *Ann. génét. 1:*41 (1959).

20. A. G. Baikie, W. M. Court Brown, P. A. Jacobs, and J. S. Milne, *Lancet* 425 (1959).

21. C. E. Ford, P. A. Jacobs, and L. G. Lajtha, *Nature 181:*1565 (1958).

22. C. E. Ford, K. W. Jones, O. J. Miller, U. Mittwoch, L. S. Penrose, M. Ridler, and A. Shapiro, *Lancet 1959:*709.

23. C. E. Ford, K. W. Jones, P. E. Polani, J. C. de Almeida, and J. H. Briggs, *Lancet 1959:*711.

24. C. E. Ford, P. E. Polani, J. H. Briggs, and P. M. F. Bishop, *Nature 183:*1030 (1959).

25. M. M. Grumbach, A. Morishima, and E. H. Y. Chu, *Abstr. I. int. Congr. endocr. Copenhagen* (1960), in Press.

26. D. G. Harnden and J. S. S. Stewart, *Brit. med. J. 2:*1285 (1959).

27. D. G. Harnden and C. N. Armstrong, *Brit med. J. 2:*1287 (1959).

28. D. A. Hungerford, A. J. Donnelly, P. C. Nowell, and S. Beck, *Amer. J. Human Gen. 11:*215 (1959).

29. P. A. Jacobs, A. G. Baikie, W. M. Court Brown, T. N. MacGregor, N. MacLean, and D. G. Harnden, *Lancet 1959:*423.

30. I. M. Nilsson, S. Bergman, J. Reitalu, and J. Waldenström, *Lancet* 2:264 (1959).

31. W. A. Russell, L. B. Russell, and J. S. Gower, *Proc. nat. Acad. Sci., Wash. 45:*554 (1959).

32. W. J. Welshons and L. B. Russell, *Proc. nat. Acad. Sci. Wash., 45:*560 (1959).

33. H. Nowakowski, W. Lenz, and J. Parada, *Acta endocrin. 30:*296 (1959).

34. E. Witschi, W. O. Nelson, and S. J. Segal, *J. clin. endocrin. Metab. 17:*737 (1957).

35. E. Witschi, *Verh. naturf. Ges. Basel 34:*33 (1922).

36. E. Witschi, *Cancer Res. 12:*763 (1952).

37. J. Beetschen, C. R. Acad. Sci., Paris 245:2541 (1957).

53

DOSAGE COMPENSATION—DEVELOPMENT OF A CONCEPT AND NEW FACTS

CURT STERN

And although the examples . . . must for the present be confined mainly to Drosophila *. . . it seems very unlikely . . . that their significance is limited to this organism.—Muller (1950).*

IT is natural that the types of problems which occupy the workers in any field of science change with the times. Old problems find their solutions and new, exciting leads call for foremost attention. But behind the front-line of advance, pockets of incompletely explored areas remain. They call for continued attention; and, often, discoveries in seemingly unrelated regions make possible new inroads.

This lecture will be concerned with the phenotypes in males and females produced by sex-linked genes. In general, these phenotypes are alike or closely resemble each other. It has been customary in this connection to quote mainly the X-linked genes of *Drosophila melanogaster,* yellow and white, miniature and forked, and many others. But the similarity of phenotypes for numerous sex-linked genes seems to be equally true for wing coloration in the moth Abraxas, for silver and gold in the fowl, for hemophilia in the dog, and for the red-green colorblindnesses and numerous other traits in man.

There are exceptions to the rule of identity or close similarity. In *Drosophila,* eosin males have lighter eye color than eosin females, the surface features of the eyes of facet males depart more

Reprinted from *Canadian Journal of Genetics and Cytology—Journal Canadien de Génétique et de Cytologie,* Vol. II, No. 2, June 1960.

The Fifth Huskins Memorial Lecture. Presented at the Annual Meeting of the Genetics Society of Canada on March 17, 1960 at the University of British Columbia, Vancouver, B. C.

from normal than those of facet females, and in the fowl the autosexing breeds which are pure for the Barred allele are lighter in the homozygous male than in the hemizygous female.

It was the exceptions which first seemed in need of interpretation. When Bridges, in 1922, applied the genic balance theory to sex determination he proceeded from a discussion of genic determination in general to that of sex-limited traits in particular. "The origin of variations in sexual and sex-limited characters" was the title of his report. The term sex-limited referred among others to examples which we now, after Goldschmidt (1920), designate as sex-controlled: eosin eye color, for instance, is not limited to one or the other sex in *Drosophila* but its degree of expression is controlled by the sexual constitution. As Bridges saw it, any fly pure for eosin should be expected to have the same shade of eosin eyes. Why was this not true? His explanation made use of an assumption of numerous modifiers of eosin everywhere in the chromosomal set, some enhancing and others diminishing the degree of pigmentation. In general, one would expect that these plus and minus modifiers would be present in even balance in any large part of the chromosomal set and thus cancel each other, but occasionally the plus modifiers might outweigh the minus modifiers, or vice versa. Males are different from females in having one X chromosome less. Usually, the X chromosomal modifiers of any gene, sex-linked or autosomal, would be closely balanced and the "removal" of an X chromosome from a female to leave a male would not disturb their specific phenotypes. For some genes, however, more plus than minus modifiers may be present in the X chromosome, and males may therefore appear more extreme in phenotype than females. For some other genes the opposite imbalance for plus and minus modifiers in the X chromosome might exist and the males be less extreme.

Bridges' interpretation was discussed sympathetically but critically by Mohr on the basis of his studies on the Notch deficiencies (1923). He had discovered that in females which lack a short section of one of the X chromosomes the genes in the homologous section of the other X chromosome, which are thus made hemizygous, often cause an "exaggerated" phenotype, deviating more from normal than in homozygous females. This exaggeration applies to mutants which have normally equal effects in the two sexes as well as to those with sex-controlled effects. For example, females with apricot in one X chromosome and a deficiency for this locus (ω) in the other X chromosome have no longer the same eye color as apricot males but are lighter, and eosin/deficiency females are as light as the typically lighter eosin males. By comparing the effects of several Notch deficiencies of different length, some of which did not include the ω locus, Mohr showed that exaggeration depends primarily on the absence in one chromosome of the very locus in question. In terms of the balance theory this means that the gene at this locus is a plus modifier which tends to darken the eye color and the sum of other genes in the deficient section act as minus modifiers. Since the loss of the plus modifier is more effective than that of the minus modifiers, the Notch section is unbalanced.

Mohr recognized that this interpretation involves a further consequence. While the loss of a short section causes exaggeration effects of the included genes, the loss of the whole X chromosome as represented by males versus females usually has little effect. "This must mean that the X is internally highly balanced for general eye color modifiers, i.e. that the darkening tendency of the normal allelomorph of white is counteracted by modifiers of opposite tendency in other parts of the X, so that the balance of eye color modifiers in the X is closely similar to the balance of eye color modifiers in the whole set of chromosomes" (l.c. p. 199).

While Mohr struggled with fitting his results into the balance theory, Goldschmidt, a few years later, cut the Gordian knot (1927). Scornfully, he pushed aside Bridges' balance theory as a purely factorial explanation invented as a result of being embarrassed by the facts and replaced it by an interpretation in terms of gene quantities. It was Goldschmidt himself who earlier had explained sex determination as a result of opposing male and female determiners. In *Lymantria* with its female heterogamy an XY zygote normally develops into a female because the F determiner outbalances the single M determiner in the single X chromosome, and an XX zygote normally develops into a male because the F determiner is outbalanced by the two M determiners. Intersexes develop when special combinations of different F and M alleles are brought together, strong F's and weak M's or weak F's and strong M's. Strength and weakness of sex genes had been considered as different quantities of two genic substances, and this scheme was now applied to genes in general. Normal and mutant alleles in *Drosophila* were assigned specific quantities such as 8 to the wild type, A, and 3 to a mutant, a. In respect to a sex-linked gene, a female then may be $AA = 16$, $Aa = 11$ or $aa = 6$, and its phenotype be normal, intermediate or mutant if each quantity leads to a different effect, or normal and mutant if threshold or other developmental phenomena make the effects of AA and Aa alike. A female with a deficiency for the A locus in one chromosome and the a allele present in the other chromosome would possess only the gene quantity 3 resulting in a phenotype more mutant than aa. "Thus . . . the curious phenomenon of exaggeration proves to be a simple consequence of the action of gene quantities and the quantitative nature of the relevant mutants" (l.c. p. 81, translated).

Goldschmidt was not concerned with the question why so often hemizygous mutant males, $a = 3$, were unlike in phenotype to the exaggerated hemizygous deficient females $aO = 3$. To him the developmental reactions leading to the phenotypes occurred in essentially different developmental systems, namely males and females. Why then expect equal effects? And, when later the unexpectedly frequent similarity of mutant males, $a = 3$, and homozygous females, $aa = 6$, was emphasized by others, Goldschmidt tended to minimize their arguments by listing the cases in which the mutant phenotypes of the females were different from those of the males.

In 1929, I made some crosses related to aspects of chromosome segregation which yielded XXY females that carried mutant alleles at the bobbed locus in both the X and Y chromosomes. Misled by the name of the mutant, bobbed, which is equivalent to "short bristled," I expected these flies with triple quantities of bobbed to be shorter bristled than the usual mutant XX females with only double quantities. Instead, they had longer, nearly normal bristles. For weeks I was unable to solve the riddle, until one morning, while awakening, I saw the answer. Two years earlier, as one of the very few tasks assigned to me by my chief, Goldschmidt had asked me to read proof of his Physiologische Theorie der Vererbung. I had recently returned to Germany from Columbia University and the vehemence of Goldschmidt's dismissal of the interpretations of the Morgan school—notwithstanding his complete recognition of the brilliance and fundamental nature of their discoveries—had blinded me to see the fruitfulness of Goldschmidt's approach. Now, suddenly, I realized that what was called a mutant for short bristles should be regarded as one for not-long-enough bristles, and that with this twist in semantics it was obvious that three doses of not-long-enough-bristle-causing alleles might lead to longer bristles than only two doses. If the normal allele stands for 8 and the mutant for 3, homo- and heterozygous normal females would be represented by quantities of 16 and 11 and homozygous XX mutants by 6, while mutant XXY females would be 9, thus approaching the wild type. That same day I tested my newly found insight against that of Goldschmidt. "What bristle length should an XXY female have if it is homozygous for bobbed, Herr Professor?" "Long bristles" was the instantaneous reply.

My findings of cumulative effects of the action of triple doses of recessive alleles obviously were the counterpart of Mohr's findings of exaggeration effects of single doses in deficiency females. So I set out to construct flies with a variety of doses of different bobbed alleles, and to interpret the results in Goldschmidtian terms. But there were some differences. Where Goldschmidt had spoken of different quantities characterizing different alleles themselves, I preferred to regard the question of the nature of genic differences as unanswerable at that time, and restricted myself to formulations in terms of quantitative differences in genic effects. As is well known, Goldschmidt himself later abandoned his quantitative theory of genic differences, and we now recognize that quantitatively different gene effects can be brought about by the actions of qualitatively different polypeptide chains which depend, presumably, on different sequences of nucleotide pairs in the DNA gene.

A major difference in views became apparent when I compared dosage effects in different genetic systems: males, diploid females, triploid females, intersexes and metasexes (= supersexes, Stern, 1959). I had found that XO males with their single dose of bobbed had much shorter bristles than XX females with two doses, and that they were similar to XX females with bobbed in one chromosome and a nearly deficiency-equivalent, lethal bobbed allele in the other. This was a noteworthy exception from the similarity of effects in the two hemi- and homozygous sexes and the exaggeration effects in deficiency females of most other X-linked mutant alleles (but it corresponded to the dissimilarity of eosin in males and females). Using the concepts of modifier systems of Bridges and Mohr I concluded that the X chromosome as a whole is neutrally balanced in regard to enhancers and inhibitors of bobbed, so that the absence of one X chromosome in bobbed males as compared to bobbed females is effective simply in terms of 1 vs. 2 doses of bobbed itself. Such a neutralizing, equal representation of the supposed numerous plus and minus modifiers of bobbed in the whole X chromosome appeared *a priori* as the most probable state of affairs. In other words, the inequality of effects of one vs. two bobbed alleles needed no explanation apart from the pure dosage effect itself. But in the same sense, the equality of effects of one vs. two doses of so many other X-linked genes stood out as an unexpected situation. They too should show the dosage effect, and its actual lack must mean that the total action of X-linked genes is balanced in such a way as to nullify the dosage action of any individual gene. Muller, in 1931, labelled this phenomenon "dosage compensation."

The problem of the expression of sex-linked genes had taken a complete turn. Bridges found no difficulty in the fact that most of them are expressed alike in males and females, but wished to account for those which expressed themselves differently. Now the exceptions seemed reasonable and the regular ones required further thought!

I proposed an evolutionary hypothesis in order to explain dosage compensation for the usual X-linked mutants and its absence for bobbed. Translated, it reads as follows (Stern, 1929 p. 289):

I assume that this peculiar situation has been produced by natural selection, in a manner which is not clearly apparent. If the different genic doses would produce different phenotypes they would, presumably, have different selective values. In this case, selection would affect the different sexes differentially which would constitute a danger to the species. If, however, such a noteworthy genic balance originates, as we actually observe it, then its retention would be favored by selection. On the other side, in respect to the *bb* genes selection could not lead to such a balance since the presence of a *bb* allele in the Y chromosome normally excludes the existence of a dosage difference between males and females. Thus no opportunity for selection was available.

This theory of dosage compensation by genic balance ran counter to Goldschmidt's way of thinking with its emphasis on males and females as basically different developmental systems. I submitted the manuscript to him as the editor of Biologisches Zentralblatt. His response, the following day, was characteristic; candid in giving his judgment, and generous in his action: "The difference between us is this. I have read your views, understand them and reject them. You read my views, did not understand them and reject them. Your paper will appear in the May issue."

Following the work on bobbed, studies on the effects of extra doses of other specific X-linked genes were undertaken by Muller, League and Offermann (1931) and the existence of compensatory effects of the rest of the X chromosome recognized. These experiments made use of fragments of X chromosomes which carried mutant alleles. The fragments were added to males and females with mutant whole X chromosomes so that the effects of two and three doses in females and of one and two doses in males could be compared with one another—in addition to the already known effects of single doses in females heterozygous for a deficiency. In 1932 Muller delivered his classic address before the Sixth International Congress of Genetics held in Ithaca, N. Y. In it he defined the new terms amorph, hypomorph, neomorph and antimorph, and devoted a special section to dosage compensation. Here a solution was offered for the problem of how natural selection could have resulted in dosage compensation for mutant alleles although the overwhelming majority of alleles in nature belong to the wild type. Muller suggested that dosage compensation had evolved for wild type alleles and that its recognition in mutant flies was only a consequence of greater ease of visual discrimination. He postulated that there must be some intrinsic difference in the effect of one as against two doses of wild type alleles even though, so far as our eye can perceive, practically the same effect is produced. Experimental evidence in favor of this suggestion was provided for the normal allele at the ω locus (Muller, 1935, 1950) and was also seen in the fact that deficiencies for certain loci lead to dominant abnormal phenotypes. Thus, in the male a single dose of the normal allele for Notch makes for normal wings while the same single dose in a female, one of whose X chromosomes lacks this locus, causes Notch wings. Mohr, at the same congress at which Muller spoke, appropriately called such loci "haplo-insufficient" (1932). It was Muller's thought that all or most X-linked loci belonged to this class even if their normal alleles often do not give striking haplo-insufficient effects in single dose. Granted the difference in effect of 1 as against 2 doses of normal X-linked alleles, selection of compensating modifiers in the rest of the X chromosome would be a natural consequence. In order to account for dosage compensation of mutant alleles it had to be assumed further that the compensators of wild type alleles acted in a like way on mutant alleles. This assumption may be substantiated by data on the effect of two doses of apricot eye color in the male as compared to four doses in the female. Such flies are available in a strain supplied by Professor M. M. Green, who was able by means of unequal crossing over to construct X chromosomes which have two apricot alleles duplicated in tandem sequence (Green, 1959). The same dosage modification observable in the equality of effects of 1 dose/male – 2 dose/female is present for the effects of 2 dose/male – 4 dose/female: the darker color of 2 dose than 1 dose males is matched by the darker color of 4 dose than 2 dose females.

It is not contradictory to Muller's interpretation that exceptions exist for which dosage compensation is not valid. This is true for eosin where 1 dose males are lighter than 2 dose females and, indeed, as light as 1 dose/deficiency females. If the products of different wild and mutant multiple alleles are qualitatively different proteins, as for instance different enzymes, then the products of compensatory genetic systems will not necessarily act alike on all of them. Rather, it is perhaps surprising that they do so often.

The concept of dosage compensation involves the existence of modifiers within the X chromosome which cancel the effect of different doses of a given gene. A particularly clear demonstration of the existence of such internal modifiers was later provided for the X-linked mutant zeste *(z)* of *Drosophila* even though this mutant happens to be not compensated (Gans 1953). Males with one dose of z (with or without a Y chromosome) have normal, red eyes while females with two doses have lemon colored zeste eyes. But males with one dose of z and 2 doses of the normal allele of white, ω^+, which is at a different locus from z, are zeste as are females with 2 such doses; and females with 2 doses of zeste and only 1 dose of ω^+ are red eyed as are males with one such dose. This shows that ω^+ acts as an internal X-chromosomal modifier of z and that the dosage of ω^+ is the decisive element in the usual sexual dimorphism of z eyes.

It has sometimes been questioned whether the heterogametic sex in various species with XX-XY (or WW-WZ) arrangement of sex chromosomes is truly hemizygous for X-linked loci, or whether the Y chromosomes may regularly be the bearers of recessive alleles of X-linked genes; for example, whether a man is hemophilic because he carries one dose of an allele for hemophilia in his X chromosome or because he carries this allele in his X chromosome plus another such allele, always present, in his Y chromosome (Sirks 1937, see also Haldane 1938). If it is assumed that the Y borne allele is an amorph then the question can hardly be answered, since presence of an amorph may be indistinguishable from absence of an allele. If the question concerns presence of a hypomorph or an otherwise active allele evidence can be obtained from a comparison of regular XY with exceptional XO individuals which carry X-linked mutants. In *Drosophila melanogaster* and *simulans* such comparisons have shown the emptiness of the Y chromosome for all tested loci except that of bobbed which is usually occupied by a dominant wild-type allele in melanogaster and by a recessive in simulans. In man the discovery of colorblind XO individuals—to be discussed below—shows the emptiness of the Y chromosome in regard to the locus for color vision. For the fowl in which the Y chromosome had been credited with a recessive allele for non-barring the evidence is less direct but also points against such a hypothesis (Cock 1953).

Even though obvious it should be stated explicitly that resemblance of effects of X-linked genes in males and females does not require dosage compensation if the alleles are amorphs. If the effect of an allele is zero then one times zero in the male should equal two times zero in the female. Thus absence of pigment in the eyes of "white" *Drosophila* provides no test for dosage compensation, but its presence in apricot Drosophilae does so. Since, in *Drosophila*, most X-linked loci have yielded series of multiple alleles the statement that dosage compensation exists for the majority of loci is based on the facts of equality of effect not of the possibly amorphic, most extreme allele, but on the equality of effects of intermediary alleles. It may be added that even an apparent amorph like white does not truly belong to this category. Mohr (1923) showed that a deficiency for the white locus gives a more extreme "ultra-white" effect than the white allele, and E. B. Lewis (unpubl.) who constructed chromosomes with quintuple representation of a white allele found that the eyes of males and females with 5 and 10 doses, respectively, are slightly pigmented, (the females are darker than the males, evidence for lack of complete dosage compensation).

No advances in the area of dosage compensation were made for more than a decade. Indeed, the concept was hardly mentioned. But in 1945 a new tool for its analysis became available. Sturtevant described a recessive autosomal gene, *tra*, which transforms females into males and made use of it for a comparison of the effect of three sexually dimorphic X-linked mutants in hemizygous males, homozygous transformed males, and homozygous females. For all three mutants which belonged to different loci the homozygous transformed males resemble homozygous females rather than hemizygous males. This seemed to prove that the normal sexual dimorphism in the expression of the three mutants is not connected with maleness or femaleness of the two developing systems.

One of the mutants used by Sturtevant was eosin which, as

pointed out earlier, shows no dosage compensation. It is, therefore, not surprising that transformed males with 2 doses of eosin
should resemble females with two doses rather than males with
one. But for at least one of the other two mutants, facet, dosage
compensation—although incomplete—was known to exist and here
the transformed males seemed to offer an opportunity for distinguishing between the two interpretations of dosage compensation: Goldschmidt's view that regarded it as a consequence of the
basic developmental differences of the two sexes, and Muller's and
my own inclination to think of the compensatory modifiers in
more general genetic terms. If the sexual developmental system as
such is responsible for the fact that the ommatidia of deficiency
females with one dose of facet are more extremely faceted than
males with one dose, then females with two doses should also be
more extreme than transformed males with two doses. The fact
that this is not the case seemed to point to dosage compensation
residing in the X chromosomes independently of their sex determining functions.

Sturtevant did not reach this conclusion explicitly, but soon Muller and Lieb made use of the transformer gene for a direct attack
(Muller 1950). Apricot eye color which had furnished one of the
best examples of essentially complete dosage compensation was
introduced into transformed males. If the resemblance of females
with 2 doses of apricot to males with 1 dose is due to the different
sex determining processes then the eye color of transformed males
with 2 doses in their two X chromosomes should resemble the
dark eye color of normal males with two doses, one in their single
chromosome and the other in a small duplication. If, however, the
modifier system resided in the X chromosome apart from its sex
determiners, then transformed males should be compensated as
are females and be as light as normal males. And so they were.

This seemed to establish that not the sex determiners but the
dosage compensators within the X chromosomes are responsible,
and the argument was strengthened by findings of Muller and his
collaborators that compensators of different X-linked genes were
not identical with one another. But once more Goldschmidt went
to the attack. In his presidential address to the 9th International
Congress of Genetics he chose dosage compensation as the first

example on which to demonstrate two "Different Philosophies of Genetics": "One [that] considers all and everything the product of selection and adaptation . . . the other [that] looks for simple facts of development . . . which might automatically produce the effect . . ." (1954).

What enabled Goldschmidt to counter the argument derived from the experimentally proven retention of dosage compensation by transformed males? Once more let him speak for himself:

> This argumentation clearly assumes that the normal 1X-males and the transformed 2X-males are identical, which means that they have the same developmental system. If the problem had been looked at, not from the point of view of modifiers but from the point of view of development, it would have turned out that the males-by-transformation have a developmental system that is female in a number of basic features. Actually, the sex-reversal flies are not males, but extreme female intersexes (= 2X-intersexes) in which some basic features of growth and differentiation (actually those of early determination) are still female. This is true for size and general growth, for time of development, for many proportions, and for the rhythm of gonad development.*

Thus, he concludes, the behavior of apricot eye color in transformed males is like that in females *because* the transformed males are actually developmentally equivalent to females. This was an ingenious way out of difficulties for Goldschmidt's philosophy. If some might be inclined to think of his interpretation of the transformer effect as a bit of sophistry—a term to which Goldschmidt was inclined in respect to the interpretations of the adherents of the opposing philosophy of genetics—it may be well to mention that Sturtevant already had considered the question whether transformed individuals are better described as intersexes rather than as males and had not completely rejected this interpretation. In a way, a stalemate had been reached.

Only last year new facts became available which may lead us farther. The discovery, by Jacobs and Strong (1959) and Ford,

---

* It is not clear what Goldschmidt meant by "rhythm of gonad development." Perhaps he referred to the fact that the testes of transformed males are reduced in size and sterile.

Polani, Briggs and Bishop (1959) in man, and by Welshons and Russell (1959) in the mouse, that sex determination in mammals depends primarily on the Y chromosome has provided us with two transformed mammalian types, the XXY human males with Klinefelter's syndrome and the XO human females with Turner's syndrome as well as the XO female mice without associated deviant phenotype. In regard to X-linked genes, the XXY males are 2 dose individuals with a male developmental system who can be compared with XX females and XY males, and the 0 females are 1 dose individuals with a female developmental system who can be compared with XY males and XX females. These comparisons are available for X-linked partial (red-green) colorblindnesses in XO, XY, XX, and XXY humans, and for scurfy and tabby XO, XY and XX mice.

In man, the effects of the X-linked alleles for red-green colorblindnesses seem to be essentially alike in males and females (but there is a greater variability in females which is not fully understood (Walls, 1959) and whose existence may possibly affect the tentative interpretations of the following discussion). Granted essential resemblance of expression in the two sexes, this is evidence for dosage compensation in respect to at least the alleles for deuteranomaly and protanomaly whose effects deviate less from normal than those of deuteranopy and protanopy. For the latter it is at present unknown whether they are amorphs and thus are immaterial for the problem of dosage compensation. For the alleles which are not at the bottom of the series, deuteranomaly and protanomaly in their usual or extreme forms, XXY Klinefelter males should give decisive evidence for the type of mechanism of dosage compensation: typical expression of the color vision defect if the compensation is independent of the sexual developmental system, but a dosage effect due to the 2X condition which expresses itself in a male instead of a female system.

Of the three colorblind Klinefelter males so far described two were deuteranomalous and one protanopic (Nowakowski, Lenz, and Parada, 1959). Their colorblindnesses were apparently typically expressed, resembling those of XY males and XX females. We may conclude, at least for deuteranomaly, that dosage compensation depends on modifiers in the X chromosomes which act independently of the sex-differentiating genes.

This conclusion would be confirmed if the female type Turner individuals with a single X chromosome, XO, also would resemble XX females in the expression of non-amorphic alleles for colorblindnesses. The only published case of colorblindness in a Turner female which can be classified with some degree of accuracy concerns deuteranopia, expressed in a typical way. Since it cannot be excluded that the allele for deuteranopia is an amorph this individual is not decisive.

In the mouse no XXY animals are known at present, but XO females have been discovered (Welshons and Russell 1959, Russell, Russell and Gower, 1959), and the expressions of two X-linked mutants have been recorded. Scurfy is a recessive sublethal gene. Females homozygous for scurfy have not been obtained but hemizygous scurfy XO females and XY males could be compared. Their phenotypes are alike, suggesting dosage compensation independently of the sex difference but this view is subject to two reservations. First, scurfy may be an amorph and, second, if it is not, the unknown XX females homozygous for scurfy may not be dosage compensated! Tabby, a dominant X-linked gene is expressed alike in XO and XX females and in XY males. Thus the second reservation made for scurfy can be dismissed for tabby. The first reservation, applied to tabby, still stands: it may be an amorph. This, however, is unlikely, since tabby is a dominant which is viable in hemizygous and homozygous state. Subject to the possibility that tabby is an amorph, it would appear to be dosage compensated and the alikeness of the tabby phenotype in XO and XX females would show that dosage compensation is founded on modifiers in the X chromosome which act independently of the sex-developmental system. It will be important to search for other X-linked mutants occurring in Klinefelter and Turner humans and corresponding "transformed" sexual types in mice and other mammals.

In connection with the foregoing treatment of dosage compensation in mammals two points still deserve attention. For one, in none of the colorblind Klinefelter and Turner humans had the chromosomal constitution been directly determined, since these cases were described prior to the discoveries of the XXY and XO nature of such persons. But since the colorblind Klinefelters were known to be sex chromatin positive and the Turners negative, it may be considered as very probable that they were XXY and XO respectively. The XO constitution of tabby but not of the scurfy mice was proven by actual chromosome counts. The other point relates to the sexual nature of the two kinds of chromosomally aberrant types. In man, the XO individuals are sterile females, with infantile development of the sexual ducts and virtual absence of gonads. It has been suggested that Turner individuals are essentially not females but represent the phenotype of the "neutral basic sex" (Jacobs, Baikie, Court Brown, Harnden, MacGregor, and MacLean, 1959). But since XO mice are fertile females, indistinguishable from XX females except perhaps by slightly reduced number of offspring, it may be argued by analogy that the gonadal agenesis of human Turners is not the expression of neutral non-female sex determination but a consequence of chromosomal unbalance which is not directly related to sex genes. It may be added that Turner individuals have a skeletal age approximately equivalent to XX females of corresponding age (Tanner, Prader, Habich, and Ferguson-Smith, 1959), a finding which is equally in accord with the view which regards the Turners as females and with viewing them as of neutral sex. The classification of Klinefelter individuals as males also requires discussion. Jacobs, Baikie, Court Brown, Harnden, MacGregor, and MacLean (1959) consider the finding of female breast development in many cases of Klinefelter's syndrome with XXY constitution as pointing to "the feminising influence of the X chromosome." In other words, they feel that the XXY constitution is an intersexual one as compared to that of XY males. I am less inclined to this interpretation, since gynecomasty may be a hormonal consequence of the abnormal testicular state rather than the result of primary sex determination, and since Klinefelter-like syndromes with gynecomasty have been observed to develop in presumably normal XY males after traumatically acquired spinal cord lesions (Planansky, Pillar, and Selback, 1956). As to skeletal growth, Tanner *et al.* have found that Klinefelters have a skeletal age equivalent to XY males but the

Klinefelter children, even before puberty, have a different growth rate as measured by length of legs. The investigators also gained the impression "that the great majority are somewhat feminine or eunchoid in appearance and distinctly lacking in mesomorphy or degree of muscularity." These observations may indeed suggest some slightly intersexual type of development but, on the other side, they may be nothing but dosage phenomena due to the presence of two X chromosomes in developmentally basically male Klinefelters. It seems premature at present to definitely assign a female determining role to the X chromosomes of mammals rather than to state that the male determining role of the Y chromosome is opposed to a female determining role of the totality of the other chromosomes, autosomes and X chromosome.

There is a peculiar inherited type of human intersexually, testicular feminization. Affected individuals possess testes and are XY chromosomally (Severinghaus 1942, Jacobs, Baikie, Court Brown, Forrest, Roy, Stewart, and Lennox 1959), but phenotypically they are females. Two such individuals from separate kindreds have been found to be colorblind, and the defect in both was classified as extreme deuteranomaly. Here the single dose of the allele for this color vision abnormality expressed itself similarly to that in typical XY males and XX females. Once again, therefore, there is no difference in expression when one dose of the X-linked allele exerts its effect in a normal male developmental system or one which is somatically a female system although, in testicular feminization, with distinctly aberrant features.

If we look at the totality of observations on colorblindness in individuals of the types Klinefelter, Turner, and testicular feminization we must admit that Goldschmidt's interpretation of dosage compensation as resulting from the normal sex difference in development and not from sex-independent modifiers can be defended on the same basis on which he refused to admit the argument from transformed males. In all cases there is some room left for regarding the unusual phenotypic sex as developmentally being an intersex. Nevertheless, it seems to me that the evidence for the intersexual nature of most of these types is very tenuous if not completely lacking. And even if one should be inclined to accept the intersex interpretation it is unexpected that dosage compensation is apparently always complete. This is as it should be on the basis of internally compensated X chromosomes *per se,* but if the developmental sex system were decisive for dosage compensation in normal males and females, why should the various intersexual systems be so adjusted? Let us not forget, however, how many points in the argument as derived from mammals are still unsettled: degree of resemblance of X-linked gene effects in different sexual groups, amorphism of alleles, and nature of the developmental sex determining systems. New facts are required, on X-linked mutants in mice, on colorblindness in man and, if possible, on other X-linked mutants such as that for glucose – 6 – phosphate dehydrogenase deficiency which are frequent enough to warrant a search not only among normal men and women but also among persons with the syndromes of Klinefelter, Turner and testicular feminization.

Before leaving the question of whether dosage compensation is accomplished by the sexual systems or by independent systems of modifiers it seems appropriate to ask whether the latter systems alone require natural selective forces for their establishment. In regard to the sexual systems Goldschmidt (1954) spoke of the "simple facts of development . . . which might automatically produce the (dosage compensation) effect. . . ." He cannot argue his case any more himself, but one wonders whether the word "automatically" can be accepted. Would it not require selection of modifiers of the sexual system themselves to make dosage compensation possible?

A newly discovered potential difficulty for all theories of selection for dosage compensation must still be mentioned. Muller (1950) pointed out that the relations between the double doses of the compensators and those of the compensated genes must be so fixed as to reduce the effect of a given dose of the compensated gene to half of the effect which would obtain in the presence of a single dose of compensators. "Such a result," Muller wrote, "would be brought out most simply in a case in which the compensators, when themselves in a single dose, reduced the primary effect to half of what it would otherwise be, and in which, when their dose was raised, their own effectiveness rose in the usual geometric manner." Thus, if the effect of a single dose of a gene is equal to

4 arbitrary units, its compensated effect would be ($\frac{1}{2}$) x (1 x 4) or 2, and the effect of two genic doses, after compensation would be ($\frac{1}{2}$)$^{(2)}$ x (2 x 4), likewise 2. "Whether this simple scheme is usually true can probably be determined definitely through quantitative studies involving several different doses of compensators," Muller added. We have recently studied 3X 2A metafemales whose three X chromosomes are homozygous for apricot. Metafemales homozygous for bobbed are known to be non-compensated, having longer bristles than 2X females which themselves have longer bristles than XO males. For apricot, on the other hand, if the simple scheme of geometric compensator effects applies, one might have expected an intensity of eye color corresponding to the expression ($\frac{1}{2}$)^3 x (3 x 4) = 1.5. This would be lighter than apricot in males and females. Actually the color in metafemales resembled closely that in the normal sexes. Apparently the effectiveness of the compensator system had increased relatively less than that of the primary gene. It is not surprising that the simple scheme is not obeyed by nature, but it is a matter for further study that dosage compensation extends to metafemales which are so rare in wild populations—and sterile besides—that they themselves cannot have been involved in selective processes for dosage compensation. Further experiments with metafemales, using other loci, should throw light on this problem.

Whatever the formal genetic system is that accounts for dosage compensation, it is a task for the future to elucidate its physiologic and biochemical basis. There are cytologic facts which have a bearing on this aspect of the phenomenon. Many years ago Offerman (1936) found that the single X chromosome in the salivary gland nuclei of male larvae of *Drosophila melanogaster* has a diameter which is nearly as great as that of the paired two X chromosomes in female larvae, and Dobzhansky (1957) has recently confirmed these observations in hybrids of certain Drosophila species. Since it was shown by Aronson, Rudkin and Schultz (1954) that the DNA content of the single X chromosome of male gland cells is only half of that of the two X chromosomes in female cells Dobzhansky has concluded that "the bloated appearance of the male X indicates accumulation in this chromosome of some products of gene activity. A male has only one X, but this single

X works apparently twice as hard as does each of the two X's in the female." These observations "may, then, be said to describe a microscopically visible counterpart of the genetic phenomenon of dosage compensation." In detail, of course, these observations are not sufficient to illustrate the fact that dosage compensation must be produced by quantitatively differential action of primary genes and modifiers.

A different cytologic device for dosage compensation is found in some organisms with diploid females and haploid males. In the honey bee and in the parasitic wasp Habrobracon the expression of most genes is identical or very similar in the two sexes. In these organisms dosage compensation seems to be required for all loci. Measurements of cell size and of the DNA content of nuclei, and counts of chromosomes show that the "haploid" males retain haploidy in their germ line but become diploid, or polyploid, in various somatic tissues, equivalent to female tissues (Speicher 1935, Merriam and Ris 1954, Risler 1954).

Dosage compensation forms one chapter in the history of genetic systems. Its analysis is not yet a closed chapter.

REFERENCES

Aronson, J. F., Rudkin, G. T., and Schultz, J. 1954. A comparison of giant X chromosomes in male and female *Drosophila melanogaster* by cytophotometry in the ultraviolet. *J. Histochem. Cytochem.* 2:458-459.

Bridges, C. B. 1922. The origin of variatons in sexual and sex-limited characters. *Amer. Naturalist* 56:51-63.

Cock, A. G. 1953. The interpretation of autosexing. *J. Genet.* 51:421-433.

Dobzhansky, Th. 1957. The X chromosome in the larval salivary glands of hybrids *Drosophila insularis* x *Drosophila tropicalis*. *Chromosoma* 8:691-698.

Ford, C. E., Polani, P. E., Briggs, J. H., and Bishop, P. M. F. 1959. A presumptive human XXY/XX mosaic. *Nature* 183:1030-1032.

Gans, M. 1953. Etude génétique et physiologique du mutant z de *Drosophila melanogaster*. *Bull. Biol. France Belg. Suppl.* 38:1-90.

Goldschmidt, R. 1920. Untersuchungen über Intersexualität. *Z. Ind. Abst. Vererb.* 23:1-199.

Goldschmidt, R. 1927. Physiologische Theorie der Vererbung. Springer, Berlin.

Goldschmidt, R. 1954. Different philosophies of genetics. *Science* 119:703-710.

Green, M. M. 1959. Putative non-reciprocal crossing over in *Drosophila melanogaster. Z. Ind. Abst. Vererb.* 90:375-384.

Haldane, J. B. S. 1938. The location of the gene for haemophilia. *Genetica* 20:423-430.

Jacobs, P. A., Baikie, A. G., Court Brown, W. M., Harnden, D. G., Mac-Gregor, T. N., and MacLean, N. 1959. Use of the term "superfemale." *Lancet,* December 19, 1959: 1145.

Jacobs, P. A., Baikie, A. G., Court Brown, W. M., Forrest, H., Roy, J. R., Stewart, J. S. S., and Lennox, B. 1959. Chromosomal sex in the syndrome of testicular feminisation. *Lancet ii of 1959:*591-592.

Jacobs, P. A., and Strong, J. A. 1959. A case of human intersexuality having a possible XXY sex-determining mechanism. *Nature 183:*302-303.

Merriam, R. W., and Ris, H. 1954. Size and DNA content of nuclei in various tissues of male, female, and worker honeybees. *Chromosoma 6:*522-538.

Mohr, O. L. 1923. A genetic and cytological analysis of a section deficiency involving four units of the X-chromosome in *Drosophila melanogaster. Z. Ind. Abst. Vererb.* 32:108-232.

Mohr, O. L. 1929. Exaggeration and inhibition phenomena encountered in the analysis of an autosomal dominant. *Z. abst. Vererb.* 50:113-200.

Mohr, O. L. 1932. On the potency of mutant genes and wild-type allelomorphs. *Proc. 6th Int. Congr. Genet.* 1:190-212.

Muller, H. J. 1932. Further studies on the nature and causes of gene mutations. *Proc. 6th Int. Congr. Genet.* 1:213-255.

Muller, H. J. 1950. Evidence of the precision of genetic adaptation. Harvey Lecture Series XLIII, 1947-1948, *1:*165-229. C. C Thomas, Springfield.

Muller, H. J., League, B. B., and Offermann, C. A. 1931. Effects of dosage changes of sex-linked genes, and the compensatory effects of other gene differences between male and female (Abstr.) *Anat. Rec. 51* (suppl.):110.

Nowakowski, H., Lenz, W., and Parada, J. 1959. Diskrepanz zwischen Chromatinbefund und genetischem Geschlecht beim Klinefelter-Syndrom. *Acta Endocrinol. 30:*296-320.

Offermann, C. A. 1936. Branched chromosomes as symmetrical duplications. *J. Genet. 32:*103-116.

Planansky, K., Pillar, S., and Selbach, G. 1956. Spinal cord lesion with hypogonadism and gynecomastia; chromosomal sex. *J. Clin. Endocrinol.* 14:1607-1613.

Risler, H. 1954. Die somatische Polyploidie in der Entwicklung der Honigbiene (*Apis mellifica* L.) und die Wiederherstellung der Diploidie bei den Drohnen. *Z. Zellforsch. 41:*1-78.

Russell, W. L., Russell, L. B., and Gower, J. S. 1959. Exceptional inheritance of a sex-linked gene in the mouse explained on the basis that the X/O sex-chromosome constitution is female. *Proc. Nat. Acad. Sci.*45:554-560.

Severinghaus, A. E. 1942. Sex chromosomes in a human intersex. *Amer. J. Anat.* 70:73-92.

Sirks, M. J. 1937. Haemophilia as a proof for mutation in man. *Genetica* 19:417-422.

Speicher, B. R. 1935. Cell size and chromosomal types in Habrobracon. *Amer. Naturalist* 69:79-80.

Stern, C. 1929. Über die additive Wirkung multipler Allele. *Biolog. Zbl.* 49:261-290.

Stern, C. 1959. Use of the term "superfemale." *Lancet,* December 12, 1959: 1088.

Sturtevant, A. H. 1945. A gene in *Drosophila melanogaster* that transforms females into males. *Genetics* 30:297-299.

Tanner, J. M., Prader, A., Habisch, H., and Ferguson-Smith, M. A. 1959. Genes on the Y chromosome influencing rate of maturation in man. *Lancet ii of 1959* (7095): 141-144.

Walls, G. L. 1959. Peculiar color blindness in peculiar people. *Arch. Ophthalmol.* 62:13-32.

Welshons, W. J., and Russell, L. B. 1959. The Y-chromosome as the bearer of male determining factors in the mouse. *Proc. Nat. Acad. Sci.* 45:560-566.

54

INDICATIONS THAT MONGOLOID IMBECILITY IS A GAMETIC MUTATION OF DEGRESSIVE TYPE

ADRIEN BLEYER, M.D.

WHETHER a mutation, even a degressive mutation, the result of a disturbance in the biologic order at the beginning of life, with its inevitable limitation of function as well as change in anatomy, may constitute disease may be open to question. The term is used in this paper chiefly because of its convenience, although I believe that any pathologic syndrome such as mongolism is in fact a "departure from health," which is the definition of disease commonly found in modern dictionaries.[1]

THREE SIGNS OF MONGOLISM

Figure 1 shows the astonishing elasticity of the skin in mongolism. The added peculiarity of redundancy makes it a useful sign of this disease. This combination is often best appreciated in the neck, especially the back of the neck, where the folds with their familiar feel may be grasped and lifted away from the underlying muscles.

The soft skin of the mongoloid imbecile, its fulness, one might say its amplitude, is of great diagnostic value. In the female, the labia majora exhibit this peculiarity so often as to afford another sign of this disease. When these characteristics are pronounced, the labia resemble small round pillows and may be quite distinctive.

A third sign of mongolism comprises the peculiarities of the nipples. They are tiny, round beads placed on a flat surface. There is a relative absence of areola. Only occasionally is this condition of help in diagnosis, although when present it may render as-

Reprinted from the *American Journal of Diseases of Children*, Vol. 47, February 1934, pp. 342-348.
Read before the St. Louis Pediatric Society, Dec. 16, 1932.

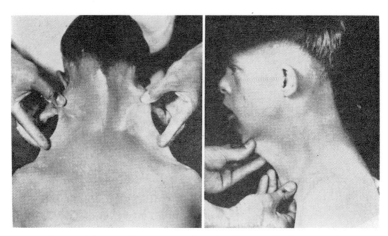

Fig. 1. Softness, fulness, elasticity and redundancy of the superficial tissues may often be detected in the nucha. When present they afford a convenient and helpful sign of mongolism (Roy H. W. M., aged 10 years).

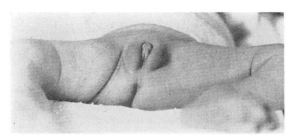

Fig. 2. The round, full labia in mongolism. Note also the redundancy of the right thigh. (Baby L., 5 days old, seen with Dr. Park White, Jr., who allowed me to use this picture.)

sistance. None of these items is pathognomonic of mongolism; they may be seen in varying degrees in apparently normal children just as the in-curved little finger which has been deemed a highly important point in the recognition of mongolism was found in about one fifth of the members of a group of persons without mongolism. So far I am aware, these signs have not been described heretofore.

THE ORIGIN OF MONGOLISM

Looking at mongoloid imbeciles is like looking at the stars; the more one looks, the more one sees. New things are always appearing, and the suggestion is aroused that much more remains hidden from view. Certainly the more one studies these persons, the less one is able to find anything normal about them. It is not unlikely that some time it may be known that no part of the entire body is spared its own particular distortion by this disease; that no organ or tissue whatever may not reveal evidence of it. It is thus probable that the symptomatology of mongolism is destined to become much more ample than it is now, and that it will be learned that imbecility is only incidental to it, the brain, like any other part of the mongoloid body, exhibiting changes that are always characteristic.[2]

If one may indulge in speculation as to the origin of mongolism, it is likely that one will go back to the embryo to find there perhaps a deviation which was present at the time of fertilization or even before fertilization which would involve the entire structure of the new being. It is thus probable that the problem of mongolism may belong to the cytologist rather than to the common-clay clinician, to whom it may be only a problem in genetics. There are two reasons for this idea: first, the clinical aspects of the disease as mentioned; namely, that the entire body seems to be involved, which, if true, fairly satisfies the requirements of a gametic origin, and second, that no two ovum pregnancy has yet been reported in which both children had mongolism, nor any monozygotic pregnancy the result of a double sperm implantation of one ovum with a single chorion and children of the same sex in which one child has a mongoloid imbecile and other was not. Alone these facts suggest, and combined they fairly indicate, that mongolism occurs with fertilization or has already occurred before it during the period of maturation either of the ovum or of the spermatozoon, and that it is here that elaboration of the subject may be most promising.

RELATED BIOLOGY

It will be recalled that the maturation of both the ovum and the spermatozoon preparatory to fertilization is characterized by the appearance of chromatin-bearing bodies known as chromosomes which are identical in number for each species. After the appearance of these bodies and their arrangement along the equator of the cell, half of their chromatin is lost and two new nuclear bodies appear; in each of these a reticulum forms in which the chromatin is again increased. Thus is reached the so-called resting period when paternal and maternal elements, both in the ovum and in the spermatozoon, may be differentiated. On fusion of the two new nuclear bodies, the number of chromosomes is reduced to one-half their original number, constituting the all-important period of reduction whereby mature ovum and mature spermatozoon may each provide half the original number of chromosomes which on fertilization will restore the number characteristic of the species, half of them being derived from each of the parents.

That these structures and these functions may be visited by some of the vicissitudes to which their progeny the embryo will be exposed, there can be little doubt. One might conceive of a disturbance in the structure of the function of the chromosomes or even perhaps of other parts of the germ cell where functions no less important are now believed to occur[3] which might elaborate itself into disease. Indeed such disturbances in structure and in the functioning of the chromosomes have already been observed—"accidents and irregularities in the nuclear make-up," as the geneticist Herbert Walter called them.[4] He said:

> During the period of unpairing of homologous chromosomes the process may not be clean-cut and complete. A piece of one chromosome may adhere to its mate thus changing its size and composition, or again a fragment of a chromosome during the complicated elimination performance accompanying the marriage ceremony of the germ cells may be shuffled out and lost, thus creating a deficient chromosome. Such accidents to the germ cells would be reflected in all the subsequent mitotic divisions of the cells derived therefrom and a mutation would result. Further, an examination of the nuclear structure of mutants frequently reveals chromosomal irregularities so that an unmistakable relation between the two phenomena undoubtedly exists.

There may be an unequal migration of the chromosomes to the poles of the germ cell during the reduction period which will result in a cell progeny having a number of chromosomes unlike the number present in the parent. An example of this occurs in the evening primrose, Enothera lamarkiana, the chromosomes of which number fourteen, whereas in one of its mutations, Enothera lata, fifteen chromosomes are found, an eight chromosome gamete joining with a normal seven chromosome gamete because, prior to the resting period, the chromosomes divided unequally. In this case instead of fourteen dividing into two groups of seven each, they divided into eight and six, so that when eight were fertilized with a normal germ cell containing seven, it produced the mutant fifteen, a mutation which de Vries called degressive because it was defective and in natural surroundings was incapable of reproducing itself.

A DEFINITION OF MUTATIONS

Perhaps the definition of a degressive mutation may be left to history, extending back to the closing decades of the last century when the terms "variation" and "fluctuation" were used to imply a change in species arising through the force of environment; the whole scheme of inheritance was based on the assumption that peculiarities or modifications acquired through use or disuse might recur in later generations and indeed that transition from one form to another through adaptation to external influences was the most fit of explanations.

Following Darwin's contribution, "The Origin of Species," in 1859, these notions became dominant and remained so for some time despite the fact that new types among both plants and animals were arising abruptly and spontaneously on every hand, which must have been most disconcerting to those who had espoused the creed of natural selection. For these unexpected forms Darwin proposed the term "sport," which continues to be used to this day, although just as he used it, in a more or less tentative, if not apologetic, way. The fact that new types or rather perhaps unknown types could arise spontaneously was the occasion for the mutation theory of de Vries, who found that new species often possessed something not present in the parent; these he called "progressive mutations." There were others which lacked something present in the parent and were therefore called "regressive mutations." Still others were defective and were called "degressive mutations," the degressive mutation being essentially defective throughout its structure and without the normal power of further propagation.

THE MENDELIAN LAW

It is now known that the reappearing types are due merely to genes which for a time had receded from view. Although genes and chromosomes had not been discovered, the term "recessive" had already been coined by Mendel to describe them, a discovery which doubtless far transcends any other contribution to genetics and which at that time, unknown to Darwin, lay slumbering in the archives of an obscure publication in Brunn, Austria.

Since the enunciation of the mendelian laws, it is no longer difficult to account for the reappearance of an unknown type, or even of the progressive or regressive types, the mating of recessive genes from both parents being responsible. The etiology of defective progeny, however, still awaits explanation, and so far as mongolism is concerned, one can at this time do no more than lean on suggestions which clinicians have made in seeking an explanation. These suggestions, it is true, comprise a somewhat formidable and more or less divergent group as is inevitable in so mysterious a situation, and aside from tuberculosis, which was strongly favored as the cause of mongolism by the early English writers, they are fairly represented in the following group:

1. Syphilis: (a) in the child and (b) the effect on the germ plasm of the parent.
2. Alcoholism in the immediate or remote parentage.
3. Shock during pregnancy or adverse environment of either parent.
4. Social position as a particular example of the latter.
5. Abnormalities of the pituitary sella.
6. Endocrine dysfunction in the child or the parent.
7. Neuropathic inheritance.
8. Consanguinity.
9. Parental age.
10. Race.
11. Sex.

An analysis of these factors by Macklin[5] and by myself[6] has served to arouse the suspicion that satisfactory information relating to the cause of mongolism is not now at hand. Further, it may be noted that the influence of sex, long recognized in relation to mentally defective persons as a class and apparently exhibiting an especially strong influence in mongolism,[7] cannot be accepted as anything more than a contributing factor. Parental age and the old hypothesis of exhaustion so generally quoted by writers on this subject are open to question.[8]

Before leaving this phase of the subject, however, it is especially interesting to recall the belief of Charles Herrman,[9] that mongolism exhibits the behavior of a true recessive unit because of which it may be expected to reappear in the general population from time to time according to the more or less exact ratios of Mendel. Unfortunately, it is in the field of pathology that the celebrated 3:1 ratios are often most difficult to follow, particularly in those diseases in which disruptions in the function of the germ cell may be assumed to have occurred and which may perhaps not duplicate the behavior of a gene of heredity on which mendelian laws are necessarily based. Certainly, however, all available data should be gathered which may bear on so interesting a suggestion.

CONCLUSIONS

1. Three signs of mongolism are described. One of them, redundancy of the folds of the neck, will usually assist in making a diagnosis. The other two are mentioned as of occasional corroborative value.

Of much greater importance is the desirability of search for additional evidence of this disease, which will be found, I believe, almost anywhere in the body if scrutiny is sufficiently close. Minute anatomy will contribute its part.

2. As to the origin of mongolism, one may perhaps speculate on the existence of an alteration in the normal number of chromosomes, just as this is known to account for the degressive mutations of plants, a very early alteration in the germ cell, a true gametic alteration which would repeat itself in every cell derived therefrom throughout the entire body. The human cell is a forty-eight chromosome cell. Whether in the mongoloid imbecile one is dealing with forty-nine or forty-seven, with fifty or forty-

six or with some other number of chromosomes must be left to the cytologist, in whose field the richest prizes in genetics now seem to lie.

Nor is it possible to reject the hypothesis of some other fixed irregularity or disturbance either of anatomy or of function of any part of the germinal cell, of which the chromosomes just now receive the largest share of attention. This irregularity owes its existence to causes not yet understood but capable of producing a defect which in this instance repeats itself with amazing faithfulness. This suggests one cause and one disturbance acting alike in the gamete and all of its progeny. In either case there seems to have been produced a true mutation which, in the language of de Vries, would be called degressive.

REFERENCES

1. Dorland, W. A. Newman, The American Illustrated Medical Dictionary, ed. 12, Philadelphia, W. B. Saunders Company, 1923. Webster: The Peerless Dictionary, Springfield, Mass., G. & C. Merriam Company, 1930.
2. Davidoff, L. M., The Brain in Mongolian Idiocy: Report of Ten Cases, *Arch. Neurol. & Psychiat. 20:*1229 (Dec.) 1928.
3. Wilson, Edmund B., The Physical Basis of Life, New Haven, Conn., Yale University Press, 1923.
4. Walter, Herbert Eugene, Genetics, ed. 3, New York, The Macmillan Company, 1930.
5. Macklin, M. T., Mongolian Idiocy: The Manner of Its Inheritance, *Am. J. M. Sc. 178:*315 (Sept.) 1929.
6. Bleyer, Adrien, Concerning the Origin of Mongoloid Imbecility, *J. Missouri M. A.,* to be published.
7. Bleyer, Adrien, The Frequency of Mongoloid Imbecility, The Question of Race and the Apparent Influence of Sex, *Am. J. Dis. Chil. 44:*503 (Sept.) 1932.
8. Brousseau, Kate, Mongolism, Baltimore, Williams & Wilkins Company, 1928.
9. Herrman, Charles, The Etiology of Mongolian Imbecility, *Arch. Pediat. 34:*494, 1917; Mongolian Imbecility as an Anthropologic Problem, *ibid. 42:*523, 1925.

55

CHROMOSOMES FOR BEGINNERS

Bernard Lennox, M.D. Durh., Ph.D. Lond., M.R.C.P., F.R.F.P.S.

I N this subject of human chromosomal anomalies we are all beginners. It is so new that even the old hands were new themselves two years ago. It has travelled so fast that it has shot past the average reader before he has had time to notice that it has begun to move, and he begins already to be frightened of it. This is a pity: the chromosomes are still essentially a very simple matter.

Classical genetics as applied to medicine demands a high level of conceptual thinking. It is a little like medieval medicine, deducing the nature of disease without even looking inside the patient; it relies on imperfect analogies with conditions in plants and insects, and on a very complex and largely mathematical system of deduction, to arrive at a purely notional model of what goes on at the chromosome level (this is not to decry its necessity or its truth, only to explain why the average brain finds it so difficult). The new methods may be still extremely crude: we are like a student watching a postmortem from the back benches of a large theatre, able to recognise that the liver is grossly enlarged or one kidney missing. But at least we can now really *see* something. They help us to understand only a corner of the field, but into that corner they shine a refreshing beam of good honest morbid anatomy, something tangible, unequivocal, simple to understand. It is well worth making a small effort to catch up with the main lines of discovery.

I have been charged with the task of making the subject intelligible to those who missed the beginning of the story. I propose to be as dogmatic as possible. I shall try to avoid saying anything demonstrably untrue; but to those who know the subject in much greater depth than I do, I hope I may be allowed to say firmly that this account is not intended for them.

Reprinted from *The Lancet*, May 13, 1961, pp. 1046-1051.

THE METHOD

Identifying Chromosomes

Let us take the bull by the horns and begin with one of those exasperating pictures with which the pages of *The Lancet* have

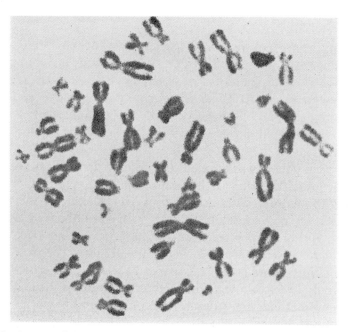

Fig. 1. A normal human mitosis, from a blood-cell culture prepared for chromosome analysis. Note that each of the 46 bodies present, though apparently double, is a single chromosome, not a pair. An example of a chromosome pair, readily recognisable as such, is offered by the two large chromosomes lying at right angles to each other in the upper left corner: these are pair No. 2—their nearness is purely fortuitous.

been so freely littered recently, and which are said to look like masses of squashed spiders. (Fig. 1.)

This is a normal mitosis—a mitosis skilfully coaxed, doctored, and stretched so that its chromosomes lie flat and separate; and stained and photographed so that everything except chromosomes is eliminated. (This is by no means as good a preparation as is possible, but it is sufficient for most purposes.)

Each of the little spiders is a chromosome (not, as you might easily suppose at first sight, a pair of chromosomes). Count them: you will find there are 46—the normal number. At first they look very much alike, but even a little attention will show that they differ a great deal in length. This is not just random variation. This will become more obvious if one examines the other point of distinction, the position of the *centromere*.

Before mitosis starts, the chromosomes have already nearly

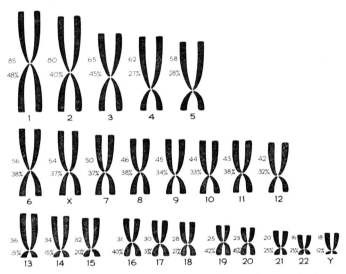

Fig. 2. An idealised chromosome set, numbered according to the internationally agreed Denver system. Note that only one of each pair is represented. The small figures beside each chromosome indicate approximately the relative length of the whole chromosome, and the proportion of the total length occupied by the short arm.

split into two chromatids, but they remain adherent at the centromere. At the crucial moment of division, the pull of the spindle splits the centromere, the chromatids separate to travel into the daughter cells and become its chromosomes in their turn. In the mitosis at which we are looking, the presence of colchicine in the brew has resulted in absence of the spindle, so that the centromere remains unsplit and the two chromatids remain tied together. The two are always exactly alike (apart from accidental bending in preparation) and whatever happens to the chromosome, it is always symmetrical. When one speaks of the "short arm" of a chromosome, one means *both* of the two shorter legs of the spider, and one tends to speak of them as though they were still fused together.

The centromere does not stain with the usual chromosome stains, and hence appears as a gap in the middle of the spider. The ratio between the lengths of the two arms separated by the centromere is constant for any one chromosome pair, and this is of great importance in identification.

If we arrange the chromosomes strictly in order of length, as has been done in fig. 2, the use of this begins to be obvious. (Fig. 2 is based on the official Denver nomenclature: note that only one of each pair is represented.) Most chromosomes, especially the big group of medium size, have the short arm about half the length of the long arm; but some have the two arms more nearly equal (1, 3, 16, 19, 20) and some are "acrocentric" with the centromere near the end (13, 14, 15, 21, 22, Y, and to a lesser extent, 4 and 5). The acrocentrics are the easiest of all to pick out. The group of middle-sized acrocentrics, 13-15, is a specially important landmark. Using fig. 3 as a guide, you should have no difficulty in picking them out in fig. 1.

The very smallest chromosomes are also acrocentric, though, especially in a photograph, it may be hard to see this clearly. But the next larger group (pairs 19 and 20) have definitely central centromeres and look like small fat starfish, and in consequence the smallest group is easy to separate. Since the Y belongs to it, there are five small acrocentrics in the normal male but only four in the female. Would it seem too much like a parlour game to suggest that you use this method to determine the sex of fig. 1?

The Chromosome Groups

Carrying on with this process, the chromosomes arrange themselves into well-defined groups (fig. 4). According to the Denver system, these are simply called group 1-3, group 4-5, group 6-12, group 13-15, group 16-18, group 19-20, and group 21-22 (less unimaginative names are used for the groups also, but as no two workers seem to use the same names it is better to stick to the simple numbers). With even a moderately good preparation, analysis of the chromosomes into these groups should be easy and unequivocal, and it should always be possible to say to which group a missing or an extra chromosome belongs—though of course it is always a good thing to have a fair number of mitoses to analyse to check the findings.

Identification of Individual Pairs

You will find that in most cases published recently all the chromosomes have been neatly paired off and numbered according to the Denver system. Do not be too much discouraged if you find it hard to see how the authors have separated off the pairs.

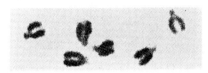

Fig. 3. The six chromosomes of group 13-15 from fig. 1. The group is very characteristic, but it is hardly possible (certainly not in this preparation) to separate them into three pairs. The apparent attachment of three of them together by their short arms is in this case not a matter of chance, but is common with the acrocentric chromosomes and perhaps reflects their association with the nucleolus—perhaps also it is a source of anomalies.

Just how complete identification can be is a matter of considerable dispute, but it is unlikely that even with the best of present-day techniques it can extend to all the pairs. Pairs 1, 2, 3, 16, and (often) the Y are certainly identifiable, but beyond this one gets into trouble. It used to be thought that pairs 13 and 21 could be identified by the presence of satellites (rather ill-named irregular whiskery excrescences on the short arm) but it seems now that these are characteristic of the acrocentrics generally rather than of individual pairs.

Take, for instance, pairs 4 and 5. It is easy to identify them as a group of four, for they have a much shorter short arm than anything at all near them in size. But to separate the two pairs is another matter. There is some random variation of chromosome length (demonstrable, for instance, between the two members of pair 1 in many individual mitoses) and this can easily be greater than the difference between the mean size of the two pairs. Perhaps in an occasional exceptionally good mitosis we may think we can make out one pair a little smaller than the other. But we can never be quite certain. So, for instance, if we had an extra chromosome in the group we should have great difficulty in deciding whether it was a 4 or a 5, though we could be quite certain it was one of the two. And so, in mongolism, though we usually

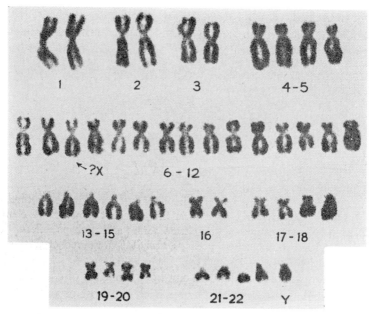

Fig. 4. The chromosomes of fig. 1 arranged in their groups. Within the groups they have been arranged as far as possible in order of length, but have not been paired off. The presence of five small acrocentrics and of only fifteen chromosomes in group 6-12 show that this is a male, although identification of the X is quite arbitrary and of the Y in this case not absolute.

assume the extra chromosome is a 21, it is still by no means certain it is not a 22.

The *6-12 group* in the middle is the biggest and most difficult to deal with. It consists of middle-sized chromosomes with the centromere neither very near the middle nor very near the end. It includes seven pairs of autosomes (which by the way means simply pairs that are always alike, as distinct from heterosomes, where the pairs are often unlike; but since in nearly all creation it is only the sex chromosomes that make unlike pairs, it has come about that autosomes in practice mean non-sex-chromosomes) and one or two X's—and so the number in the group is normally 15 in men and 16 in women. It is well defined by the distinctive wishbones 13-15 below and the almost equally distinctive pincers 4-5 above, and so it is fairly easy to count how many there are in the group (and so incidentally to obtain an independent check on sex). It is very much harder to separate the pairs within the group. Obviously one can tell one end of the group from the other: one will not mistake a 6 or a 7 for an 11 or a 12. How far one can go beyond this is a matter of dispute into which there is not much point in entering here.

It is not even certain which is the X, though it is generally supposed to be the second largest, coming between pairs 6 and 7. It is nearly always, however, possible to find an independent check of the number of X's present by nuclear sexing. With a very few exceptions (interesting in themselves, but not such as to destroy the rule) where nuclear sexing indicates one or more extra X's, the corresponding number of extra chromosomes are found in the 6-12 group, and it is always reasonable therefore to assume that this excess is due to X's.

These doubts as to the defensibility of exact identification of the whole chromosome set must not be thought to interfere at all with the reliability of the findings in the vast majority of published cases. There have been one or two mistakes, but not such as to cause damage. It does not really matter whether the mongol chromosome is a 21 or 22: it must be one or the other, and when circumstances arise that make it necessary to decide which it is, the circumstances themselves will probably contain the seeds of the solution.

Technique

This is no place to describe methods in detail. Perhaps what the general reader most needs to know is that they are increasingly reliable but still not easy. It is probably less difficult to analyse a well-prepared mitosis than to prepare one well. Probably it should not be attempted by any group unless at least one well-qualified person is prepared to devote full time to it.

There are three chief sources of the mitoses needed for study.

All depend on tissue-culture techniques, but the length of cultivation varies widely. Classical tissue-culture methods, aiming at the production of a single layer of cells growing rapidly on a flat glass surface, can give very beautiful results; but they are costly in time, labour, and skill. The first relatively simple technique depended on the ability of marrow cells to continue dividing when kept in suspension in tissue-culture media for twelve hours or so. The most recent method uses the white cells of the blood, and depends on a curious property of phytoagglutinin extracted from French beans. If one precipitates the red cells from a blood sample with this material and then incubates the white cells in the remaining plasma (plus synthetic tissue-culture medium) an unexplained burst of mitoses occurs about the third day. This method not only avoids sternal puncture but gives better results, and is almost universally used at present.

In the later stages of all methods colchicine is an almost invariable ingredient. It stops mitoses in mid-career, so that they accumulate and are easier to find. Also, by breaking up the spindle, it allows the chromosomes to separate, instead of lying bunched together in the familiar star-shaped mass. This spreading process is helped by making the cells swell (just before fixation) with hypotonic solutions, and by flattening them out on the slide either by judicious squashing or by air drying. There is a good deal of green fingers involved in all these processes.

Prospects

He would be a brave man who would attempt to predict the lines of future development. It may be that the present breakthrough is already near the limit of our progress for a long time —that technique will improve in simplicity and reliability, but not very much in resolving power, so that even the ability to distinguish all the chromosome pairs with certainty will still elude us. We need either bigger chromosomes or higher magnifications. For the latter ultraviolet photography might help a little, but electron microscopy will have to travel a long way before it can give useful results. Bigger chromosomes would be best of all, but we know of no way of producing them.

The tantalising thing is that a relatively small increase in resolution might yield tremendous dividends. Naturally occurring enlarged chromosomes (the giant chromosomes of the salivary glands of dipteran larvæ, or the lamp-brush chromosomes of frog eggs) show an enormous amount of detail which enables one not only to identify the individual chromosome but also to localise events along its length with great exactitude. It is nearly certain that human chromosomes, if only we could see them clearly enough, possess intensely varied individual patterns. If only we could grow them a few times their present size, or magnify them a few more diameters, we should begin to see these patterns. There seems to be no immediate prospect of either being achieved; but in this subject pessimists are continually being confounded.

Examination of meioses would of course help, at least with the pairing-off problem. But there is no known way of producing meioses artificially. Ovarian meiosis is hardly ever accessible in man; and, though testicular biopsy is a simple enough procedure, a very large proportion of the most interesting cases have disorders of spermatogenesis which make it useless. Even given a good active testicular biopsy, the technical problems of obtaining from it a preparation comparable to modern mitotic cultures have not yet been overcome.

APPLICATIONS OF THE METHOD

Detectable Chromosome Abnormalities

From what I have said so far it should be clear that any change in the chromosomes has to be gross to be visible at all with present methods. We can count the total number of chromosomes accurately, and if the number is wrong we may be able to say which is missing or in excess. If there is a structural abnormality of a chromosome we may be able to recognise it, but only if it is relatively massive. We may be able to recognise a loss of half a micron from a chromosome 22, because this is nearly half its long arm, but a much larger loss from a chromosome 1 will pass without notice. And the amount of genetic material in half a micron of a chromosome must be colossal. (The number of distinguishable loci in the average chromosome appears to be of the order of 100,000.)

Dismiss from your mind every idea that the genetic lesion of traditional Mendel-inherited disorders like hæmophilia or phenyl-ketonuria could possibly be demonstrated by the kind of method we are discussing. These depend on a disorder of the deoxyribo-nucleic acid chain—perhaps the misplacement of a single base in the chain, one dash written for a dot in an enormously long Morse code message. It is like hoping to detect a single false note in a recording of a symphony speeded up so fast that we hear the whole in a second. The most we can manage at present is to identify the symphony from its length and the position of its main interval. Even if a whole movement were substituted by one from another symphony, we should only be able to recognise the fault if it was one of very different length from the original.

Possible Anomalies

When we consider the amount of genetic material concerned in even the smallest visible chromosome lesions, it is astonishing that any of them can be compatible with life. The answer to this is that, of the great variety of lesions, only a very small num-ber are seen in practice. One is concerned here, of course, only with lesions that affect the whole body: what is compatible with survival of a part of the body—and especially of a tumour—is a very different matter. Tumours especially are capable of huge chromosome variations: but they do not have to achieve viability on their own account.

Loss, for instance, of one whole chromosome (*monosomy*, be-cause only one of a pair remains) is nearly always fatal, and so is loss of a substantial fraction of one chromosome. Gain of an extra chromosome is not so bad, though still bad: every variety of *trisomy* (i.e., the presence of three chromosomes of a kind in-stead of the normal pair) is damaging, but several varieties at least are compatible with life and one even with reproduction.

Loss or gain of the sex chromosomes seems to be especially well tolerated. Both contain relatively little genetic material for their size, and, since there is a normal variation in the number of each kind, there must be a tolerance to such variations which is not called for with the autosomes. (To take one simple example of the way this can work, any autosome may carry lethal recessives which are bound to be exposed in the monosomic condition: but, since both are single in the male, the Y cannot and the X is most unlikely to carry any such lethal factors.) Whatever the reason, it is a fact that sex-chromosome monosomy (a single X or XO) is the only form of monosomy yet recognised, and all or nearly all the cases with more than one extra chromosome have involved the sex chromosomes.

Clinical Manifestations

Between lesions that are too big for survival and lesions that are too small to be recognised, the ground is narrow. There are four well-established and reasonably common syndromes, and a great number of rarer variants, less well studied. Of the four main syndromes, three involve sex chromosomes, one an autosome; three are trisomies with 47 chromosomes, one a monosomy with 45; three are old syndromes revived, one is wholly new. Any one of these four is a study in itself: what follows is the barest bones.

(a) Trisomy-21 (*mongolism*).—No description in needed of this familiar, common (1 in 600 births) and precisely defined form of congenital mental defect. Its cause is now demonstrably the presence of an extra chromosome 21. As to *how* the anomaly produces mongolism we are literally clueless, but the fact is there. (Mental defect—and sterility—seem especially common consequences of chromosome anomalies, but neither is constant: XO interferes little with intelligence and XXX is often fertile.) A very few mongols have the normal 46 chromosomes, but these are the "translocation" cases (see below) in which the bulk of the extra 21 is still present but attached to another chromosome.

(b) Trisomy-X (the *XXX syndrome*).—These cases are women, often mentally defective, but otherwise unremarkable. They are often fertile, producing normal offspring. Probably they account for something under 1% of female mental defectives and something under 0.1% of all female births. This is the latest of the four syndromes to be described, and the only one that is not an easy clinical spot diagnosis. It carries its hallmark, however, in the buccal smear, where the duplicated sex-chromatin bodies in the nuclei are very characteristic. Cases with four or more X chromosomes occur, but much more rarely: the abnormality is probably always greater than with simple XXX. With each extra X the number of sex-chromatin bodies increases in step, the total being just one less than the number of X chromosomes in each case.

(c) Trisomy-XY *(XXY Klinefelter's syndrome).*—These cases, in most respects normal males, have small testicles (tubular atrophy and Leydig-cell hyperplasia) and infertility as their only constant features. Eunuchoidism, gynæcomastia, and mental defect also feature prominently in any series. After puberty clinical diagnosis is not difficult, bilateral small soft testes without other obvious cause being always very suggestive of it. The presence of sex chromatin in the buccal smear will clinch the diagnosis. Anatomically normal male external genitalia and a chromatin-positive buccal smear are practically diagnostic of XXY. (Note that some cases of Klinefelter's syndrome are not due to chromosomal anomaly, but these are chromatin-negative.) Something over 0.2% of all male births, over 1% of male mental defectives, and over 3% of men with organic infertility are XXY. Again there are rarer and more severely affected variants with a larger number of X's, some also probably with additional Y's, and mosaic mixtures.

(d) Monosomy-X *(XO Turner's syndrome).*—This is the most complex disorder and fairly certainly the least common of the four. The classical syndrome is well known and well defined: a dwarf woman, with absent or grossly hypoplastic gonads and the endocrine consequences of this, and with in addition a variety of more or less constant associated stigmata—webbed neck, irregular ears and hairline, cubitus valgus, shield shaped chest with wide-spaced nipples, peripheral œdema in infancy, cardiovascular defects, including coarctation, and others. Fertility is very rare but intelligence little if at all affected.

Besides the straight syndrome there are many marginal varieties. Incomplete XO's are probably as common as the complete form: either only part of the second X is missing or, more often, the patient is a mosaic, with an admixture of XX or XY or XXX cells. In addition there is a confusing group of cases too diverse to discuss here, with some part of the clinical syndrome but no chromosomal anomaly.

Clinical diagnosis of Turner's syndrome is usually easy, at least after puberty. A buccal smear is of obvious value: the XO cases are chromatin-negative (though an exception to this is claimed) and the mosaics give intermediate patterns which may, however, need some experience to interpret. A surprisingly large proportion of cases of primary amenorrhœa are due to chromosomal anomalies, and such cases should always have at least a buccal smear (which will uncover also cases of testicular feminisation, though this is not due to a chromosomal anomaly).

(e) Other abnormalities.—These begin to be numerous, and cannot be dealt with adequately here. Trisomies have been claimed for quite a few chromosome pairs, and some (especially one in the 13-15 group, and one in the 17-18) are well established. The cases are all mentally defective children with multiple congenital defects, and the numbers of cases are too few for the certain definition of syndromes, though it is most probable that syndromes corresponding to each viable trisomy will be established in time. Multiple trisomies (especially the mongol-Klinefelter combination, $3 \times 21 + XXY$) occur. Translocations, deletions, and perhaps other chromosome lesions are also involved, and may be even harder to relate to clinical syndromes. Mosaics also must be included, though those recognised so far have all been related to the four main syndromes. One triploid child, with trisomy of all pairs and 69 chromosomes in all, is the most extreme anomaly yet recorded.

ORIGIN OF THE ANOMALIES

Almost certainly, the usual cause of the commoner and the grosser chromosomal anomalies is the process of *non-disjunction*. During the preparation for reduction division during meiosis, the two chromosomes of each pair come briefly together (the only time when they are paired off naturally) before they separate to go one to each daughter cell (haploid, with twenty-three chromosomes). If this process goes wrong, either by failure of pairing-off or by failure of separation of the pair once formed, both members of one pair may find themselves in one gamete. For example, if we consider the presumed origin of mongolism by non-disjunction in the mother (Fig. 5) it is easy to see how faulty division of the oocyte can result in a cell with two 21's and another with none at all. Each normal male spermatozoon brings its single 21, and when it fertilises an ovum with two 21's, the result is a zygote with three, which results in a mongol. If it fertilises an ovum with no 21's, the final zygote has only one, and this must die at some early stage of pregnancy.

Most simple trisomies can be explained in this way. Non-disjunction increases with the age of the mother: hence the clear evidence of a maternal-age effect, at least in mongolism and the XXX syndrome. The above account disregards the existence of a second meiotic division which, however, usually results in duplication of the products of the first, so that four cells (two with two 21's, and two with no 21's, in the example given are produced instead of two: all four survive as gametes in the male, but three are lost as polar bodies in the female. Cases with more than three X's suggest that in the case of that chromosome at least the non-disjunction can be repeated in the second division, so that in the extreme case the four nuclei resulting would be XXXX, O, O and O.

Though the term non-disjunction should, properly speaking, only be applied to the meiotic defect, something very similar can also occur in mitosis, both daughter chromosomes derived from one chromosome passing into one of the daughter cells. It appears that this can sometimes happen at a very early stage. For instance, at least two women are known whose bodies consist of mosaics of roughly equal numbers of XO and XXX cells. One can only suppose that such a woman began as a normal XX zygote, but that at its first division "non-disjunction" occurred with one of the X's, both of whose daughter chromosomes passed into one daughter cell, and thus of the two cells produced one had an X too many and the other an X too few. Not all mosaics arise in this way: thus, for instance, an XXY/XY mosaic may arise by early loss of an X from what was originally an XXY ovum—a remarkable example, if this is true, of accidental reversion to normal.

Translocation is so far much less important, though translocations too small to see may be common. A translocation is an exchange of material between two chromosomes of different pairs
(exchange with the other member of the same pair is a normal
part of meiosis). Simple exchange between two chromosomes has

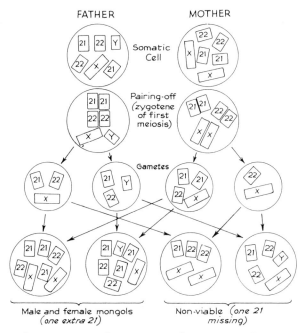

Fig. 5. Non-disjunction producing mongolism. Most of the chromosomes
have been omitted, leaving only the sex chromosomes and pair 22 (which
behave normally) and pair 21 which behave normally in the father and
undergoes non-disjunction in the mother. Both 21's pass into one ovum,
so that after fertilisation the offspring have three 21's and are mongols.
The ovum without a 21 cannot produce a live child. (Second meiosis and
polar bodies have been disregarded.)

little immediate effect (all the genetic material is still there)
though there may be defects arising from imperfections at the
new joints. Since, however, the chromosomes affected are now
different (sometimes very widely different) from their original
partners, they cannot pair off properly during meiosis, and irregularities may arise in the offspring in consequence. Thus in some
families a translocation may exist which has the effect of attaching

the bulk of one 21 to another larger chromosome: in itself the translocation does not matter, and it may be carried through several generations, but it so affects meiosis that occasional members of the family acquire an extra dose of 21 and so appear as mongols, thus giving rise to the most important variety (even if rare) of familial mongolism. This is the only chromosomal anomaly yet recognised as transmissible: all the other anomalies so far known stop at the one case in which they appear.

There are other kinds of chromosomal lesion, of which deletion (loss of part of a chromosome) is the simplest, and this has occasionally been blamed for disease in man.

ACQUIRED CHROMOSOME ANOMALIES

All the diseases so far discussed are congenital, demanding a lesion already present in the fertilised ovum or (for mosaics) its immediate successors. The new techniques have so far only increased our knowledge of acquired lesions in two ways. In the first place, it has been shown that in most cases of chronic myeloid leukæmia there is a deletion of part of one of the smallest autosomes—a 21 or a 22. And in the second, it has been shown that a single dose of 250 rad of deep x-rays to the spine, or 100 mC. of radioiodine, produces a shortlived but surprisingly abundant crop of chromosomal anomalies. These are both profoundly interesting observations which cannot be discussed further here.

> In an attempt to set down the essential facts intelligibly in the least possible space I have left out all the history, all the people, and all the original references. There are too many of the latter to give them all and to choose would be invidious. If I have failed to give credit where it is abundantly due, I apologise, but I have at least been consistent. Fortunately, so large a fraction of the formative papers in the subject have appeared in *The Lancet* that the earnest inquirer is recommended to begin with the issue of April 4, 1959, and work steadily through all the issues from then until now, using the index as far as it is available. Nearly all the people who matter are represented. You will find it heavy going in places, but most of it makes good sense, and it is a wonderful story.
>
> Weaker vessels may find the editorials of April 4, 1959 (p. 715), Sept. 26, 1959 (p. 448), May 4, 1960 (p. 1118), July 23, 1960

(p. 191), Nov. 12, 1960 (p. 1068), and Feb. 25, 1961 (p. 433), especially the first and the last three, a better historical introduction than this, and a useful source of all but the most recent references.

The mitosis was prepared by Miss Elizabeth Boyd, the photograph by Mr. G. Kerr, and the diagrams by Mr. R. Callander.

HUMAN CHROMOSOME BIBLIOGRAPHY*
1956-60

1956

BARR, MURRAY L. Cytological Tests of Sex. *Lancet, i:*47.

FORD, C. E. and J. H. HAMERTON. A Colchicine, hypotonic citrate, squash sequence for mammalian chromosomes. *Stain Technology, 31:*247.

FORD, C. E. and J. L. HAMERTON. The chromosomes of man. *Acta Genet.,* 6:264-266.

FORD, C. E. and J. L. HAMERTON. The chromosomes of man. *Nature,* 178:1020-1023.

FRITZ-NIGGLI, H. Die Chromosomen im menschlichen Mamma-Karzinom. *Acta Unio Internat. Conta Cancrum, 12:*623-637.

HANSEN-MELANDER, E.; S. KULLANDER; and Y. MELANDER. Chromosome analysis of a human ovarian cystocarcinoma in the ascites form. *J. Nat. Cancer Inst., 16:*1067-1081.

HSU, T. C. and P. S. MOORHEAD. Chromosomal anomalies in human neoplasms with special reference to the mechanisms of polyploidization and aneuploidization in the HeLa strain. *Ann. N. Y. Acad. Sc., 62:*1083-1094.

HSU, T. C.; R. K. ROBINS; and C. C. CHENG. Studies on 4 APP: antineoplastic action *in vitro. Science, 123:*848-849.

KOLLER, P. C. Cytological variability in human carcinomatosis. *Ann. N. Y. Acad. Sc., 63:*793-816.

LEIGHTON, J.; I. KLINE; and H. C. ORR. Transformation of normal human fibroblasts into histologically malignant tissue *in vitro. Science, 123:*502-503.

LENNOX, B. Nuclear sexing: a review incorporating some personal observations. *Scott. Med. J., 1:*97-121.

LEVAN, A. Chromosomes in cancer tissue. *Ann. N. Y. Acad. Sc., 63:*744-789.

LEVAN, A. Chromosome studies on some human tumors and tissues of normal origin, grown *in vivo* and *in vitro* at the Sloan-Kettering Institute. *Cancer, 9:*648-663.

* Reprinted from *The Human Chromosome Newsletter*, No. 3, by kind permission of its editors, Dr. D. G. Harnden and Miss Patricia A. Jacobs, Western General Hospital, Edinburgh, and Dr. D. A. Hungerford of Philadelphia, Dr. M. L. Barr, London, Ontario, Dr. J. A. Böök of Uppsala, Sweden, Dr. J. de Grouchy, of Paris, France, Dr. W. Kosenow, Munster, Germany, Dr. J. Lejeune of Paris, France, and Dr. S. Makino of Hokkaido University, Japan.

LEVAN, A. Self-perpetuating ring chromosomes in two human tumours. *Hereditas, 42*:366-372.

MANNA, G. K. Handling human chromosomes by a coumarin technic. *Stain Technol., 31*:45-49.

MOORE, A. E.; C. M. SOUTHAM; and S. S. STERNBERG. Neoplastic changes developing in epithelial cell lines derived from normal persons. *Science, 124*:127-129.

MOORHEAD, P. S. and T. C. HSU. Cytologic studies of HeLa, a strain of human cervical carcinoma. III. Durations and characteristics of the mitotic phases. *J. Nat. Cancer Inst., 16*:1047-1066.

POLANI, P. E.; M. H. LESSOF; and P. M. F. BISHOP. Colour blindness in "ovarian agenesis" (gonadal dysplasia). *Lancet, ii*:118.

TJIO, J. H. and A. LEVAN. The chromosome number of man. *Hereditas, 42*:1-6.

1957

BARR, M. L. and K. L. MOORE. Chromosomes, sex chromatin, and cancer. *Canad. Cancer Conf., 2*:3-16.

BARR, MURRAY L. Cytologic Tests of Chromosomal Sex. *Progress in Gynecology, 3.*

BENDER, M. A. X-ray induced chromosome aberrations in normal diploid human tissue cultures. *Science, 126*:974-975.

DANON, M. and L. SACHS. Sex chromosomes and human sexual development. *Lancet, ii*:20.

FERGUSON-SMITH, M. A.; B. LENNOX; W. S. MACK; and J. S. S. STEWART. Klinefelter's Syndrome. Frequency and Testicular Morphology in Relation to Nuclear Sex. *Lancet, ii*:167.

HSU, T. C. and P. S. MOORHEAD. Mammalian chromosomes *in vitro*. VII. Heteroploidy in human cell strains. *J. Nat. Cancer Inst., 18*:463-471.

HSU, T. C.; C. M. POMERAT; and P. S. MOORHEAD. Mammalian chromosomes *in vitro*. VIII. Heteroploid transformation in the human cell strain Mayes. *J. Nat. Cancer Inst., 19*:867-873.

ISING, U. and A. LEVAN. The chromosomes of two highly malignant human tumors. *Acta Path. et Microbiol. Scand., 40*:13-24.

KLINGER, HAROLD P. and KURT S. LUDWIG. A Universal Stain for the Sex Chromatin Body. *Stain Technology, 32*, No. 5.

KODANI, M. The karyotype of man with the diploid chromosome number of 48. Proc. Internat. Genetics Symp., 1956, Tokyo and Kyoto. *Cytologia*, suppl. vol., pp. 103-107.

KODANI, M. Three diploid chromosome numbers of man. *Proc. Nat. Acad. Sc. 43*:285-292.

MANNA, K. G. A study on chromosomes of the human nonneoplastic and neoplastic uterine tissues. Proc. Internat. Genetics Symp., 1956, Tokyo and Kyoto, *Cytologia*, suppl. vol., 182-187.

MOORE, K. L. and M. L. BARR. The Sex Chromatin in Human Malignant Tissues. *Brit. J. of Cancer*, 11:384.

REITALU, J. Observation on the so-called sex chromatin in man. *Acta Geneticae Medicae et Gemellologiae*, 6:393-402.

SOUTHAM, C. M.; A. E. MOORE; and C. P. RHOADS. Homotransplantation of human cell lines. *Science*, 125:158-160.

SYVERTON, J. T. Comparative studies of normal and malignant human cells in continuous culture. Cellular Biology, Nucleic Acids and Viruses. *Special Publ. N. Y. Acad. Sci.*, 5:331-340.

WENDT, G. G. and B. E. WOLF. Die Chromosomenzahl beim Menschen. *Dtsch. med. Wachr.*, 82(43):1832-1836.

YERGANIAN, G. Cytologic maps of some isolated human pachytene chromosomes. *Amer. J. Human Genetics*, 9:42-54.

YOSIDA, T. H. and T. TABATA. Karyological study on the normal somatic and malignant tumour cells in the human. *Ann. Rep. Nat. Inst. Genet.* (Japan) 8:25.

1958

ASHLEY, D. J. B. Discrepancies in the Diagnosis of Genetic Sex by Leucocyte Morphology. *Lancet*, i:240.

ASHLEY, D. J. B. and C. H. JONES. Sex Reversal: Ovarian Tissue associated with Male Nuclear Sex. *Lancet*, i:74.

ASHLEY, D. J. B. and E. A. THEISS. Nuclear Sex of Patients with Testicular Tumour. *Science*, 128:1434.

CHU, E. H. Y. and N. H. GILES. Chromosome complements and nucleoli in normal human somatic cells in culture. *Proc. X Int. Cong. Genetics*, 11:50 (abstr.).

CHU, E. H. Y. and N. H. GILES. Comparative chromosomal studies on mammalian cells in culture. I. The HeLa strain and its mutant clonal derivatives. *J. Nat. Cancer Inst.*, 20:383-401.

CORNWELL, J. G. and W. HERRMANN. Intersexuality in mentally deficient patients. *Acta Endocrinol.*, 27:369.

EDITORIAL, Sex Reversal. *Lancet*, i:89.

ELMHOLT, L. On the chromosome number of human sternal marrow. *Acta Path. et Micro. Scand.*, 43:241.

FERGUSON-SMITH, M. A. Chromatin-Positive Klinefelter's Syndrome (Primary Microrchidism). *Lancet*, i:928.

FERGUSON-SMITH, M. A. Gonadal Dysgenesis. *Lancet*, i:1176.

FERGUSON-SMITH, M. A. and I. B. MUNRO. Spermatogenesis in the presence of Female Nuclear Sex. *Scot. Med. Jour.*, 3:39.

FORD, C. E.; P. A. JACOBS; and L. G. LAJTHA. Human somatic chromosomes. *Nature*, 181:1565-1568.

GRUMBACH, M. M. and M. L. BARR. Cytologic tests of chromosomal sex in relation to sexual anomalies in man. *Rec. Progr. Hormone Res.*, N. Y., 14:255-334 (L).

Hsu, T. C.; L. Milofsky; and R. Fuerst. Studies on 4-aminopyrazolo (3,4-d) pyrimidine: reversal of cellular damage in the HeLa stain. *Tex. Rpts. Biol. and Med.*, 16:472-478.

Kodani, M. Studies on Human Chromosomes—A Review. *La Kromosomo*, 34/36:1246.

Kodani, M. The supernumerary chromosome of man. *Amer. J. Human Genetics*, 10:125-140.

Kodani, M. Three chromosome numbers in whites and Japanese. *Science*, 127:1339-1340.

Levan, A. Cancerogenesis. A genetic adaptation on the cellular level. *Overdruck Achste Jaarboek van Kankeronderzoek en Kankerbestrijding in Nederland*, pp. 110-126.

Levan, A. Cancer Chromosomes, *Xth International Congress of Genetics*, Montreal, Aug. 20-27.

Nowell, P. C.; D. A. Hungerford; and C. D. Brooks. Chromosomal characteristics of normal and leukemic human leukocytes after short-term tissue culture. *Proc. Amer. Assoc. for Cancer Res.*, 2:331-332 (abstr.).

Polani, P. E.; P. M. F. Bishop; B. Lennox; M. A. Ferguson-Smith; J. S. S. Stewart; and A. Prader. Colour vision studies and the X chromosome constitution of patients with Klinefelter's Syndrome. *Nature*, 182:1092.

Prader, A.; J. Schneider; J. M. Francés; and W. Züblin. Frequency of the true (Ch. +ve) Klinefelter's Syndrome. *Lancet*, i:968.

Puck, T. T. Action of radiation on mammalian cells. III. Relationship between reproductive death and induction of chromosome anomalies by X-irradiation of euploid human cells *in vitro*. *Proc. Nat. Acad. Sc.*, 44:772-780.

Puck, T. T.; S. J. Cieciura; and A. Robinson. Genetics of somatic mammalian cells. III. Long-term cultivation of euploid cells from human and animal subjects. *J. Exp. Med.*, 108:945-956.

Ruddle, F. H.; L. Berman; and C. S. Stulberg. Chromosome analysis of five long-term cell culture populations derived from nonleukemic human peripheral blood (Detroit strains). *Cancer Res.*, 18:1048-1059.

Serr, D. M.; M. A. Ferguson-Smith; B. Lennox; and J. Paul. Representation of the X chromosome in intermitotic nuclei in man. *Nature*, 182:124.

Tjio, J. H. and T. T. Puck. Genetics of somatic mammalian cells. II. Chromosomal constitution of cells in tissue culture. *J. Exp. Med.*, 108:259-268.

Tjio, J. H. and T. T. Puck. The somatic chromosomes of man. *Proc. Nat. Acad. Sc.*, 44:1229-1237.

Wakabayashi, M. and T. Ishihara. Cytological studies of tumors, XXVI. Chromosome analysis of a human mammary carcinoma. *Cytologia*, 23:341-348.

Weicker, H. and K. H. Terwey. "The number of the chromosomes in the erythroblasts." *Klin. Wchnschr.*, 36:1132-1138. (Abstracted in *Blood*, 15:931 (1960).)

1959

Awano, I. and F. Tuda. The Chromosomes of Stomach Cancers and Myelogenous Leukaemias in Comparison with normal human complex. *Jap. J. Genet., 34*:220.

Baikie, A. G.; W. M. Court Brown; P. A. Jacobs; and J. S. Milne. Chromosome studies in human leukaemia. *Lancet, ii*:425-428.

Barr, M. L. Sex Chromatin and phenotype in man. *Science, 130*:679.

Barr, M. L.; E. L. Shaver; D. H. Carr; and E. R. Plunkett. An unusual sex chromatin pattern in three male mental defectives. *J. Ment. Defic. Res., 3*:78.

Barr, M. L. The Chromosomes of Man. *The Canadian Med. Assoc. J., 81*:192.

Bearn, J. G. Nuclear Chromatin of Anencephalic Foetuses. *Lancet, i*:24.

Bender, M. A. X-ray induced chromosome aberrations in mammalian cells *in vivo* and *in vitro. Internat. J. Radiation Biol.* (special suppl.):103-113.

Böök, J. A. Chromosomal variations in man and their clinical significance. *Uppsala LäkFören. Förh., 64*:7-8.

Böök, J. A.; M. Fraccaro; and J. Lindsten. Cytogenetical observations in mongolism. *Acta Paediatrica, 48*:453-468.

Carpenter, P. J. and Edith L. Potter. Nuclear Sex and Genital malformation in 48 cases of renal agenesis with especial reference to non-specified female pseudohermaphroditism. *Amer. J. Obstr. and Gynec., 78*:2, 235.

Chu, E. H. Y. and N. H. Giles. Qualitative and quantitative analyses of X-ray induced human chromosome aberrations in cultures of normal diploid somatic cells. *Genetics, 44*:503-504.

Chu, E. H. Y. and N. H. Giles. Human chromosome complements in normal somatic cells in culture. *Am. J. Human Genet., 11*:63-79.

Editorial, How Common Is Sex Reversal? *Lancet, i*:237.

Editorial, The Sex of Teratomas. *Lancet, ii*:777.

Ferguson-Smith, M. A. The Prepubertal Testicular Lesion in Chromatin-Positive Klinefelter's Syndrome (Primary Micro-Orchidism) as seen in mentally handicapped Children. *Lancet, i*:219.

Ford, C. E. Chromosomes of man. *Brit. Med. J., ii*:1330-1331.

Ford, C. E. and R. H. Mole. Chromosome studies in human leukaemia. *Lancet, ii*:732.

Ford, C. E.; K. W. Jones; O. J. Miller; U. Mittwoch; L. S. Penrose; M. Ridler; and A. Shapiro. The chromosomes in a patient showing both mongolism and the Klinefelter syndrome. *Lancet, i*:709-710.

Ford, C. E.; K. W. Jones; P. E. Polani; J. C. de Almeida; and J. H. Briggs. A sex-chromosome anomaly in a case of gonadal dysgenesis (Turner's syndrome). *Lancet, i*:711-713.

Ford, C. E.; P. E. Polani; J. H. Briggs; and P. M. F. Bishop. A presumptive human XXY/XX mosaic. *Nature, 183*:1030-1032.

FRACCARO, M. Chromosomal variations in anomalies of sexual development. *Uppsala LäkFören. Förh., 64*:8.

FRACCARO, M.; K. KAIJSER; and J. LINDSTEN. Chromosome complement in gonadal dysgenesis. *Lancet, i*:886.

FRACCARO, M.; K. KAIJSER; and J. LINDSTEN. Chromosome complement in parents of patient with gonadal dysgenesis (Turner's syndrome). *Lancet, ii*:1090.

FRACCARO, M. and J. LINDSTEN. Observations of the so-called "sex chromatin" in human somatic cells cultivated *in vitro. Exp. Cell Res., 17*:536-539.

FRACCARO, M. and P. O. NYMAN. Effects of 8-ethoxycaffeine on human somatic cells cultivated *in vitro. Exp. Cell Res., 17*:536-539.

FRACCARO, M. and P. O. NYMAN. Effects of 8-ethoxycaffeine on human somatic cells cultivated *in vitro. Uppsala LäkFören. Förh., 64*:232-235.

GALTON, M. and K. BENIRSCHKE. Forty-six chromosomes in an ovarian teratoma. *Lancet, ii*:761-762.

HARNDEN, D. G. and C. N. ARMSTRONG. The chromosomes of a true hermaphrodite. *Brit. Med. J., ii*:1287-1288.

HARNDEN, D. G.; J. H. BRIGGS; and J. S. S. STEWART. Nuclear chromatin of anencephalic foetuses. *Lancet, ii*:126-127.

HARNDEN, D. G. and J. S. S. STEWART. The chromosomes in a case of pure gonadal dysgenesis. *Brit. Med. J., ii*:1285-1287.

HARRIS, H. Human Biochemical Genetics. Cambridge Univ. Press. viii + 310 pp.

HSU, T. C.; L. MILOFSKY; R. K. ROBINS; and C. C. CHENG. Studies on 4-aminopyrazolo (3,4-d) pyrimidine: action of derivatives and analogues on HeLa cells. *Antibiotics and Chemotherapy, 9*:333-336.

HUNGERFORD, D. A. Chromosomes and Intersexuality. *Lancet, ii*:98.

HUNGERFORD, D. A.; A. J. DONNELLY; P. C. NOWELL; and S. BECK. The chromosome constitution of a human phenotypic intersex. *Am. J. Human Genet., 11*:215-236.

ISHIHARA, T. A chromosome study in five near-diploid human tumors. *Jap. Jour. Genet., 34*:23-27.

ISHIHARA, T. Cytological studies of tumors. XXXI. A chromosome study in a human gastric carcinoma. *Gann, 50*:403-408.

ISHIHARA, T. Some aspects on the chromosomes of a human gastric carcinoma in the ascites form. *Jap. Jour. Genet., 34*:28-33.

JACOBS, P.; A. G. BAIKIE; W. M. COURT BROWN; H. FORREST; J. R. ROY; J. S. S. STEWART; and B. LENNOX. Chromosomal sex in the syndrome of testicular feminization. *Lancet, ii*:591-592.

JACOBS, P. A.; A. G. BAIKIE; W. M. COURT BROWN; D. G. HARNDEN; T. N. MACGREGOR; and N. MACLEAN. Use of the term "superfemale." *Lancet, ii*:1145.

JACOBS, P. A.; A. G. BAIKIE; W. M. COURT BROWN; T. N. MACGREGOR; N. MACLEAN; and D. G. HARNDEN. Evidence for the existence of the human "super female." *Lancet, ii*:423-425.

JACOBS, P. A.; A. G. BAIKIE; W. M. COURT BROWN; and J. A. STRONG. The somatic chromosomes in mongolism. *Lancet, i*:710.

JACOBS, P. A. and A. J. KEAY. Somatic chromosomes in a child with Bonnevie-Ullrich syndrome. *Lancet, ii*:732.

JACOBS, P. A. and J. A. STRONG. A case of human intersexuality having a possible XXY sex-determining mechanism. *Nature, 183*:302-303.

LEJEUNE, J. Le mongolisme, maladie chromosomique. *La Nature, 3296*:522.

LEJEUNE, J.; M. GAUTIER; and R. TURPIN. Les chromosomes humains en cultur de tissus. *C. R. Acad. Sci.*, Paris, *248*:602-603.

LEJEUNE, J.; M. GAUTIER; and R. TURPIN. Étude des chromosomes somatiques de neuf enfants mongoliens. *C. R. Acad. Sci.*, Paris, *248*:1721-1722.

LEJEUNE, J.; M. GAUTIER; and R. TURPIN. The chromosomes of man. *Lancet, i*:885.

LEJEUNE, J. and R. TURPIN. Somatic Chromosomes in Mongolism. Meeting Annual, *Amer. Ass. Ment. Nerv. Dis. Res.*, New York.

LEJEUNE, J.; R. TURPIN; and M. GAUTIER. Le mongolisme, maladie chromosomique (trisomie). *Bull. Acad. Nat. Méd., 143* (11 and 12):256-265.

LEJEUNE, J.; R. TURPIN; and M. GAUTIER. Le mongolisme premier exemple d'aberration and autosomique humaine. *Annales de Génétique, 1*:41-49.

LEVAN, A. and T. C. HSU. The human idiogram. *Hereditas, 45*:665-674.

LINDSTEN, J. Chromosomal aberrations induced by ionizing radiation in human cells grown *in vitro*. *Uppsala LäkFören. Förh., 64*:8-9.

MAKINO, S.; T. ISHIHARA; and A. TONOMURA. Chromosome conditions in thirty human tumors. *Proc. Jap. Acad., 35*:252-256.

MAKINO, S.; T. ISHIHARA; and A. TONOMURA. Cytological studies of tumors, XXVII. The chromosomes of thirty human tumors. *Z. Krebsforsch., 63*:184-208.

MAKINO, S. and M. SASAKI. On the chromosome number of man. *Proc. Japan Acad., 35*:99-104.

MOORE, KEITH L. Sex Reversal in Newborn Babies. *Lancet, ii*:217.

NACHTSHEIM, H. Chromosomenaberrationen beim Säuger und ihre Bedenutung für die Entstehung von Missbildungen. *Naturwissensch., 46*:637-645.

NAKANISHI, Y. H.; M. V. FERNANDES; M. MIZUTANI; and C. M. POMERAT. On the chromosome numbers of human amnion cells in primary and strain cultures. *Tex. Repts. Biol. and Med., 17*:345-353.

NAKANISHI, Y. H.; M. MIZUTANI; and C. M. POMERAT. Smoke condensates on lung cells in tissue culture with special reference to chromosomal changes. *Tex. Repts. Biol. and Med., 17*:542-590.

NILSSON, I. M.; S. BERGMAN; J. REITALU; and J. WALDENSTRÖM. Hæmophilia in a "girl" with male sex-chromatin pattern. *Lancet, ii*:264-266.

NORRYD, C. The chromosomes of three human cell strains. *Hereditas, 45*:499-460.

NOWAKOWSKI, H.; W. LENTZ; and J. PARADA. Diskrepenz zwischen chromatinbefund und genetischem Geschlecht beim Klinefelter-syndrom. *Acta Endocr., 30*:296.

Penrose, L. S. Outline of Human Genetics. Wiley, New York. xii + 146 pp.

Polani, P. E. Nuclear Chromatin of Anencephalic Foetuses. *Lancet, ii*:240.

Polani, P. E. Sex Reversal: Genetic, Chromosomal and Nuclear Sex. *Lancet, i*:629.

Polani, P. E. and J. II. Briggs. Chromosomes of man. *Brit. Med. J., ii*:1330.

Rabotti, Giancarlo. Ploidy of Primary and Metastatic Human Tumours. *Nature, 183*:1276.

Rothfels, K. H.; A. A. Axelrad; L. Siminovitch; E. A. McCulloch; and R. C. Parker. The origin of altered cell lines in cultures from mouse, monkey, and man, as indicated by chromosome and transplantation studies. *Canad. Cancer Conf.*, 3:189-214.

Stern, C. Colour-blindness in Klinefelter's syndrome. *Nature, 183*:1452-1453.

Stern, C. The chromosomes of man. *J. Med. Educ.*, 34:301-314. (Reprinted in *Am. J. Human Genet., 11*, No. 2, part 2.)

Stern, C. Use of the term "superfemale." *Lancet, ii*:1088.

Stewart, J. S. S. The Chromosomes in Man. *Lancet, i*:833.

Stewart, J. S. S. Genetic factors in intersexes. *Proc. Roy. Soc. Med.*, 52:817-818.

Stewart, J. S. S. Testicular feminisation and colour-blindness. *Lancet, ii*:592-594.

Tabata, T. A chromosome study in some malignant human tumors. *Cytologia*, 24:367-377.

Tanner, J. M.; A. Prader; H. Habich; and M. A. Ferguson-Smith. Genes on the Y chromosome influencing rate of maturation in man. *Lancet, ii*:141-144.

Tjio, J. H.; T. T. Puck; and A. Robinson. The somatic chromosomal constitution of some human subjects with genetic defects. *Proc. Nat. Acad. Sc.*, 45:1008-1016.

Tonomura, A. A chromosome survey in six cases of human uterine cervix carcinomas. *Jap. J. Genet.*, 34:401-406.

Turpin, R.; J. Lejeune; J. Lafourcade; and M. Gautier. Aberrations chromosomiques et maladies humains. La polydyspondylie à 45 chromosomes. *C. R. Acad. Sci.*, Paris, 248:3636-3638.

Valberg, L. S. Hæmophilia in a "girl" with male sex-chromatin pattern. *Lancet, ii*:466.

The chromosomes of man. *Lancet, i*:715-716.

Human chromosomal abnormalities. *Lancet, ii*:448-450.

Chromosomes of man. *Brit. Med. J.*, No. 5159, Nov. 21, 1959.

Yosida, T. H. Chromosomal Alteration and the Development of Tumors. *Zschr. f. Krebsforschung*, 63:209.

1960

Atkin, N. B. A single heteropycnotic chromosome in a human tumour. *Exp. Cell Res.*, 20:214-215.

578   *Genetic Mechanisms in Human Disease*

ATKIN, N. B. Cell-division in carcinoma during radiotherapy. A criterion of response to treatment. *Lancet, ii*:778-781.

ATKIN, N. B. Sex chromatin and Chromosomal variation in Human Tumours. *Acta Union Internationale Contre Le Cancer*, 16, No. 1.

AWANO, I. and F. TUDA. The Chromosomes of Human Somatic Cells. *La Kromosomo, 44/45*:1459.

BAHNER, F.; G. SCHWARZ; D. G. HARNDEN; P. A. JACOBS; H. A. HIENZ; and K. WALTER. A fertile female with XO sex chromosome constitution. *Lancet, ii*:100-101.

BAIKIE, A. G.; W. M. COURT BROWN; K. E. BUCKTON; D. G. HARNDEN; P. A. JACOBS; and I. M. TOUGH. A possible specific chromosome abnormality in human chronic myeloid leukaemia. *Nature, 188*:1165-1166.

BAIKIE, A. G.; W. M. COURT BROWN; and P. A. JACOBS. Chromosome studies in leukaemia. *Lancet, i*:168.

BAIKIE, A. G.; W. M. COURT BROWN; and P. A. JACOBS. Chromosome studies in leukaemia. *Lancet, i*:280.

BAIKIE, A. G.; W. M. COURT BROWN; and P. A. JACOBS. Chromosome constitution of mongols with leukaemia. *Lancet, i*:1251.

BARR, M. L. Sexual dimorphism in interphase nuclei. *Am. J. Human Genet., 12*:118-127.

BARR, M. L. and D. H. CARR. Sex chromatin, sex chromosomes, and sex anomalies. *Canadian Med. Assoc. J., 83*:979-986.

BAYREUTHER, K. Chromosomes in primary neoplastic growth. *Nature, 186*:6-9.

BERGMAN, S.; J. REITALU; H. NOWAKOWSKI; and W. LENZ. The chromosomes in two patients with Klinefelter syndrome. *Ann. Hum. Genet., 24*:81-88.

BISHOP, P. M. F. and P. E. POLANI. True hermaphroditism and Klinefelter's syndrome. *Lancet, ii*:928-929.

BLANK, C. E.; A. BISHOP and J. P. CALEY. Example of XY/XO Mosaicism. *Lancet, ii*:1450.

BLOISE, W.; L. M. DE ASSIS; C. BOTTURA; and I. FERRARI. Gonadal dysgenesis (Turner's syndrome) with male phenotype and XO chromosomal constitution. *Lancet, ii*:1059-1060.

BÖÖK, J. A. Mongolism and other conditions associated with chromosome variations. *Uppsala LäkFören. Förh., 65*:1-2.

BÖÖK, J. A. and B. SANTESSON. Further studies in clinical cytogenetics. Lunds Universitets Arrskrift. (In press.)

BÖÖK, J. A. and B. SANTESSON. Malformation syndrome in man associated with triploidy (69 chromosomes). *Lancet, i*:858-859.

BOTTURA, C. Chromosome analysis. *Lancet, ii*:1092-1093.

BOTTURA, C. and I. FERRARI. A simplified method for the study of chromosomes in man. *Nature, 186*:904-905.

CARTER, C. O.; J. L. HAMERTON; P. E. POLANI; A. GUNALP; and S. D. V.

WELLER. Chromosome translocation as a cause of familial mongolism. *Lancet, ii*:678-680.

CHU, E. H. Y. The chromosome complements of human somatic cells. *Am. J. Human Genet., 12*:97-103.

COURT BROWN, W. M.; P. A. JACOBS, and R. DOLL. Interpretation of chromosome counts made on bone-marrow cells. *Lancet, i*:160-163.

CROOKE, A. C. and M. D. HAYWARD. Mosaicism in Klinefelter's Syndrome. *Lancet, i*:1198.

DE ASSIS, L. M.; D. EPPS; C. BOTTURA; and I. FERRARI. Chromosomal constitution and nuclear sex of a true hermaphrodite. *Lancet, ii*:129-130.

DE CARLI, L.; F. NUZZO; B. CHIARELLI; and E. POLI. Trisomic condition of a large chromosome in a woman with mongoloid traits. *Lancet, ii*:130-131.

DE GROUCHY, J.; S. COTTIN; M. LAMY; A. NETTER; A. NETTER-LAMBERT; R. TREVOUX; and G. DELZANT. Un Cas de Dysgenesie Gonadique a Formule Chromosomique Male (XY) Normale. *Rev. Franc. Etudes Clin. et Biol., 5*:377-381.

DOBZHANSKY, T. The present evolution of man. *Sci. Amer., 203*:206.

EDWARDS, J. H. Painless skin biopsy. *Lancet, i*:496.

EDWARDS, J. H.; D. G. HARNDEN; A. H. CAMERON; V. M. CROSSE; and O. H. WOLFF. A new trisomic syndrome. *Lancet, i*:787-789.

ENGEL, D. Chromosome Anomalies in "Bleb Diseases." *Lancet, 2*:369.

ENGSTROM, W. W. and F. J. STODDARD. Gonadal Dysgenesis: Ovaries in association with Chromatin-Negative Patterns in Somatic Cells. *J. Clin. Endocrin. & Metab., 20*:780-5.

FERGUSON-SMITH, M. A. Cytogenetics in man. *A.M.A. Arch. Int. Med., 105*:627-639.

FERGUSON-SMITH, M. A. Nuclear sex and the sex chromosomes. *J. Chronic Dis., 12*:203-210.

FERGUSON-SMITH, M. A. and A. W. JOHNSTON. Chromosome abnormalities in certain diseases of man. *Ann. Int. Med., 53*:359-371.

FERGUSON-SMITH, M.A.; A. W. JOHNSTON; and S. D. HANDMAKER. Primary amentia and micro-orchidism associated with an XXXY sex-chromosome constitution. *Lancet, ii*:184-187.

FERGUSON-SMITH, M. A.; A. W. JOHNSTON; and A. N. WEINBERG. The chromosome complement in true hermaphroditism. *Lancet, ii*:126-128.

FORD, C. E. Human cytogenetics: its present place and future possibilities. *Am. J. Human Genet., 12*:104-117.

FRACCARO, M. Cell cultures for human genetic studies and concluding remarks. *Am. J. Human Genet., 12*:134-138.

FRACCARO, M. X-ray induced Chromosome Aberrations in Mammalian Cells. *Intern. Jour. of Rad. Biol.* (Supplement, p. 117).

FRACCARO, M.; D. IKKOS; J. LINDSTEN; R. LUFT; and K. KAIJSER. A new type of chromosomal abnormality in gonadal dysgenesis. *Lancet, ii*:1144.

FRACCARO, M.; K. KAIJSER; and J. LINDSTEN. Chromosomal abnormalities in father and mongol child. *Lancet, i*:724-727.

FRACCARO, M.; K. KAIJSER; and J. LINDSTEN. A child with 49 chromosomes. *Lancet, ii*:899-902.

FRACCARO, M.; K. KAIJSER; and J. LINDSTEN. Further cytogenetical observations in gonadal dysgenesis. *Ann. Hum. Genet.*, Lond., *24*:205-211.

FRACCARO, M.; K. KAIJSER; and J. LINDSTEN. Somatic chromosome complement in continuously cultured cells of two individuals with gonadal dysgenesis. *Ann. Hum. Genet.*, *24*:45-61.

FRACCARO, M. and J. LINDSTEN. A child with 49 chromosomes. *Lancet., ii*:1303.

FRACCARO, M. and J. LINDSTEN. The human chromosome complement determined in somatic cells cultivated *in vitro*. *Folia Hered. Pathol.*, *9*:185-190.

FRACCARO, M.; C. A. GEMZELL; and J. LINDSTEN. Plasma level of growth hormone and chromosome complement in four patients with gonadal dysgenesis (Turner's syndrome). *Acta Endocrin.*, *39*:496.

FRASER, J. H.; J. CAMPBELL; R. C. MACGILLIVRAY; E. BOYD; and B. LENNOX. The XXX syndrome: frequency among mental defectives and fertility. *Lancet.*, *ii*:626-627.

GAGNON, J. Les Chromosomes de l'homme. *L'union Médicale du Canada*, *89*:1286.

GAGNON, J.; N. KATYK-LONGTIN; and J. C. SINNOT. Le syndrome des malformations multiples arsocié à la dysgenese gonadique (syndrome de (Turner) à formule chromosomique XO. *L'Union Médicale du Canada*, *89*:1227.

GEERTS, S. J. More chromosome anomalies. *Lancet, ii*:766-767.

GORDON, R. R.; F. J. P. O'GORMAN; C. J. DEWHURST; and C. E. BLANK. Chromosome count in a hermaphrodite with some features of Klinefelter's syndrome. *Lancet, ii*:736-739.

GORDON, R. R.; F. J. P. O'GORMAN; C. J. DEWHURST; and C. E. BLANK. True hermaphroditism and Klinefelter's syndrome. *Lancet, ii*:982.

GRIBOFF, S. I. and R. LAWRENCE. Non-Disjunction of the Chromosomes as a Cause of Congenital Defects: Known and Potential Combinations. *Jour. of Mount Sinai Hospital*, *27*:591.

GRIBOFF, S. I. and R. LAWRENCE. A Proposed Genetic Theory for the Pathogenesis of certain congenital gonadal defects. *Lancet*, *1*:602.

GRUMBACH, M. M. Some Considerations of the Pathogenesis and Classification of Anomalies of Sex in Man. *Clinical Endocrinology*, *1*:407.

GRUMBACH, M. M.; A. MORISHIMA; and E. H. Y. CHU. On the sex chromatin and the sex chromosomes in sexual anomalies in man; relation to origin of sex chromatin. *Proc., First Intern. Cong. Endocrin.*, Copenhagen.

HALE, A. J. and S. J. WILSON. The deoxyribonucleic acid content of the nuclei of leukaemic leukocytes. *Lancet, i*:577-578.

HARNDEN, D. G. Abnormalities of Chromosome Constitution and defects of sex development (Abstract). *Proc. Royal Soc. of Med.*, 53:493.

HARNDEN, D. G. The Chromosomes. *Recent Advances in Human Genetics* (ed. Penrose). Churchhill, London, pp. 19-38.

HARNDEN, D. G. A human skin culture technique used for cytological examination. *Brit. J. Exp. Pathol.*, 41:31-37.

HARNDEN, D. G.; O. J. MILLER; and L. S. PENROSE. The Klinefelter-mongolism type of double aneuploidy. *Ann. Hum. Genet.*, 24:165-169.

HAUSER, VON G. A.; F. GLOOR; G. STALDER; J. BODIS; M. KELLER; J. GOERRE; and W. L. GOUW. XX-chromosomale Gonadendysgenie mit Granulosa-Thekazell-Tumor und Feminierung. *Sonderab. aus. der Schweiz Med. Wschr.*, 90:1486.

HAYWARD, M. D. Sex chromosome mosaicism in man. *Heredity*, 15:235-240.

HAYWARD, M. D. and B. D. BOWER. Chromosomal trisomy associated with the Sturge-Weber syndrome. *Lancet, ii*:844-846.

HIRSCHHORN, K.; W. H. DECKER; and H. L. COOPER. Human intersex with chromosome mosaicism of type XY/XO. *New Eng. J. Med.*, 263:1044-1048.

HIRSCHHORN, K.; W. H. DECKER; and H. L. COOPER. True hermaphroditism with XY/XO mosaicism. *Lancet, ii*:319-320.

HIRSCHHORN, K.; H. COOPER; and O. J. MILLER. Gonadal Dysgenesis (Turner's Syndrome) with Male Phenotype and XO chromosomal constitution. *Lancet, ii*:1449.

HSIA, D. Y-Y. Medical genetics. *New Eng. J. Med.*, 262:1172-1178, 1222-1227, 1273-1278, 1318-1323.

HSU, T. C. and D. S. KELLOGG, JR. Primary cultivation and continuous propagation *in vitro* of tissues from small biopsy specimens. *J. Nat. Cancer Inst.*, 25:221-235.

ISHIHARA, T. and S. MAKINO. Chromosomal conditions in some human subjects with non-malignant diseases. *Texas Rep. Biol. Med.*, 18:427.

IVERSON, S. Sex Chromatin in Somatic Nuclei. *Lancet, ii*:1347.

JACOBS, P. A.; D. G. HARNDEN; W. M. COURT BROWN; and A. G. BAIKIE. Trisomic condition of a large chromosome. *Lancet, ii*:368.

JACOBS, P. A.; D. G. HARNDEN; W. M. COURT BROWN; J. GOLDSTEIN; H. G. CLOSE; T. N. MACGREGOR; N. MACLEAN; and J. A. STRONG. Abnormalities involving the X-chromosome in women. *Lancet, i*:1213-1216.

JAMES, J. The Sex Chromatin: Single or Double? *Lancet, ii*:368.

KAPLAN, W. D. More Chromosome Anomalies. *Lancet, ii*:934.

KOCH, GERHARD. Outras considerações sobre o Mongoloidismo-uma aberção cromosómica. *O Medica* No. 481.

KOCH, G. Neure Beobachtungen uber die Atiologie des Mongilismus. *Arztl. Prax.* 141.

KOSENOW, W. Neue Ergebnisse der Chromosomenforschung und ihre Bedentung fur die klinische Pathologie. *Arch. Kinderhk, 162*:219.

KOSENOW, W. Das Ullrich-Turner-Syndrom in heutiger sicht. *Münch. med. Wschr.*, 102:24.

LANMAN, J. T.; B. S. SKLARIN; H. L. COOPER; and K. HIRSCHHORN. Klinefelter's syndrome in a ten-month-old mongolian idiot. *New Eng. J. Med.*, 263:887-890.

LEHMANN, O. and H. FORSSMAN. Chromosome complement in a mongoloid mother, her child, and the child's father. *Lancet, i*:498.

LEHMANN, O. and H. FORSSMAN. Chromosomes in the Sturge Weber Syndrome. *Lancet, ii*:1450.

LEHMANN, O. and H. FORSSMAN. Klinefelter's syndrome and mongolism in the same person. *Acta Paed.*, 49:536.

LEJEUNE, J. Le Mongislisme-Trisomie dégressive. *Ann. de Génét.*, 2:1.

LEJEUNE, J. On two possible markers of chromosomal aberrations induced by X-rays in human cells. *Internat. Jour. of Rad. Biol.* (Supplement).

LEJEUNE, J.; R. TURPIN; and R. DECOURT. Abérrations chromosomiques et maladies humaines: Syndrome de Klinefelter XXY à 46 chromosomes par fusion centro T-T. *Comptes Rendus*, 250, 2468.

LEJEUNE, J.; R. TURPIN; and M. GAUTIER. Étude des chromosomes somatiques humains. Technique de culture de fibroblastes "in vitro." *Rev. Franç. Étude Clin. Biol.*, 5:406.

LEJEUNE, J.; R. TURPIN; and M. GAUTIER. Analyse caryotypique de trois pseudo-hermaphrodites masculins. *Comptes Rendu.*, 250:618.

LENNOX, B. Use of the term "superfemale." *Lancet, i*:55.

LEON, N.; I. FERRARI; and C. BOTTURA. Chromosomal constitution in a case of Klinefelter's syndrome. *Lancet, ii*:319.

LENZ, W. Genetisch bedingte Störungen der embryonalen Geshlechtsdifferenzierung. *Dtsch. med. Wschr.*, 85:268.

LEVAN, A. and T. C. HSU. The chromosomes of a mongoloid female, mother of a normal boy. *Hereditas*, 46:770-772.

McKUSICK, V. Chromosomes in Marfan's Disease. *Lancet, i*:1194.

MAKINO, S. and M. SASAKI. Chromosome constitution in normal human subjects and in one case of true hermaphroditism. *Proc. Jap. Acad.*, 36:156.

MAKINO, S. and M. SASAKI. A study of the somatic chromosomes in the Japanese. *Jap. J. Genet.*, 35:228.

MAKINO, S.; A. TONOMURA; and E. MATSUNAGA. Chromosome studies in ten cases of mongolism (Preliminary Report). *Proc. Jap. Acad., 36,* (12).

MAKINO, S.; A. TONOMURA; S. TAKAI; and E. MATSUNAGA. Chromosome studies in four human phenotypic intersexes (Preliminary Report). *Proc. Jap. Acad., 36,* (12).

MARTIN, L. Gonadal dysgenesis (Turner's syndrome) with male phenotype and XO chromosomal constitution. *Lancet, ii*:1199.

MILES, C. P. Morphology and Functional Relations of Sex Chromatin in cultured Amnion Cells. *Experimental Cell Research*, 20:324-337.

MILES, C. P. Karyotypes in Klinefelter's and Turner's Syndrome. *Lancet,* *i*:603.

MILLER, O. J. Developmental Sex Abnormalities. *Recent Advances in Human Genetics* (ed. Penrose). Churchhill, London, pp. 39-55.

MILLER, O. J.; U. MITTWOCH; and L. S. PENROSE. Spermatogenesis in man with special reference to aneuploidy. *Heredity, 14*:456 (abstr.).

MITTWOCH, U. More chromosomal abnormalities. *Lancet, ii*:597.

MOORHEAD, P. S.; W. J. MELLMAN; and D. M. BATTIPS. Human autosomal anomalies in a sibship of six. *Genetics, 45*:1001 (abstr.).

MOORHEAD, P. S.; P. C. NOWELL; W. J. MELLMAN; D. M. BATTIPS; and D. A. HUNGERFORD. Chromosome preparations of leukocytes cultured from human peripheral blood. *Exper. Cell Res., 20*:613-616.

MOSER, H. Modern approaches to the study of mammalian cells in culture. *Experimentia, 16*:385-398.

MOSIER, H. D.; L. W. SCOTT; and L. H. COTTER. Frequency of Positive Sex Chromatin Pattern in Mental Deficiency. *Pediatrics, 25*:291.

NACHTSHEIM, H. Chromosomenaberrationen beim Menschen und ihre Bedeutung für die Entstehung von Missbildungen. *Naturwiss., 47-* (16):361-371.

NOWAKOWSKI, H.; W. LENZ; S. BERGMAN; and J. REITALU. Chromosomen-befunde beim echten Klinefelter-Syndrom. *Acta Endocrin., 34*:483-495.

NOWELL, P. C. and D. A. HUNGERFORD. A minute chromosome in human chronic granulocytic leukemia. *Science, 132*:1497 (abstr.).

NOWELL, P. C. and D. A. HUNGERFORD. Chromosome studies on normal and leukemic human leukocytes. *J. Nat. Cancer Inst., 25*:85-109.

NOWELL, P. C. and D. A. HUNGERFORD. Aetiology of leukemia. *Lancet,* *i*:113-114.

OEHME, J. Chromosomenveränderungen bei Leukämie. *Dtsch. med. Wschr.,* 85 (18):817-818 (Übersichten).

PATAU, K. The identification of individual chromosomes, especially in man. *Am. J. Human Genet., 12*:250-276.

PATAU, K.; D. W. SMITH; E. THERMAN; S. L. INHORN; and H. P. WAGNER. Multiple congenital anomaly caused by an extra autosome. *Lancet, i*:790-793.

PENROSE, L. S.; J. R. ELLIS; and J. D. A. DELHANTY. Chromosomal trans-locations in mongolism and in normal relatives. *Lancet, ii*:409-410.

POLANI, P. E.; J. H. BRIGGS; C. E. FORD; C. M. CLARK; and J. M. BERG. A mongol girl with 46 chromosomes. *Lancet, i*:721-724.

POLI, E. Extra chromosomes and Barr chromatin bodies. *Lancet, ii*:46-47.

POLI, E. Paramongoloidismo. *Atti Accad. Med. Lomb. Sed., 15*:2.

POWSNER, E. R. and L. BERMAN. Number of chromosomes in the human cell. *Nature, 188*:1045-1046.

PUCK, T. T.; A. ROBINSON; and J. H. TJIO. Familial primary amenorrhea due to testicular feminization: A human gene affecting sex differentiation. *Proc. Soc. Exptl. Biol. and Med., 103*:192-196.

RABOCH, J. and O. BLEHA. Uber ein echtes Klinefelter-syndrom mit Kompletter Spermiogenese. *Endocrinologie 39*:203.

SALLER, K. Der mongoloide Schwachsinn (Morbus Langdon Down)—Genese & Prophylaxe. *Münch. med. Wschr., 102*:70.

SANDBERG, A. A.; L. H. CROSSWHITE; and E. GORDY. Trisomy of a large chromosome. *J. Am. Med. Assoc., 174*:221-225.

SANDBERG, A. A.; G. F. KEOPF; L. H. CROSSWHITE; and T. S. HAUSCHKA. The chromosome constitution of human marrow in various developmental and blood disorders. *Am. J. Human Genet., 12*:231-249.

SANDERSON, A. R. Rapid Nuclear Sexing. *Lancet, i*:1252.

SASAKI, M. and MAKINO, S. The chromosomal constitution of a human hermaphrodite. *Texas Rpts. Biol. Med., 18*:493.

SCHÖYER, N. H. D. Aetiology of leukaemia. *Lancet, i*:229.

SMITH, D. W.; K. PATAU; E. THERMAN; and S. L. INHORN. A new autosomal trisomy syndrome: multiple congenital anomalies caused by an extra chromosome. *J. Pediatrics, 57*:338-345.

STERN, C. Mechanisms of meiotic non-disjunction in man. *Nature, 187*:804-805.

STERN, C. *Principles of Human Genetics*. Second edition. Freeman, San Francisco and London. x + 753 pp.

STERN, C. The determination of sex. *Triangle, 4*:131-135.

STERN, C. The Fifth Huskins Memorial Lecture. Dosage compensation—development of a concept and new facts. *Canadian J. Genet. Cytol., 2*:105-118.

STEWART, J. S. S. Genetic mechanisms in human intersexes. *Lancet, i*:825-826.

STEWART, J. S. S. Chromosome analysis. *Lancet, ii*:651.

STEWART, J. S. S. Mechanisms of meiotic non-disjunction in man. *Nature, 187*:804-805.

STEWART, J. S. S. Gonadal Dysgenesis: The Genetic Significance of Unusual Variants. *Acta Endocrinologica, 33*:89.

STEWART, J. S. S. and A. R. SANDERSON. Fertility and oligophrenia in an apparent triplo-X female. *Lancet, ii*:21-23.

STOLTE, L. A. M.; H. I. AM. V. KESSEL; J. C. SEELEN; G. A. J. TIJDINK. Chromosomes in hydatidiform moles. *Lancet, ii*:1144-1145.

TJIO, J. H.; T. T. PUCK; and A. ROBINSON. The human chromosomal satellites in normal persons and in two patients with Marfan's syndrome. *Proc. Nat. Acad. Sc., 46*:532-539, 759.

TOUGH, I. M.; K. E. BUCKTON; A. G. BAIKIE; and W. M. COURT BROWN. X-ray-induced chromosome damage in man. *Lancet, ii*:849-951.

WARKANY, J. Etiology of mongolism. *J. Pediatrics, 56*:412-419.

WITSCHI, EMIL. Sex reversal in animals and in man. *Amer. Scientist, 48*:399-414.

YOUNG, W. J.; T. MERZ; M. A. FERGUSON-SMITH; and A. W. JOHNSTON. Chromosome number of the chimpanzee, *Pan troglodytes. Science, 131:-*1672-1673.

A proposed standard system of nomenclature of human mitotic chromosomes. *Lancet, i:*1063-1065; *Am. J. Human Genet., 12:*384-388; *J. Am. Med. Assoc., 174:*159-162; etc.

Agreement on human chromosomes. *Lancet, i:*1118.

More chromosome anomalies. *Lancet, ii:*191-192.

Account of the First International Conference on Congenital Malformations, London, July 18-22, under auspices of the National Foundation. *Lancet, ii:*257-258 (1960).

The mongol chromosome and some others. *Lancet, ii:*1068-1069.

Triple X-sex. *J. Am. Med. Assoc., 174 (2):*176-177.

Supplementary References

1956

DIXON, A. D. and TORR, J. B. D. Sex chromatin in oral smears. *Brit. med. J.,* 2:799.

DIXON, A. D. and TORR, J. B. D. Postmortem persistence of sex chromatin. *J. forensic Med., 3:*161.

DIXON, A. D. and TORR, J. B. D. Sex chromatin as an aid to the identification of sex in forensic medicine. *Nature, 178:*797.

FUCHS, F. and RIIS, P. Ante-natal sex determination. *Nature, 177:*330.

GLENISTER, T. W. Determination of sex in early human embryos. *Nature,* 177:1135.

EDITORIAL. Annotation on Chr. Number of Man. *Brit. med. J., 1:*353.

1957

ASHLEY, D. J. B. Occurrence of sex chromatin in the cells of the blood and bone marrow in man, *Nature, 179:*969.

DIXON, A. D.; and TORR, J. B. D. Sex determination of human tissues from cell morphology. *J. forensic Med., 4:*11.

PARK, W. W. The occurrence of sex chromatin in chorionepitheliomas and hydatidiform moles, *J. Path. Bact., 74:*197.

PARK, W. W. Sex chromatin in early human embryos. *J. Anat.* (Lond.), 91:396.

RIIS, P. A sex difference in the chromatin structure of peripheral blood lymphocytes, *Nature, 179:*784.

SERR, D. M.; SACHS, L.; and DANON, M. Diagnosis of foetal sex during pregnancy, *Surg. Gynec. Obstet., 104:*157.

SILVA-INZUNZA, E. Sexing cells. *Brit. med. J., 1:*1182.

STEVENSON, A. C. and McCLARIN, R. H. Determination of the sex of human abortions by nuclear sexing the cells of the chorionic villi. *Nature, 180*:198.

TAVARES, A. S. Nuclear sex in undifferentiated carcinomata. *J. Path. Bact.,* 74:25.

EDITORIAL. Symposium on Nuclear Sex. *Brit. med. J., ii*:760.

1958

ASHLEY, D. J. B. Occurrence of sex chromatin in the basal cells of the epidermis and in basal cell carcinomata. *Nature, 181*:427.

DAVIDSON, W. M.; FOWLER, J. F.; and ROBERTSON SMITH, D. Sexing the neutrophil leukocytes in natural and artificial blood chimaeras. *Brit. J. Haemat.,* 4:231.

DIXON, A. D. and TORR, J. B. D. Chromosomal sex and abnormal sexual development. *Brit. med. J.,* 2:388.

GRAY, J. The Y Chromosome in Man. *Lancet, 1*:970.

GRAY, J. Diagnosis: nuclear sexing. *Brit. med. J.,* 2:566.

KLINGER, H. P. and SCHWARZACKER, H. G. Sex chromatin in polyploid nuclei of human amnion epithelium. *Nature, 181*:1150.

ROBERTSON SMITH, D. and DAVIDSON, W. M. Symposium on Nuclear Sex (Heinemann, London).

TERNI, M. and LO MONACO, G. B. Coltura continua di cellule derivate da embrione umano. Lo Sperimentale, 108, p. 177.

EDITORIAL. Annotation on determining sex. *Brit. med. J.,* 1:93.

EDITORIAL. Annotation on sexing of tumour cells. *Brit. med. J.,* 1:1292.

1959

DAVIDSON, W. M. and ROBERTSON SMITH, D. *Human Chromosome Abnormalities* (King's College Hospital Symposium). Staples Press, London.

GAUTIER, M. Etude des chromosomes humains sur culture de tissus. *Bull. Mem. Soc. Med. Hop.,* 28-29:956.

LUERS, T. Die Chromosomen des Menschen. Umschau, Heft 4.

MILES, C. P. Sex chromatin in cultured human tissue. *Nature, 184*:476.

MYERS, L. M. Sex chromatin in normal tissues and non teratomatous tumours. *J. Path. Bact.,* 78:29.

MYERS, L. M. Sex chromatin in teratomas. *J. Path. Bact.,* 78:43.

STEVENSON, A. C. Observations on the results of pregnancies in women resident in Belfast. III. Sex ratio with particular reference to nuclear sexing of chorionic villi of abortions. *Ann. hum. Genet.,* 23:415.

EDITORIAL. A major advance in Human Genetics. Eugenics Review, *51*: (32 new series) 66.

EDITORIAL. Human chromosomal abnormalities; a conference at King's College Hospital. *Brit. med. J.,* 2:1089.

1960

ANDERS, G.; PRADER, A.; HAUSCHTEK, E.; SCHARAR, K.; SIEBENMANN, R. E.; and HELLER, R. Multiples sex chromatin und complex chromosomales mosaik bei einem Knaben mit Idiotic und multiplen missbildungen. *Helvet. Paediat. Acta.*, 15:515.

ATKIN, N. B. and Ross, A. J. Polyploidy in human tumours. *Nature, 187*:579.

AUSTIN, C. R. Memoirs to the Society for Endocrinology No. 7 (Cambridge Univ. Press).

BAHNER, F.; SCHWARZ, G.; HIENZ, H. A.; and WALTER, K. Turner-Syndrom mit Voll Ausgeluldeten Sekundaren Geschlechtsmerkmalen und Fertilitat. *Acta Endocrinologica*, 35:397.

BARR, M. L. Cytogenetics in Mental Deficiency Research. *Canad. Med. A. J.* 83:1164.

CARTER, C. O. Chromosome Abnormalities in Man. *Nature, 186*:683.

CHIARELLI, B.; NUZZO, F.; DE CARLI, L.; and AULISA, A. B. Morphometric analysis of human chromosomes. *Atti A. Genet. ital.*, 5:265.

COWIE, V.; COPPEN, A.; and NORMAN, P. Nuclear sex and body build in schizophrenia. *Brit. med. J.*, 2:431.

DAVIDSON, W. M. Sex determination, diagnostic methods. *Brit. med. J.*, 2:1901.

DE CARLI, L. and CHIARELLI, B. Variabilita nel numero dei chromosomi tra cloni ed entro cloni in due ceppi stabilizzati di cellule umane coltivate in vitro. *Atti A. Genet. ital.* (Pavia), 5:225.

DE LE CHAPELLE, A. and HORTLING. Frekvensen av Klinefelters syndrom och gonadal dysgenesi vid oligofreni. *Nordisk Medicin*, 63:256.

DI TORO, R. Su alcuni recenti contributi in terna di etiologia delle malformazioni congenite. *La Pediatria*, Fax. 11—Anno LXVIII.

FERGUSON-SMITH, M. A. and JOHNSON, A. W. The Human Chromosomes in Disorders of Sex Differentiation. Transactions of Assocn. Amer. Physicians 73: p. 60.

FISCHLER, E. and LARCHY, R. Mongolism associated with acute congenital leukaemia. Report of a case. Helvetica Paediatrica Acta. Vol. 15 (1960) Fax 3, p. 253.

FORD, C. E. The Chromosomes of normal human somatic and leukaemic cells (abstract). *Proc. roy. Soc. Med.*, 53:491.

GANDINI, E. and CEPPELLINI, R. Eterogeneita per il gruppo ABO, per l'emoglobina Fe per il numero cromosomico in corso di leucemia. *Atti A. Genet. ital.* (Pavia) 5:283.

KLINGER, H. P. and SCHWARZACHER, H. G. The Sex Chromatin and Heterochromatic Bodies in Human Diploid and Polyploid Nuclei. *J. of Biophys. and Biochem. Cytology*, 8:345.

KOCH, G. Neuras consideraciones sobre el tema del mongolismo como alteracion cromosomica. *Fol. clin. int.* (Barcelona), 10/9, 354.

MAKINO, S. and ISHIHARA, T. Chromosomes of some human subjects with non-malignant diseases. *Proc. of the Japan Acad.* (1960), 36, no. 3.

NOWELL, P. C. Phytohemagglutinin: An initiator of Mitosis in Cultures of Normal Human Leukocytes. Cancer Research Vol. 20:462.

OLMSTEAD, E. G.; PFEIFFER, E. W.; and HILL, A. Incidence of Intersexuality in Mentally Retarded Female Patients as determined by Nuclear Chromatin Patterns. *Am. J. Med. Sc.*, *240*:308.

PENROSE, L. S. Human Genetics. *New Scientist*, *8*:129.

POLANI, P. E. Anomalie cromosomiche nell'uomo. *Atti A. Genet. ital.*, (Pavia), *5*:51.

SHAPIRO, A. and RIDLER, M. A. C. The incidence of Klinefelter's syndrome in a mental deficiency hospital. *J. ment. defic. Res.*, *4*:48.

TONOMURA, A. The Cytological Effect of Chemicals on Tumors. VIII. Observations on Chromosomes in a Gastric Carcinoma treated with Carzinophilin. Gann, *51*:47.

EDITORIAL. Annotation on genetics and leukaemia. *Brit. med. J.*, *2*:1662.

1961

ACHESON, R. M. and ZAMPA, G. A. Skeletal Maturation in Ovarian Dysgenesis and Turner's Syndrome. *Lancet*, *i*:917.

ALLEN, G. *et al.* Mongolism. *Lancet*, March.

ALVAREZ, W. C. Human Genetics—The Next Big Step Forward in Medicine. *Conn. Med. J.*, *25*:(3), 148.

BAIKIE, A. G.; JACOBS, P. A.; McBRIDE, J. A.; and TOUGH, I. M. Cytogenetic Studies in Acute Leukaemia. *Brit. med. J.*, *i*:1564.

BARR, M. and FAIRLEY, G. H. Circulating Antibodies in Reticulosis. *Lancet*, *i*:1305.

BERGEMANN, E. Geschlectschromatinbestimmungen am Neugeborenen. *Schweiz. Med. Wschr.*, *91*:292.

BLANK, C. E.; GORDON, R. R.; and BISHOP, A. Atypical Turner's Syndrome. *Lancet*, *i*:947.

BLUMEL, J.; OHNUKI, Y.; and AVA, A. Chromosome Anomaly in Two Cases of Cerebral Palsy, a Brother and a Sister. *Nature*, *189*:154.

BÖÖK, J. A.; GUSTAVSON, K. H.; and SANTESSON, B. Chromosomal Abnormality in a Mongolism-like Syndrome. *Acta Paediat.*, *50*:240.

BÖÖK, J. A.; SANTESSON, B.; and ZETTERQUIST, P.: Translocation Heterozygosity in Man. *Lancet*, *1*:167.

BÖÖK, J. A.; SANTESSON, B.; and ZETTERQUIST, P.: Association between Congenital Heart Malformation and Chromosomal Variations. *Acta Paediat.*, *50*:217.

BOTTURA, C.; FERRARI, I.; and VEIGA, A. A. Chromosome Abnormalities in Waldenstrom's Macroglobulinaemia. *Lancet*, *i*:1170.

BOYD, E.; BUCHANAN, W. W.; and LENNOX, B. Damage to Chromosomes by Therapeutic Doses of Radioiodine. *Lancet*, *1*:977.

BRUNN PETERSON, G. and THERKELSEN, A. J. Observations on Satellited Human Chromosomes. *Lancet*, *i*:1229.

BUCKTON, K.; HARNDEN, D. G.; BAIKIE, A. G.; and WOODS, G. E. Mongolism and Leukaemia in the Same Sibship. *Lancet*, *i*:171.

CARR, D. H.; BARR, M. L.; and PLUNKETT, E. R. An XXXX Sex Chromosome Complement in Two Mentally Defective Females. *J. Canad. Med. A.* 84:136.

CARR, D. H.; BARR, M. L.; and PLUNKETT, E. R. A probable XXYY sex determining mechanism in a mentally defective male with Klinefelter's syndrome. *Canad. Med. A. J.* 84:873.

CARR, D. H.; BARR, M. L.; PLUNKETT, E. R.; GRUMBACH, M. M.; MORISHIMA, A.; and CHU, E. H. Y. An XXXY Sex Chromosome Complex in Klinefelter Subjects with Duplicated Sex Chromatin. *J. Clin. Endocrinol. and Metab.* 21:491.

CHU, E. H. Y.; WARKANY, J.; and ROSENSTEIN, R. B. Chromosome Complement in a Case of the "Male Turner Syndrome." *Lancet, i*:786.

CLARKE, C.; EDWARDS, J. H.; and SMALLPEICE, V. 21-Trisomy/Normal Mosaicism. *Lancet, i*:1028.

COTTIN, S. Les chromosomes des cellules cancéreuses en culture. Thèse Doctorat Médecine, Paris.

COURT BROWN, W. M. New Perspectives in Leukaemia. *New Scientist,* 9:97.

CRAWFURD, M. D'A. and ELLIS, J. R. The Chromosome Constitution of the Sturge-Weber Syndrome. *Lancet, i*:826.

DE CARLI, L.; MODIANO, G.; NUZZO, F.; and DE ANDREIS, M. Studio sulla persistenza degli antigeni di un gruppo sanguigno in cellule coltivate in vitro e loro possibile impiego come marcatori genetici. *Atti A. genet. Ital.,* Pavia, 6:99.

DE CARLI, L.; MURTHY, Y. K. S.; and MARIN, G. Studio di una variante morfologica del ceppo EUE. *Atti A. genet. Ital.,* Pavia, 6:87.

DE GROUCHY, J. Les chromosomes humains. *La Vie Med.,* 42:13.

DE GROUCHY, J.; LAMY, M.; FREZAL, J.; and RIBIER, J. XX/XO Mosaics in Turner's Syndrome. *Lancet, i*:1369.

DE LA CHAPELLE, A. Factor stimulating Cell Division in Cultured Leucocytes. *Lancet, i*:1348.

DELHANTY, J.; ELLIS, J. R.; and ROWLEY, P. T. Triploid Cells in a Human Embryo. *Lancet i*:1286.

EBERT, J. D. First International Conference on Congenital Malformations. Summary and Evaluation. *J. Chron. Dis., 13*:91.

EDWARDS, J. H. Barr Bodies. *Lancet, i*:616.

FERGUSON-SMITH, M. A. Modern Trends in Endocrinology (second series), Butterworth, London. p. 299. Genetic factors in disorders of sexual differentiation.

FERGUSON-SMITH, M. A. Chromosome Abnormalities with Congenital Disease. *Mod. Med.* (Minneap.) 29:77.

FERGUSON-SMITH, M. A. Trisomy of a Large Chromosome. *J.A.M.A.,* 175:414.

FERGUSON-SMITH, M. A. and HANDMAKER, S. D. Observations on the Satellited Human Chromosomes. *Lancet, i*:638.

FERRIER, P.; SHEPARD, T.; GARTLER, S.; and BURT, B. Chromatin Positive Gonadal Dysgenesis and Mosaicism. *Lancet, i*:1170.

FORD, C. E. Die Zytogenese der Intersexualitat des Menschen. In *Die Intersexualitat* (ed. Overzier) p. 90. Georg. Thieme, Stuttgart.

FORD, C. E. The cytogenetics of sex in man. *Eugenics Review, 53*:21.

FORSSMAN, H. and LEHMANN, O. Translocation-carrying Phenotypically Normal Males and the Down Syndrome. *Lancet, i*:1286.

FRACCARO, M.; IKKOS, D.; LINDSTEN, J.; LUFT, R.; and TELLINGER. Testicular Germinal Dysgenesis, (Male Turner's Syndrome). *Acta Endoc., 36*:98.

GALL, J. C. Nomenclature in Genetics. *Lancet, 1*:673.

GARDNER, L. I. *Molecular Genetics and Human Disease.* Thomas, Springfield, p. 153, p. 182, p. 255.

GAUTIER, M. Etude du corporscule chromatinien sur fibroblastes cultives in vitro. *Bull. Mem. Soc. Med. Hop.,* Paris, 77:345.

GRAY, J. Hypospadias with 47/XXY Karyotype. *Lancet, i*:722.

GRAY, J. Gonadal Dysgenesis (Turner's Syndrome) with Male Phenotype and XO chromosomal constitution. *Lancet, i*:53.

GRIBOFF, S. I.; and LAWRENCE, R. The Chromosomal Aetiology of Congenital Gonadal Defects. *Amer. J. med., 30*:544.

GUSTAVSON, K. H. and HÖÖK, O. The Chromosomal Constitution of the Sturge Weber Syndrome. *Lancet, i*:559.

HALL, B. The Chromosomal Constitution of the Sturge Weber Syndrome. *Lancet, i*:559.

HANHART, VON E. Aktuelles aus der allgemeinen und Humangenetik. *Schweiz. Med. Wschr., 91*:721.

HANHART, E.; DELHANTY, J. D. A.; and PENROSE, L. S. Trisomy in Mother and Child. *Lancet, i*:403.

HAYWARD, M. D. and BOWER, B. D. The Chromosomal Constitution of the Sturge Weber Syndrome. *Lancet, i*:558.

HAYWARD, M. D.; CAMERON, A. H.; and WOLFF, O. H. Chromosomes in Paediatrics. *Postgraduate Med. J., 37*:268.

ISRAELSOHN, W. J. and TAYLOR, A. I. Chromatin Positive Presumed Klinefelter's Syndrome. (Survey of Boys in London Schools for Educationally Subnormal Children) *Brit. med. J., i*:633.

JACOBS, P. A.; HARNDEN, D. G.; BUCKTON, K.; COURT BROWN, W. M.; KING, M.; MCBRIDE, J. A.; MACGREGOR, T. N.; and MACLEAN, N. Cytogenetic Studies in Primary Amenorrhoea. *Lancet, i*:1183.

JOHNSTON, A. W. The Chromosomes in a Child with Mongolism and Acute Leukaemia. *New England J. Med. 264*:591.

KINLOUGH, M. A.; ROBSON, H. N.; and HAYMAN, D. L. A simplified method for the study of chromosomes in man. *Nature, 189*:420.

LAFOURCADE, J. La determinisine genetique du sexe. *Rev. Prat., 11*:649.

LEJEUNE, J. and TURPIN, R. Chromosomal Aberrations in Man. *Am. J. Hum. Gen., 13*:175.

LENNOX, B. Chromosomes for Beginners. *Lancet*, *i*:1046.

LINDSTEN, J. New Type of Chromosomal Mosaicism in Ovarian Dysgenesis. *Lancet*, *i*:1228.

MACKINNEY, A.; STOHLMAN, F.; and BRECHER, G. Kinetics of Leukocyte Proliferation in Vitro. *Clinical Research*, 9:163.

MAINX, F. Sex-determination in Man and in Diptera. *Lancet*, *i*:673.

MAKINO, S. and SASAKI, M. A study of Somatic Chromosomes in a Japanese Population. *Am. Jour. Hum. Gen.*, 13:47.

MEIGHAN, S. S. and STITCH, H. F. Simplified technique for examination of chromosomes in the Bone Marrow of Man. *Canad. Med. A. J.*, 84:1004.

MILES, C. P. Human Chromosome Anomalies: Recent Advances in Human Cytogenetics. *Stanf. med Bull.*, 19:1.

MITTWOCH, U. Sex under the Microscope. *New Scientist*, No. 231.

MITUS, W. J.; MEDNICOFF, B.; WITTELS, B.; and DAMESHEK, W. Neoplastic Lymphoid Reticulum Cells in the Peripheral Blood: A Histochemical Study. *Blood*, *17(2)*:206.

MOORHEAD, P.; MELLMAN, W. J.; and WENAR, C. A familial chromosome translocation associated with Speech and Mental Retardation. *Am. J. Hum. Gen.*, 13:32.

NUZZO, F.; DE CARLI, L.; and CHIARELLI, B. Analisi morfologica degli assetti cromosomici in un ceppo di cellule umane stabilizzate in vitro. *Atti A. genet. Ital.*, Pavia, 6:111.

OHNO, S. and MAKINO, S. The Single-X Nature of Sex Chromatin in Man. *Lancet*, *i*:78.

OIKAWA, K. and BLIZZARD, R. M. Chromosomal Studies on Patients with Congenital Anomalies simulating those of Gonadal Aplasia—including a case of true gonadal and sex reversal. *New England J. Med.*, *264*:1009.

PATANELLI, D. J. and NELSON, W. O. Sex Chromatin and Chromosomes in Man. *Postgrad. Med.*, 29:3.

PATAU, K. Chromosome Identification and the Denver Report. *Lancet*, *i*:933.

PENROSE, L. S. Chromosomes and Disease, *Tr. med. Soc.*, 76:64.

PENROSE, L. S. and DELHANTY, J. Triploid Cell Cultures from a Macerated Foetus. *Lancet*, *i*:1261.

ROBINSON, A. The Human Chromosomes. *Amer. J. Dis. Child.*, *101*:379.

RUSSELL, L. B. and CHU, E. H. Y. An XXY Male in the Mouse. *P.N.A.S.*, 47:571.

SALMON, C. and BERNARD, J. New Observation of a "Weak A" Antigen in a Patient with Acute Leukaemia. *Revue Française d'Etudes Cliniques et Biologiques*, 5:912.

SASAKI, M. Observations on the modification in size and shape of chromosomes due to technical procedure. *Chromosoma*, 11:514.

SCHOYER, N. H. D. The Philadelphia Chromosome. *Lancet*, *i*:559.

SCHOYER, N. H. D. The Philadelphia Chromosome. *Lancet*, *i*:826.

SERINGE, P.; BACH, C.; LOEWE-LYON, S.; HALLEZ, J.; BOCQUET, L.; and

VERON, P. Les differentes varietes de pseudo-hermaphrodisme feminin ne relevant pas de l'hyperplasie surrenale congenitale. *Sem. Hop.*, 37:57.

SHAH, P. N. Male Pseudohermaphrodite with a female chromosomal complement. *J. Clin. Endocr. and Metab.*, June, 1961.

SHAW, M. W. Association of Acrocentric Chromosomes with the Centromere Region of Chromosome No. 1. *Lancet, i*:1351.

SLIZYNSKI, B. M. The pachytene stage in mammalian oocytes. *Nature*, 189:683.

STEIKER, D. D.; MELLMAN, W. J.; BONGIOVANNI, A. M.; EBERLEIN, W. R.; and LEBOEUF, G. Turner's Syndrome in the Male. *J. Pediat.*, 58:321.

STEWART, J. S. S. and SANDERSON, A. Sex Chromatin Body in Normal Human Testis. *Lancet, i*:79.

STEWART, J. S. S. and SANDERSON, A. Chromosomal Aberration after Diagnostic X-irradiation. *Lancet, i*:978.

THULINE, H. C. and PRIEST, J. H. Pregnancy in a 14-year-old Mongoloid. *Lancet, i*:1115.

TOUGH, I.; COURT BROWN, W. M.; BAIKIE, A. G.; BUCKTON, K.; HARNDEN, D. G.; JACOBS, P. A.; KING, M.; and MCBRIDE, J. A. Cytogenetic Studies in Chronic Myeloid Leukaemia and Acute Leukaemia associated with Mongolism. *Lancet, i*:411.

TRUJILLO, J. M.; STENIUS, C.; OHNO, S.; and NOVACK, J. Translocation Heterozygosity in Man. *Lancet, i*:560.

TURPIN, R. and LEJEUNE, J. Chromosome Translocations in Man. *Lancet, i*:616.

VAHARU, T.; PATTON, R. G.; VOORHESS, M. L.; and GARDNER, L. I. Gonadal Dysplasia and Enlarged Phallus in a girl with 45 Chromosomes plus a "fragment." *Lancet, i*:1351.

VAN WIJCK, J. A. K.; STOLTE, L. A. M.; VAN KERSEL, H. S. A. M.; and TYJDINK, G. A. J. A Trisomic Child of a Hyperthyroid Mother. *Lancet, i*:887.

WALD, N.; BORGES, W. H.; LI, C. C.; TURNER, J. H.; and HARNOIS, M. C. Leukaemia Associated with Mongolism. *Lancet, i*:1228.

ZELLWEGER, H. and MIKAMO, K. The Chromosomal Constitution of the Sturge-Weber Syndrome. *Lancet, i*:826.

EDITORIAL. Chromosomal abnormality in chronic myeloid leukaemia. *Brit. med. J., i*:347.

EDITORIAL. Clinical Aspects of Genetics. Royal College of Physicians of London. *Brit. med. J.*, 1:1026.

EDITORIAL. Normal and Leukaemic haemopoiesis. *Brit. med. J. i*:1595.

EDITORIAL. Chromosome Abnormalities and Congenital Malformation of the Heart. *Brit. med. J., i*:1747.

EDITORIAL. The Philadelphia Chromosome. *Lancet, i*:433.

EDITORIAL. The Numbering of Chromosomes. *Lancet, i*:928.

EDITORIAL. The Clinical Significance of Research on Human Sex Chromosomes. *J. Canad. Med. A.* 84:167.

EDITORIAL. Leukaemia and Mongolism. The Medical Officer C.V., 164.